BACTERIOPHAGES

MARK H. ADAMS

WITH CHAPTERS BY

E. S. ANDERSON, *Central Enteric Reference Laboratory,*
Central Public Health Laboratory, London

J. S. GOTS, *University of Pennsylvania, Philadelphia*

F. JACOB, *Pasteur Institute, Paris*

E.-L. WOLLMAN, *Pasteur Institute, Paris*

ELECTRON MICROGRAPHS BY

E. KELLENBERGER, *The University, Geneva*

1959

INTERSCIENCE PUBLISHERS, INC., NEW YORK

Interscience Publishers Ltd., London

INTERSCIENCE PUBLISHERS, INC.
250 Fifth Avenue, New York 1, N. Y.

For Great Britain and Northern Ireland:
INTERSCIENCE PUBLISHERS, LTD.
88–90 Chancery Lane, London, W.C. 2

PRINTED IN THE UNITED STATES OF AMERICA
BY MACK PRINTING COMPANY, EASTON, PA.

PREFACE

Phage research, after a fitful history during its first twenty years, had all but died out in the middle 1930's. In the textbooks of bacteriology, the bacteriophages, if they were mentioned at all, figured as a curiosity item, unconnected with the rest and disposed of in a couple of pages at most. Today, phage research is vigorously pursued in many outstanding laboratories in this country, in France, and to a lesser extent in other countries. There are perhaps 100 people directly engaged in basic research. In addition, the field has become well known to many scientists in other fields: genetics, biochemistry, virology, immunology, to name the most important. Indeed, there is every reason for the popularity of phage research, and for the interest in its results on the part of other scientists. Phage research has become so interwoven with these other fields that it is quite difficult to extricate it from its entangling alliances, and to present it as a unit.

The author of this book, Mark Adams, has a large share in recent developments, by his own research, by his teaching at New York University, and by two special contributions: the phage course at the Biological Laboratory in Cold Spring Harbor, and the review on the methods in phage research first published in *Methods in Medical Research*, Vol. 2, 1950, and now reprinted in revised form as an appendix to the present volume. The phage course in Cold Spring Harbor was instituted in 1945. Mark Adams took it the second year, and taught it since then every summer, except two. In this course were trained many of those who are presently engaged in phage research, and in addition many who are interested in related fields acquired through it a critical understanding of the phage literature. It thus served to bring phage research out of its isolation, and to foster the many links to other parts of modern biology. The review on Methods is a classic, and easily the paper most often referred to in the current phage literature. The sentence "the methods employed in this work are those described by Adams, etc.," is almost like a ritual invocation used by every phage worker, with a sigh of relief, relieving him of the necessity of an otherwise burdensome chore.

Phage research has also been discussed in, and its knowledge disseminated through, numerous, perhaps too numerous, review articles, but there has been no book covering the whole field since 1926, long before the modern era of this field. The fact is that the literature on this subject has grown so complex as to deter everybody, except Mark Adams. I do not believe, in fact, that anybody, besides Adams, had the qualifications for this task. Adams started writing this book several years ago, and even he, in spite of his tremendous knowledge, critical ability, and superb expository gifts, found the going very hard. On October 17, 1956, Mark Adams died, of an acute infection, at the age of 44. At that time about three-quarters of the chapters of this book were in a semi-finished state, the rest not begun. Some of the chapters had been finished recently, and were up to date. Some had been written several years ago and needed additions and revision. All of them needed some editing. At the request of Mrs. Adams, a committee consisting of A. D. Hershey, R. D. Hotchkiss, A. M. Pappenheimer, Jr., and E. Racker, in consultation with the publisher, went over the manuscript and decided that several specialists should be invited to write the missing chapters, while Hershey volunteered to edit the others. After proceeding with this plan for some time, it became clear that the editorial job was greater than anticipated, and could not be completed by one man within a reasonable length of time. Accordingly, an inquiry was sent around asking for volunteers for the editing of individual chapters, the over-all editorial responsibility to remain in the hands of Hershey. This inquiry met with a wide response, and the plan was promptly executed.

Accordingly we now have before us, for the first time in thirty years, a book on bacteriophages, reasonably complete, reasonably up to date, and reasonably elementary; useful, we trust, to every student of modern biology in the widest sense. We also have before us a monument to Mark Adams, our unforgettable friend.

Pasadena, California   M. DELBRÜCK
May, 1958

EDITORS' PREFACE

At the time of his death on October 17, 1956, Mark Adams had written all but four chapters of the present book. Messrs. Anderson, Gots, Jacob, and Wollman contributed the remainder, completing the text according to Adams' plan.

The original chapters were written over a period of several years. They had to be revised, completed, and brought up to date, with a minimum of editorial changes. The necessary work was done by S. Benzer, G. Bertani, M. Delbrück, A. Garen, W. Harm, R. M. Herriott, A. D. Hershey, F. Lanni, R. G. E. Murray, F. W. Stahl, G. S. Stent, G. Streisinger, J. D. Watson, and J. J. Weigle. Hershey is responsible for the form in which these chapters now appear.

E. Kellenberger and his colleagues furnished many electron micrographs, and assisted in the selection and presentation of those appearing in this book. Unless otherwise stated, specimens were prepared by Kellenberger's agar filtration method (see Chapter XI), shadowed with uranium oxide, and translated to film in the RCA-EMU 2 microscope.

Appreciation is due the Year Book Publishers, Inc., Chicago, Illinois, for permission to reprint, as an appendix to this volume, "Methods of Study of Bacterial Viruses," from Vol. 2 of *Methods of Medical Research*. The appendix was edited by Rollin D. Hotchkiss and Nancy Collins Bruce.

Carnegie Institution of Washington　　　　　　　　A. D. HERSHEY
Cold Spring Harbor, New York　　　　　　　　　　*for the editors*
June, 1958

CONTENTS

CHAPTER I

INTRODUCTION

1. Definition

The name bacteriophage was given by F. d'Herelle to a bacteriolytic substance that he isolated from feces. Now usually shortened to phage, it means "eater of bacteria" and refers to the remarkable ability of bacteriophages to bring about lysis of growing bacterial cultures. More remarkable still was d'Herelle's evidence that the lysis is accompanied by production of more phage; the lytic agent is transmissible in series from culture to culture of susceptible bacteria.

Today phages are universally recognized to form a group of bacteria-specific viruses, that is, ultramicrobes of diverse character exhibiting all the signs of a long history of manifold variation, adaptation, and specialization. D'Herelle himself subscribed to this view only in part: he considered all bacteriophages to belong to a single variable species. In so doing he, and many of the opponents of the virus theory, ignored or denied the strongest evidence for it, with the unfortunate result that some of the ostensibly fundamental research on phages was for a decade or more directed along fruitless channels.

The lytic cycle recognized by d'Herelle was such a striking aspect of bacteriophage activity that other aspects were largely ignored. However, a nonlytic phase of reproduction has been rediscovered recently, causing phage research to branch out in new directions. Certain strains of bacteriophage when infecting a susceptible bacterial culture are able to enter into an intimate symbiotic relationship in which the host cell continues to multiply, carrying the virus intracellularly in a noninfective condition for an indefinite number of cell divisions. This

1

delicately balanced phase of viral growth in which the infected host cell and its carried "prophage" multiply at the same rate has been termed "lysogenesis" or "lysogeny." Infection leading to lysogeny is now thought to produce a modification of the genetic apparatus of the bacterial cell and often results in changes in bacterial properties, a striking example being the conversion of avirulent strains of diphtheria bacilli to toxigenic potency by infection with an appropriate phage.

Under certain conditions some bacteriophages can attack and kill susceptible bacteria with no evidence of bacterial lysis or of phage multiplication. In these circumstances the phage particle behaves as an antibiotic rather than as a virus. In fact certain antibiotics produced by bacteria, the colicins and pyocins, are rather similar to bacteriophages in certain of their properties. For these reasons the colicins as well as phages will be discussed in this book.

2. Discovery of Bacteriophages

There is no doubt that numerous early bacteriologists saw and described signs of phage action in bacterial cultures. However, no intensive investigation of these phenomena was undertaken prior to the appearance of a brief but provocative paper by F. W. Twort (1915). This British bacteriologist described an acute infectious disease of staphylococci that produced marked changes in colonial morphology. The infective agent was filterable and could be passed indefinitely in series from colony to colony. Twort considered various hypotheses to explain this phenomenon; among others that it was a filterable virus analogous to the virus pathogens of animals and plants. Twort's remarkable paper contained in essence the present concept of the nature of bacteriophage, yet the paper remained unnoticed by scientists and Twort failed to pursue the matter further, perhaps because of his wartime duties in the British Army.

In 1917, Felix d'Herelle, a Canadian bacteriologist working at the Pasteur Institute in Paris, published his independent discovery of "bacteriophage." In a noteworthy series of papers he reported and correctly interpreted many of the significant aspects of bacteriophage action, and in 1921 published his classic book entitled *Le bactériophage: son rôle dans l'immunité.*

D'Herelle, stimulated by the announcement that hog cholera was due to the synergistic action of a bacterium and a virus, was searching for evidence of such a mixed etiology for bacillary dysentery in man. He prepared Chamberland filtrates of stools of dysentery patients and added these filtrates to young cultures of Shiga's bacillus. He incubated the mixtures overnight intending to inject the supposed mixture of bacterium and virus into experimental animals next day. To his surprise some of the culture fluids were clear and sterile. He filtered some of the lysed cultures and inoculated fresh cultures of Shiga's bacillus with the filtrates, keeping other cultures of the bacterium as uninoculated controls. On incubation overnight he found the control cultures to be turbid as expected while the bacterial cultures inoculated with the filtrates were completely clear. The "lytic principle" could be passed indefinitely from culture to culture using each time for phage inoculum a bacteria-free filtrate of the previous culture. This behavior suggested to him an ultravirus, pathogenic for bacteria, destroying its host cells as it multiplied. During the next few years bacteriophages were found for a variety of pathogenic bacteria such as staphylococci, cholera vibrio, and typhoid bacteria. Because of the susceptibility of pathogenic bacteria to phages, and because of the wide distribution of phages in nature, d'Herelle suspected that they played a role in resistance to and recovery from disease.

D'Herelle shares with Twort credit for the discovery of phages and did much of the basic research concerning them. In addition his ideas relating phages to immunity to disease attracted the general attention of medical scientists, indirectly yielding both practical and theoretical benefits. The importance of the role of bacteriophages in natural control of infectious disease has not been assessed to this day, however.

A vast amount of research was devoted to possible therapeutic applications of bacteriophages between 1920 and 1940. In most cases results were equivocal or disappointing but in certain diseases such as cholera there was some evidence for a favorable effect of phage therapy.   Interest in this application has largely subsided since the introduction of the more convenient chemo-therapeutic agents.   The early hopes of effective medical use stimulated much valuable work on host range, immunological properties, stability and variation, and other attributes of bac-teriophages.   Many of the well-known names in bacteriology and immunology are found in the phage literature of this period: J. Bordet, Costa Cruz, Doerr, A. Fleming, Hauduroy, Levaditi, Prausnitz, and Topley.   Also during this period a few men made phage research their life work.   Included in this group besides d'Herelle are Asheshov, Bronfenbrenner, Flu, Gratia, and the elder Wollmans.   These scientists were inter-ested in the biology of bacteriophages as well as in possible ap-plications and made many contributions of fundamental impor-tance.   During the second decade of phage history appear a few men whose work combined biological "feeling" and quantitative methods in the modern manner: Burnet, M. Schlesinger, and C. H. Andrewes.   The contributions of these older phage workers and of a very large contemporary school form the subject matter of this book.

3. Nature of Bacteriophages

In his original publication, Twort (1915) considered the na-ture of his as yet unnamed lytic agent, asking if it was similar to bacteria, protozoa, or to the filterable viruses; whether it was a filterable stage in the life cycle of the micrococcus affected; or whether perhaps it was a bacterial enzyme, produced autocatalyt-ically while destroying the bacterium that produced it.   A much more elaborate series of hypotheses is discussed in d'Herelle's book (1926).   Of these hypotheses two only have survived to the present: the "precursor" theory and the "virus" theory.   An active controversy between the proponents of these two theories continued for many years and stimulated much experimental work as well as verbiage.

According to the precursor theory bacteriophages are endogenous, existing in bacteria as precursors which either spontaneously or after stimulation are transformed into characteristic lytic substances, much as trypsinogen can be converted into trypsin. This theory was supported by Gildemeister (1921), Bordet (1925), Northrop (1939a), Kreuger and Scribner (1939), and Felix (1953). Much of the experimental support for it was derived from studies on lysogenic bacteria, to be discussed presently.

According to the virus theory the bacteriophages are autonomous microbes analogous to plant and animal viruses but obligately parasitic on bacteria. This hypothesis was adopted very early in his work by d'Herelle and seemed obvious to most virologists once something had been learned about the biology of viruses in general. In the light of current knowledge this theory amounts to very little, however, since both autonomy and parasitism as applied to viruses are terms difficult to define. Some current views are presented below in connection with theories concerning the origins of viruses.

As is often the case in the historical development of a scientific field each of the rival hypotheses can now be construed as part of the truth; each was incomplete by itself. The current concept of the nature of bacteriophage is a synthesis of the old ideas plus a few novel ideas developed recently. Somewhat as a typical bacillus may exist in the spore state or the vegetative state, a typical bacteriophage may exist in three states, called prophage, vegetative phage, and mature phage. Phages exist outside of the host cell in mature form, metabolically inert and resembling very crudely the spore state of bacteria. Following adsorption to the host cell, part of the phage particle penetrates within and may begin to multiply. When it does, the multiplying, intracellular state of the phage particle differs in many respects from mature phage and has been termed vegetative phage in recognition of its almost unlimited reproductive capacity. Some phages, called temperate, are distinguished by the fact that they can exist in a third state, prophage, as well. When a mature temperate phage particle infects a susceptible bacterial cell it may be transformed either to the vegetative state leading to destruction of the host cell, or to the prophage state in which it enters into the hereditary symbiotic relationship with the host cell known as lysogeny. This relationship has been termed symbiotic rather than parasitic because it may be readily surmised that the lysogenic condition is of great survival value to both phage and host cell.

The recognition that temperate phages could exist in three distinct states served to unify the precursor and virus theories. The endogenous precursor in lysogenic bacteria is simply the phage-specific prophage state of temperate phages. This synthesis of the opposing concepts was clearly foreseen by Burnet and McKie (1929). The status of precursor theories as applied to infection by exogenous phages is still unclarified, however.

Recent research has demonstrated a marked similarity in physical, chemical, and biological properties between bacteriophages and other viruses. The similarity has stimulated much research in which bacteriophages have been used as models for animal viruses, even in extensive screening programs for antibiotics against viruses. To a limited extent this procedure has already justified itself, but it is doubtful whether the homology can be pursued very far. It is possible that bacteriophages and other viruses have evolved from quite distinct ancestors, as the following paragraphs suggest. The facts that the known bacteriophages contain deoxyribonucleic acid whereas several typical plant and animal viruses contain ribonucleic acid may prove more significant than the rather casual resemblances demonstrated so far.

4. Origin of Bacteriophages

Theories of the origin of bacteriophages have been closely associated with theories of their nature. Many diverse ideas have been proposed, most of which fall into one of two categories, the "creation" hypothesis or the "degeneration" hypothesis. The creation hypothesis considers that viruses are the direct descendants of some very primitive form of life that originated prior to the evolution of organized cells (Oparin, 1938). This hypothesis is not very useful or satisfying, but it could be true for some or all phages, or for some or all viruses. The degeneration hypothesis considers that viruses have gradually evolved from more complicated forms of life by the loss of all protoplasm unnecessary to the peculiar mode of existence bacteriophages have chosen. This hypothesis has a certain intellectual appeal in that it is easy to visualize intermediate steps in the degenerative process, and progressive loss by bacteria of synthetic abilities is subject to experimental study. This hypothesis avoids the problem of the ultimate origin of life, which is not necessarily related to the problem of the origin of viruses, and it provides for the independent evolution of different viruses. By this hypothesis there is no need to assume that animal viruses and bacteriophages are derived from a common progenitor.

Recent studies of the phenomenon of lysogeny have lent credence to a variant of the degeneration hypothesis that may be called the "mutation" hypothesis (Lwoff, 1953). According to this hypothesis a series of mutations occurring in a segment of the genetic material of a bacterium has conferred on that segment a certain degree of autonomy. The mutations resulted in the synthesis of a specific kind of protein covering to protect the segment of genetic material from damage by the extracellular environment and to facilitate the transfer of the genetic material from one cell to another. It is not impossible that bacteriophages may have evolved from a primitive mechanism of sexuality originally developed for the purpose of transfer of genetic materials between bacterial cells. At least certain bacteriophages are able to perform that function at present. According to this hypothesis the phage genetic material would be a modified form of the bacterial genetic material, yet sufficiently like the homologous segment of bacterial gene stuff to undergo genetic recombination with it or even to replace it. This hypothesis is consistent with the observed fact that the genetic material of certain temperate phages can associate more or less permanently with definite genetic loci in the hereditary apparatus of the host cell, and thus become part of that apparatus. Once temperate phages have evolved they could be irreversibly transformed into virulent phages by further mutations. It is suspected that certain virulent phages have retained the ability to undergo genetic recombination with host cells. Host range mutations of a virulent phage might permit it to attack hosts with which it had no genetic affinity whatever and so ultimately to give rise to hypervirulent phages that have lost all resemblance to any known bacterial strains. According to this hypothesis different phage strains may have completely independent phylogenies and a given phage may be much more closely related to its host cell phylogenetically than to other phages. It is clear that if this hypothesis has any validity there may be no phylogenetic relationship between bacteriophages and any other type of virus. The resemblances of phages to plant and animal viruses may be superficial and due to their filling of similar ecological niches. Referring to bacteriophages as bacterial viruses may convey some information about their way of life but it should carry no implications about their origins.

5. Lysogeny

From what has been said above it is clear that the phenomenon of lysogeny has played a central role in the formulation of ideas about bacteriophages. Because of its significance to all aspects of phage research today, lysogeny must be discussed early in this book. Literally, the term means production of lysis and refers to the habit of bacterial strains that characteristically produce a bacteriophage capable of lysing other bacterial strains. Unfortunately the term has been applied to two entirely distinct phenomena with consequent confusion in thinking and definition.

One of these phenomena results from the contamination of a partially susceptible bacterial strain with a bacteriophage. In such cases it is sometimes technically difficult to rid the bacteria of the phage. D'Herelle (1930) referred to this phenomenon as "symbiose bactérie-bactériophage," a name that reflects his interpretation of lysogeny. He assumed that the bacterial population was composed of individuals covering a considerable spectrum of susceptibility to phage action, while the phage population covered a considerable range of virulence. The most virulent phage particles would multiply at the expense of the most susceptible bacteria and in this way bacteria and phage particles would be perpetuated in mixed culture. D'Herelle refused to recognize any other explanation for lysogenic strains of bacteria. An essentially similar idea was proposed by Delbrück (1946b) for a phenomenon he called "pseudolysogenesis," in which the contaminating phage reproduced at the expense of phage-susceptible bacteria produced by mutation during growth of a phage-resistant culture. Pseudolysogenic bacterial strains have been termed "carrier strains" by Lwoff (1953).

In contrast to pseudolysogenic or carrier strains are those bacterial strains that exhibit true lysogeny. In such strains the prophage multiplies as an integral part of the genetic apparatus of each bacterial cell. During bacterial growth the conversion of prophage to vegetative phage occurs spontaneously with a small but characteristic frequency, for example in one cell per million cell generations, as evidenced by the lysis of an occasional cell to liberate infective phage particles. In some but not all lysogenic cultures the natural frequency of productive lysis may be greatly increased by exposure to ultraviolet light, X-rays, nitrogen mustard, peroxides, and certain other agents. The biochemical mechanism of such "induction" is unknown.

It has been repeatedly demonstrated that each bacterial cell in a lysogenic culture is capable of transmitting the potentiality of phage production to its progeny in the absence of contact with exogenous phage. With inducible strains of bacteria, for instance, it is possible with suitable doses of ultraviolet light to cause at least 90 per cent of the cells to lyse and liberate viable phage particles (Lwoff, Siminovitch, and Kjeldgaard, 1950). In the classic experiment of den Dooren de Jong (1936), spores of a lysogenic strain of *Bacillus megaterium* were heated above lethal temperatures for free phage particles without killing the spores.   Each spore on germination gave rise to a lysogenic culture.   Similar conclusions had been reached from studies on a lysogenic strain of *Salmonella enteritidis* by Burnet and McKie (1929) who wrote that "the permanence of the lysogenic character makes it necessary to assume the presence of bacteriophage or its *anlage* in every cell of the culture, i.e., it is a part of the hereditary constitution of the strain."

For many years the manner of release of phage particles from lysogenic bacterial cells was a subject of dispute.   One popular theory proposed that the phage was secreted by the growing bacterial culture in the manner of extracellular bacterial enzymes (Northrop, 1939b).   An alternative theory held that the occasional disintegration of a bacterial cell liberated a number of phage particles in a way that was already familiar to students of the virulent phages (Burnet, 1929a).   This question was finally settled by the work of Lwoff and Gutmann (1950) who demonstrated by the use of micromanipulator techniques that phage particles were not secreted by multiplying lysogenic bacteria, but appeared in groups simultaneously with the disintegration of single bacterial cells.

The recent revival of interest in lysogeny begins with important reinvestigations of the phenomenon by Lwoff and Gutmann (1950), Bertani (1951), and the Lederbergs (1953). These papers are all the more interesting because they record three quite different experimental approaches.

Lwoff (1953) lists the characteristic signs of lysogeny as follows:

1. In a lysogenic culture lysogenesis is a property of every cell and every spore.

2. Bacteria of a lysogenic culture generally can adsorb the mature phage produced by the culture, but are not damaged by it.

3. Lysis of lysogenic bacteria by enzymes, by other phages, or by mechanical means does not liberate mature phage particles.

The intracellular phage in lysogenic bacteria is noninfectious; it is prophage.

4. Infection of a susceptible bacterial culture by a temperate phage may result in the conversion of a considerable proportion of the bacterial cells to the lysogenic condition, potentially capable of liberating the same kind of phage that was used to infect them.

5. Lysogenic bacteria can multiply without liberating mature phage and can undergo many cell divisions in the absence of external phage without losing the lysogenic propensity.

6. Lysis of single lysogenic bacterial cells spontaneously or after a characteristic latent period following induction is accompanied by the release of many mature phage particles. Lysogeny is potentially lethal to the bacterial cell.

One may define lysogenic bacteria as bacteria in which the capacity to produce bacteriophage is a hereditary property perpetuated without intervention of mature phage particles.

Lysogenic bacteria are very common in nature and probably constitute the principal reservoir of bacteriophages. Lysogeny resembles in some respects the phenomenon of latency in animal and plant viruses, but work in the latter fields has not progressed to the point that permits one to judge the validity of the analogy. The phenomenon of lysogenesis is intimately related to the problems of bacterial genetics and has already served as a powerful tool in the study of genetic structure and function in certain genera of bacteria. These and other aspects of lysogeny will be discussed in detail in later chapters.

6. Classification of Phages

Phages are conveniently described as typhoid phages, staphylococcal phages, or coliphages, meaning phages attacking the indicated types of bacteria. In addition, phages are known by individual designations, such as lambda, T1, or P8, which serve to identify the particular phage. These specific symbols usually have no meaning in themselves, except to indicate that the phage came from a particular collection. The coliphages T1, T2,

. . . T7, for instance, were collected by Demerec and Fano (1945) and have in common only the ability to infect a strain of *Escherichia coli* known as B.   In this instance, but in relatively few others, the phages have been classified by other means.   They fall into four groups of "related" phages: T1; T2, T4, T6; T5; T3, T7.   In this instance the phages within a single group are morphologically identical, and serologically related but not identical.   In the following pages we shall frequently speak of related phages, meaning two or more phages having a common host, common morphology, and usually also some common antigens.   A given "wild-type" phage and its mutants are always related in this sense, as far as is known.   In much of the earlier work on phages unclassified specimens, often no longer available, were used.   These can only be described as "a staphylococcal phage," or "a coli-dysentery phage."   When a phage is referred to by a symbol without indication of host specificity, it is likely to be one of the better known coli-dysentery phages. These remarks will serve to indicate the meaning, or lack of it, of names of phages referred to in this book.   General problems of taxonomy are discussed in the final chapter.

CHAPTER II

THE INFECTIVE PROCESS

As d'Herelle found, the inoculation of a growing culture of susceptible bacteria with an appropriate bacteriophage results in a few hours in lysis of the bacterial cells and an increase in the amount of bacteriophage far above that added. D'Herelle conceived of this phenomenon as an infection of the bacterial host cell by a virulent virus particle which as a result of its multiplication brought about death and dissolution of the host cell. He noted that in order for lysis to occur the host cells must be growing in an appropriate physical and chemical environment. It is not difficult to find environmental conditions of temperature, pH, salt concentration, or chemical composition in which the host cells will multiply but lysis will not occur.

For convenience in discussion d'Herelle divided the infective process into arbitrary stages: (1) adsorption of the phage particle to the host cell, (2) penetration of the phage particle into the bacterium, (3) the intracellular multiplication of the virus, and (4) the lysis of the host cell and release of phage progeny. This division is peculiarly appropriate from the experimental viewpoint and leads to the following interpretation of the lytic process.

If to an actively growing fluid culture of susceptible bacteria one adds a single phage particle, it will adsorb to a bacterial cell, multiply therein, and eventually cause the cell to lyse. On lysis about 100 phage particles will be liberated thus completing one growth cycle. The 100 phage progeny from the first cycle will then infect 100 bacteria to initiate the second growth cycle. The progeny of the second cycle will initiate a third cycle and so the process will continue at an exponential rate until all susceptible bacteria are lysed.

Similarly, if to a film of susceptible bacteria growing on an agar surface one adds a phage particle, it will adsorb to a bacterium and initiate the first lytic cycle. The phage progeny from the first cycle will infect neighboring bacteria to initiate the second cycle, thus producing a spreading lesion in the bacterial film. Eventually this process will result in a readily visible sterile area in the film of growing bacteria, the bacteria-free area being known as a plaque. Under ideal conditions each infective phage particle will produce a plaque, so that plaque counts give a simple and reproducible measure of the number of phage particles present in a sample inoculated on the assay plate.

1. The One-Step Growth Experiment

The over-all aspects of the infective cycle are most conveniently studied by means of the one-step growth experiment of Ellis and Delbrück (1939), which gives the minimum *latent period* of intracellular virus growth and the average *burst size*. The latent period is defined as the minimum time between the adsorption of phage to host cell and the lysis of the host cell with release of phage progeny. The burst size is the mean yield of phage particles per infected bacterium. Each of these characteristics can be determined by other techniques, but the one-step growth experiment enables both to be determined at once. The technique is as follows:

1. Phage and bacteria are mixed at concentrations that permit rapid adsorption.

2. After a suitable adsorption period the mixture is diluted into antiphage antibody to stop adsorption and inactivate unadsorbed phage.

3. After sufficient time for antibody action the mixture is further diluted in growth medium so that each sample will contain about 100 infected bacteria.

4. The suspension of infected bacteria is sampled at intervals until lysis is completed and each sample is assayed by the plaque count method.

Each infected bacterium if plated before lysis will produce one plaque. If permitted to lyse before plating each bacterium liberates a considerable number of phage particles each of which will produce a plaque. Therefore the plaque count of successive samples remains constant until the end of the latent period when lysis begins. From this time the plaque count increases with each sample until all infected bacteria have lysed, after which it remains constant at the new higher level. The final count of liberated phage particles divided by the initial count of infected bacteria gives the average burst size.

The dilution of the adsorption mixture at the end of the adsorption period is an essential feature of the experiment because it prevents further adsorption. If the suspension of infected bacteria were not diluted, much of the phage released by the early lysing bacteria would be adsorbed onto yet unlysed bacteria and initiate secondary cycles of infection.

The antiphage antibody inactivates unadsorbed phage without affecting the multiplication of adsorbed phage (Delbrück, 1945b). If unadsorbed phage were not inactivated the early plaque counts would include unadsorbed phage as well as infected bacteria and the estimate of the burst size would be too small.

The one-step growth technique has been discussed in some detail because its significance has not been understood by all phage workers. This technique enables one to determine very simply the effect of changes in the physical and chemical environment on the duration of the infectious cycle and on the yield of virus per infected host cell.

2. Adsorption

Adsorption of phage to host cell is the stage in the infectious cycle which is most readily accessible to laboratory study and hence best known. If adsorption is prevented the infectious process cannot proceed and the host cells continue to multiply as if the phage were not present. One crucial factor in adsorption is the ionic environment, so one of the first things to consider in

studying any new bacterium-phage system is the effect of varying the salt concentration in the growth medium. An unfavorable salt concentration can prevent phage adsorption. It is
probable that antiphage antibody acts in part by interfering
with adsorption, and antibacterial antibodies can also prevent
adsorption by coating the bacterial receptor sites.

The specificity of the phage-bacterium relationship is in most
cases determined by the adsorption process. When a coliphage
for instance fails to attack a particular strain of *E. coli*, the failure
is usually due to lack of adsorption. Certain exceptions to this
generalization will be noted in later chapters. The adsorption
process is remarkably specific. A single mutation on the part
of a host cell can result in loss of ability to adsorb a particular
bacteriophage, without loss of susceptibility to other closely related phages. The bacteriophage by a single mutation can
gain the ability to adsorb to a particular host without other detectable change in viral properties.

Another interesting aspect of adsorption specificity is the requirement for *adsorption cofactors* by certain phages. A particularly well studied example is a tryptophan requiring variant of
coliphage T4 which fails to adsorb to its host cell unless tryptophan or certain other substances are present in the medium.
The tryptophan reacts reversibly with the phage, changing it
from a particle incapable of adsorption to a particle which adsorbs with high efficiency (T. F. Anderson 1948a). This "sen-
sitization" of the phage particle to adsorption can be counter-
acted by indole (Delbrück, 1948). Since *E. coli* can convert tryptophan into indole, we have a bacterium converting a substance essential for the attack by a hostile virus into a substance
which renders the virus innocuous. This is antibiosis on a
primitive level.

An important observation by T. F. Anderson (1951) gives
further evidence for a high order of specificity in the adsorption
process. Stereoscopic electronmicrographs show that the tailed
bacteriophages T2, T4, and T6 attach to the host cell by the tips
of their tails only.

3. Penetration

Very little is known about penetration, the second step in the infectious process. It has been assumed that the phage particle must penetrate into the host cell interior, since microscopic studies have quite clearly demonstrated that the phage progeny are formed intracellularly and released on rupture of the host cell membrane. Either the parental phage particle must penetrate the membrane or one must invoke biological action at a distance as great as the membrane thickness. Convincing evidence of penetration was obtained by Hershey and Chase (1952) using T2 coliphage labeled with either radioactive phosphorus or sulfur. The phosphorus labels the phage nucleic acid while the sulfur labels the sulfur-containing proteins. Hershey and Chase found that if the infected bacteria were subjected to violent agitation in a Waring Blendor shortly after infection, a remarkable fractionation of the labels took place. The high shearing forces of the Waring Blendor resulted in the liberation of 75 per cent of the radioactive sulfur but only 15 per cent of the phosphorus into the medium, the remaining radioactivity staying with the bacteria. The treatment did not interfere with the infective process; the cells remained capable of yielding phage progeny. The radioactive sulfur-labeled substance which was shaken loose by the Waring Blendor was precipitable by antiphage serum and could be readsorbed to sensitive bacteria, that is, it had the biological specificity of the phage particle. The reasonable conclusion is that the sulfur-containing proteins of the infecting bacteriophage particles remain on the host cell surface from which they can subsequently be shaken loose, while the nucleic acid of the phage particle penetrates into the host cell. The experiment completely alters the problem of phage penetration since it is evident that the intact phage particle does not penetrate and only certain parts of the particle participate in phage reproduction. These parts may well gain entrance by some enzymatic damage to the host cell membrane produced by viral enzymes, or by viral stimulation of host cell enzymes. Evidence for enzymatic activity on host cell materials is particularly good for the influenza group of animal viruses (Hirst, 1948), for phages T2 and T4 (Barrington and Kozloff, 1956; Koch and Weidel, 1956b), and for a *Klebsiella* phage (Adams and Park, 1956). This topic is discussed in Chapter XI.

4. Multiplication

Of the basic mechanisms of intracellular phage multiplication very little is known. As usual where knowledge is meagre, hypothesis is rampant. We will not consider hypotheses but merely describe briefly those events that are known to occur during multiplication of phages related to T2.

One type of information is obtained from the survival curves of infected bacteria as a function of dosage of ultraviolet or X-ray irradiation (Luria and Latarjet, 1947). The plaque-forming ability of infected bacteria is as susceptible to ultraviolet inactivation immediately after adsorption as is that of unadsorbed phage. However, within a few minutes after adsorption the infected bacteria become far more resistant to inactivation than they were earlier. It is probable that this marked increase in resistance is correlated with the first replication of the phage nucleic acid in the interior of the host cell. The inactivation curves remain exponential until nearly half way through the latent period and then rapidly become multiple hit curves. Apparently there are few potential virus particles in the cell for the first half of the latent period, but then the mean number of potential virus particles per infected host cell rapidly increases. During the initial quiescent period the cytological appearance of the infected bacterium changes markedly, the "nuclear bodies" disintegrate, and the chromatin appears to migrate to the cell periphery. About the middle of the latent period the cell begins to fill with granular chromatin (Luria and Human, 1950).

Chemical studies of infected bacteria during the latent period have also been of interest. Following phage adsorption cell division stops. The synthesis of certain adaptive enzymes is inhibited but energy metabolism as judged by respiration continues (Cohen, 1949). Synthesis of ribose nucleic acid almost stops but protein synthesis continues. The synthesis of bacterial deoxyribose nucleic acid (DNA) stops but after a short lag the synthesis of phage DNA begins. The synthesis of phage protein and DNA then continues until bacterial lysis occurs (Hershey, Garen, Fraser, and Hudis, 1954).

A third approach to a knowledge of intracellular multiplication consists in stopping virus synthesis by chilling or by metabolic poisons such as cyanide at appropriate intervals in the latent period. The infected cells are then lysed by secondary means such as a second phage or sonic vibrations and the lysates are assayed to determine the mean number of mature phage particles present per infected host cell. By such means it has been found that no mature, infectious phage particles are present intracellularly until half-way through the latent period. Then the number of mature phage particles increases as a linear function of time until shortly before lysis (Doermann, 1952).

In such circumstances it is useful to distinguish between two kinds of phage particles, mature or infective particles and immature, noninfective, vegetative particles. The mature phage particle is the typical extracellular stage which is assayed by its plaque forming ability. The immature or vegetative phage particle is the intracellular stage, undergoing multiplication, potentially capable of producing mature phage particles but not detectable by the plaque count method because it is noninfectious.

The following picture of phage multiplication emerges from these observations:

1. The phage particle adsorbs to the host cell surface.

2. Certain reproductively essential components of the phage penetrate to the cell interior, expendable portions being discarded at the cell surface. The phage particle thus changes from the mature to the vegetative condition.

3. The host cell stops dividing, certain synthetic reactions stop, and extensive cytological changes occur.

4. Synthesis of phage protein and phage DNA start, and the irradiation inactivation curves become multiple hit, indicating that phage multiplication has started.

5. At about the mid-point of the latent period, conversion of vegetative phage particles into mature phage begins and the number of infective particles found per cell increases until host cell lysis occurs.

It should be noted that this picture applies specifically to T2 and related coliphages. The details of the reproductive cycle may be quite different for other phages. Much additional information about the reproduction of bacteriophages has been obtained from nutritional studies, tracer experiments, and genetic analysis, which will be reported later in appropriate chapters.

5. Lysis of Host Cell and Release of Phage Progeny

Of the last stage in the infectious process, lysis of the host cell, almost nothing is known. Lysis is not dependent on the accumulation of mature phage particles because lysis will occur even when phage multiplication is interrupted by chemicals such as cyanide (Cohen, 1949) or proflavine (Foster, 1948). No general method of temporarily interrupting the lytic process is known except chilling, which slows down all enzymatic reactions. Many chemical agents will interfere with phage growth but the application of such agents soon leads to irreversible changes and failure of lysis.

The latent period of growth of certain phages can be greatly prolonged by the phenomenon of "lysis inhibition" (Doermann, 1948a) but the mechanism of this is not understood. Lysis may be induced before the end of the latent period by "lysis from without" by massive doses of phage (Delbrück, 1940b), by sonic vibration (Anderson and Doermann, 1952a), or in certain cases by enzymes such as lysozyme (Lwoff, Siminovitch, and Kjeldgaard, 1950). Towards the end of the normal latent period the infected bacteria become increasingly fragile and some lysis will result from laboratory manipulations such as pipetting (Levinthal and Visconti, 1953). This pre-burst fragility of the bacterial membranes has led to the erroneous conclusion from the examination of electronmicrographs that the bacterial cell wall ruptures before the end of the latent period and that the phage particles then mature in the extruded cell sap (Wyckoff, 1949a).

Lysis of the host cell accompanied by release of virus particles is readily demonstrated by direct observation in the dark field microscope. The bacteria can be observed to disintegrate at a time corresponding to the end of the latent period. At the moment of disappearance of each bacterium a cloud of scintillating particles is released in numerical agreement with the known burst size (d'Herelle, 1926; Merling-Eisenberg, 1938; Pijper, 1945). Release of phage particles is coincident with lysis of the host cell also in lysogenic bacteria, as demonstrated by micromanipulation techniques (Lwoff and Gutmann, 1950).

6. Lysis in Fluid Media

We have described the sequence of events when a few phage particles are added to a growing culture of susceptible bacteria. The phage particles adsorb and in due course the infected bacteria lyse liberating the phage progeny. These then adsorb to unlysed bacteria initiating a second cycle of infection. The infectious cycles follow one another, the phage population increasing in each cycle by a factor equal to the burst size, until all susceptible bacteria have lysed. The final phage population is usually of the order of ten to several hundred times the maximum bacterial population achieved. The theoretical phage yield would be the bacterial population multiplied by the average burst size. The actual yield is often less because some of the liberated phage is lost by readsorption to yet unlysed bacteria or to bacterial fragments. The over-all time required for lysis depends principally on the latent period and the number of phage particles inoculated, and to a lesser extent on the adsorption rate and the bacterial concentration.

If the entire bacterial population is susceptible to the phage, the culture after lysing will remain clear indefinitely. However, if the culture contains a few phage-resistant variants, the lysed culture will on further incubation become turbid again due to multiplication of the variant cells. The mutant bacterial population will be resistant to most of the phage particles, but it not infrequently happens that a large phage population contains a few variant phage particles with an extended host range, capable of attacking the phage resistant bacteria. These *host range mutant* phage particles will multiply at the expense of the mutant bacterial population and may cause a second clearing of the culture. The second lytic episode may be followed by a third turbidity if the bacterium has produced a mutant which is resistant to the host range mutant of the phage. Bacterial and phage mutations will be discussed in more detail in later chapters.

The physiological state of the bacterial population is another important factor in the lysis of fluid cultures. The latent period is minimal and the burst size largest when the bacteria are growing in the logarithmic phase in a nutritionally adequate medium. If the bacterial population has passed from the logarithmic growth phase into the stationary phase, the cells become poor hosts for phage growth, and lysis becomes very slow or may not occur (Delbrück, 1940b).

7. Lysis on Solid Media

If 10^8 bacteria are spread on the surface of an agar plate, and then incubated, they will grow as a multitude of minute colonies which soon become confluent giving a uniform film or "lawn" of bacterial growth. The bacteria will continue to grow until exhaustion of nutrients or accumulation of toxic products interferes. If a single phage particle is placed on the plate early in the growth of the bacterial film, it will adsorb to a bacterium and initiate an infectious cycle. The phage progeny remain localized at the site of lysis, and gradually radiate from this site by a slow diffusion through the agar. In this process neighboring bacteria will be attacked and lysed, increasing the phage population further. Eventually the zone of lysis may become large enough in area to be readily visible to the naked eye as a circular zone devoid of bacteria. These cleared areas were observed by d'Herelle who called them "tâches vierges" (virgin spots), or "plages" (beaches). In German they are called "Löcher" (holes), and in English "plaques" or "clearings."

The plaque size and morphology are characteristic features for a particular phage-bacterium combination, and may vary for different phages grown on the same bacterial host or for the same phage grown on different bacterial hosts. Also the plaque size and morphology may change as a result of a single step mutation on the part of the phage.

The plaque size increases during incubation of the inoculated plate, usually reaching a maximum after 8 to 12 hours, although there is sometimes a further slow increase in size on longer incubation. Plaque development does not continue indefinitely because it is dependent on active growth of the host bacteria. When bacterial growth slows because of exhaustion of nutrients, the lysis of infected bacteria is interfered with and the burst size is markedly reduced.

Another factor affecting size of plaques is the size of the individual virus particle. Elford and Andrewes (1932), who measured the particle size of a number of strains of bacteriophage by filtration through collodion membranes, noted that there was a rough inverse relationship between particle size and plaque size. They suggested that a small particle diffuses more rapidly than a large particle and consequently that, during the limited time available for plaque development, a population of small particles will radiate farther from a common center than will a population of large particles. In spite of the fact that this is a valid generalization and that its physical basis is readily understood it has been repeatedly criticized and does not invariably hold (Felix, 1953). In fact, plaque size may be limited by many factors other than diffusion. Such factors are the burst size, latent period, and adsorption rate. The meaning of the general correlation between plaque size and phage particle size may be questioned because there is also a tendency for small particle phages to have short latent periods.

The role of adsorption in affecting size of plaques has been noted several times. If a phage particle does not adsorb to a bacterium to initiate the first infectious cycle until late in the development of the bacterial lawn the result will obviously be a small plaque or perhaps no visible plaque. It is typical of slowly adsorbing phage-bacterium systems that a single plate will show great diversity of plaque sizes, those particles adsorbing early producing much larger plaques than those adsorbing late (Wahl and Blum-Emerique, 1952a; Sagik, 1954). That this is the correct explanation can be demonstrated by adsorbing the phage particles to bacteria in fluid medium, inactivating or removing the unadsorbed phage, and then plating the infected bacteria. This results in a much greater uniformity of plaque size than when free phage is plated because all plaques start to develop at about the same time.

Since the diffusion rate is often a limiting factor, anything that interferes with diffusion will reduce the plaque size. The concentration of agar in the plating medium is important for this reason, a more dilute agar permitting development of larger plaques. The agar layer method of Gratia (1936c) using a diluted agar in the upper layer is a useful means for increasing plaque size over that obtained by the classical spreading technique.

Another factor which may affect plaque size and morphology is the genetic constitution of the phage particle. Phage T2r^+ when plated on strain B of $E.$ $coli$ produces a small, fuzzy plaque. Phage T2r, derived from T2r^+ by mutation, gives a larger plaque with a sharp outline. The difference is due to the phenomenon of "lysis inhibition" (Doermann, 1948a) caused by superinfection with phage during the latent period. These plaque type mutants have been of great value in the study of bacteriophage genetics (Chapter XVIII).

The clearness or opacity of the plaque is a characteristic feature of the phage-host pair. If the bacterial culture is completely susceptible, containing no resistant bacteria, the resultant plaques will be clear. If a small proportion of resistant bacteria is present the plaques will be clouded by scattered minute colonies. If large numbers of resistant bacteria are present the plaques will be turbid and may be completely overgrown and invisible on longer incubation. This may also occur if the phage particles are able to convert a considerable proportion of the sensitive bacteria into the lysogenic condition.

In certain cases plaque development is accompanied by the release of a soluble lytic enzyme of much smaller particle size than the phage and which produces a spreading halo of lysis around the plaque. This lytic substance does not reproduce itself and in certain cases is a capsule hydrolyzing enzyme (Humphries, 1948; Adams and Park, 1956). It will diffuse across bacteria-free areas on the agar to alter the appearance of bacteria that are beyond reach of the more slowly diffusing phage particles (Sertic, 1929a).

An additional morphological peculiarity of certain plaques should be noted. One sometimes observes on large plaques, which are turbid because of the growth of resistant bacteria, small subsidiary plaques developing on the secondary turbidity. These small plaques are due to host range mutants which are produced during phage growth in the parent plaque. These secondary plaques are quite analogous to papillae on bacterial colonies, and are illustrated by Wahl and Blum-Emerique (1952a).

The importance of plaques in phage research is two-fold. They furnish a highly accurate and reproducible assay method for counting the number of viable phage particles present in a given sample of phage preparation, and they furnish most of the characters by which hereditary variation in phages is studied.

CHAPTER III

ENUMERATION OF BACTERIOPHAGE PARTICLES

Quantitative work with bacteriophages depends on simple and accurate means of counting the particles. It is essential to be able to determine relative numbers of phage particles in different samples with precision and it is often important to be able to measure the absolute number of particles.

Three principal assay methods have been used: (*1*) plaque counts on nutrient agar plates seeded with phage-susceptible bacteria, (*2*) dilution end-points using lysis of fluid bacterial cultures as an indicator for presence of phage, and (*3*) measurements of the length of time required for lysis of a standard fluid bacterial culture.

1. Plaque Counts

Only the first method mentioned is generally useful. The method was originally described by d'Herelle in 1917. An appropriate dilution of a phage preparation is mixed with a concentrated suspension of susceptible bacteria and an aliquot of the mixture is spread on the surface of an agar plate. On incubation the bacteria grow as a film, spotted with circular clear areas or plaques produced by the lytic action of the bacteriophage. D'Herelle found that large amounts of phage could be recovered from the plaques, but that none was present in the unlysed areas of the plate. Since the number of plaques obtained was directly proportional to the amount of phage preparation spread on the plate, the plaques could be understood as phage colonies containing the descendents of single phage particles. It does not follow, however, that every phage particle will produce a plaque. Although the plaque count is a good relative assay method, it will not give the absolute number of phage particles present in the inoculum.

If the same phage preparation is assayed under different environmental conditions it is immediately obvious that the plaque count has no absolute significance. A change in salt concentration can change the assay of coliphage T2 1,000-fold, while omission of tryptophan can reduce the plaque count of certain strains of phage T4 by a factor of 10^4. Assaying the same phage preparation on a series of different susceptible bacterial strains will often result in a different assay value with each host. Such observations led to the concept of *efficiency of plating* (Ellis and Delbrück, 1939).

The *relative* efficiency of plating (EOP) can be defined as the plaque count obtained under a given set of conditions relative to the plaque count under standard conditions; for instance, the EOP of phage T2 on *E. coli* strain B/6 is 0.8 of that on strain B. For such comparative purposes it is reasonable to use as standard those conditions that are found to give the highest plaque count. However, it is unwise to assume that such standard conditions enable one to count all the potentially infective phage particles present in the inoculum.

The *absolute* efficiency of plating may be defined as the plaque count relative to the total number of phage particles present in the sample. At present there are few practicable methods for determining the absolute efficiency of plating. One method compares the plaque count obtained per unit volume of phage preparation with an electron microscopic count. Luria, Williams, and Backus (1951) made measurements of this kind. The phage was suspended in a solution containing a known concentration of polystyrene latex particles, and the mixture was sprayed upon specimen screens for electron microscopy. All morphologically characteristic phage particles and all latex particles were counted in a number of fully visible droplet patterns. The latex particle count was used to determine the total volume of counted droplets, and the phage particle count then gave the phage concentration within the sampling errors of the two counts. The electron microscopic count was then compared with the plaque count obtained per unit volume of mixture. Such comparisons were made with a number of preparations of phages T2, T4, and T6. The ratio of plaque-forming units to visible particles varied from 0.4 to 1.4, falling below unity for 8 preparations and rising above for 3. These results indicate that the assay methods for T2, T4, and T6 have an absolute EOP greater than 0.5. The low EOP for most of the preparations probably indicates that they contained noninfective particles. A mechanism of origin of noninfective particles of phage T2 has been identified by Sagik (1954), and it is likely that similar principles apply to other phages.

A considerably less accurate way of measuring the absolute EOP involves determinations of the weight of the infective particle by two independent methods. For phage T2 the dry weight per infectious unit in purified preparations (Herriott and Barlow, 1952) is about twice the weight of a single particle as measured by hydrodynamic methods (Taylor, Epstein, and Lauffer, 1955). The correspondence indicates an absolute EOP of about 0.5 and also shows that the phage preparations are not grossly impure.

A modification of d'Herelle's plaque counting method, called the *agar layer method*, is almost universally used by phage workers. This method was invented by Gratia (1936c) and independently by Hershey, Kalmanson, and Bronfenbrenner (1943a). About 2 ml. of melted 0.6 per cent agar is cooled to 45° C. and inoculated with a drop of a concentrated suspension of the host bacterium. A measured volume of phage suspension is then added and the entire mixture poured over the surface of a hardened layer of nutrient agar. After the upper agar layer has solidified the plate is incubated. The bacteria grow as a multitude of tiny colonies within the soft agar layer, fed by the layer underneath, forming an opaque background against which plaques are easily seen. Advantages of the agar layer method are: (*1*) phage samples up to 1 ml. in volume can be plated per petri dish; (2) the time required for plating each sample is less than 30 seconds; (3) the plaque size is larger than that given by the spreading method; and (4) the efficiency of plating is often higher. The agar layer method has permitted accurate kinetic study of reactions that were too rapid to be followed by other methods of phage assay, and has been indispensable in genetic studies relying on recognition of different types of plaque.

2. Dilution End-Points

The dilution end-point method consists in finding the smallest amount of the phage preparation that will bring about lysis of a growing culture of susceptible bacteria. Subject to the assumption that one phage particle will cause lysis, this method measures the number of particles. However, if the adsorption is poor or phage multiplication slow, lysis may occur only when a considerable number of phage particles are inoculated, and so the phage population will be grossly underestimated. In such cases the estimate can be improved by testing for presence of phage in all tubes in which lysis failed.

This method can be made quite precise by multiplying the number of tubes tested at the limiting dilution. The phage preparation is diluted to the point where each sample should contain about one phage particle. Then 50 young cultures of the host bacterium are each inoculated with a sample of the diluted phage preparation and incubated. Each tube is then checked for lysis or for presence of phage. If the test for infective particles is reliable, the proportion of cultures in which phage multiplication did not occur will be equal to e^{-n}, from which n, the mean number of infective particles per sample, can be computed. The measurement fails unless roughly half but not more of the tubes tested prove to contain phage, which means that the method is too laborious for routine assays. It is indispensable, however, in certain types of experiment, and the student of phage should be familiar with the Poisson distribution, of which the computation mentioned is an application. The accuracy of experimental results obtained by this method can be computed (Haldane, 1939).   Phage assays by this method should check closely with assays by the agar layer method if both media are optimal for phage multiplication.   This is one way of defining the relative efficiency of plating.

3. Measurement of Lysis Time

A kinetic method of phage assay was developed by Krueger (1930), for use with rapidly lysing phages, which gives precise and reproducible results within certain limits.   The procedure is to add appropriate dilutions of phage to tubes containing standard suspensions of actively growing host cells, and to determine the length of time required for lysis to reduce the bacterial turbidity to an arbitrary end-point.   The time of lysis is inversely proportional to the logarithm of the initial phage concentration over a considerable range.   A standard phage preparation is assayed in parallel with the unknown and the activity of the unknown is expressed in terms of an arbitrary unitage defined for the standard.   One defect of the method is that it does not give the assay in terms of infectious phage particles but only in amounts relative to the standard.   This defect could be remedied by determining the content of infective particles in the standard phage preparation by one of the methods discussed above. Another defect is that the method is applicable only to free phage particles.   A suspension of phage after adsorption to host cells will assay higher than the same amount of free phage because the time required for adsorption is not included in the observed lysis time for the adsorbed phage but is included in the case of the standard phage suspension.   Therefore the application of the kinetic assay method to the study of phage adsorption (Krueger, 1931) and intracellular multiplication (Krueger and Northrop, 1930) has led to erroneous interpretations of the data. The method has been applied successfully to the assay of phages for anaerobic bacteria when for technical reasons the plaque count method did not give satisfactory results (Gold and Watson, 1950).   The method may well have other applications and should be considered whenever plating methods are unsatis-factory.

One or another of these assay methods should suffice for most purposes. A few other methods have been used for special purposes. The use of the electron microscope to determine the total number of morphologically typical phage particles in a known volume of suspension has been mentioned above. A method that involves the ability of phage particles to kill the host cell on adsorption is particularly suitable to the assay of phage inactivated by ultraviolet light. On adsorption the phage particles are distributed over the host cell population in accordance with the Poisson distribution. The viable bacterial population is accurately determined before and after phage adsorption. The proportion of the bacterial population that survives is equal to e^{-n} where n is the mean number of lethal particles adsorbed per bacterium. Then n times the initial number of bacteria per unit volume gives the number of phage particles, per unit volume, adsorbed and capable of killing. Conditions should be such that most of the phage particles present are adsorbed to bacteria and the value of n should be greater than one (Luria and Dulbecco, 1949).

4. Intracellular Phage

Mature phage particles present in yet unlysed bacteria present a special assay problem. An infected bacterium if plated before bursting will form only a single plaque regardless of how many mature phage particles it may produce. However, the number of mature phage particles present in the bacterium at any time during the latent period may be determined by interrupting phage development by chilling or by chemical agents, and liberating the mature phage by breaking open the infected bacteria by biological, enzymatic, or physical means (Doermann, 1952; Anderson and Doermann, 1952a). The average number of mature phage particles per bacterium liberated by premature lysis may then be determined by plaque counting methods.

A peculiar biochemical feature of phage T2 and its relatives has been exploited for the analysis of vegetative phage within infected bacteria. The nucleic acid of this serological group of phages contains the unique base hydroxymethylcytosine (Wyatt and Cohen, 1953). This base may be readily distinguished from the other bases present in bacterial or phage nucleic acids by paper chromatography of acid hydrolyzates of the nucleic acid fraction, and may be determined quantitatively. It is therefore possible to distinguish the DNA of phage T2 from host cell DNA and to determine quantitatively the total amount of phage DNA present per infected cell. The amount of mature phage DNA per cell can be calculated from plaque counts on prematurely lysed infected bacteria. The amount of phage DNA present as vegetative phage in the infected bacteria can be calculated by subtracting the mature phage DNA from the total phage DNA. This method has been used by Hershey, Dixon, and Chase (1953) to study the intracellular multiplication of phage T2.

Another method for assay of intracellular phage substances is based on the high specificity of phage antigens. The antibody that neutralizes phage infectivity reacts with a protein situated on the phage tail but fails to react with any substances present in uninfected bacteria. The relative amount of neutralizing antibody present in a sample of serum can be accurately determined (see Chapter VIII). Phage tail antigen will combine with phage neutralizing antibodies and so decrease the neutralizing ability of the serum. This "serum-blocking power" of phage antigens can be calibrated in terms of phage particle equivalents and used as a measure of the total amount of phage tail antigen present in infected bacteria when they are prematurely lysed at various times during the latent period. The amount of phage tail antigen already included in mature phage particles can be calculated from the mean number of mature phage particles present and the known antigen content per phage particle. The difference between the content of total tail antigen and mature phage tail antigen gives the phage tail antigen not yet built into mature phage at the time of premature lysis (DeMars, 1955). Similar techniques have been used to determine the amount of phage-specific complement-fixing antigen present at various times in the latent period (Y. T. Lanni, 1954).

It is evident that the speed and accuracy of assay methods for extracellular and intracellular mature phage and for various phage components have been major factors in the very rapid increase in knowledge of phage reproduction. The introduction of plaque counting methods into the field of animal virology by Dulbecco (1952c) is permitting a parallel development in this field.

CHAPTER IV

SIZE AND MORPHOLOGY OF BACTERIOPHAGES

The presence of phage particles inside the infected bacterial cell and the release of these particles on bursting of the cell were seen in the dark field microscope by d'Herelle (1926) and photographed by Merling-Eisenberg (1938). The agglutination of phage particles by antiphage serum was photographed in the ultraviolet microscope by Barnard (Burnet, 1933c). Although there is no difficulty in seeing light scattered by the larger phages under these conditions, they are not resolved by light microscopes. Consequently our knowledge of the morphology of the particles begins with their examination under the electron microscope.

1. Electron Microscopy of Bacteriophage Particles

The electron microscope was first applied to the study of phages by Ruska (1940) and Pfankuch and Kausche (1940). It was soon clear that the particles are striking and characteristic in shape (Ruska, 1943; Luria, Delbrück, and Anderson, 1943). Most of the phages examined resemble tadpoles, with long tails attached to spherical, cylindrical, or polyhedral heads. Some phages at first thought to be tailless spheres revealed on closer examination polyhedral shapes and a rudimentary tail (Williams and Fraser, 1953). In numerous instances the tail proves to be a specialized organ for attachment to bacteria; very likely all phages possess such an organ (T. F. Anderson, 1953). Micrographs of several phages are shown in Figures 1, 2, and 3 and the frontispiece of this book.

TABLE I

Phage Morphology in Electron Microscope

Subject	Reference
Book on Electron Microscopy	Wyckoff (1949b)
Review on Bacteriophages	Ruska (1943)
Coli phage T1	Williams and Fraser (1953)
Coli phage T2	Williams and Fraser (1953)
Coli phage T4	Williams and Fraser (1953)
Coli phage T6	Williams and Fraser (1953)
Coli phage C16	Giuntini, Lépine, Nicolle, and Croissant (1947)
Coli phage T7	Williams and Fraser (1953)
Coli phage T5	Williams and Fraser (1953)
Salmonella pullorum phage	Baylor, Severens, and Clark (1944)
Erwinia carotovora phage	Chapman, Hillier, and Johnson (1951)
Streptococcus lactis phage	Cherry and Watson (1949)
Streptomyces griseus phage	Koerber, Greenspan, and Langlykke (1950)
Bacillus megaterium phage	McLauchlan, Clark, and Boswell (1947)
Streptococcus lactis phage	Parmelee, Carr, and Nelson (1949)
Corynebacterium diphtheriae phage	Toshach, S. (1950)
Mycobacterium smegmatis phage	Whittaker (1950)
Streptococcus lactis phage	Williamson and Bertaud (1951)
Bacillus subtilis phage	Giuntini, Lépine, Nicolle, and Croissant (1947)
Salmonella paratyphoid B phage	Giuntini, Lépine, Nicolle, and Croissant (1947)
Staphylococcus phage (Twort)	Giuntini, Lépine, Nicolle, and Croissant (1947)
Staphylococcus phage K	Hotchin (1954)
Pseudomonas aeruginosa phage	Schultz, Thomassen, and Marton (1948)
Many phages	Terada (1956)

Although many phages have now been examined (Table I), it is unfortunate that no morphological comparison has been made of a large group of phages classified also by other means. From the study of a small group, it appears that morphological features will aid in classification of phages much as they do in classification of other organisms (Delbrück, 1946b).

Microscopic measurement of size of virus particles is complicated by shrinkage and distortion on drying, increase of size by shadowing with metals, and difficulties in calibration.   These difficulties have been minimized in various ways (Anderson, 1951; Williams, 1953).   Some very careful measurements have been published by Williams and Fraser (1953).   Estimates of

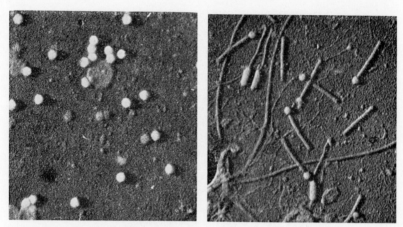

Figure 1. Phages of diverse morphology.   Left, phage T3, unpurified lysate.   × 46,000.   Unpublished.   Right, two phages carried by a lysogenic strain of *Bacillus cereus* (Kellenberger and Kellenberger, 1952).   Unpurified lysate, ×40,000.   Unpublished.

particle size of several bacteriophages by electron microscopy and other methods are given in Table II.

Further information about the structure of several phages has been obtained by degradation of the particles in various ways. Coliphage T2 and its relatives, and the staphylococcal phage K, are subject to osmotic shock (Anderson, 1949; Hotchin, 1954). To observe this, the phages are suspended in concentrated solutions of sodium chloride and, a few minutes later, water is dumped in.   The phage particles lose their characteristic infectivity.   Microscopic examination now reveals empty, but more or less intact, phage ghosts.   Herriott (1951a) showed that the ghosts, after treatment with deoxyribonuclease, contained most of the phage proteins and retained ability to adsorb to and kill bacteria. The phage nucleic acid presumably escapes through cracks in the phage head and may be seen in electron micrographs as long filaments about 20 A in thickness (Williams, 1953). These phage particles consist, therefore, of a nucleic acid core surrounded by a membrane responsible for the overall

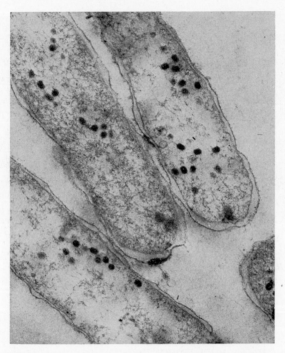

Figure 2. Phage T2 seen inside bacteria infected 40 minutes earlier. Ultrathin sections prepared as described by Kellenberger, Ryter, and Schwab (1956). ×32,400. Unpublished.

shape of the particle (T. F. Anderson, Rappaport, and Muscatine, 1953). T5, as shown in a somewhat different manner, is similarly constructed (Lark and Adams, 1953).

Some additional features of the tail structure of phages T2 and T4 have been resolved in considerable detail. Kellenberger and Arber (1955) observed stepwise changes in the morphology of these phages during the action of oxidizing agents (Figure 3). Williams and Fraser (1956) described degradation products produced by freezing and thawing. Both groups reached essentially similar conclusions about the structure of the phage tail, which may be described as follows. The tail is composed of a rigid central core or pin running the full length, and an outer tubular sheath. The sheath itself is composed of two

Figure 3. Left, phage T2, purified preparation of normal particles.   ×31,-500. Unpublished. Right, T2 particles treated with hydrogen peroxide showing alteration of tail structure.   ×32,500. Reproduced from E. Kellenberger and W. Arber, 1955, *Z. Naturforsch.*, **10b**, 698, with permission.

parts. The half proximal to the head of the particle retains its integrity under the influences mentioned, and is occasionally obtained in detached form, when its hollow structure becomes evident. The distal half of the tail sheath is readily removed, and yields long slender fibrils, probably four per phage particle, in the process. These fibrils may be coiled about the tail pin, or may already exist partly as free ends, in the natural state. The central pin often shows a knob at one end, to which remnants of fibrils may or may not be adhering. Isolated pins were ob-

TABLE II
The Sizes of Bacteriophages

Phage	Ultra-filtration,[a] mμ	Centrifugation,[b] mμ	Diffusion, mμ	X-rays, mμ	α-rays or deuterons, mμ	Electron micrographs	
						Head, mμ	Tail, mμ
T2	—	54[c]	107[c]	50[d]	—	65 × 95	25 × 100[e]
T4	—	—	55[f]	50[d]	—	65 × 95	25 × 100[e]
T6	—	54[g]	94[g]	50[d]	—	65 × 95	25 × 100[e]
C16	90	90[h]	—	50[i]	66[j]	65 × 70	150[k]
WLL	90	65[l]	—	—	—	—	—
Staph K	90	65[l]	—	40[m]	50[m]	55	225[n]
T5	—	45[g]	—	—	—	65	10 × 170[e]
T1	—	—	—	38[d]	28[o]	50	10 × 150[e]
D20	50	50[h]	—	—	—	—	—
T3	—	—	36[f]	38[d]	—	47	10 × 15[e]
T7	—	43[g]	—	33[l]	—	47	10 × 15[e]
C13	37	—	—	—	—	—	—
S13	21	16[l]	—	16[m]	16[m]	—	—
φ × 174	—	16[p]	—	17[p]	18[p]	—	—

[a] The limiting pore diameter (Elford, 1938) times the factor 0.83 (Lea, 1946).
[b] Computed from sedimentation constant only (Putnam, 1950).
[c] Taylor, Epstein, and Lauffer (1955).
[d] Watson (1950).
[e] Williams and Fraser (1953).
[f] Polson (1948).
[g] Putnam (1954).
[h] Schlesinger or Bechold and Schlesinger from Elford (1938).
[i] Luria and Exner (1941).
[j] Holweck, Luria, and Wollman (1940).
[k] Giuntini, Lépine, Nicolle, and Croissant (1947).
[l] Elford (1938).
[m] Lea and Salaman (1946).
[n] Smiles, Welch, and Elford (1948).
[o] Pollard and Forro (1949).
[p] Lépine, Bonét-Maury, Boulgakov, and Giuntini (1944).

served earlier in unpurified lysates by Herriott and Barlow (1952). A very similar structure for the tail of the staphylococcus phage K had been surmised by Hotchin (1954). The functional significance of this structure is discussed by Williams and Fraser (1956).

Discontinuity of internal structure of the phage head is noticeable in certain types of preparation (Luria, Delbruck, and Anderson, 1943; Terada, 1956). Unlike the tail structure described above, which undoubtedly reflects functional differentiation, the appearance of the head contents may depend on accidents of drying (T. F. Anderson, Rappaport, and Muscatine, 1953).

2. Ultrafiltration

Some of the earliest attempts to measure the size of phage particles sought to determine the largest pore diameter of collodion membranes through which the particles could not pass. The method was chiefly developed by Elford, whose review (Elford, 1938) is the source of the information given here. The method is based on the following principles.

A series of graded collodion membranes can be prepared by systematically varying the solvent mixture from which the membrane is precipitated. Measurements of the rate of flow of water through such membranes yield, with the aid of hydrodynamic theory, a nominal average pore diameter. Finally, an empirical factor, arrived at by testing substances of known particle size, relates the average pore diameter of the membrane to the size of particles it will hold back. This factor presumably corrects for heterogeneity of pore size, adsorption, electrostatic effects, and other imponderables. (Adsorption is minimized by suspending the phage in peptone solutions.) Elford multiplied the hydrodynamic pore diameter of the coarsest membrane that would fail to pass phage by factors varying between 0.33 and 0.50, depending on the membrane, to obtain the diameter of the phage particle. The sizes he determined have proved to be somewhat too small. Approximately correct diameters are obtained from

Elford's data by increasing his empirical factor to 0.83 (Lea, 1946). Nevertheless, Elford's data were for a long time the best information available as to size and diversity of size of different phages. The relative sizes he determined were remarkably exact. This is shown in Table II, which lists Lea's corrections to Elford's estimates.

The method is still useful. Now that a number of phages of known size are available, it should be possible to estimate the comparative size of an unknown phage with considerable precision. The usefulness of the method is all the greater since it does not require the phage to be purified or concentrated. For some of the smaller phages, not yet identifiable in the electron microscope, probably no better method is available.

Ultrafiltration is also useful for concentrating and purifying phages (Elford, 1938) and for isolating phage-specific materials smaller in size than phage particles (Burnet, 1933b; DeMars, 1955).

3. Analytical Centrifugation

Centrifugal measurements of particle size of phages were also attempted some years ago. Ingenious methods were developed to follow the sedimentation of infective particles by plaque counts under conditions in which no sedimentation boundary is established. This work is reviewed by Elford (1938). The application of the modern optical ultracentrifuge to the study of phages is described by Hook, Beard, Taylor, Sharp, Beard (1946), Putnam (1950), and Taylor, Epstein, and Lauffer (1955).

Sizes of some phage particles calculated from sedimentation constants are given in Table II. These are computed without correction for water content and departure from spherical shape, which means that they are underestimates that have, in fact, no exact meaning. From combined sedimentation and diffusion measurements, the true particle weight can be calculated. In this way Taylor, Epstein, and Lauffer (1955) found the dry weight of a particle of T2 to be 3.3×10^{-16} grams. Putnam's

(1950) estimate for T6 is very similar. This corresponds to a particle diameter of 75 mμ, which should be understood as the diameter of a phage particle dried and compressed to a sphere of density 1.5. These hydrodynamic measurements of the particle weight of T2 and T6 are the only satisfactory ones of their kind for any phage.

Taylor, Epstein, and Lauffer (1955) also measured the wet density of T2 by sedimentation in a sucrose gradient. The density found, 1.27, calls for a water content of 37.5 per cent, a natural particle weight of 5.3 $\times$ 10^{-16} grams, and a spherical diameter of 92 mμ. If anything this water content is probably underestimated, because sucrose may extract water from phage (Anderson, Rappaport, and Muscatine, 1953).

Phages T2 and T6 exist in two reversibly interconvertible forms. One, sedimenting and diffusing the more rapidly, predominates at pH 5, the other at pH 7. According to Taylor, Epstein, and Lauffer (1955), these probably differ only in shape. It is possible that these differences reflect different states of the tail fibrils described earlier.

4. Diffusion Constants

Measurements of diffusion coefficients are needed for the proper interpretation of sedimentation constants, and also lead directly to an equivalent particle diameter computed on the assumption of spherical shape (Putnam, 1950). Early applications of diffusion measurements by the porous disk method to phages (Northrop, 1938; Kalmanson and Bronfenbrenner, 1939) yielded erroneous results and improbable theories. What was measured was not diffusion but flow of solvent through the disk (Hershey, Kimura, and Bronfenbrenner, 1947). Polson (1948) measured reasonable diffusion constants of phages T3 and T4 but Polson and Shepard (1949) studying the same two phages again decided that T4 must be self-motile. In all these attempts, efforts were made to measure diffusion of infective particles in dilute solutions. None of them proved very successful.

Diffusion of phage T6 across an optically visible boundary was carefully studied by Goldwasser and Putnam (1951). They found that the particles diffused like spheres 94 mμ in diameter, in excellent agreement with physical predictions. Similar results were obtained by Taylor, Epstein, and Lauffer (1955) for T2.

5. Electrophoresis

The mobility of particles in an electric field yields information about the sign and density of charges on their surfaces, but does not permit any estimate of size. Only phage T6 has been studied in this way (Putnam, 1950). The particles were negatively charged down to pH 5.2, below which measurements were not attempted. Only one rather diffuse boundary was observed for the best preparations. Since reversal of the electric field did not sharpen the boundary, no evidence for electrophoretic inhomogeneity was obtained. The relatively slow mobility suggested a protein, rather than a nucleic acid, surface.

6. Ionizing Radiations

Certain radiations such as electrons, protons, deuterons, neutrons, alpha particles, gamma rays, and X-rays are called ionizing radiations because in traversing matter they produce ion pairs by ejecting electrons from atoms. This ionization is often followed by chemical change, which if it occurs in an essential molecule can result in death of cells and viruses. All viruses and many single-celled organisms are inactivated by ionizing radiations as an exponential function of the dose of radiation. This has been interpreted as indicating that a single ionization is sufficient to inactivate (Lea, 1946). One may readily determine the dose of radiation which will produce an average of one lethal event per organism; that is the 37 per cent survival dose. Since the density and something about the spatial distribution of ionizations produced by a given dosage of various radiations are known, it is possible to calculate from the 37 per cent survival dose the size of the target in which ionizations must be produced in order that inactivation results. A description of the *target theory* and of the methods of calculating the target size from the 37 per cent survival dose of ionizing radiations is given by Lea (1946). For small viruses the calculated target size is within experimental error the same as the virus size, indicating that a cluster of ionizations anywhere within the virus particle may be lethal. However for larger viruses the target size has been found to be smaller than the size of the virus particle. The larger viruses are heterogeneous in sensitivity containing considerable amounts of material that is relatively insensitive to irradiation. The target size will be a minimum estimate of the virus particle size. When the target size is determined using two different kinds of radiation such as X-rays and alpha particles, the results are usually in good agreement in the case of small viruses. However with larger viruses the target size determined from alpha particle data is larger than that calculated from X-ray data. This has been taken to mean that with the larger viruses the target is not a uniformly sensitive sphere as assumed in the theory but is structurally complex. That the particles of the larger viruses are structurally complex is evident from electron micrographs, and the inactivation data extend this complexity even into that portion of the particle which is radiation sensitive. Further applications of the target theory to the study of size and structure of viruses are discussed by Pollard (1953, 1954).

Size of bacteriophages determined with the aid of target theory are included in Table II for comparison with sizes determined by other methods. These have been derived from graphs given by Lea (1946) and more recent data. It should be realized that the theory involves arbitrary assumptions that render interpretation doubtful (Watson, 1950). In particular it is assumed that two or more ion pairs are wasted for each lethal ionization within the phage particle, the number depending on target size and kind of radiation.

7. Nonionizing Radiations

Ultraviolet and visible light can also inactivate viruses. However, the mechanism of inactivation is quite different from that of ionizing radiations. In the case of the relatively low energy ultraviolet and visible radiations, entire quanta of radiation are absorbed by specific chemical structures. Under suitable conditions the energy absorbed may be enough to break chemical bonds and inactivate viruses. Since the energy is absorbed only by certain structures, the rate of killing gives no information about the size of the virus particle. It was thought at one time that there was an inverse relationship between sensitivity to ultraviolet light and virus particle size. However, lambda, the phage carried by the lysogenic strain K12 of *E. coli*, is 13 times more resistant to ultraviolet radiation than is coliphage T5, which is about the same size (Weigle and Delbrück, 1951). The various physiological effects of ionizing and nonionizing radiations will be considered in detail in Chapter VI.

8. Weight of the Infectious Particle

For those phages that have been isolated in highly purified form, the dry weight of the infectious particle has usually been determined. If the dry density is known the particle size can be calculated from the relation

$$\text{Particle weight} = 4\pi R^3/3 \times \text{density}$$

where R is the radius of a sphere of mass and density equal to those of the dried phage particle. Sizes calculated in this way from available data are summarized in Table III, and may be compared with particle sizes of the same viruses obtained by other methods and summarized in Table II. As might be expected particle size estimated in this way is somewhat larger than the size obtained by other methods. Any impurity in the phage preparation would increase the dry weight per infective particle, and any inactivation of phage during purification, or an efficiency of plating less than unity, would have the same ef-

TABLE III

Sizes of Phage Particles Estimated from Particle Weights

Phage	Dry particle weight $\times 10^{-16}$ g.	Particle diameter,[a] mμ	Reference
T2	10	110	Hook, Beard, Taylor, Sharp, and Beard (1946)
T2	5	86	Herriott and Barlow (1952)
T6	7.5	100	Putnam (1954)
WLL	4.3	83	Schlesinger (1934)
T7	4.0	80	Putnam (1954); Kerby, Gowdy, Dillon, Dillon, Csaky, Sharp, and Beard (1949)
Staph. muscae	18	134	Northrop (1938)

[a] Calculated for a measured or assumed density of 1.5 grams per cubic cm.

fect. However, the purity of the best preparations is excellent, and at least half the particles form plaques (Luria, Williams, and Backus, 1951). Therefore the particle weight of T2 given by Herriott and Balrow (1952) is overestimated by a factor less than two, and the particle diameter by less than 26 per cent.

9. Summary

The well-studied phage particles are sperm-shaped structures containing, in the head portion, mostly nucleic acid surrounded by a protein membrane, often hexagonal in cross section, to which the tail is attached. From some phages, the membrane and tail can be isolated as a functionally intact "ghost" following osmotic shock. Different phages range in size from approximately 0.1 micron in diameter to a poorly defined minimum of perhaps 20 mμ. They also show characteristic differences in shape and structure.

Sizes of these particles can be measured in three more or less satisfactory ways. Electron microscopy is the most informative. It probably underestimates size in general, because of unavoidable shrinkage on drying. Analytical centrifugation, supplemented by measurements of diffusion, hydration, and wet density, also yields precise information. Weight measurements of purified preparations, related directly or indirectly to electron-microscopic counts of particle number, together with independent estimates of chemical purity, are now feasible.

All the available methods have been applied only to T2. For this phage the particle "diameter" in mμ is 65 to 95 in electron micrographs, 75 by sedimentation and diffusion, and 86 to 110 computed from the weights per infective particle, all referring to dried particles. These estimates are consistent with an equivalent spherical diameter of about 90 mμ and other characteristics of the natural particles as determined by hydrodynamic methods.

In addition, very simple methods, such as ultrafiltration or measurements of sensitivity to X-rays or beta rays, suffice to classify one phage in relation to others. These methods are available in instances where the other methods fail.

CHAPTER V

EFFECTS OF PHYSICAL AND CHEMICAL AGENTS (EXCEPT RADIATIONS) ON BACTERIOPHAGE PARTICLES

The commonly studied bacteriophages are extraordinarily stable under appropriate conditions. The infective titer may fall at the rate of one per cent per day, or often much less. Needless to say, the stability depends on many environmental factors, some of which act differently on different phages. A knowledge of these factors is of immediate concern to anyone interested in the concentration, purification, or preservation of phage.

Phages are generally stable in their own lysates provided these are free from specific inactivating agents (receptor substances) derived from the lysed bacteria, and contain suitable electrolytes. The absence of general poisons is more or less guaranteed by the fact that the phage grew in the first place. Purified phages are generally stable in neutral, buffered solutions, prepared from glass-distilled water, containing 0.1 M sodium chloride, 0.001 M magnesium chloride, and, if the phage concentration is low, a small amount of gelatin. The effects of receptor substances, if these are not completely removed, can be minimized by choosing conditions unfavorable for specific interaction, but these conditions vary greatly from phage to phage. Low temperatures, of course, favor stability, especially if other conditions are suboptimal.

In addition to these purely practical considerations, the study of inactivation of phages under controlled conditions has yielded important information about the structure and function of phage particles. Much of the recent systematic work has dealt with the effects of radiations, which will be considered separately in Chapter VI. This chapter describes the effects of other physical and chemical agents on phage particles. Some of the agents that have been studied tend to be phage-specific in their action, and can be used as aids to the classification of phage types (Burnet, 1933e). This application is discussed in Chapter XXII.

1. Effect of pH

Bacteriophages are usually stable over the pH range of 5 to 8. At low temperatures the range can often be extended to pH 4 and pH 9 or 10. T2 can be precipitated at pH 4 without loss of infectivity (Herriott and Barlow, 1952). Curves showing stability as a function of pH are given for purified preparations of coliphage T2 by Sharp, Hook, Taylor, Beard, and Beard (1946), of coliphage T6 by Putnam, Kozloff, and Neil (1949), and of coliphage T7 by Kerby, Gowdy, Dillon, Dillon, Csaky, Sharp, and Beard (1949). Some kinetic data on phages C16 and S13 are given by Wahl and Blum-Emerique (1947) over the pH range between 3 and 8.

2. Urea and Urethane

Both urea and urethane denature proteins and inactivate enzymes. They also inactivate viruses. Burnet (1933e) in his studies on the classification of the dysentery-coli phages used susceptibility to inactivation by concentrated solutions of urea as a differential characteristic. He found large differences in rate of inactivation from one strain to another. Sato (1956) studied the action of urea on phage T4 and observed minimal inactivating effects at temperatures near 15°. Urea has been used also to extract nucleic acid from phage T2 (Cohen, 1947a). The effect of urethane on the thermal inactivation of coliphage T5 was investigated by Foster, Johnson, and Miller (1949). The thermal inactivation rate was increased by urethane at all concentrations above 0.05 M, the first-order velocity constant increasing as the 2.3 power of the urethane concentration. The

Arrhenius constant (see Glossary) was somewhat increased by the presence of urethane. The authors suggest that there may be more than one urethane-catalyzed reaction involved in phage inactivation.

3. Detergents

Because of the marked bactericidal effects of soaps and other detergents, these agents were tested quite early for possible virucidal effects. Vaccinia virus and influenza virus are rapidly inactivated by detergents while poliomyelitis virus is resistant. The earlier literature was reviewed by Stock and Francis (1940) in connection with studies on the effects of soaps on influenza virus. These authors found that influenza virus was rapidly inactivated by oleic, linoleic, and linolenic acid soaps at pH 7.5 without impairment of antigenicity. Burnet and Lush (1940) tested dodecyl sodium sulfate, sodium deoxycholate, and saponin on a number of animal viruses and also on phages C16, D6, D44, two salmonella phages and two staphylococcus phages. All of the phages were resistant to inactivation by the three detergents although many of the animal viruses were rapidly inactivated. Klein, Kalter, and Mudd (1945) tested a number of cationic and anionic detergents on vaccinia virus, phage T2, a shigella phage, and a staphylococcus phage. Excepting phage T2 which was resistant to all the detergents tested, all the viruses were susceptible to inactivation by some of the detergents. Putnam, Miller, Palm, and Evans (1952) noted that phage T7 but not T6 was rapidly inactivated by the cationic detergent dodecyltrimethylammonium chloride. However, phage T6 is inactivated by $M/1,000$ benzyldodecyldimethylammonium chloride and less effectively by cetyltrimethylammonium bromide and dodecyl sodium sulfate (Putman, Kozloff, and Neil, 1949).

Certain detergents cause the separation of protein from nucleic acid of tobacco mosiac virus, permitting the reconstitution of virus particles from the separate components (Fraenkel-Conrat, 1956). Dodecyl sodium sulfate has been used in a similar manner for the isolation of nucleic acid from T2 (Mayers and Spizizen, 1954).

Bacteria are generally more sensitive to detergents than are bacteriophages, suggesting the use of detergents to rid phage-containing materials of bacteria (Kalter, Mordaunt, and Chapman, 1946). Detergents presumably act by denaturing proteins and cell membranes. Their properties are summarized in a symposium (Anson, 1946).

4. Chelating Agents

Chelating agents are chemicals that form undissociated complexes with metal ions. Lark and Adams (1953) found that citrate, ethylenediaminetetraacetate and -triphosphate accelerated the inactivation of phage T5 at low salt concentrations. These substances may act by forming a complex with some cation bound to the phage particle. Stocks of phage T5 are heterogeneous with respect to susceptibility to the action of chelating agents, since inactivation curves are not exponential with respect to time.

5. Mustard Gas

Mustard gas and nitrogen mustard are of biological interest not only because they inactivate enzymes and kill viruses and microorganisms but also because of their mutagenic activity. Mustard gas was tested on a variety of microorganisms, viruses, enzymes, and on the pneumococcus transforming principle by Herriott (1948). Among the test objects were coliphage T2 and a staphylococcus phage. The phages were inactivated in accordance with first-order kinetics, the velocity constants being of the same order of magnitude as those found for microorganisms but larger than those for enzymes. Luria and Dulbecco (1949) reported that nitrogen mustard inactivated T2 and T6. An analysis of the effect of mustards on phages might help to elucidate the nature of the so-called radiomimetic action of mustards. Herriott and Price (1948) found that mustard-killed bacterial cells still retain their ability to serve as hosts for phage multiplication, another resemblance to the action of radiations.

6. Alcohols

Cold aqueous solutions of glycerine and ethyl alcohol do not inactivate most phages, and in fact cold 30 per cent alcohol at pH 5.4 has been used to precipitate phage T6 as one step in the concentration and purification of this virus (Putnam, Kozloff, and Neil, 1949). Undiluted glycerine and ethanol cause rapid inactivation of phages (d'Herelle, 1926). Bronfenbrenner (1925) studied the effect of salts on the stability of phages during alcohol and acetone precipitation and concluded that suitable mixtures of monovalent and divalent cations were preferable to pure salts in stabilizing the phage. Wahl and Blum-Emerique (1949a) used alcohol precipitation to purify phage C16, and Hotchin (1954) used acetone to precipitate phage K.

7. Other Chemicals

The enzyme poisons, cyanide and fluoride, do not damage phages in concentrations that are lethal to bacteria. Cyanide has been used to stop phage development without inactivating phage particles at desired times in the latent period (Doermann, 1952). Thymol and chloroform are bactericidal but do not inactivate phages. Any of these substances can be used to preserve phage lysates (Wahl and Blum-Emerique, 1949b; Frédéricq, 1952a, Séchaud and Kellenberger, 1956).

Formaldehyde inactivates bacteriophages, but Schultz and Gebhardt (1935) reported that formalin inactivated staphylococcus phage could be reactivated by dilution. Labaw, Mosely, and Wyckoff (1949) noticed a large difference between coliphage T1 and phages T2 and T4 in susceptibility to inactivation by formaldehyde.

There are many observations to the effect that mercuric ion inactivates phages. Krueger and Baldwin (1934) found that the rate of inactivation of staphylococcus phage K by $HgCl_2$ followed first-order kinetics to 99 per cent inactivation and then slowed. With 2.8 per cent $HgCl_2$ a phage stock titering 5 $\times$ 10^9 per ml. could be completely inactivated in a few days. Treatment of such a stock with hydrogen sulfide followed by centrifugation resulted in complete reactivation. Essentially similar results were obtained by Wahl (1939, 1946c) with six different phages, which differed, however, in rate of inactivation.

Oxidizing agents such as peroxide, halogens, ozone, and permanganate rapidly inactivate viruses. In contrast mild reducing agents have no harmful effect and Wahl and Blum-Emerique (1946) have suggested the addition of hydrosulfite to protect phage preparations from oxidation during storage. Contrary to general expectation, however, Alper (1954) suggests that phage S13 is inactivated by the reducing action of hydrogen peroxide. In support of this he finds that the inactivation by peroxide is accelerated by exclusion of oxygen, that mild oxidizing agents like chlorate and iodate do not inactivate the phage, and that ascorbic acid does. The question calls for systematic work.

8. Sonic Vibration

High intensity sonic vibrations imparted to a fluid medium by a vibrating crystal or diaphragm can denature proteins and destroy bacteria. They have been used to liberate enzymes from bacteria by rupture of the bacterial cell walls (Shropshire, 1947). The effect of intense sonic vibration on the seven coliphages of the T group and on their common host, strain B of E. coli, was studied by T. F. Anderson, Boggs, and Winters (1948) using the Raytheon magneto-striction apparatus operating at about 9,000 cycles per second. The inactivation followed the kinetics of a first order reaction and there was a large variation in sensitivity among the phage strains tested. The small particle phages T1, T3, and T7 were relatively resistant (99 per cent inactivation in 60 minutes) whereas the large particle phages T2, T4, T5, and T6 were sensitive (99 per cent inactivation in about 5 minutes). The host bacteria were somewhat more resistant than the large phages but much more sensitive than the small phages.   T. F. Anderson and Doermann (1952a) applied this information in studies of the intracellular development of phage T3 (Chapter XI).

Anderson and Doermann (1952b) also tested the effect of sonic vibration on phage that had been inactivated with antibody.   Phage T3 was treated with anti-T3 serum to a phage survival of 10^{-4}.   After dilution, treatment of the neutralized phage with sonic vibrations resulted in a 40-fold increase in phage titer, presumably due to breaking of the bonds linking antibody molecules to phage particles.

9. Surface Denaturation

Proteins are rapidly denatured when subjected to the unbalanced forces existing at gas-liquid or liquid-liquid interfaces, and physiologically active proteins such as enzymes and toxins are thus inactivated.   The first quantitative study of this phenomenon with phages was made by Campbell-Renton (1942). She found that all the phages tested were rather rapidly inactivated when aqueous solutions were vigorously shaken in air. In one experiment for which detailed data are given the inactivation was first order to a survival of less than 10^{-4}, except for an initial lag of 25 minutes due to the presence of 100 μg. per ml. of peptone in the medium.   The inactivation could be greatly retarded by increasing the concentration of peptone, and accelerated by omitting peptone.

The same phenomenon was studied by Adams (1948) with the seven coliphages of the T group.   Surface inactivation occurred very rapidly in a chemically defined diluent at the gas-liquid interfaces formed by bubbling or shaking with air or nitrogen. Under conditions of vigorous shaking the inactivation kinetics were first order with a low temperature coefficient, as might be expected of a reaction in which the rate-limiting step is diffusion of the virus particles into the region of the interface.   The reaction rate was nearly independent of pH over most of the stability range of the phages but was greatly accelerated near the acid and alkaline ends of this range. The first-order velocity constants differed from one phage type to another, ranging from 0.05 to 1.2 per minute. The velocity constant calculated from the data of Campbell-Renton is 0.06 per minute.

Surface inactivation can be completely prevented by adding enough protein to the diluent to saturate the gas-liquid interface and prevent access of the virus to the surface. For this purpose 10 to 100 μg. of gelatin per ml. of solution are adequate. Surface inactivation must be considered whenever virus preparations are diluted in buffer solutions free of protein or peptones, especially when surface-volume ratios become large. Similar losses can be expected at solid-liquid interfaces, and call for similar precautions.

The effect of denaturation at liquid-liquid interfaces has not been studied systematically. Garen (personal communication) isolated DNA from phage T2 by shaking aqueous suspensions with chloroform. Hotchin (1954), on the other hand, reported no inactivation of phage K on shaking with isobutanol-chloroform mixtures; he used this method as a step in purification of the phage. From what has been said above the effects should depend very much on total concentration of phage and other proteins.

10. Heat Inactivation

D'Herelle (1926) noted that several phages were inactivated by heating at 75° C. for 30 minutes, whereas some survived and some did not after heating at 70° C. Observations of this type led to the notion of a qualitatively defined inactivation temperature, characteristic for each phage, analogous to the thermal death point used to report the results of similar tests with bacteria. Such qualitative information sufficed for practical purposes, and led to the use of heat treatment in lieu of filtration to eliminate bacteria from phage preparations.

Quantitative study of the effects of heating showed that phages are inactivated in accordance with first-order kinetics. The temperature coefficient of inactivation is very high, the Arrhenius constant being of the order of 100 kilocalories (Krueger, 1932).   The only known reaction with such a high coefficient at laboratory temperatures is the heat denaturation of proteins. Presumably heat inactivation of phages is the result of denaturation of this kind.   Some data from the literature on Arrhenius constants and the temperature range tested are given in Table IV.

TABLE IV
Arrhenius Constants for Heat Inactivation of Phages

Phage	Activa- tion energy, cal.	Temper- ature range, ° C.	Reference
In broth			
Staph K	101,000	51–62	Krueger (1932)
Coli T5	170,000	above 65	Foster, Johnson, and Miller (1949)
Coli T5	5,000	below 65	Foster, Johnson, and Miller (1949)
Coli T5	86,000	63–73	Adams (1949a)
Coli T5st	100,000	65–75	Lark and Adams (1953)
Coli T1	106,000	65–70	Adams (1949a)
Coli T1	73,600	60–70	Pollard and Forro (1949)
Coli T1	95,000	60–75	Pollard and Reaume (1951)
Coli T7	77,000	55–60	Adams (1949a)
Coli T7	60,700	45–60	Pollard and Reaume (1951)
Coli T3	105,000	47–60	Pollard and Reaume (1951)
Coli T4	131,000	65–70	Adams (1949a)
Coli T2	71,700	60–74	Pollard and Reaume (1951)
Staph phage	137,000	above 65	Chang, Willner, and Tegarden (1950)
Staph phage	14,000	below 65	Chang, Willner, and Tegarden (1950)
In dry state			
Coli T1	27,500	95–145	Pollard and Reaume (1951)
Coli T3	19,100	20–47	Pollard and Reaume (1951)
Coli T7	12,700	25–60	Pollard and Reaume (1951)

From the table it may be noted that two values for the Arrhenius constant are given for phage T5 by Foster, Johnson and Miller (1949) and for a staphylococcus phage by Chang, Willner, and Tegarden (1950). In both cases the value below 65° C. is exceedingly low, 5,000 and 14,000 calories. These low values are probably due to chemical inactivation of the phages by some substance in the broth diluent, which becomes inappreciably slow in comparison with thermal inactivation above 65° C. With these two exceptions, all Arrhenius constants recorded for wet phage are above 70,000 calories.

The inactivation constants for dry phages listed in Table IV are difficult to interpret because drying itself inactivates most phages and subsequent heating may merely continue the drying process. Phage T1 is exceptionally resistant to drying, however, and the dried phage is notably resistant to heat. The low Arrhenius constant in this instance may, therefore, reflect the effect of drying on thermal denaturation. These results suggest further experiments, as discussed by the authors (Pollard and Reaume, 1951).

It is obvious that different determinations of the Arrhenius constant for the same phage do not always agree. A significant clue to these discrepancies is found in the paper of Foster, Johnson, and Miller (1949). These authors failed to obtain a first-order inactivation rate for phage T5 in broth. However, the addition of 0.01 N MgCl$_2$ to the broth resulted in typical first-order curves with a velocity constant about half that found in the absence of added magnesium salt. The addition of phosphate accelerated the inactivation. Since broth is not a chemically defined medium it is not likely to give reproducible results from one lot to another.

In chemically defined media the heat susceptibility of phages depends very markedly on the chemical composition of the medium. Nanavutty (1930) found a coliphage to be inactivated 10 times faster in saline than in broth. Burnet and McKie (1930) found several phages to be far more susceptible to heat inactivation in 0.1 N solutions of sodium or potassium salts than in broth. The addition of magnesium or calcium salts made the salt solutions equivalent to broth as far as phage stability was concerned. Similar results were obtained by Gratia (1940).

The coliphage T5 belongs to the same class, and its response to heating has been studied in detail by Lark and Adams (1953).

T5 is maximally resistant to heat at cation concentrations exceeding $M/1,000$ for magnesium or $M/1$ for sodium, and maximally sensitive at concentrations less than $M/10^5$ for magnesium or $M/10$ for sodium. The span of inactivation rates at 50° C. (measured indirectly) between these two extremes is about 1×10^7. These and other characteristics of the dependence on cations presumably indicate complex formation between cations and some heat-labile phage protein. In its stable form, the complex resists heating to 70° C.; in its least stable form the phage is rapidly inactivated at 30° C., or even below in the presence of chelating agents. Inactivation of the phage by heat is accompanied by release of nucleic acid into the solution. The resulting nucleic acid-free ghosts do not adsorb to bacteria. Further details of the physical and biological characteristics of heat inactivation are given by Lark and Adams (1953).

Coliphage T5 mutates to a form, T5st, that is about 1,000 times more heat resistant in 0.1 N NaCl than is the parental wild type (Lark and Adams, 1953). The two forms do not differ in heat sensitivity at high salt concentrations. They differ, therefore, in the manner of interaction with cations. The mutant occurs with a frequency of about 10^{-7} in wild type stocks initiated from single plaques, but on repeated subculture accumulates until it may amount to 10 per cent of the population. Wild type stocks of phage T5 also contain a phenotypically heat-resistant form composing about 0.1 per cent of the population. The phenotypically heat-resistant particles have the same stability as the heat-resistant mutants but differ in that the property of heat resistance is lost on a single growth cycle in the host bacterium. Similar phenotypically heat-resistant particles have been found in stocks of phages BG3, 29 alpha, and PB which are serologically related to phage T5 (Adams, 1953a). No satisfactory explanation for the origin of these phenotypically heat-resistant particles is available at present.

Another example of nonheritable heat resistance was observed in a coliphage by Fischer (1950). The heat resistance increased on rapid subculture and decreased on storage at room temperature. It may be related to the cofactor independence of nascent phage T4 (E.-L. Wollman and Stent, 1952).

11. Hydrostatic Pressure

The effect of high pressure on the heat stability of phages was investigated by Foster, Johnson, and Miller (1949). Pressures of 10,000 pounds per square inch were found to increase the stability of phages T1, T2, and T5, but to accelerate the inactivation of phage T7. The change of velocity constant for inactivation of phage T5 with changing pressure indicated that thermal inactivation of this phage was characterized by a volume increase of activation of 113 cubic centimeters per mole. This is the type of effect usually found in protein denaturation.

12. Osmotic Shock

The production of ghosts from phages T2, T4, T6, and K by osmotic shock, first described by T. F. Anderson, has already been noted in Chapter IV. The phenomenon shows that phages are rapidly penetrated by simple electrolytes, glycerol, sometimes by sucrose, and even more rapidly by water. Sudden reduction of salt concentration presumably causes water to enter the particle until the membrane ruptures, permitting the internal contents to leak out more or less completely. Gradual changes in salt concentration do not have this effect (T. F. Anderson, Rappaport, and Muscatine, 1953).

Purely mechanical considerations suggest that the principal damage should occur to the membrane of the head and this seems to be so, since the tail structure of the ghost remains morphologically and functionally intact (Herriott, 1951a; Kellenberger and Arber, 1955). The same considerations probably explain in part the resistance of the smaller phages T1, T3, T5, and T7 to osmotic shock (Anderson, 1949). Other factors are probably involved as well, however. Anderson, Rappaport, and Muscatine (1953) describe variants of T6 differently sensitive to osmotic shock, and an unexpected temperature-dependence in some of them.

The discovery of osmotic shock was of the greatest importance in contributing to an understanding of the structure (Chapter IV) and function (Chapter XIV) of phage particles.

The properties of the ghosts produced by osmotic shock of T2 have been studied in some detail. All observers agree that they kill bacteria with a low efficiency varying between 10 and 50 per cent. That ghosts can adsorb to bacteria without killing them is especially clear from the microscopic observation of Bonifas and Kellenberger (1955) and the metabolic studies of French and Siminovitch (1955), which show that the surviving bacteria are damaged. Multiplication and protein synthesis are interrupted for about 80 minutes, and ability to support growth of superinfecting phage is temporarily lost. Since infection with live T2 does not interrupt protein synthesis, it appears that ghosts and phage damage the cell in different ways. For this reason it is incorrect to say that the killing power of T2 resides in its protein coat; the death of the cell penetrated by a ghost could be due, for example, to leakage of material through fissures in the ghost. This consideration, as well as the observed low efficiency of killing by ghosts, does not support the idea sometimes expressed that phage T2 belongs to a necessarily virulent species.

13. Summary

Substances or conditions that denature proteins or react chemically with proteins or nucleic acids inactivate phages. The effects tend to be phage-specific, and sometimes help in classification of phages. Substances that react reversibly such as formaldehyde and mercuric ions cause reversible inactivation under appropriate conditions. Specific enzyme poisons such as cyanide, fluoride, and dinitrophenol have no effect on phage particles. These substances, as well as thymol and chloroform, can be used to kill or inhibit bacteria and molds in the preparation and preservation of phage stocks.

Several protein denaturants, as well as osmotic shock, can be used to liberate nucleic acid from phage particles. Osmotic shock also permits isolation of the proteinaceous ghost of certain phages in relatively undamaged form.

CHAPTER VI

EFFECTS OF RADIATIONS ON PHAGE PARTICLES

The discussion of the action of various physical and chemical agents on the viability of bacteriophages will now be continued by a consideration of the effects produced in phage particles which have been exposed to various sorts of radiations. The irradiation of bacteriophages has been a very useful tool in the elucidation of their structure and physiology, and it may be said that with bacteriophages radiobiological methods have found one of their most profitable applications. Diverse types of bacteriophages have at some time or other been subjected to radiations of almost all parts of the electromagnetic spectrum, ranging in wavelength from the infrared (3,000,000 to 7,600 A) through the visible (7,600 to 4,000 A) and ultraviolet (4,000 to 130 A) to the X-ray regions (100 to 0.1 A), and extending even to the most highly energetic radiations of extremely short wavelength emitted by radioactive substances and those produced in the accelerators of atomic physics. The body of literature concerned with this subject is already so large that not all of the results can be discussed here. The reader may find further information in a number of specialized reviews (Lea, 1946; Bowen, 1953; Luria, 1955; Pollard, 1954; Kleczkowski, 1957; Stent, 1958).

1. Visible Light

Wahl and Guelin (1942) observed that the small phage S13 is particularly sensitive to inactivation by light, being killed by radiations from the visible part of the spectrum at a much greater rate than the large phage C16. Wahl (1946b) found by use of appropriate filters that the wavelength of the active radiations is in the vicinity of 4,500 A, or in the blue region. He also observed that, like S13, a large subtilis phage is sensitive, while the phages coli 36 and streptococcus B563, like C16, are resistant to inactivation by visible light. This differential action of visible radiations is presumably due to some difference in the chemical composition of these phage strains, in that only the light-sensitive phage types contain some pigment which absorbs blue light. Wahl and Latarjet (1947) examined the inactivation spectrum of S13 more critically and found that light of wavelengths greater than 5,550 A is ineffective, the efficiency of inactivation increasing with decreasing wavelength down through 3,650 A. Throughout this part of the spectrum phage S13 is more radiosensitive than phage C16. Between 3,130 and 3,650 A, an inversion of the relative sensitivities of these two phage strains occurs, so that at shorter wave lengths in the ultraviolet C16 becomes more radiosensitive than S13. The kinetics of inactivation of S13 by light at both 3,650 and 4,500 A are complex in that the first 75 per cent of the phage particles are killed according to an exponential survival curve (see Glossary) of greater slope than the rate of inactivation of the remaining 25 per cent. A change of temperature from 17 to 37° C. does not change the rate of inactivation of phage S13 at 4,500 A, indicating that the lethal action results from a direct photochemical effect. The effectiveness of the incident energy in the visible region at 4,500 A is only 10^{-4} of that in the ultraviolet region at 2,537 A, although no data are available for such a comparison in terms of the absorbed energy. The differential sensitivity of phages to visible light may be an important clue to their chemical structure, although no information appears to be as yet at hand concerning the nature of the material which absorbs the blue light.

The *photodynamic action* of dyes on a bacteriophage was investigated by Clifton (1931) who observed that addition of 0.01 per cent methylene blue to a suspension of a staphylococcus phage has no effect on the viability of the phage particles as long as the suspension is kept in the dark but results in complete inactivation within 5 minutes after the suspension is placed in light.   The presence of 0.01 per cent cysteine gives complete protection against such photodynamic action, for which also oxygen appears to be essential, since no inactivation takes place in the light in a nitrogen atmosphere.   Similar results were reported by Perdrau and Todd (1933).   Burnet (1933e) investigated the photodynamic action of methylene blue on a series of coli-dysentery phages.   He found marked differences in sensitivity, differences which were correlated not with particle size but rather with serological classification.   Hence photodynamic sensitivity, like sensitivity to visible light, is of taxonomic significance, although here too the chemical basis for such differential behavior is as yet unknown.   Krueger Scribner, and Mecracken (1940) reported the photodynamic inactivation of a "phage precursor."   In these experiments, a reduced yield of phage was encountered after illumination prior to infection of the host bacteria in the presence of 10^{-6} M methylene blue, a treatment which was said not to reduce the bacterial colony count.   Since the assays in this experiment were made by Krueger's kinetic method, it is difficult to interpret such results. Illumination of bacteria in the absence of methylene blue suppresses their capacity to produce phage without killing them (Dulbecco and Weigle, 1952; Latarjet and Miletic, 1953; Hill, 1956).

Yamamoto (1956) studied the relation between structure of dyes and photodynamic inactivation of the T series of coliphages, and observed competitive interactions between effective and ineffective dyes.   Welsh and Adams (1954) found that photodynamic action on T2 destroys infectivity three times faster than it destroys the host-killing property of the particles.   No photoreactivation or multiplicity reactivation could be demonstrated.

2. Ultraviolet Light

Of all the agents capable of inactivating bacteriophages, ultraviolet light has been studied most extensively and has shown the most diverse and interesting effects.   Besides simply inactivating phage particles, ultraviolet light produces important physiological and genetic effects, such as inducing phage development in lysogenic bacteria, causing a growth-delay in the phage particles surviving irradiation, stimulating genetic recombination, and exerting a mutagenic action. Some of the effects of ultraviolet light, furthermore, are reversible under appropriate conditions. Ultraviolet light has also been used to study the course of intracellular phage development. The possibilities of ultraviolet light as a tool in phage research appear to be far from exhausted.

a. Lethal Effect

Repeated observations of the lethal effect of ultraviolet light on bacteriophages have been made ever since 1922 (see d'-Herelle, 1926). The first quantitative study appears to have been carried out by Baker and Nanavutty (1929). These authors found that the inactivation of a shiga phage is an exponential function of the dose of ultraviolet light to a survival of 10^{-5}. By use of filters it was possible to determine that wavelengths above 3,000 A are harmless and that the wavelength of maximum effectiveness is somewhere below 2,650 A. Gates (1934), using a monochromator to isolate single emission lines, studied the inactivation of a staphylococcus phage and found that the kinetics of inactivation follow a simple exponential at all wavelengths studied from 2,300 to 2,970 A. The energy output of the radiation source was determined at each wave length by means of a thermopile, thus permitting a determination of the action spectrum for the ultraviolet inactivation of this phage. It was found that the incident energy required to inactivate a given fraction of the phage population decreases continuously between 2,950 and 2,600 A, then increases to a peak at 2,400 A and finally decreases again toward 2,300 A. Northrop (1938) determined the ultraviolet absorption spectrum of purified staphylococcus phage and found it to be very similar in shape to Gates' action spectrum. Analogous investigations carried out subsequently to determine the action spectra of ultraviolet inactivation of T1, T2, and the megaterium phage M5 (Fluke and Pollard, 1949; Zelle and Hollaender, 1954; Franklin, Friedman, and Setlow, 1953) and of the ultraviolet absorption spectra of suspensions of purified T6 (Putnam, Kozloff, and Neil, 1949), T2 (Cohen and Arbogast, 1950b), and T7 (Putnam, Miller, Palm, and Evans, 1952), showed that in all these cases both action and absorption spectra are very similar to the typical absorption spectrum of purified nucleic acids, which displays a maximum absorption near the wavelength of 2,600 A. It seems probable, therefore, that the inactivating photons of ultraviolet light are absorbed by the phage nucleic acid. The quantum yield, i.e., the number of phage particles inactivated per quantum absorbed, has been estimated for T1 and T2 at various wavelengths by Zelle and Hollaender (1954). These authors found that the yield for either phage is only about 3×10^{-4} throughout the range of wavelengths from 2,200 to 3,000 A.

Campbell-Renton (1937) compared the effects of ultraviolet irradiation on five strains of phage and found the inactivation to be an exponential function of dose. The ultraviolet sensitivity of these strains, measured as the slope of the exponential survival curve, varied over a ten-fold range. Latarjet and Wahl (1945) compared the ultraviolet inactivation of phages C16 and S13 and found that while the survival curves for both types are exponential, phage S13 has only $1/_3$ the ultraviolet sensitivity of phage C16, although S13 contains only about $1/_{30}$ as much nucleic acid as C16 (Sinsheimer, 1957). The nucleic acid of S13, therefore, appears to be intrinsically more sensitive to ultraviolet light than that of C16. It is possible that the same difference in chemical composition which is responsible for the very different sensitivities of these two phage strains to visible light is also responsible for the greater intrinsic ultraviolet sensitivity of S13. In this connection it may be noted that although T4 is indistinguishable from T2 and T6 in size and morphology, it has only one half the ultraviolet light sensitivity of its two relatives. Streisinger (1956a) traced the difference in ultraviolet sensitivity of these three strains to a single genetic locus. Phage lambda is inactivated by ultraviolet light at only $1/_{13}$ the rate of phage T5, although these two phages have almost the same size (Weigle and Delbrück, 1951). As we will see later, there is much evidence that different strains of phages react very differently towards ultraviolet light.

Latarjet and Morenne (1951) found that phage T2 is inactivated slowly when irradiated by Mazda fluorescent lamps of the daylight type. Examination of the radiations emitted by these lamps showed that appreciable amounts of radiant energy emanate at wavelengths from 3,130 A down to 2,890 A, and calculations indicate that these radiations can account for the observed rate of phage inactivation. The kinetics of inactivation by fluorescent lamps are not strictly exponential but follow a "3-hit" curve, which suggests that the mechanism of ultraviolet inactivation of these phages may be more complex than had been imagined previously. A downward concavity of the exponential survival curve has also been noted at low doses of ultraviolet light for phages T2, T4, T5, and T6, but the significance of these deviations from first-order kinetics is not known. In contrast, the ultraviolet light survival curves of phages T1, T3, and T7 show an upward concavity at low survival values, as if a fraction of the phage is inactivated at a slower rate than the bulk of the population (Dulbecco, 1950). This break in the survival curve of such phages, as well as the low intrinsic ultraviolet sensitivity of the salmonella phage P22, led Garen and Zinder (1955) to propose that some of the particles in ultraviolet-irradiated populations of such phage types are reactivated by homologous genetic material present in the nuclear structures of the bacterial host cell. A comprehensive discussion of this hypothesis is given by Stent (1958).

b. Growth-Delaying Effect

Luria (1944) noted that the latent period of bacteriophage particles surviving moderate doses of ultraviolet light is considerably increased. This observation indicates that phage particles can be damaged by the action of absorbed ultraviolet quanta without being killed, and hence that ultraviolet light can produce more than one kind of lesion.   The growth delay increases with increasing dosage of ultraviolet light and is not hereditary, in the sense that progeny of affected phage particles reproduce themselves with normal latent period.   The magnitude of the effect varies from one phage type to another, the growth delay for a given dose of ultraviolet being much greater with phages T1 and T7 than with T2.   Setlow, Robbins, and Pollard (1955) determined the ultraviolet action spectrum of the growth delaying effect in T1 and found that wavelengths near 2,600 A, the absorption peak of nucleic acids, have the maximum effect.   This suggests that extension of latent period, like inactivation, results from the absorption of radiation by nucleic acid.

c. Host Killing

Luria and Delbrück (1942) discovered that ultraviolet inactivated T2 phage particles, though no longer able to reproduce themselves, are still capable of killing phage-susceptible bacterial cells.   By determining the proportion of surviving bacteria after infection with various amounts of ultraviolet-inactivated phage particles, these authors demonstrated that the adsorption of a single irradiated phage particle suffices to kill the host cell. A dose of ultraviolet light that reduces the number of plaque-forming particles to 10^{-6} of their initial number leaves $1/_3$ of the original phages still able to kill susceptible bacteria.   The host-killing property of phage T2, therefore, is enormously more resistant to ultraviolet light than the viability of the phage. Heat, in contrast to ultraviolet light, destroys both of these activities at the same rate.   Microscopic examination of bacteria infected with ultraviolet inactivated T2 particles shows that such cells do not multiply and do not lyse.   Cohen and Arbogast (1950c) demonstrated that infection of bacteria with heavily irradiated T2 phages arrests synthesis of both ribonucleic acid and deoxyribonucleic acid.

Cytological methods were employed by Luria and Human

(1950) to study the effects of phage infection on the chromatinic structures of the bacterial host cells. These authors also observed the effects of infection with ultraviolet-inactivated T1, T2, and T7 phages. It was found that ultraviolet-inactivated phages, like normal unirradiated particles, cause marked alterations of cell structure. The details of this work will be discussed in a later chapter. Luria and Human also followed the synthesis of material absorbing ultraviolet light at 2,600 A in bacteria infected with normal and with irradiated phages. They found that infection with irradiated T1 or T2 phages causes some increase in optical density at 2,600 A, but at a much slower rate than in uninfected bacteria. It may be concluded, therefore, that although ultraviolet-inactivated phage particles are unable to reproduce themselves, they can nonetheless cause extensive changes in the infected bacterium, changes which ultimately result in the death of the host cell.

d. Interference

Luria and Delbrück (1942) found that infection of bacteria with ultraviolet-inactivated T2 phages makes it impossible for unirradiated particles of T1 to multiply in these cells. In this respect, ultraviolet-inactivated T2 phages behave exactly as do active T2 particles. In contrast, ultraviolet-inactivated T1 phages do not interfere with the multiplication of active T2 phage. Infection of bacteria with ultraviolet-inactivated phages also results in interference with induced enzyme synthesis under the same conditions under which active phages produce such interference (Luria, 1950). These results demonstrate that ultraviolet-inactivated phage particles still possess some of the physiological properties of active phages.

e. Photoreactivation

Kelner (1949) discovered while working with ultraviolet-inactivated conidia of *Streptomyces griseus* that visible light has the remarkable ability of restoring viability in this material. Since this observation, there have been numerous reports of the photoreversal of radiation lesions in a number of different organisms. Photoreactivation of bacteriophages was discovered independently by Dulbecco (1950), who observed that ultraviolet-inactivated phages can be reactivated by exposure to visible light, but only after their adsorption to susceptible bacteria. Visible light does not reactivate unadsorbed ultraviolet-irradiated phages, nor induce phage development in bacteria illuminated just before infection with such phages. The rate of photoreactivation of adsorbed phage particles is a function of the temperature, increasing by a factor of two in the interval from 25 to 37° C. These observations suggested that photoreactivation depends on some enzyme system present in the bacterial host cell but absent from the phage particles. Attempts to obtain photoreactivation of free phages in cell-free extracts of bacteria have thus far been unsuccessful, although photoreactivation of ultraviolet-inactivated transforming DNA has recently been demonstrated in extracts of *E. coli* (Goodgal, Rupert, and Herriott, 1957). Photoreactivation of adsorbed phages is not inhibited by cyanide or anaerobiosis. The rate of photoreactivation is a linear function of the intensity of the reactivating light at low intensities and approaches a maximum value at high intensities, at which point some factor other than absorption of light quanta becomes rate limiting. Light of wavelength near 3,650 A possesses the maximum efficiency of photoreactivation, although the entire wavelength range from 3,000 to 5,000 A is effective. If ultraviolet-inactivated phages are adsorbed to rapidly growing bacteria and the infected cells are incubated for various lengths of time before exposure to photoreactivating light, it is found that the maximum amount of photoreactivation attainable decreases rapidly. If such phages are adsorbed to resting bacteria, however, the complexes remain photoreactivable at 37° C. for at least 70 minutes. The rate of photoreactivation at a given light intensity is less in resting than in rapidly metabolizing bacteria.

Only a portion of ultraviolet-inactivated phage particles is photoreactivable. The fraction of the phage population capable of forming plaques after maximum photoreactivation decreases as an exponential function of the dose of ultraviolet light, but less rapidly than the fraction which survives in the dark, i. e., in the absence of photoreactivation. If the absorption of ultraviolet light in a given type of phage has a probability a of producing a photoreactivable lethal lesion and probability $1-a$ of producing a nonphotoreactivable lethal lesion, then a is said to be the photoreactivable sector of ultraviolet damage in this phage strain. The ratio of the slope of the dose-survival curve after maximum photoreactivation to the slope of the dose-survival in the dark, or in the absence of photoreactivation, is then evidently $1-a$. The photoreactivable sector a may vary from unity (complete photoreactivability) to zero (no photoreactivability) in different phage strains. Experimental values for the photo-reactivable sectors of the 7 T phages are: $T1 = 0.68$; $T2 = 0.56$; $T4 = 0.20$; $T6 = 0.44$; $T3 = 0.39$; $T7 = 0.35$; $T5 = 0.20$. These values show no simple correlation with any of the other properties of the phage concerned; for instance, the three closely related phages T2, T4, and T6 are seen to differ widely in their photoreactivable sectors. In spite of this, the photoreactivable sector is a remarkably reproducible characteristic of a particular phage strain, although it depends on the physical conditions under which the ultraviolet light has been administered (Hill and Rossi, 1954). The photoreactivable sector also depends somewhat on the type of host cell to which the ultraviolet-in-activated phage particles have been adsorbed (Dulbecco, 1955).

By means of experiments in which phage-infected bacteria were exposed to flashes of photoreactivating light rather than to continuous illumination it could be shown by Bowen (1953) that photoreactivation consists of at least two steps. One, a temperature-sensitive dark reaction (i. e., one for which no light is required) appears to precede a second, temperature-insensi-tive light reaction (for which light is required). Bowen pro-posed that the function of the dark reaction is to generate those substances which absorb the visible radiations and thus become "activated" for the reactivation process. Lennox, Luria, and Benzer (1954) carried out experiments in which phage-bacterium complexes were inactivated by ultraviolet light, photoreactivated and then subjected to a second ultraviolet irradiation. They observed that photoreactivated complexes have the same ultraviolet sensitivity as nonreactivated complexes and inferred from this fact that photoreactivation probably constitutes a direct reversal of the primary ultraviolet damage, rather than a by-pass mechanism.

f. Multiplicity Reactivation

When assaying phage stocks inactivated by ultraviolet irradiation, Delbrück and Bailey noticed that the plaque counts of surviving phage particles appear to depend on the relative proportions of phage particles and bacteria in the plating mixture. Luria (1947) investigated this titration anomaly further and discovered the phenomenon of multiplicity reactivation. An ultraviolet-inactivated phage particle, though unable to reproduce itself, is, as we have already seen, far from physiologically inert. It may kill the host cell, interfere with the multiplication of other phages, or even regain its ability to reproduce after exposure to visible light. Now if two or more such ultraviolet-inactivated phage particles are adsorbed to the same host bacterium, then there exists a good chance that they may cooperate in some way so that this multi-infected cell lyses and liberates viable progeny phage particles. This is multiplicity reactivation, which can be demonstrated readily with phages T2, T4, T6, and T5. It is, however, barely or not at all detectable with T1, T3, T7, and lambda. Luria formulated a theory of multiplicity reactivation in terms of genetic exchange of undamaged parts between irradiated phage particles, a theory whose essence, though not its particulars, later work has shown to be indeed the most likely explanation of this phenomenon. The detailed results of studies on multiplicity reactivation, as well as those of an associated phenomenon, cross reactivation, will be considered in Chapter XVIII.

3. Ionizing Radiations

Most investigators of the effects of ionizing radiations, i.e., radiations belonging to the shortest wavelength sector of the electromagnetic spectrum, have been interested in the interpretation of inactivation data in terms of the "target theory." It was hoped that development of the target theory would yield information about the size and shape of the radiation-sensitive structures in viruses (Latarjet, 1946; Lea, 1946). Some of the calculated target sizes have already been presented in Chapter IV, and their relation to phage particle sizes determined by other means has been discussed. Recently, an increased emphasis has also been placed on the study of the physiological effects of ionizing radiations on phage particles, stimulated, no doubt, by the amazing variety of effects produced by ultraviolet (nonionizing) radiation.

Extensive discussions of the chemical effects of ionizing radiations and possible mechanisms for their biological action can be found in Lea (1946) and in Hollaender (1954). We may state briefly here that the effects of ionizing radiations may be classed under two categories: direct and indirect. Direct effects are produced when an ionization occurs directly in the substance under investigation, whereas indirect effects are caused by chemical agents produced by the action of ionizing radiations on the solvent molecules. Irradiation of pure water produces highly reactive but unstable free radicals, such as OH, H, and O_2H, as well as more stable peroxides. The presence of dissolved oxygen increases the toxic and mutagenic effects of ionizing radiations, while the presence of sulfhydryl compounds and certain simple organic substances reduces these effects.

The irradiation of dry substances will result in direct effects only, since there is no solvent. Irradiation of dilute solutions will result in both direct and indirect effects, while irradiation of concentrated solutions will result in predominance of direct effects and a relative decrease in indirect effects. The addition of certain kinds of solutes will protect against the indirect effects because the added solute molecules will react preferentially with the radiation-activated solvent molecules—free radicals and peroxides—in competition with the material under study. Since target volumes are calculated on the assumption that the lethal action has resulted from energy absorbed within the physical domain of the biological structure whose death is being followed, it is important to remember that target-size estimates of bacteriophages can be based only on experiments in which exclusively direct effects come into play. Indirect effects must be excluded by the addition of protective substances.

Luria and Exner (1941) found, while studying the inactivation of phages with X-rays, that the inactivation rate in distilled water or buffers is very much greater than the rate in nutrient broth. The addition of gelatin to water, however, gives maximum protection, so that the rate of X-ray inactivation of phages suspended in this medium is no greater than that in broth. Egg albumin and serum albumin also protect against this indirect effect, while sugars do not. Alper (1948) made similar observations of the protective effect of proteins and attributed the indirect effect to the lethal action of hydrogen peroxide. Latarjet (1942) had considered this possibility but his experiments indicated that not enough peroxide is produced to account for the indirect effect on phage C16. It seems to be generally agreed that although some peroxides are produced by ionizing radiations, the major portion of the indirect effect is due to short-lived radicals generated in the water (Alper, 1954). Latarjet and Ephrati (1948) investigated a number of simple chemical substances for protective action against the indirect effect. They found that glucose, sucrose, alanine, and histidine confer little or no protection, while thioglycolic acid, tryptophan, cysteine and cystine, glutathione, ascorbic acid, and phenylalanine possess considerable protective power. The presence or absence of oxygen has no effect on the inactivation rate either in the presence or absence of protective substances.

The properties of X-ray-inactivated phages may be compared with those of ultraviolet-inactivated phages discussed in the previous section of this chapter, principally on the basis of an extensive investigation by Watson (1950, 1952) of the physiological modifications produced in bacteriophages by both direct and indirect effects of X-irradiation. To study the direct effect, phage preparations were irradiated in broth. It was found that T2 phage particles inactivated by the direct effect are still adsorbed to bacteria as efficiently as active T2 particles. Not all the inactivated phage particles, however, are able to kill the host cells on adsorption, the host-killing property being abolished by X-irradiation at $1/3$ the rate at which plaque-forming ability is lost. X-ray-inactivated T2 particles are also able to interfere with the multiplication of active T1 phages, the interfering power being inactivated by X-rays at the same rate as the host-killing property. X-ray-inactivated T2 phages retain their ability to cause "lysis from without," and are even more effective in this regard than unirradiated phage particles. Cytological observations on bacteria infected with X-ray-inactivated T2 phages show nuclear disintegration and chromatinic change, analogous to those observed with ultraviolet-inactivated T2 phages. The proportion of inactivated phage particles capable of inducing these cytological changes is the same as the proportion capable of killing the host cell, so that host cell death appears to be the result of the phage-induced destruction of the nuclear apparatus. The ability of $T2r^+$ phage particles to cause "lysis inhibition" is retained after X-irradiation even after the host-killing property has been abolished. Photoreactivation can also be detected in X-ray-inactivated T2 phages, but in a much smaller proportion of the phage particles than after ultraviolet inactivation. Both multiplicity reactivation and cross reactivation of X-ray-inactivated T2 and T4 phages exists and will be considered in detail in Chapter XVIII. It is evident that X-irradiation permits one to isolate several physiological properties of the phage particles. It is also evident that the effects of X-rays are quite distinct from those of ultraviolet light, suggesting that the nature of the lesions produced by these two types of radiation are different. This is also indicated by the fact that a population of T2 bacteriophages inactivated by ionizing radiations is no longer able to inject all of its DNA into the bacterial host cells, whereas a similar population inactivated by ultraviolet light to the same extent is still able to do so (Hershey, Garen, Fraser, and Hudis, 1954). It would appear that T2 phage is a rather complex organism, which can be functionally dissected by means of radiations.

The indirect inactivation of viruses by X-irradiation in the absence of protective substances is in reality an inactivation by chemical agents generated by the radiant energy. These chemical agents, as stated above, are of two kinds: the short-lived free radicals and the long-lived "peroxides." Because of the brief life of the free radicals, their range of action is short, and only those radicals produced in the water of hydration of the phage particles can have an appreciable probability of causing physiological damage. The properties of phage particles damaged by the short-lived radicals (indirect effect) can be studied by ir-

TABLE V

The Properties of Bacteriophage T2 Inactivated by X-rays and Ultraviolet Light[a]

Inactivating agent	Rate of inactivation	Adsorption	Bacterial killing ability	Photoreactivation	Multiplicity reactivation
Direct effect of X-rays	Exponential	Normal	Lost at a rate $1/3$ the rate of inactivation	+	+
Indirect effect of X-rays	Cumulative damage	Greatly reduced	Uncertain because of poor adsorption	−	Uncertain because of poor adsorption
After effect of X-rays	Cumulative damage	Slightly reduced	Lost at slow rate	−	++
Ultraviolet light	Nearly exponential	Normal	Normal	++++	++++

[a] From J. D. Watson, *J. Bacteriol.*, **63,** 473 (1952), with permission.

TABLE VI

The Sensitivity of Various Bacteriophages to Ionizing Radiations

Bacteriophage		Environment during irradiation	Radiation	Inactivation dose[a] $\times 10^{-6}$ roentgen	Reference
Host	Strain				
Coli-dysentery	C16	Broth	X-ray	0.054	Wollman and Lacassagne (1940)
	C16	Broth	X-ray	0.040	Luria and Exner (1941)
	C16	Broth	X-ray	0.039	Holweck, Luria, and Wollman (1940)
	C16	Broth	X-ray	0.075	Latarjet (1942)
	C16	Broth	α-ray	0.3	Holweck, Luria, and Wollman (1940)
	T2, T4, T6	Broth	X-ray	0.04	Watson (1950)
	T2	Broth	X-ray	0.034	Latarjet (1948)
	T5	Broth	X-ray	0.035	Buzzell and Lauffer (1952)
	Tl(P28)	Broth	X-ray	0.09	Luria and Exner (1941)
	T1	Broth	X-ray	0.085	Watson (1950)
	C13	Broth	X-ray	0.12	Luria and Exner (1941)
	T7	Broth	X-ray	0.085	Watson (1950)
	lambda	Broth	X-ray	0.11	Epstein and Englander (1954)
	C36	Broth	X-ray	0.10	Wollman and Lacassagne (1940)
	C36	Dry	γ-ray	0.21	Lea and Salaman (1946)
	C36	Dry	X-ray	0.43	Lea and Salaman (1946)
	C36	Dry	α-ray	0.94	Lea and Salaman (1946)
	S13	Broth	X-ray	0.39	Wollman and Lacassagne (1940)
	S13	Dry	γ-ray	0.58	Lea and Salaman (1946)
	S13	Dry	X-ray	0.99	Lea and Salaman (1946)
	S13	Dry	α-ray	3.50	Lea and Salaman (1946)
	T105α	Broth	X-ray	0.059	Wollman and Lacassagne (1940)
Salmonella	P22	Broth	X-ray	0.11	Garen and Zinder (1955)
Pyocyanea	P8	Broth	X-ray	0.083	Tobin (1953)

TABLE VI (*Continued*)

Bacteriophage		Environment during irradiation	Radiation	Inactivation dose[a] $\times 10^{-6}$ roentgen	Reference
Host	Strain				
Megaterium		Broth	X-ray	0.09	Wollman and Lacassagne (1940)
Subtilis		Broth	X-ray	0.044	Wollman and Lacassagne (1940)
Staphylococcus	K	Broth	X-ray	0.054	Wollman and Lacassagne (1940)
	K	Broth	X-ray	0.045	Luria and Exner (1941)
	K	Dry	γ-ray	0.079	Lea and Salaman (1946)
	K	Dry	X-ray	0.109	Lea and Salaman (1946)
	K	Dry	α-ray	0.45	Lea and Salaman (1946)
Streptococcus	B	Broth	X-ray	0.20	Exner and Luria (1941)
	C	Broth	X-ray	0.11	Exner and Luria (1941)
	D	Broth	X-ray	0.06	Exner and Luria (1941)

[a] Inactivation dose = dose required to reduce titer of phage population to the fraction $1/e$.

radiating dilute phage suspensions in buffer, though some fraction of the population must also be inactivated by the direct effect under these conditions. The long-lived peroxides, in contrast, may continue to cause damage long after the irradiation has ceased. Watson (1952) called this second kind of indirect action after effect. The properties of phage particles damaged by after effect can be studied by diluting phages into medium previously heavily X-irradiated and allowing the after effect to occur in the absence of any direct irradiation of the particles themselves. The results of such studies are summarized in Table V, where the physiological properties of phages inactivated by ultraviolet light and by direct, indirect, and after effects of X-rays are presented. It is evident from this summary that the damage caused by indirect and after effects is quite different from that caused by direct effect or ultraviolet light.

Buzzel and Lauffer (1952) studied the effect of X-rays on phage T5 under conditions in which either the direct effect or the indirect effect was predominant, and then investigated the sensitivity to heat inactivation of the surviving phage population. It was found that the survivors of the direct effect irradiation have the same sensitivity to heat inactivation as an unirradiated control population, while the survivors of the indirect effect irradiation are far more heat-sensitive than the control. The chemical agents responsible for the indirect effect thus increase the heat-sensitivity of the survivors. The fact that the survivors of the indirect effect are already modified in some way was also shown by Watson (1952) who found that such survivors have an increased X-ray sensitivity upon a second exposure to indirect effects, i.e., that the indirect effect is cumulative (see also Alper, 1954). In contrast, Watson found that direct damage is not cumulative, i.e., that there is no evidence for "sublethal" direct lesions.

For purposes of reference, the available data for the sensitivity of various phages to ionizing radiations are presented in Table VI.

4. Decay of Radiophosphorus

It was discovered by Hershey, Kamen, Kennedy, and Gest (1951) that T2 and T4 bacteriophages lose their infectivity upon the decay (half-life of two weeks) of radiophosphorus P^{32} atoms incorporated into their DNA. The kinetics of this inactivation proceed in such a manner that the surviving fraction of the population is an exponential function of the proportion of P^{32} atoms which have decayed by the time of assay. The rate of inactivation is proportional to the specific radioactivity of the medium in which the phage has been grown and is independent of the phage concentration during decay, provided that the particles are stored in sufficiently great dilution in a medium which contains protective substances against any indirect effects produced by radiations attending the radioactive decay.   These observations indicate that the death of each radioactive phage particle is the consequence of the disintegration of one of its own atoms of P^{32}.   It is possible to calculate the fraction of all radioactive disintegrations which are actually lethal to the phage particles in which they occur, on the basis of the inactivation rate and the number of P^{32} atoms per phage known to have disintegrated at various times.   This fraction is approximately 0.1 in the case of T2 and T4, an efficiency of killing so high that it is possible to show by means of reconstruction experiments that the ionizations produced on the way out of the virus particles by the hard β electrons emitted at each P^{32} disintegration cannot be the principal cause of death.   Instead, a short range consequence of the radioactive disintegration, like the transmutation of phosphorus to sulphur or the recoil energy sustained by the decaying nucleus, must be responsible for the loss of infectivity.   When the lethal effects of P^{32} decay were similarly studied in phages T1, T3, T5, T7, and lambda (Stent and Fuerst, 1955) and in the salmonella phage P22 (Garen and Zinder, 1955), it was found that the efficiency of killing per P^{32} disintegration is very nearly the same in all of these strains, i.e., that approximately one out of every ten P^{32} disintegrations kills any phage particle in which it occurs.   This efficiency depends on the temperature at which radioactive decay is allowed to take place, rising from a minimum value of 0.04 at $-196°$ C. to 0.3 at $+65°$ C. (the value of 0.1 holding only at $+4°$ C.) (Stent and Fuerst, 1955; Castagnoli, Donini, and Graziosi, 1955a, 1955b).   On the basis of these findings, Stent and Fuerst inferred that the efficiency of killing reflects the double-stranded helical Watson-Crick structure of the DNA which harbors the decaying P^{32} atoms.   They proposed that the high proportion of nonlethal decays derives from the possibility that the physiological function of the DNA macromolecules can be preserved even after radioactive decay has interrupted one of the two single polynucleotide strands and that the small proportion of lethal decays represent disintegrations which have resulted in a complete cut of the DNA double helix.

Phage particles inactivated by decay of P^{32} can still participate in cross reactivation (Stent, 1953; Stahl, 1956), indicative that the lethal radioactive disintegrations destroy only part of the viral genome. The details of these experiments will be considered in Chapter XVIII. It has not been possible, however, to detect any multiplicity reactivation of phage particles inactivated by decay of P^{32}. The ability to give the lytic and lysogenic responses are both destroyed by P^{32} decay at the same rate in the temperate phages lambda and P22.

5. Summary

The group of physical agents whose effects on bacteriophages have been considered in this chapter includes various forms of radiant energy, such as visible and ultraviolet light and ionizing radiations, as well as the energy released by radioactive decay. In the case of radiant energy, the inactivation of phage particles is seen to result from the chemical reactions caused by the absorption of the electromagnetic quanta, whereas in the case of radioactive decay the local energy suddenly generated in the vicinity of the disintegrating atom appears to be responsible for the lethal effect. Inactivation by these agents is often highly specific, involving only certain properties of the phage particle and leaving other properties unharmed. A thorough investigation of the mechanisms by which bacteriophage particles are inactivated may reveal much information about the complexities of structure and function in viruses. The results already obtained and discussed here serve as an indication of what may be accomplished.

CHAPTER VII

CHEMICAL COMPOSITION

In order to determine the chemical composition of a virus one must be able to isolate and purify adequate amounts of it. Appropriate criteria of purity must be applied if the analyses are to have any validity. Therefore, these subjects will be discussed before presentation of the available data on chemical composition. An extensive review, "Bacteriophages," by Putnam (1953) includes methods of concentration and purification, criteria of purity, and determination of size, density, and chemical composition of purified bacteriophages. A similar review by Beard (1948), "Purified Animal Viruses," includes some material on bacteriophages.

1. Concentration and Purification

In general, it is unusual to obtain more than 10^{10} phage particles per ml. in lysates prepared on a large scale. However, lysates of the even-numbered T phages are now easily obtainable which titer up to 5×10^{11} per ml., or 250 mg. of phage per liter. The first successful purification of phage was achieved by Schlesinger (1933a) using coliphage WLL related to the T2-C16 serological group. The host bacteria were grown in a chemically defined medium to avoid contamination of the product with peptones and proteins from the starting material. Bacteria and large particle debris were removed by bacteriological filters. The phage was concentrated by means of collodion membranes of a pore size sufficiently small to retain the phage particles. The concentrated phage was further purified by high speed centrifugation. Modern criteria of purity were not yet available, but comparison of Schlesinger's results with recent data indicates that his phage preparations were probably as pure as any up to date.

Northrop (1938) concentrated and purified a staphylococcus phage by applying the techniques so successfully used for enzyme purification. The host bacteria were grown in a yeast extract medium, and after phage lysis was complete much nonphage material was removed by precipitation with lead acetate. The supernatant fluid was concentrated *in vacuo* to 1/20 of its volume and digested with trypsin, which does not harm the phage. The phage was then precipitated with ammonium sulfate and further purified by ammonium sulfate fractionation.

Kalmanson and Bronfenbrenner (1939) concentrated and purified a strain of coliphage T2, using collodion membranes. Hershey, Kalmanson, and Bronfenbrenner (1943a) prepared highly concentrated phage suspensions by simply washing the phage from the surface of agar plates on which large populations of bacteria had been lysed. From 10^{11} to 10^{12} phage particles per ml. were obtained in this way. This method was further developed and applied to the seven coliphages of the T series by Swanstrom and Adams (1951), with resultant phage concentrations about ten-fold greater than those obtained with broth lysates. This method was applied by Cohen and Arbogast (1950a) and Marshak (1951) and is useful in laboratories with limited centrifuge facilities. Fraser (1951a) developed an apparatus for growing bacteria in batches up to 6 liters under conditions of vigorous aeration. He obtained yields of phage T3 of better than 10^{11} per ml. in large scale lots.

Coliphage T2 had been concentrated on a large scale from fluid lysates by means of the Sharples continuous flow centrifuge (Hook, Beard, Taylor, Sharp, and Beard, 1946). The concentrated phage suspensions were then further purified by sedimentation in a high speed vacuum centrifuge. Similar methods were used by Kerby, Gowdy, Dillon, Dillon, Csaky, Sharp, and Beard (1949) for the purification of coliphage T7 and by Putnam, Kozloff, and Neil (1949) for the purification of coliphage T6. In the latter paper are preliminary reports of the fractionation of phage concentrates with alcohol in the cold and by acid precipitation at pH 4.2. These methods were also applied to the purification of phage T7 by Putnam, Miller, Palm, and Evans (1952).

Herriott and Barlow (1952) reported yields of 2 to 5 $\times$ 10^{11} per ml. of phage T2 in a chemically defined medium. Apparently, adequate aeration brought about by vigorous shaking is the explanation of the high yields, as in the case of the results with phage T3 of Fraser (1951a) noted above. The phage stocks were filtered through a calcined diatomaceous earth (Celite) to remove bacterial debris, and the phage was precipitated in the cold by acid at pH 4.0. The precipitated phage was resuspended at pH 6.5 and treated with deoxyribonuclease, after which it was purified by differential centrifugation.

A fairly simple method of preparing T2 phage lysates in 10 liter quantities was described by Siegel and Singer (1953). A defined medium was aerated by forcing air through a sintered glass tube and lysates which titered 2 to 5 $\times$ 10^{11} per ml. were produced. Wyatt and Cohen (1953) obtained lysates titering up to 1 $\times$ 10^{12} per ml. through the use of a thin film of enriched medium in which cells at 3 $\times$ 10^9 per ml. were multiinfected.

Wahl and Blum-Emerique (1949a) used alcohol precipitation for concentration of phage C16 with good recovery of activity. Wahl, Terrade, and Monceaux (1950) used successive adsorption and elutions from calcium phosphate for concentration and purification of a salmonella phage. Northrop (1955b) again applied salting out and enzymatic treatment to purify a megaterium phage, which is inactivated by repeated centrifugation.

2. Criteria of Purity

Certain criteria of purity have been discussed from another viewpoint in Chapter IV. From its dry weight and density one can calculate the diameter of the infective particle. If the size calculated in this way is larger than the true size but the efficiency of plating is high, the discrepancy must be attributed to aggregation or gross impurity in the phage preparation. This is a rather crude criterion of purity but it suffices to discredit many claims in the literature that pure phage has been prepared. Direct examination in the electron microscope can detect aggregates of phage as well as contaminating particles with sedimentation properties similar to those of phage particles.

The analytical centrifuge is useful for detecting impurities with a slower rate of sedimentation than the phage particles. It also gives a measure of the homogeneity of the preparation with respect to particle size and density (Putnam, 1953). Electrophoresis is a useful technique for detecting impurities which have a different mobility in the electric field (Putnam, 1953). Optical analysis of diffusion at a phage-buffer boundary has been used also as a test for homogeneity of preparations of phage T6 (Putnam, 1953). The specific infectivity of preparations will be low if a fraction of the phage particles are not infective for any reason. Such a preparation might well react as though it were homogeneous by any other test. An inhibitor of phage T2 which produces a low specific infectivity has been observed in certain phage lysates but fortunately Sagik (1954) and others have found methods for separating it from the phage.

An immunological criterion of purity has been used by Cohen and Arbogast (1950a). The most probable impurity in phage purified by differential centrifugation is particulate bacterial debris which should react with antibacterial antibodies to give a precipitate. Cohen obtained such precipitates with purified phage preparations and demonstrated that ribonucleic acid was removed in the precipitate, so that treatment with antiserum was a method of purification as well as a test of purity. Serum proteins could then be removed by centrifugation. The immunological criterion was used by Kozloff and Putnam (1949) and by Herriott and Barlow (1952).

The constancy of certain properties of the phage preparation such as infectivity per mg. nitrogen, infectivity per unit of turbidity (extinction at 4,000 A) and infectivity per unit of absorbancy (extinction at 2,600 A) was used as a criterion of homogeneity of purified T2 phage by Herriott and Barlow (1952). The phage was assayed for these properties before and after fractionation by alcohol precipitation, adsorption with alumina or copper hydroxide, centrifugation, acid precipitation, adsorption to host cells, and treatment with antibacterial sera.

The criteria of purity offered by an investigator for his analyzed preparations are an essential part of his evidence for any unusual analytical results claimed. This point is too often disregarded.

TABLE VII

Elementary Composition of Purified Bacteriophages
(per cent of dry weight)

Phage	C	N	P	H	Reference
WLL	42	13.2	3.7	6.4	Schlesinger (1934)
T2(PC)	49.3	14.0	0.07	7.9	Kalmanson and Bronfenbrenner (1939)
T2	—	11.8	3.7	—	Cohen and Anderson (1946)
T2	42	13.4	5.0	—	Taylor (1946)
T2	—	16	5.2	—	Herriott and Barlow (1952)
T6	—	13.3	3.95	—	Kozloff and Putnam (1949)
T7	—	14.7	4.2	—	Csaky, Beard, Dillon, and Beard (1950)
Staphylococcus	41	14.3	4.8	5.3	Northrop (1938)

3. Elementary Composition

Elementary analyses are available for only three serologically distinct groups of phages, the staphylococcus phage of Northrop, coliphage T7, and the group of phages closely related to T2. Although these analyses (Table VII) are in good agreement among themselves it is probably unwise to make generalizations about phage composition from such a restricted sample. The only seriously discrepant result is the low phosphorus content reported by Kalmanson and Bronfenbrenner, which can probably be discarded as an error. It is specially noteworthy that the assays on coliphage WLL by Schlesinger in 1934 are in such excellent agreement with later results on T2 and T6.

TABLE VIII

Gross Chemical Components of Phages

(per cent by weight)

Phage	Protein	DNA[a]	RNA[b]	Carbohydrate	Lipid	Reference
T2	—	37	0	—	—	Cohen and Anderson (1946)
T2	51	42	4	12	2	Taylor (1946)
T2	40	50	<1	—	<1	Herriott and Barlow (1952)
T6	—	42	3	—	—	Kozloff and Putnam (1949)
T7	49	41	—	17	<1	Csaky, Beard, Dillon, and Beard (1950)

[a] DNA = deoxyribonucleic acid.

[b] RNA = ribonucleic acid.

4. Gross Chemical Components

The few analyses available on the protein, carbohydrate, lipid, and nucleic acid components of bacteriophages are sumarized in Table VIII. There seems to be general agreement that the phages analyzed are about half protein and half nucleic acid of the deoxyribose type. The intrinsic lipid and ribonucleic acid of phage T2 appears to be very small, if any. On the basis of the radioactivity in the mononucleotide fraction of phage T2 produced from a P^{32}-labeled medium, Volkin and Astrachan (1956c) placed the upper limit of the ribonucleic acid content of this phage at 0.025 per cent and argued that the distribution of radioactivity was such that even this quantity is probably an impurity.

The protein of phage T2 is physically separable into two kinds (Hershey, 1955). One of these is the coat or "ghost" of the phage particle and the other is a relatively small soluble protein. The latter is probably mixed with the DNA in the phage head for it is injected into the cell, and it is readily liberated into the medium following osmotic shock which releases the DNA. The amino acid analyses of these two protein components are not distinctively different.

The carbohydrate of T2 is part of the nucleic acid, but that of T7 may be in part a constituent of the phage particle or an impurity. It is desirable to have additional analyses of this type, since only two serologically distinct groups of phages have been analyzed and this is an inadequate sample from which to draw general conclusions about the chemical nature of phages.

The gross chemical composition of the few phages analyzed is quite different from the composition of any plant or animal virus which has been analyzed (Beard, 1948). The known bacteriophages are characterized by a large content of deoxyribonucleic acid (DNA). The well known plant viruses contain ribonucleic acid (RNA) exclusively, usually in relatively small amounts. Two, and perhaps three, animal viruses contain predominantly RNA. The latter include the carefully studied PR8(A) and Lee(B) strains of influenza virus (Ada, 1957) which are reported as having 0.9 per cent RNA and 0.1 per cent DNA, and MEF-1 poliomyelitis virus (Schwerdt and Schaffer, 1955) which analyzed 24 per cent RNA and 1 per cent DNA. Nearly 10 per cent RNA was found in Eastern equine encephalitis virus by Taylor, Sharp, Beard, and Beard (1943). Wyatt (1952) reported DNA in some insect viruses.

5. Amino Acids, Nucleotides, and Bases

Polson and Wyckoff (1948) published the first amino acid analyses for phage T4. The phage was purified by centrifugation, hydrolyzed, and the amino acids separated by paper chromatography. No criteria of purity were presented and the authors seem to have reservations about the significance of the results. Luria (1953a) reported amino acid analyses of T2 and T4 bacteriophages from his laboratory. Fraser and Jerrell (1953) described in more detail the amino acids in preparations of T3. Hershey (1955) analyzed several protein fractions from T2. The results are summarized in Table IX. The phage proteins do not differ markedly in composition from plant and animal virus proteins but are quite different from the histones and protamines that form part of the nucleoproteins of higher organisms.

TABLE IX

Amino Acid Analyses of Some Bacteriophages

Amino acid	T2[a]	T2[b]	T4[a]	T4[c]	T3[d]
Aspartic acid	10.5	10–14	—	12	11.7
Glutamic acid	—	13–15	—	12	10.5
Glycine	17.2	4–6	12	7.3	9.8
Alanine	—	6–10	—	9.4	9.7
Valine	6.5	6–8	6.1	6.5	6.6
Leucine	5.7	12–15	5.6	6.5	9.8
Isoleucine	7.4		5.5	3.9	4.9
Serine	5.7	4.5–6	2.3	4.8	2.9
Threonine	5.7	4.5–6	6.1	7.0	5.3
Cystine	0.2	0.1–0.4	—	—	—
Methionine	3.0	1–2	2.35	< 1.3	1.7
Proline	3.7	3.6–5	—	5.0	4.2
Phenylalanine	5.0	7.5–9	5.3	4.2	3.5
Tyrosine	4.5	3–9	4.6	3.7	4.2
Tryptophan	0.9	—	—	—	—
Histidine	1.0	0.6–2.5	0.64	<2.6	1.7
Lysine	7.4	4.7–7	4.2	8.5	6.3
Arginine	5.6	3.6–5.3	4.0	6.5	7.2

[a] Luria (1953a), results of microbiological assays expressed as per cent of phage protein.

[b] Hershey (1955), results for C^{14}-labeled acid-insoluble protein by radiochemical analysis after separation on paper chromatograms, showing distribution of carbon as per cent of total recovered.

[c] Polson and Wyckoff (1948), separation by paper chromatography and ninhydrin assay, expressed as per cent of recovered amino acids.

[d] Fraser and Jerrell (1953), separation by ion exchange chromatography, analysis by ninhydrin reaction expressed as per cent of recovered amino acids.

Early analyses of the constituents of phage nucleic acids yielded conflicting results. Kozloff, Knowlton, Putnam, and Evans (1951) reported the isolation from phage T6 of adenine, guanine, thymine, and cytosine, but the relative proportions of the bases were not determined. Weed and Cohen (1951), while studying transfer of host cell pyrimidines to phage T6, isolated thymidylic acid, deoxycytidylic acid, and adenine from the phage. Smith and Wyatt (1951) reported the presence of adenine, guanine, cytosine, and thymine in both T5 and T2. Marshak (1951) found adenine, guanine, and thymine in phage T2 but made the rather startling observation that neither cytosine nor 5-methylcytosine could be found, although cytosine was present in phage T3. Marshak also noted that the absorption spectrum for the guanine isolated from phage T2 was abnormal suggesting the possibility of contamination of the guanine with some other base. The confusion was finally resolved by Wyatt and Cohen (1953) who reported that phages T2, T4, and T6 contain neither cytosine nor 5-methylcytosine, but contain instead a new base, 5-(hydroxymethyl)cytosine. Some analyses on the nucleic acids of phages are given in Table X. A few additional data are given by Lwoff (1953). It appears that only T2, T4, and T6 contain 5-(hydroxymethyl)cytosine.

TABLE X

The Molar Proportions of Nucleic Acid Bases in Phages

Base	T5[a]	T2[b]	T2, T4, T6[c]	T6[d]	T2[e]	T7[f]
Adenine	34	33	33	33	32	26
Guanine	21	17	18	24	17	24
Cytosine	11	—	—	—	—	24
HMC[g]	—	—	17	—	16	—
Thymine	35	31	33	—	35	26

[a] Smith and Wyatt (1951).

[b] Marshak (1951), absolute values arbitrary.

[c] Wyatt and Cohen (1953).

[d] Koch, Putnam, and Evans (1952), absolute values arbitrary.

[e] Hershey, Dixon, and Chase (1953).

[f] Lunan and Sinsheimer (1956).

[g] 5-(Hydroxymethyl) cytosine.

The presence of glucose in glucosidic linkage with 5-(hydroxymethyl)cytosine (HMC) of T2, T4, and T6 is clearly indicated by work from several laboratories. The presence of a hexose in the material released from T4 by a specific lipocarbohydrate was first mentioned by Jesaitis and Goebel (1953). Sinsheimer (1954) independently found glucose attached to some but not all of the HMC released from T2 phage DNA by the combined action of pancreatic deoxyribonuclease and purified venom phosphodiesterase. Volkin (1954b) reported similar results for T2, T4, and T6 phages, except that in T4 he found one mole of glucose for each mole of HMC. In addition, he found no glucose in T1 phage. Sinsheimer (1956) confirmed the difference between T2 and T4, and found that glucose content is one of several characters showing unusual inheritance in crosses between T2 and T4 (Streisinger and Weigle, 1956).

Cohen (1956) reported that the r mutants of T2, T4, and T6 contain higher glucose/deoxyribose ratios than do the wild type phages. Sinsheimer's (1956) analytical results do not support this finding so that clarification must await further studies.

6. Extinction Coefficients of Phage Preparations

An analytical quantity of some interest to phage workers is the light absorption at 2,600 A since this is a measure of the nucleic acid content of the virus particle. However, there has been no uniformity in the presentation of data. The absorbancy has been expressed as extinction coefficient per infective phage particle, per morphologically typical phage particle, or per mg. of phage phosphorus per ml. In some cases the extinction coefficient has been corrected for light scattering, in some cases not. This lack of uniformity makes comparison of data difficult. The expression of analytical results in terms of the infective particle is very convenient for the analyst but is only of comparative value because of unknown contamination of phage preparations with inactive phage particles and uncertainties in the efficiency of plating. Luria, Williams, and Backus (1951) avoided these difficulties by giving the absorbancy per morphologically typical phage particle counted in the electron microscope. Examples of the available data are given in Table XI. They express optical densities per cm. divided by phage concentrations in visible particles per ml., plaque-forming particles per ml., and mg. of phosphorus per ml., insofar as the data given permit. In many instances values are given for the best of numerous preparations that vary considerably. These variations depend in part on variable content of noninfective phage particles in the preparations but, as the data of Luria, Williams, and Backus (1951) show, depend also on other impurities that contribute to the absorbancy or light scattering by the preparation.

TABLE XI

Extinction Coefficients of Phage Preparations

Phage	cm.^{2}/10^{12} particles	cm.^{2}/10^{12} plaques	cm.^{2}/mg. P
T2[a]	—	8.3	300
T2[b]	4.5[c]	8.8[c]	—
T2[d]	—	6.0	310
T4[b]	2.9[c]	7.3[c]	—
T4[e]	—	6.7	270
T6[b]	5.0[c]	7.4[c]	—
T6[f]	—	—	260
T6[g]	—	—	363
T5[e]	—	5.0[c]	—
T5[h]	—	32	300
T7[f]	—	2.7[c]	255
DNA[g]	—	—	278

[a] Herriott and Barlow (1952).

[b] Luria, Williams, and Backus (1951).

[c] These figures are about 20 per cent low relative to the others owing to correction for scattering.

[d] Hershey, Dixon, and Chase (1953).

[e] Hershey, Kamen, Kennedy, and Gest (1951).

[f] Putnam, Miller, Palm, and Evans (1952).

[g] Cohen and Arbogast (1950b).

[h] Smith and Wyatt (1951).

Measurements of extinction provide a rapid and convenient method of assay of phage during purification, and the extinction per plaque-forming particle of the final product is an excellent measure of contamination by impurities that contain nucleic acid, on the one hand, or of the efficiency of the plaque count on the other.

7. Phosphorus and Nitrogen Contents per Infective Particle

The content in phosphorus and nitrogen per plaque-forming particle has been frequently measured, and a few data are given in Table XII. The phosphorus content of some additional phages is cited by Lwoff (1953) and Stent (1958). The results are only moderately consistent among themselves and with the expectations based on size measurements, composition, and absolute infectivity. The results for T5 given by Smith and Wyatt (1951) illustrate the uncertainties that are inseparable

TABLE XII

Phosphorus and Nitrogen per Plaque-Forming Particle

(μg./10^{11} particles)

Phage	Phosphorus	Nitrogen	Reference
T2	2.0	—	Hershey, Dixon, and Chase (1953)
T2	3.7	10	Hook, Beard, Taylor, Sharp, and Beard (1946)
T2	2.8	8.3	Herriott and Barlow (1952)
T4	2.3	—	Cohen and Arbogast (1950a)
T6	3.3	10	Kozloff and Putnam (1949)
T6	3.4	—	Cohen and Arbogast (1950a)
WLL	1.6	5.7	Schlesinger (1934)
T1	1.7	—	Labaw (1953)
T7	1.3	—	Labaw (1953)
T7	0.82	—	Lunan and Sinsheimer (1956)
T7	1.5	5.3	Putnam, Miller, Palm, and Evans (1952)
T7	1.5	5.0	Csaky, Beard, Dillon, and Beard (1950)
T5	3.8	—	Labaw (1953)
T5	10	36	Smith and Wyatt (1951)
Staphylococcus	6.7	20	Northrop (1938)
Megaterium	—	17	Northrop (1955b)

from measurements of this type. The ratio of nitrogen to phosphorus indicates that the material consists of phage particles but the plaque count is improbably low. The phosphorus (or nucleic acid) content per particle is important for several reasons (Stent, 1958) and reliable ways to determine it need to be developed.

8. Summary

The few phages that have been analyzed contain deoxyribonucleic acid and protein in approximately equal amounts and very little else. This distinguishes them from most living things including most of the other viruses, excepting perhaps certain animal sperm and some insect viruses.

A few phages, notably T2, contain a chemically unique nucleic acid. Phage proteins have been relatively little studied. Most of the protein of T2 is membrane material. It is not unusual with respect to amino acid composition.

CHAPTER VIII

ANTIGENIC PROPERTIES

Early studies on the antigenic properties of bacteriophages have been reviewed by d'Herelle (1926) and Burnet, Keogh, and Lush (1937). The latter reference gives an excellent discussion of the mechanism of the antigen-antibody reaction from the kinetic viewpoint and, in addition, contains much experimental material which has not been published elsewhere.

Bordet and Ciuca (1921) first demonstrated that injection of rabbits with phage lysates stimulates the production of phage-neutralizing antibody. Their antisera also contained agglutinins for the host bacterium. The injection of host bacteria, however, failed to stimulate the production of phage-neutralizing antibody. Otto and Winkler (1922) were able to remove all bacterial agglutinins by absorption with host bacteria without affecting the antiphage properties of the serum. These findings demonstrated that phage is antigenically distinct from its host.

It was early recognized that antiphage sera had considerable specificity, inactivating the homologous and some heterologous strains of phage but not others. The fact that serological relationship was correlated with other properties of bacteriophages was not generally appreciated, however, until the taxonomic work of Burnet and Asheshov.

Since these early experiments it has been found that the activity of antiphage antibodies is not confined to neutralization. The addition of a sufficiently concentrated suspension of phage particles to homologous antiserum results in visible aggregation of the virus particles followed by settling of the clumps as a precipitate. By suitable ultrafiltration methods one can separate from phage lysates soluble substances possessing the antigenic specificity of the phage particles. When antiphage antibody is allowed to react with such substances it loses its ability to neutralize phage. Some, if not all, phage-antiphage systems fix complement. These and other properties of anti-phage sera will now be discussed in more detail.

1. Preparation of Antiphage Sera

Rabbits are the most convenient animals to use for antibody production, and most of the serological work with phage has been done with rabbit sera. The phages themselves are non-toxic and nonpathogenic for animals and can usually be in-jected in large amounts without damage to the recipient. Crude phage lysates, however, may contain toxic bacterial sub-stances, such as the endotoxins of the enteric bacteria and the much more potent exotoxins of the corynebacteria and clos-tridia. In such cases the toxins must first be removed by frac-tionation or inactivated. For many purposes it is desirable to purify the phages before using them for immunization, since adequate purification will result in the absence of host-cell antibodies from the resultant antisera (Kalmanson, Hershey, and Bronfenbrenner, 1942). If crude phage preparations are used it may be necessary to remove host-cell antibodies by absorption with bacterial suspensions. This is essential, for instance, in studies involving complement fixation.

Stimulation of antibody production requires the administra-tion of adequate quantities of antigenic material. The daily injection of about 10^{10} virus particles (about 10 μg.) for five days will usually result in the presence of considerable neutralizing antibody in serum obtained one week after the last injection. Repetition of this course of immunization will further increase the antibody titer. The final result does not seem to depend greatly on the route (intravenous, intraperitoneal, or subcu-taneous) by which antigen in administered. Use of the sub-cutaneous route, however, is least likely to lead to toxic or ana-phylactic reactions. Since there are large differences in antibody response from one rabbit to another, it may be desirable to immunize at least three rabbits with the same phage preparation. Judged by the neutralization test, antisera prepared against certain phages, such as T2, T3, T4, T6, and T7, usually have very high homologous antibody titers in comparison with antisera against others, such as Tl and T5, which may be relatively weak. Such differences do not necessarily reflect corresponding differences in antibody concentration, since the rate of neutralization may easily depend on other factors as well. Actually, a very few determinations have been made of the absolute antibody content of antiphage sera.

The effect of adjuvants on phage antigenicity has been very little studied, probably because most phages are already excellent antigens. Wahl and Lewi (1939) obtained a marked improvement in the antigenicity of a low-titer *B. subtilis* phage by adsorption to alumina. Intraperitoneal injection of 3×10^8 particles of unadsorbed phage gave little or no antibody response. Injection of the same amount of absorbed phage resulted two weeks later in an antiserum giving 90 per cent inactivation at a dilution of $1/_{50}$. The titer increased to $1/_{200}$ in a month. This technique may be useful to workers dealing with low-titer temperate phages.

Phages retain antigenicity, in some instances without appreciable loss, following careful inactivation of their infectivity by heat, formaldehyde, ultraviolet irradiation (Muckenfuss, 1928; Schultz, Quigley, and Bullock, 1929; Nagano and Takeuti, 1951; Pollard and Setlow, 1953; Miller and Goebel, 1954); phenol, photodynamic action of methylene blue (Burnet, Keogh, and Lush, 1937); osmotic shock, and sonic vibration (F. Lanni and Lanni, 1953; Nagano and Oda, 1954). Phage which has been "overneutralized" by homologous antibody is, however, nonantigenic in guinea pigs, even after treatment with papain (Kalmanson and Bronfenbrenner, 1943; Nagano and Takeuti, 1951).

The antigenicity of premature lysates of a staphylococcal phage has been studied by Rountree (1952); of purified T2 "doughnuts" by Lanni and Lanni (1953); of proflavine lysates of T4, and of T4- and T3-infected bacteria by Barry (1954); and of infected and lysogenic *B. megaterium* by Miller and Goebel (1954). The antigenicity of ultrafiltrable phage-related materials is discussed below.

2. Multiplicity of Phage Antigens

Until a few years ago it was believed, simply because there was no contradictory evidence, that each strain of phage possessed a single kind of antigen. Accordingly, all of the specific effects of antiphage serum were interpreted in terms of the reaction of a single antibody (neutralizing antibody) with the virus particles. In an extensive study, Lanni and Lanni (1953) (see also Rountree, 1952; De Mars, Luria, Fisher, and Levinthal, 1953) presented clear evidence for the existence of at least two distinct antigens in phage T2. One of the antigens, which appears to be localized in the phage tail, reacts with neutralizing antibody. The primary measurable effect of this reaction is neutralization of infectivity; under appropriate conditions virus aggregation and complement fixation can also be demonstrated. The second antigen, which appears to be localized in the phage head, participates in specific aggregation and complement fixation, but does not react measurably with neutralizing antibody. The two antigens are confined to the surface structures (protein) of the virus; thus far, the internal contents, liberated by osmotic shock, have given no sign of serological activity (see also Hershey and Chase, 1952; Hershey, 1955). The available evidence indicates that staphylococcal phage 3A (Rountree, 1952) and phage T5 (Fodor and Adams, 1955) likewise possess two distinct antigens, only one of which reacts with neutralizing antibody. Evidence bearing on the serological heterogeneity of the phage tail will be discussed in later sections.

The failure until recently to recognize the antigenic complexity of phage attaches considerable doubt to many of the structural interpretations given to early serological observations.

3. Neutralization of Phage Infectivity

When a phage preparation is mixed with homologous antiserum there is a progressive decrease in the number of plaque-forming particles. The inactivation process can be interrupted at any time by diluting the phage-antibody mixture below the antibody concentration at which collisions between the reactants occur at a significant rate. Following this dilution there is, in general, no detectable reversal of the inactivation process; the titer of surviving phage does not increase. Apparently, dissociation of the phage-antibody complex does not occur at a measurable rate (Burnet, Keogh, and Lush, 1937; Hershey, 1943; see, however, Andrewes and Elford, 1933b; Jerne and Avegno, 1956). Attempts to facilitate dissociation by the addition of formalin-inactivated phage to bind the antibody were unsuccessful (Hershey, 1943). The addition of soluble phage antigen, however, appeared to have a slight reactivating effect (Burnet, 1933b). Although in most instances antibody does not appear to dissociate from the phage particles spontaneously, there is evidence that it can be removed by certain methods. Kalmanson and Bronfenbrenner (1943) found that neutralized phage could be completely reactivated by digestion of the antibody with papain providing the antibody had not been too concentrated or the serum treatment too prolonged. Apparently, if a sufficiently large number of antibody molecules had reacted with the phage particle, the inactivation became irreversible. Anderson and Doermann (1952b) succeeded in obtaining more than a 30-fold increase in titer of a neutralized preparation of phage T3 by subjecting it to sonic vibration.

In the cited reactivation experiments with papain and sonic vibration the concentration of phage during preliminary treatment with antiserum was sufficiently high in most instances as to admit the possibility that part, at least, of the plaque-count decrease was due to specific aggregation. It is not certain, therefore, to what extent the observed reactivation can be ascribed to reversal of neutralization, as opposed to disaggregation of virus clumps. However, Hershey (1943) found that papain can reactivate phage which has been treated with serum under conditions minimizing the possibility of specific aggregation. These successful attempts to reactivate neutralized phage particles indicate that antibody does not kill or destroy phage particles. Presumably, it interferes with some step in the interaction of the intact virus particle with the host cell. The nature of this interference will be discussed in a later section.

From the foregoing discussion, it is clear that neutralizing antibody acts on the phage particles themselves, rather than on the host cell. Pretreatment of host cells with phage antibodies has no effect on the infectious process. Delbrück (1945b) found that, following phage adsorption to the host cell, the infected bacteria are immune to antiphage serum throughout the latent period (see, however, Lieb, 1953; Gross, 1954a; Nagano and Mutai, 1954a). The resistance of infected bacteria to antiphage serum is of great importance in phage technology because it permits the inactivation of unadsorbed phage without affecting the multiplication of phage which is already adsorbed.

Although complement is not required for specific neutralization, it can modify the neutralization of T1 and T2 (Hershey and Bronfenbrenner, 1952). Complement and properdin together, but not separately, inactivate T2 in the absence of specific antibody (Van Vunakis, Barlow, and Levine, 1956).

4. Properties of Incompletely Neutralized Phage Preparations

Following the treatment of phage preparations with antiserum, the surviving infectious particles are not normal. Andrewes and Elford (1933b) reported that the survivors of antibody treatment produced smaller plaques than normal. They interpreted this as indicating a delay in the initiation of the infectious process. The surviving particles also failed to pass through bacteriological filters and collodion membranes which were freely permeable to the same phage particles prior to serum treatment. This might be ascribed to increase of particle size or change of surface charge due to an antibody coating, or to aggregation of phage particles. Frequency distribution curves for plaque sizes of phage C16 before and after treatment with antiserum are given by Burnet, Keogh, and Lush (1937). The distribution for the incompletely neutralized preparation was bimodal with one maximum at less than $1/_3$ the peak plaque diameter of the unimodal curve for normal phage particles. Surprisingly, Delbrück (1945b) failed to find any difference between normal T2 phage and serum-survivors at the 1 per cent level with respect to adsorption, latent period, or burst size (cf. Adams and Wassermann, 1956). The reason for the discrepant observations with these closely related phages is not obvious.

Gough and Burnet (1934) extracted from suspensions of the host bacterium a phage-inhibiting agent (PIA) which was able to inactivate phage particles in much the same manner as antiphage sera. They regarded the extract as a solution of the bacterial receptors for phage adsorption. Burnet and Freeman (1937) investigated the effect of PIA on phage preparations which had been inactivated to the extent of 90 per cent with dilute antiphage sera. The survivors of serum inactivation proved to be very resistant to the inhibiting action of PIA whereas the untreated phage population was 99 per cent inactivated by PIA. This is further evidence that phage antibody can modify the properties of phage particles without inactivating them. It also suggests that the isolated PIA is not identical to the receptor substance on the bacterial surface, since the survivors of the serum action are still able to infect the host cell although they are resistant to the action of PIA.

Another very striking property of partially neutralized phage preparations was demonstrated by Hershey, Kalmanson, and Bronfenbrenner (1944) using a variant of phage T2. The variant adsorbed very poorly to bacteria in a salt-free medium and had a relative efficiency of plating of 10^{-4}. In a medium containing 0.1 N NaCl the phage adsorbed well and the efficiency of plating was about half of that under optimal conditions. The phage was treated with very dilute antiphage serum (dilution 10^{-5})to a survival of about 0.2. The plaque count in a salt-free medium of the survivors of serum treatment was *increased* 1,000-fold as compared with that of the untreated phage preparation. Treatment with a small amount of antiserum had the same effect on phage infectivity as an increase in salt concentration. It is probable that these effects of salt and of antiserum on phage infectivity are due to effects on electrostatic charge (see Cann and Clark, 1955), although this explanation was discarded by the authors. This problem will be discussed further in the chapter on phage adsorption.

It is not certain at present which of the several antibodies in antiphage serum is responsible for the effects described above. A peculiar antibody which stabilizes the activated state of a tryptophan-requiring strain of T4 has recently been described (Jerne, 1956).

5. Complement Fixation

Early results (d'Herelle, 1926) left considerable doubt as to the ability of phage-antiphage systems to fix complement. These doubts have been dispelled in recent years by studies showing not only that such systems do, in fact, fix complement but also that complement fixation offers a valuable quantitative tool for the study of those phage antigens and phage-related materials that do not react with neutralizing antibody. An example is the work of Lanni and Lanni (1953) in their demonstration of a serological relationship between T2 doughnuts and T2 phage and their use of antidoughnut sera for studying the structure of the infective virus particle. The scope of the procedure is not restricted, however, to such antigens.

Other recent studies illustrate further the broad applicability of complement fixation to problems of phage structure and growth. In confirmation of the discovery of Hershey and Chase (1952) with T2, Lanni (1954) showed that the bulk of the complement-fixing antigens of infecting particles of T5 remained outside the infected host cells. Previous work had suggested instead that the complement-fixing antigens of T5 (Rountree,

1951b) and of staphylococcal phage 3A (Rountree, 1952) disappeared during the early stages of infection. Both workers observed that newly synthesized complement-fixing antigens appeared and increased intracellularly a few minutes before mature virus. Miller and Goebel (1954) injected lysogenic cells of *B. megaterium* into rabbits and failed to demonstrate the production of phage-specific, complement-fixing, or neutralizing antibodies. Since nucleic acids have not, in general, been found antigenic, this negative result, which extended an earlier failure by F. Lanni (cited by Lwoff, 1953), accords with the current conception that prophage consists of DNA. Fodor and Adams (1955) used complement fixation in analyzing the antigenic relationship of T5, the related phage PB, and T5 × PB hybrids. Details of a photometric complement titration are given by Lanni (1954).

6. Specific Aggregation

Schlesinger (1933a) observed the aggregation of phage WLL particles by antiphage serum using the dark field microscope. Burnet (1933c) demonstrated that phage C16 gave a visible precipitate when mixed with antiserum. Photographs of the aggregated phage particles, taken by Barnard with the ultraviolet microscope, are included in Burnet's paper. A visible precipitate was formed when antiserum was mixed with phage C16 at all concentrations above about 2×10^9 particles per ml. For smaller virus particles a considerably higher concentration is needed to give a visible precipitate, since the amount of precipitate formed is dependent on the total mass of antigen added. The relationship between the size of an antigenic particle and the concentration of particles needed to give a visible precipitate has been discussed by Merrill (1936). This author also discussed the relationships between particle size and the minimal concentration required for complement fixation and for the stimulation of antibody production. These relationships should be of considerable value to virologists. Ignorance of them has been responsible for much wasted effort.

The phage-antibody system could be readily investigated by the techniques of the quantitative precipitation reaction, but the only attempt at such a study was made by Hershey, Kalmanson, and Bronfenbrenner (1943a) using coliphage T2. The authors concluded that the nitrogen of phage lysates which was specifically precipitable by phage antibodies corresponded to less than 10^{-13} mg. N per lytic unit. Chemical analyses of purified T2 phage preparations by various investigators agree with a figure for the nitrogen content of the lytic unit which is close to 10^{-13} mg. (Chapter VII). The amount of antibody nitrogen capable of precipitating with phage T2 was found to be 0.6 mg. per ml. for a serum with a K value of about 360 minutes^{-1}. It would be of interest to know the ratio between antibody content and K value for various other antiphage sera.

With sera of low neutralizing antibody content, it is possible to follow specific aggregation of phage by observing the consequent reduction in plaque count (Lanni and Lanni, 1953; Fodor and Adams, 1955).

7. Agglutination of Phage-Coated Bacteria

Individual cells of susceptible bacterial strains are able to adsorb a considerable number of phage particles. Delbrück (1940a) found that cells of *E. coli* became saturated after adsorption of from 20 to 250 phage particles depending on the physiological condition of the cells. Burnet (1933a) investigated the serological properties of such phage-coated cells using formalin-killed bacteria to avoid lysis. The formalinized bacteria were suspended in a high-titer phage stock for an hour, then centrifuged and washed to remove unadsorbed phage. These phage-coated bacteria were less susceptible than uncoated bacteria to agglutination by antibacterial sera, but were readily agglutinated by antiphage serum which had no effect on uncoated bacteria. The agglutination was phage-specific. Absorption of the serum with phage-coated bacteria depressed both the agglutinating and the phage-neutralizing activities. The result is interesting since it suggests that antigens capable of binding neutralizing antibody exist elsewhere than at the tip of the phage tail. More work is needed, however, before this interpretation is accepted.

Burnet also performed cross-absorption experiments using serologically related phages. Absorption with bacteria coated with homologous phage reduced the neutralization titer for homologous and heterologous phages alike, whereas bacteria coated with heterologous phage absorbed antibody against this phage but had little effect on the titer against homologous phage. This type of experiment permits one to make an antigenic analysis of a series of related phages. Antiphage sera can also be absorbed with phage concentrates, the precipitated phage particles being removed by low-speed centrifugation (Hershey, Kalmanson, and Bronfenbrenner, 1943a, 1943b; Hershey, 1946a). An advantage of the use of phage-coated bacteria is that the adsorption of the phage particles to the bacteria serves to concentrate and purify them in one step. It should be kept in mind, however, that those phage antigens which are located at or near the site of adsorption to host cells may not be accessible to antibody.

8. Specific Soluble Substances

The first evidence for a soluble substance having the antigenic specificity of phage particles was obtained by Asheshov (1925). He filtered a phage preparation through a collodion membrane of a pore size small enough to retain the phage particles. The immunization of rabbits with the phage-free filtrate resulted in the production of specific phage-neutralizing antibody. Burnet (1933b) prepared sterile ultrafiltrates of high-titer stocks of coliphage C16 using Gradocol membranes of a suitable permeability to retain all the phage particles. The ultrafiltrates immunized rabbits with the production of neutralizing antibody for phage C16. The ability of the ultrafiltrate factor to react with antibody was most conveniently detected by mixing it with antiphage C16 serum and observing a decrease or blocking of the phage-neutralizing activity of the serum.   The antibody-blocking effect showed the serological specificity of phage C16. The ultrafiltrate factor was not adsorbed by phage-sensitive bacteria and had no bacteriolytic activity.   It was relatively heat resistant, requiring treatment at 90° C. for 30 minutes for inactivation.   On this basis Burnet suggested that it might be a polysaccharide.

DeMars, Luria, Fisher, and Levinthal (1953) demonstrated the presence of similar specific soluble substances in bacteria infected with coliphages T2, T4, or T5.   The substances were liberated from the infected bacteria during the latent period by premature lysis, and were separated from phage particles and bacteria by ultrafiltration through collodion filters.   The quantity of ultrafiltrable specific antigen increased during the latent period.   What is probably the same type of substance was liberated from bacteria infected with phage T2 or T6, in which normal phage development had been prevented by the addition of proflavine (see also DeMars, 1955; Barry, 1954).   The ultrafiltrable fraction had the same serological specificity as the infecting phage.   At equivalent antibody-blocking activity the ultrafiltrable fraction from T2 lysates had roughly the same complement-fixing activity as intact virus (Lanni and Lanni, 1953).

Crude T2 lysates contain a second noninfectious antibody-blocking component, which appears to be intermediate in size between the ultrafiltrable component and the infectious virus particle (Lanni and Lanni, 1953; DeMars, 1955).   The latter reference should be consulted for details of the measurement of antibody-blocking agents and for a description of their intracellular development.   Actually, the antibody-blocking measurement may be regarded as an abbreviated absorption experiment, in which the absorbing agent and its attached antibody are allowed to remain in the system during subsequent measurement of residual neutralizing activity.

Lanni (1954) has found that at least one-half of the total phage-specific complement-fixing activity of T5 lysates is associated with a noninfectious fraction which sediments more slowly than the virus.

Efforts to isolate phage antigens by degradation of the virus particle have met with partial success (Lanni and Lanni, 1953; DeMars, 1955; see also Hershey, 1955).

9. Kinetics of Neutralization

It had been recognized since the work of Prausnitz (1922) that the neutralization of phage activity by antiserum was a relatively slow process, and that a small proportion of the phage population resisted inactivation by antibody. There seems to have been no further attempt to study the kinetics of phage neutralization until the work of Andrewes and Elford (1933a). These authors systematically varied the concentrations of antiserum and of phage in the reaction mixture, and determined the decrease in the number of infectious phage particles as a function of time. The "percentage law" is a summary of their experimental results: "over a very wide range a given dilution of serum neutralized in a given time an approximately constant percentage of phage, however much phage there was present." This relationship held from concentrations of a few hundred phage particles per ml. up to at least 10^8 per ml., and for serum concentrations from 10^{-4} to undiluted. Although this relationship between phage and antibody is taken for granted by phage workers today, it was very startling at the time of its discovery, and its implications are still not understood or appreciated by many immunologists and virologists.

Burnet, Keogh, and Lush (1937) presented kinetic measurements for the inactivation of various phages by antiserum. In most cases the proportion of active virus decreased logarithmically with time after a slight initial lag. The rate of inactivation was directly proportional to the concentration of antiserum. The inactivation was assumed to be the result of a collision between a phage particle and an antibody molecule. Since the reaction is usually carried out in the presence of a large excess of antibody, phage neutralization does not decrease the concentration of antibody perceptibly. Therefore, the kinetics is that of a first-order reaction, represented by the equation:

$$-dP/dt = KP/D$$

Integration gives the very useful result:

$$K = \frac{2.3D}{t} \log_{10} (P_0/P)$$

in which K is the velocity constant with the dimension minute^{-1}, D is the dilution of serum (100 for serum diluted 1/100, etc.), t is the time in minutes, P_0 is the phage assay at zero time, and P is the phage assay at time t.

Burnet found that the kinetics of neutralization of phage C16 agreed satisfactorily with this equation at serum concentrations from $1/30$ to $1/30,000$. Phage neutralization was logarithmic to an inactivation of more than 99 per cent, but then the rate slowed, the survivors appearing to be more resistant. Most of the phages studied by Burnet behaved in this manner, including a streptococcal phage and a staphylococcal phage as well as various immunological types of enterophages. However, he noted that the neutralization of coliphages in serological group 3 deviated markedly from a first-order reaction, and that a relatively large proportion of the phage population was resistant to inactivation by even high concentrations of antiserum. Delbrück (1945b) found that the neutralization of T2 and T7 obeyed the equations above, but that neutralization of Tl did not. The rate of inactivation of Tl decreased progressively throughout the course of the reaction. Similar anomalous behavior has been observed with phages related to T5 (Adams, 1952), with the M phages of *B. megaterium* (Friedman and Cowles, 1953), and with D20, a relative of Tl (Adams and Wade, 1955).

The value of K, the velocity constant, is a characteristic of a particular lot of serum and may vary from one rabbit to another or from one bleeding to another from the same animal. The K value is a convenient measure of the neutralizing potency of a serum, a high K value indicating a high titer. Once the K value of a sample has been determined, it can be substituted in the equation and used to calculate the dilution, D, of this serum required to inactivate any desired fraction of the phage in any given time. The range of inactivation over which the equation is applicable must be determined by experiment. For most purposes an inactivation of 90 to 99 per cent is adequate and within the range of first-order kinetics.

Any phage-antibody system which follows first-order kinetics will necessarily obey the percentage law of Andrewes and Elford. The law is more general, however, since it applies also to phages in serological group 3, which do not follow first-order kinetics.

Hershey, Kalmanson, and Bronfenbrenner (1943a) found that the inactivation of phage T2 by antiserum followed first-order kinetics, the K value being independent of D, t, and P_0 up to a concentration of about 10^9 phage particles per ml. Above this concentration, aggregation of phage particles by antiserum resulted in an increased K value.

Kalmanson, Hershey, and Bronfenbrenner (1942) studied some of the variables influencing the rate of neutralization of phage T2 by antibody. A particularly careful study of the reaction using highly diluted antiserum confirmed the initial lag in the neutralization that had been noted by Burnet. Analysis of the convexity of the inactivation curve suggested that between 2 and 3 antibody molecules must react with each phage particle on the average for neutralization to occur. Neutralization of T2 by antibody thus appeared to be a multi-hit process. However, it is now known (Sagik, 1954) that a large fraction of the phage particles in certain stocks of T2 are unable to form plaques when plated directly, but become infective during treatment with antiserum. The inhibited particles may also be activated in other ways, for example, by heating or by lowering the salt concentration. Activated stocks showed no sign of deviation from first-order neutralization kinetics (Cann and Clark, 1954). Since allowance must be made for genetic differences in the lines of T2 employed by different workers and for differences in antisera, these findings do not necessarily explain all examples of multi-hit neutralization kinetics (see Park, 1956).

The temperature coefficient for the velocity constant K was determined by Burnet, Keogh, and Lush (1937) for phage C16. The K value at 0, 37, and 45° C. was 45, 930, and 1350 minutes^{-1}, respectively, the Q_{10} thus being about 2.1. Similar studies were made by Kalmanson, Hershey, and Bronfenbrenner (1942) with the serologically related phage T2. The K value was found to be 0.05 seconds^{-1} at 0° C. and 0.7 seconds^{-1} at 37° C., corresponding to a Q_{10} of about 2. The Arrhenius constant was determined by Hershey (1941) to be about 11,000 cal. per mole. The meaning of these estimates has been placed in doubt by the finding of Cann and Clark (1954) that the neutralization of activated T2 (see above) shows a Q_{10} of only 1.4, suggesting that the process is limited solely by diffusion. However, their measurements, unlike earlier ones, were made using media of low salt concentration.

Essentially all serological work with viruses has been done with antiserum diluted either in physiological saline or in broth containing added salt because such diluents are conventional in serology. Recently Jerne (1952) and Jerne and Skovsted (1953) reported that physiological diluents actually inhibited phage neutralization, monovalent cations above 10^{-2} M and divalent cations above 10^{-3} M being inhibitory. Optimum rates of inactivation were obtained in 10^{-3} M NaCl containing a few μg. per ml. of certain proteins which appeared to act as cofactors. Highly diluted normal serum, egg white, and crystalline lysozyme were effective as cofactors. An anti-T4 serum with a K value of 600 minute^{-1} in broth gave under optimal conditions a K value of 100,000 or more. The kinetics were first order to a phage survival of 10^{-3} to 10^{-4}. It has long been recognized that salt concentration has a marked effect on reactions involving colloidal particles because of surface charges, but no one had anticipated such an astonishing effect on the rate of the antigen-antibody reaction. Additional data and discussion of these effects are given by Cann and Clark (1954, 1955).

Hershey (1941) discussed the absolute rate of the phage-antiphage reaction, giving theoretical equations from which the maximum rate could be calculated. The calculations and some of the discussion in this paper are incorrect because of erroneous concepts of the nature and size of phage T2 current at that time. However, recalculation using Hershey's methods and more modern data indicates that the actual inactivation rates observed by Jerne are of the same order of magnitude as the maximum rate attainable assuming that every collision resulted in antibody attachment. Control of the ionic environment and the use of cofactors in Jerne's experiments resulted in increasing the number of effective collisions between antibody molecules and susceptible sites on the phage particle to nearly the theoretical limit.

A theoretical analysis of the neutralization of T4 is given by Mandell (1955).

10. Anomalous Neutralization Behavior

A fact which puzzled Andrewes and Elford (1933a) was that neutralization of their phages proceeded rapidly until 90 to 99 per cent of the phage was inactivated and then slowed down rather abruptly, the residual phage activity appearing to be very resistant to neutralization. They demonstrated that this could not be due to exhaustion of antibody and hence must be due to inhomogeneity of the phage population with respect to susceptibility to inactivation. That this inhomogeneity was not genetic in origin was demonstrated by subculturing plaques of phage particles which had survived treatment with antiserum. The descendants proved to be normally susceptible to neutralization by antiserum.

The possibility that the inhomogeneity was caused by the action of antiserum itself, combining with the phage particles in such a way as to make them resistant to neutralization, was next considered. This possibility was discarded because the resistant survivors of the action of $1/100$ serum were inactivated by $1/10$ serum at the same rate as untreated phage particles; however, the description of this experiment leaves much to be desired. Attempts to correlate resistance to antiserum with other properties such as heat resistance, ability to adsorb to host cells, age of phage stock, and plating efficiency on different bacterial hosts were unsuccessful.

Delbrück (1945b), dealing with the anomalous neutralization behavior of Tl, suggested that the inhomogeneity might be inherent in the virus population or, more likely, that it might develop during the course of the reaction as a result of attachment of antibody at noncritical sites on the phage. Although many samples of anti-Tl serum are like that described by Delbrück in failing to follow first-order kinetics, Hershey (personal communication) found that anti-Tl sera from two rabbits gave excellent first-order inactivation curves. Similarly, Fodor and Adams (1955) found only one antiserum, of some dozen prepared against various strains of the T5 serological group, which gave good first-order neutralization curves. It is not clear, therefore, whether the observed neutralization anomalies reflect an inherent heterogeneity of phage preparations, to which not all rabbits respond, or a heterogeneity which is acquired during interaction with certain samples of antiserum. Nor is it clear that the responsible serum factor is necessarily specific antibody. According to Hershey and Bronfenbrenner (1952) anomalous neutralization behavior may be an uncontrolled effect of complement. Recent studies (Van Vunakis, Barlow, and Levine, 1956) show that serum properdin, together with complement, have nonspecific effects which could confuse the study of specific neutralization. Unfortunately, nonspecific serum effects have not received explicit attention in most studies of anomalous neutralization behavior.

11. Host Dependence of Serum-Survivor Assay

It has been known for many years (d'Herelle, 1926) that different assay hosts may give different estimates of the fraction of unneutralized phage in a given phage-antiserum mixture. Kalmanson and Bronfenbrenner (1942) analyzed this host effect with a strain of T2 that plated on certain strains of Shiga and Flexner dysentery bacteria with very nearly the same efficiency as on *E. coli*. The host-range properties and susceptibility to neutralization by antiserum were independent of the bacterial strain used as host for production of phage stocks. When the kinetics of neutralization were studied by plating replicate samples of serum-phage mixtures on each of the three host strains, it was found that the rate of neutralization was decidedly greater when measured with the Shiga and Flexner hosts than when measured with *E. coli* (see also Friedman, 1954; Tanami and Miyajima, 1956). This was interpreted to mean that a certain fraction of the initial phage population lost its ability to produce plaques on the dysentery strains while retaining its infectivity for *E. coli*. Subculture of these "monovalent" survivors on *E. coli* resulted in a "polyvalent" phage stock with full infectivity for all three host species. Reaction with antiserum had seemingly produced a phenotypic modification of host range. Bronfenbrenner had previously been able to produce the same kind of modification of host range in this phage by mild heat treatment.

The authors suggested (see also Tanami and Miyajima, 1956) that their experiments provide evidence for a serological heterogeneity inherent in individual phage particles. In the present conceptual framework, this heterogeneity would be a feature of the phage tail. It is not necessary, however, to postulate heterogeneity, either of antibody-attachment or of host-attachment sites, in order to explain the results. The differential host effects could easily be due to minor differences in the phage receptor sites on the several bacterial hosts, such that there would be differences in bonding strength between phage and the different hosts. In the random reaction of antibody molecules with uniform antigen sites on the phage particles, the virus surface could be so altered that certain of the particles would adsorb abortively, or even be unable to adsorb, to the dysentery host cells, whereas stronger bonds with *E. coli* would still allow productive interaction. Both of these interpretations attribute the observed effects to antibody-induced phenotypic modification of host range, as opposed to selection from a genetically uniform, phenotypically heterogeneous population (see Lanni and Lanni, 1956). Direct evidence that "monovalent" survivors have indeed reacted with antibody in a significant fashion is contained in a brief note by Lanni and Lanni (1957).

12. Inheritance of Antigenic Specificity

The perpetuation of serological character of phages during continued subculture indicates, of course, that antigenic structure is genetically stable. On the other hand, the existence of phage strains which show partial serological cross-reaction implies the possibility of mutations affecting serological behavior.

Efforts to demonstrate serological mutation in phage, by examining either the survivors of prolonged serum action or mutants selected for nonserological markers, have generally been unconvincing (d'Herelle and Rakieten, 1934, 1935; Burnet and Freeman, 1937) or unsuccessful (Luria, 1945a; Hershey, 1946a, 1946b). Recent reports, however, indicate that some success may have been achieved in isolating serological mutants of a *Xanthomonas pruni* phage (Eisenstark, Goldberg, and Bernstein, 1955) and of T5 (Lanni and Lanni, 1956, 1957). Detailed verification of these briefly reported observations could make the antigenic structure of these phages amenable to ordinary genetic analysis.

Several workers, proceeding along a different line, have obtained valuable information by examining hybrids obtained from crosses of serologically related phages. Fodor and Adams (1955) have shown that certain T5 × PB hybrids resemble one or the other parent serologically, while others resemble both parents to some extent. By contrast, Streisinger (1956b) found that the genetic determinants of serological specificity in T2 and T4 are allelic and inseparable from the host-range determinants. Progeny from T2 × T4 crosses possessed the serological genotype of one or the other parent, but never of both. Interestingly, the first-cycle T2 × T4 progeny were found to fall into three phenotypic classes: the two parental classes, and a class with mixed serological phenotype (Streisinger, 1956c). The quantitative distribution among these classes was independent of genotype (Chapter XVI).

At the moment, it is not possible to give a unique structural interpretation to the particles, obtained in either the T5 × PB or the T2 × T4 crosses, which resemble both parents serologically. It is tempting to draw the conclusion that they contain two distinct tail antigens, corresponding to the distinct parental antigens. They could, however, contain neither of these but a third antigen, which cross-reacts with both antibodies. In this respect, serological data obtained with cross progeny are no less ambiguous than data obtained by cross-absorption analysis of related phage strains. This ambiguity, clearly stated for phage workers by Hershey and Bronfenbrenner (1952) and Luria (1953a), is conveniently overlooked by most serologists. But while the heterogeneity of the tail antigen has proved elusive, there can be no question of the heterogeneity of neutralizing antibody. The simple demonstration that exhaustive absorption of an antiserum with heterologous phage removes part but not all of the antibody for the homologous phage proves that the neutralizing antibody molecules in the serum are not all alike. Unfortunately for structural interpretations, it is well known that a single antigen can stimulate the production of a variety of antibody molecules.

13. Mechanism of Phage Neutralization

We shall briefly review the observations that seem especially relevant to the mechanism of neutralization by antibody.

1. Neutralized phage can be reactivated by treatment with proteolytic enzymes or high frequency sound. Hence, antibody molecules do not destroy the phage, but interfere mechanically with infection by their presence at the phage surface.

2. Although a particle of phage T2 can accommodate a total

of about 4,600 antibody molecules (Hershey, Kalmanson, and Bronfenbrenner, 1943b, Hershey, Kimura, and Bronfenbrenner 1947), not more than two or three molecules, and possibly only one, actually participate in neutralization, regardless of how many attach.

3. Depending on the conditions of preparation, neutralized phage may absorb to host cells normally, poorly, or not at all (Burnet, Keogh, and Lush, 1937; Hershey and Bronfenbrenner, 1952; Nagano and Mutai, 1954b; Nagano and Oda, 1955). It may even adsorb to one host, which it proceeds to infect, but not to another, for which it has been neutralized (Lanni and Lanni, 1957). A normal particle which has already adsorbed to a host cell may or may not be resistant to neutralization.

4. The tip of the phage tail is the site of adsorption to the host (T. F. Anderson, 1952).

5. Following adsorption of a normal phage particle, the phage DNA enters the host cell, while the phage protein (ghost) remains outside and can be stripped off without interfering with phage reproduction (Hershey and Chase, 1952). Hence, infection consists in the injection of phage nucleic acid into the bacterium, this process being mediated by the phage tail in a way which is not yet clear. Neutralized phage that succeeds in adsorbing to a host cell does not inject its DNA (Nagano and Oda, 1955; Tolmach, 1957).

6. Neutralizing antibody is just one of several species of antiphage antibody. There is evidence that its action is confined to the phage tail, while other antibodies react mainly with the phage head (Lanni and Lanni, 1953).

These observations clearly indicate that the phage tail is critically important for neutralization. It would appear that attachment of one or a few antibody molecules at appropriate sites on the tail can render the virus noninfectious either by preventing adsorption, or by interfering with injection if the virus remains capable of adsorbing. Reaction of adsorbed virus with antibody, after injection of the DNA, would have no consequence for the infection. How antibody manages to prevent injection without preventing adsorption is not known, but mechanisms are not difficult to imagine. Nor is it difficult to understand, in outline, how attachment of antibody at other sites on the phage might even, by altering the distribution of surface charges or in other ways, facilitate adsorption rather than inactivate the phage (Hershey, Kalmanson, and Bronfenbrenner, 1944; Sagik, 1954; Jerne, 1956).

CHAPTER IX

HOST SPECIFICITY

Because the bacteriophages are obligate intracellular parasites of bacteria, the properties of the host cell must be of major interest to the virologist. Of particular concern are those properties which permit a bacterium to serve as a host for phage multiplication or which render it immune to phage attack. As is true of plant and animal viruses, phage strains vary in their host specificity. This specificity was obvious to early phage workers and led to the practical classification of these viruses into such categories as coliphages, staphylophages, streptococcal phages, and cholera phages. Although the utility of such a classification is evident, it has no phylogenetic significance, any more than has a classification of mammalian viruses based on tissue tropisms or host pathology. The role of host specificity in the classification of phages will be discussed in Chapter XXII on phage taxonomy.

1. Microbial Hosts for Phages

It would be a difficult task to list all the bacterial hosts for phages that have been recorded in the literature. Such a list would include bacterial strains belonging to the following genera: *Pseudomonas*, *Xanthomonas*, *Vibrio*, *Rhizobium*, *Chromobacterium*, *Micrococcus*, *Gaffkya*, *Neisseria*, *Streptococcus*, *Lactobacillus*, *Corynebacterium*, all genera of *Enterobacteriaceae*, *Pasteurella*, *Brucella*, *Bacillus*, *Clostridium*, *Mycobacterium*, *Streptomyces*, *Nocardia*, and probably others. There are some bacteria such as the pneumococci and the spirochaetes for which phages have never been found. More highly organized microbial forms such as yeasts, molds, algae, and protoza also seem to be free of phages, unless the kappa substance of paramecia (see Sonneborn, 1955) might be considered a relative of the viruses.

121

2. Host Ranges of Bacteriophages

D'Herelle (1926) noted that some phage strains were highly specific attacking only certain strains in a single species of bacterium, while other phage strains possessed "multiple virulences" enabling them to attack bacteria in different genera. He noted one pure phage strain which attacked several species of shigella, several strains of *E. coli*, and some strains of paratyphoid B. Phage strains capable of attacking only a single bacterial species were termed "monovalent," while phages capable of attacking two or more bacterial species were called "polyvalent" (Kalmanson and Bronfenbrenner, 1942). The difficulty with this terminology is that the term polyvalent phage was also applied to mixtures of phages prepared for therapeutic use, and it is often difficult to tell in the early literature whether a "polyvalent phage" was a "pure line phage" or a mixture of phages.

It is evident that the host ranges of some phages cut across the lines of bacterial classification. A *Pasteurella pestis* phage, for instance, also lyses some salmonella and some shigella species (Lazarus and Gunnison, 1947). Such extensive host ranges are also observed with certain strains of plant and animal viruses.

The host range is a useful characteristic for the identification of phage strains. For instance the closely related coliphage strains T2, T4, and T6 are similar in most respects but may be readily distinguished by their host ranges on appropriate mutants of their common host, strain B of *E. coli* (Demerec and Fano, 1945). Mutant B/6 is resistant to T6 but susceptible to T2 and T4, whereas mutant B/3,4 is resistant to T4 but susceptible to T2 and T6. Similarly B/2 is resistant only to T2.

The host range is not an invariant characteristic of a phage strain, however, because the host range can alter as a result of phage mutation, or as a result of phenotypic modification. Also the phage susceptibility of the indicator bacterial strains may be changed by several methods. These modifications of host range will be discussed later.

3. Host Specificity in Adsorption

D'Herelle (1926) demonstrated that centrifugation of a mixture of phage and host bacteria, following a brief incubation, resulted in sedimentation of 98 per cent of the phage with the bacteria. Because of the generality of this phenomenon, d'Herelle concluded that adsorption is an essential first step in phage multiplication. He also showed that bacteria which are not able to adsorb a given phage cannot serve as hosts for its multiplication. The reverse, however, is not necessarily true.

Burnet (1927) in an extensive study of the host ranges of a group of salmonella phages noted a high correlation between the possession of certain heat stable agglutinogens (the O or somatic antigens) and susceptibility to certain bacteriophages. Smooth to rough mutation in these salmonella strains was correlated with a loss of the heat stable antigens and with loss of susceptibility to the phages. At the same time the bacteria acquired sensitivity to a new group of phages, specific for rough salmonellas (Burnet, 1929b). Certain of these rough salmonella strains were able to undergo the reverse mutation to smooth, simultaneously becoming resistant to the "rough-specific" phages and reacquiring susceptibility to the "smooth-specific" phages. Although the correlation between antigenic structure and phage susceptibility was not complete, it was evident that susceptibility or resistance to certain groups of phage was dependent on the presence or absence of certain host cell antigens (Burnet, 1930). The susceptibility to other phages was dependent on surface substances which apparently were not agglutinogens.

An interesting example of phage specificity is seen in the typhoid phage reported by Sertic and Boulgakov (1936b) which attacks H (flagellated) strains but not O (nonflagellated) strains. Phage-resistant mutants are invariably nonmotile, nonflagellated, and lacking in H-antigen. The growth of phage-susceptible, motile strains on agar containing phenol results in the loss of flagella and confers phage resistance on the population. The phage is also inhibited in typhoid strains possessing Vi antigen.

Mutation with loss of Vi antigen makes such strains susceptible to phage.

Further examples of a relationship between host antigenic structure and phage susceptibility are found in the dysentery bacteria (Burnet and McKie, 1930), the typhoid bacterium (Craigie and Yen, 1937; Sertic and Boulgakov, 1936a), *Vibrio cholerae* (Asheshov, Asheshov, Khan, and Lahiri, 1933) and *E. coli* (Sertic and Boulgakov, 1937). A good review and discussion of the role of bacterial antigens in protecting bacteria against the attack of certain phages is given by Nicolle, Jude, and Diverneau (1953). In most cases the protective antigens seem to act by preventing the phage from adsorbing to the receptor sites by mechanical interference. This may be, however, an over-simplified concept. The evidence for a higher order of chemical specificity in the adsorption of phage to host cell will be presented in Chapter X.

Bacterial cultures are not necessarily homogeneous in their ability to adsorb a given phage. Wahl (1953) has called "semi-resistant" those bacterial strains which appear to be heterogeneous in receptivity. Such strains contain bacteria that are able to adsorb the phage and bacteria that are not. The cell types do not breed true and must therefore be considered either as phenotypic modifications or as genetic changes recurring at high rates, similar perhaps to the diphasic variation of salmonella strains.

4. Host Specificity in Infection

Some bacteria are able to adsorb phages very well but fail to serve as host cells for phage multiplication. Lysogenic bacteria, for example, usually adsorb the phage they carry in the latent (prophage) state, but are not affected by it. Lysogenic bacteria are therefore said to be immune to superinfection. Lysogenic bacteria are susceptible to lysis by other phages however.

Some phage-resistant bacterial mutants retain the ability to adsorb the phage to which they are resistant. For instance, a mutant of *E. coli* called B/1 adsorbs coliphage T1 in a reversible manner. Its resistance to infection is not due solely to failure of attachment. A different mutant of the same strain of *E. coli*, called B/1,5, is resistant to phage T1 because of failure of adsorption (Garen and Puck, 1951). There are numerous other references in the literature to phage-resistant variants that adsorb the phage to which they are resistant. In such cases the mechanism of resistance is not known.

Some bacteria adsorb a phage, are killed by it, but fail to liberate viable phage progeny. In such cases the phage simulates an antibiotic and the bacterium cannot be considered a host for the phage. Although the individual bacterial cell is killed, the ultimate result may be protection of the bacterial culture because the adsorbed phage particle is destroyed. In some cases a bacterium may either respond in this way to phage attack or may respond normally with phage multiplication depending on environmental conditions such as nutrients or temperature. Literature references to the antibiotic action of phages have been collected by Frédéricq (1952b), and "abortive infection" is discussed in Chapter XV.

5. Acquisition of Phage Resistance by Mutation

Bacteria may become resistant to phage attack either by mutation or by becoming lysogenic. Since the mechanisms of these processes are distinct, they will be discussed separately.

A mutation is a permanent, heritable, modification in some property of a cell. Mutations occur spontaneously during cell reproduction. Since mutation is typically a rare event, mutants are usually detected by the use of appropriate selective agents in the environment. For instance the presence of phage-resistant mutants in a population of phage-susceptible cells may be detected by plating the population with an excess of phage. The phage-susceptible bacteria are destroyed and the phage-resistant mutant cells produce colonies which may be readily subcultured and free of phage.

That the mutation occurs spontaneously prior to the addition of the selecting agent has been demonstrated by the fluctuation test of Luria and Delbruck (1943), the replica plating technique of Lederberg and Lederberg (1952), and the redistribution test of Newcombe (1949). Methods for the determination of mutation rates have been discussed by Newcombe (1948), Lea and Coulson (1949), and Armitage (1953). Measured mutation rates to phage resistance are of the order of 10^{-7} to 10^{-10} mutations per bacterial division.

Mutation to phage resistance may involve any of a number of distinct physiological mechanisms. Resistance to infection correlated with the failure of phage adsorption has been noted above. Lack of adsorption may be due to the absence of the receptor substance to which the phage particle normally becomes attached. When this receptor substance happens to be a major antigen of the bacterial cell, its loss by mutation may be readily detected by immunological techniques. If the receptor substance is nonantigenic or is a minor antigen, it may be more difficult to discover the reason for failure of adsorption. Failure of adsorption may also be due to the covering of the receptor substance by some other bacterial layer, as in the mutation from rough to smooth in the salmonellas. In this case the acquisition of the O antigen results in loss of susceptibility to the "rough specific" salmonella phages (Burnet, 1930). Mucoid variants of phage-susceptible bacteria are usually phage-resistant because the masses of slime material interfere with phage adsorption (Gratia, 1922). Doubtless other mechanisms may play a role in the acquisition of phage-resistance by mutation, but these have not been studied.

Phage-resistant mutants of bacteria very often retain a normal susceptibility to some phages while becoming resistant to others. Such mutant strains are of considerable value in phage research since they can be used as specific indicators to demonstrate the presence of a particular strain of phage in a mixture.

The nomenclature used for phage-resistant mutants was originated by Burnet and McKie (1933) and modified by Demerec and Fano (1945). Strain B of *E. coli* is susceptible to phage-T1 through T7. A phage-resistant mutant isolated by means of phage T3 is designated B/3. If this mutant is found to be resistant also to phages T4 and T7 it is called B/3,4,7. If a subsequent mutation confers resistance also to T6, it is named B/3,4,7/6, each mutational step being distingished by a bar.

Mutations to phage resistance have been extremely important in the development of bacterial genetics, because of the ease with which they can be selected, and because of their great variety.

Certain mutations to phage resistance are accompanied by the loss of the ability to synthesize growth factors such as tryptophan (E. H. Anderson, 1946) or proline (E.-L. Wollman, 1947). Selecting for phage resistance in these cases is thus an easy way to obtain biochemical requirements in bacterial strains. Since rates of mutation to phage resistance are easily measured, this type of mutation has been extensively used to test for the ability of various physical and chemical agents to induce mutations (see, for instance, Novick and Szilard, 1951b). Because of the variety of properties which may be associated with resistance to a given phage (resistance to certain other phages, biochemical requirements, colony type, etc.), often several mutant types can be easily distinguished among all the resistant mutants that are selected with a given phage. One obtains thus a "mutation pattern" which can be used as a test of the specificity of various agents capable of inducing mutations (Bryson and Davidson, 1951). More information on this general subject will be found in the book by Braun (1953).

Bacterial mutations involving a change from resistance to sensitivity are more difficult to study because of lack of selective agents for isolation of the mutant strains. An exception is found in the phages specific for rough and smooth strains of salmonella studied by Burnet (1929b), which can be used for selection in both directions. In other cases phage-sensitive variants can be selected because of morphological differences from the phage-resistant parent stocks; for example, in *E. coli* (Nelson, 1927), *Sh. dysenteriae* (Arkwright, 1924), and *Sh. sonnei* (Miller and Goebel, 1949).

6. Acquisition of Phage Resistance by Lysogenization

The adsorption of a temperate phage to a susceptible bacterial cell may have either of two results; the bacterium may be lysed with release of phage progeny, or the bacterium may be converted to the lysogenic condition, in which the cell and its progeny are permanently endowed with the potentiality of producing phage. This potentiality is controlled by a latent, non-infectious form of the infecting phage, the prophage, which is carried by lysogenic cells and inherited as part of their genetic make-up. To unify the terminology of lysogenic cultures it has been agreed to use the notation of Williams Smith (1951a). In this system the symbol designating the latent phage is placed in parentheses after the symbol designating the bacterial culture. For instance if *Pseudomonas aeruginosa* strain 13 is lysogenic for phage strain 8, the notation is 13(8). Lysogeny is discussed in Chapter XIX. Only a few facts concerning the effects of lysogenization on host specificity will be mentioned here.

It has been noted before that lysogenic bacteria are immune to superinfection by the phage of the type they carry as prophage, although adsorption occurs normally. Burnet and Lush (1936) first realized that the acquisition of phage resistance by lysogenization is a very different process from the acquisition of resistance by mutation. These authors reported that from 10 to 20 per cent of effective contacts between phage and susceptible bacteria resulted in conversion of the bacteria to the lysogenic condition. The conversion was not attributable to genetic heterogeneity in the bacterial population.

Bertani (1953a), using the temperate enterophage P2, was able to convert up to 40 per cent of the infected cells of strain Sh of *Shigella dysenteriae* to the lysogenic form, Sh(P2). The susceptible strain, Sh, is subject to lysis by the 7 coliphages of the T group, and, of course, by P2. The lysogenic strain, Sh(P2), adsorbs all these phages but is resistant to lysis by P2, T2, T4, T5, and T6. Strain Sh(P2) is lysed by phages T1, T3, and T7 only. In this case conversion of the bacterium to the lysogenic condition results in the acquisition of resistance not only to the carried phage, but also to a number of unrelated virulent phages. Several other examples of this phenomenon are known and will be discussed later on. Infection with a latent phage would appear to be a valuable protective mechanism to the bacterium. The intimate details of this acquired resistance to virulent phages are unknown, but must be rather specific since the bacterium remains susceptible to lysis by certain other phages.

Lysogenization may produce phage-resistance in still another way. Salmonella strains of group E_2 (somatic antigens 3,15) are lysogenic for a phage which can be demonstrated by means of indicator strains from group E_1 (somatic antigens 3,10). Strains of group E_1, which become lysogenic for such a phage, lose at the same time the ability to adsorb the phage (Uetake, Nakagawa, and Akiba, 1955). In this case lysogenization is accompanied by a change in the surface of the host cell, such that adsorption is blocked. The change can be demonstrated serologically, since the lysogenized strains have also lost antigen 10 and gained antigen 15. If such lysogenic strains are exposed to antiserum specific for antigen 15, antigenic variants can be obtained which have lost antigen 15, and show now antigen 10. These variants are not lysogenic any more, and are susceptible to the phage, thus confirming the close association of the lysogenic condition with the change in the cell surface.

7. Phage Mutations Affecting Host Range

D'Herelle (1926) considered the extension of host range of a phage preparation to be an adaptive process which he called "acquisition of virulence." His procedure of adaptation was to grow two bacterial strains in mixed culture, add a phage active for one strain and watch for lysis. If lysis was not evident the culture was filtered and the filtrate used to inoculate a fresh mixed culture, this process being repeated until lysis occurred. Then the "adapted" phage was isolated by repeated subculture on its new bacterial host. A better method is to spread the same mixture of bacterial strains and phage on the surface of agar plates, because the presence of a host range mutant is promptly made evident as a plaque.

Unfortunately the earlier experimenters did not examine critically the properties of the "adapted" phage strains and consequently certain of their claims should probably be discounted. For instance d'Herelle claimed to have adapted a staphylococcus phage to lyse a strain of Shiga's bacillus. It is probable that this "adaptation" was the result of phage contamination, especially as the fully adapted phage had lost its lytic power for the staphylococcus strain. No such radical alteration of host range has been reported in recent years.

What appears to be the first clear description of the isolation of host range variants of a phage was given by Sertic (1929b). His experiments will be briefly summarized using his nomenclature for the phage and host cell variants. Cells of strain Fb of *E. coli* were lysed by strain beta of phage Fcz except for a few cells of a phage resistant bacterial mutant called Fbr1. If a lawn of variant Fbr1 was inoculated with phage strain beta, isolated plaques were obtained with a frequency about 1/1,000 that of the plaques obtained on the parent host strain Fb. By successive single plaque isolations on strain Fbr1, a pure culture of host range variant beta/r1 was obtained, which was able to lyse both bacterial strains, Fb and Fbr1. By inoculating host strain Fbr1 with phage variant beta/r1 a second phage resistant mutant Fbr2 was obtained. Mutant bacterial strain Fbr2 was completely resistant to phage strain beta, but when inoculated with phage beta/r1 yielded a few plaques of a new variant, beta/r2. Sertic pointed out that by this two stage process he was able to obtain a variant phage virulent for a bacterial strain which was completely resistant to the original phage.

Many reports of host range mutants of bacteriophages have since appeared, many of them dealing with adaptation of phages to attack new host strains in the development of phage typing methods. In most cases the authors have presented no evidence to prove that the "adapted" phage was actually derived from the supposed parent.

The significance of this omission was demonstrated by Rountree (1949b) in an investigation of the serological relationships of a number of staphylococcal phages. She found that typing phages 42C and 42D were serologically unrelated to phage 42B although all were supposed to have been derived from a common source, strain 42. Strain 42 had been adapted to host strain 36 to give phage strain 42A; 42A was adapted to host strain 1307 to give 42C, which on adaptation to host strain 1363 became 42D. On investigation Rountree found that host strain 36 was lysogenic, carrying a latent phage which was capable of lysing host strain 1307. This latent phage from host strain 36 proved to be serologically related to phage strain 42C and 42D. Therefore the phage strains 42C and 42D were derived from a contaminating phage from a lysogenic host strain used for passage and were not host range mutants of strain 42. Since the frequency of lysogenic strains is high in many bacterial species, this source of confusion must be kept in mind. Serological relationship is the minimum evidence required to demonstrate derivation by mutation, and resemblance in other properties should be looked for as well. These requirements were clearly stated by Craigie and Felix (1947) in discussing the standardization of the Vi typing phages for *S. typhi*.

Luria (1945a) in a detailed study of host range variants of phages T1 and T2 applied the fluctuation test to demonstrate the spontaneous mutational origin of these variants. The mutant phage particles proved to be indistinguishable from their parents in serological specificity and in growth characteristics on the common host strain B of *E. coli*. They appeared to differ only in host range. The frequency of these host range mutant virus particles in small independent culture lysates was of the order of 10^{-8}.

Hershey (1946b) demonstrated the existence of several independent host range mutations of phage T2 and that in mixed infection experiments genetic recombination between host range and plaque type mutants could occur (Hershey and Rotman, 1949). In further studies Hershey and Davidson (1951) found that host range mutations of phage T2 occurred at two different gene loci, and that three different mutant alleles might occur at one of these loci.

The host range mutants of phages T1 and T2 just mentioned have gained the ability to adsorb to indicator strains of bacteria. Phage mutants are also known that are able to overcome the immunity produced by the lysogenic condition, which has a different basis. The temperate phage P2, mentioned in the preceding section, does not lyse lysogenic cells Sh(P2), although it does absorb onto them. Rare mutants of phage P2 are found, which are able to lyse Sh(P2) cells. This mutation is commonly associated with the loss of the ability to establish lysogeny in susceptible cells (Bertani, 1953a). In a similar case involving the temperate coliphage lambda, it is possible to demonstrate genetic recombination between the factor imparting virulence and other mutations affecting the plaque type (Jacob and Wollman, 1954).

These studies have demonstrated conclusively the mutational nature of some examples of host range variation in bacteriophages. It has become evident in recent years that host range modifications may occur by mechanisms other than mutation of the virus. These phenotypic modifications of host range will be discussed next.

8. Phenotypic Modification of Host Range

A phenotypic modification of the properties of an organism implies a nonhereditary change, usually attributable to some environmental influence. A phenotypic modification is reversible in the immediate descendants of the organism in the absence of the causal environmental factor. Numerous examples of phenotypic alterations in phages have been discovered in recent years. Some examples involving host range are described below.

a. Phenotypic Mixing

The first clear example of a phenotypic modification in host range was brought to light in consequence of an observation reported by Delbrück and Bailey (1946). When bacteria were mixedly infected with the closely related phages T2 and T4, up to 90 per cent of the bacterial population liberated both T2 and T4 phage particles when plated on the mixed indicator bacteria B/2 and B/4. However when plated on B/4, the indicator for phage T2, only a small proportion seemed to yield T2. The authors concluded that the liberated T2 particles had a low efficiency of plating on B/4 as compared with that on mixed indicator.

This paradoxical result was explained by Novick and Szilard (1951a) who found that bacteria mixedly infected with T2 and T4 might liberate three kinds of phage particles, typical T2, typical T4, and particles with the genotype of T2 but the host range phenotype of T4. The latter particles adsorbed to host strains B and B/2 but not to B/4. After one passage through either B or B/2, the phage reverted to its T2 phenotype and henceforth would multiply on B/4 but not on B/2. This explains why such particles produced plaques on mixed indicators or on strain B, but not on either B/2 or B/4 by itself. In this case the T4 phenotype was the result of the presence of particles having the genotype of T4 in the mixedly infected bacteria. Since the T4 host range characteristic is replaced by the T2 phenotype on subculture, these particles must be genotypically T2.

b. Host-Controlled Variation

Another type of phenotypic host range modification was discovered by Luria and Human (1952). This involves a phage resistant mutant of *E. coli* called B/3,4,7 (2,6). This mutant may be isolated from cultures of *E. coli* strain B by the selective action of T3, T4, or T7 but not by T2 or T6. It is resistant to T3, T4, and T7 because of failure of these phages to adsorb, but it's resistance to T2 and T6 is of a different kind. When concentrated T2 and T6 phage stocks are plated with this bacterial mutant, a clear, sterile area results; but if the phage stocks are progressively diluted, this effect is lost without ever passing through a level of dilution at which discrete plaques are formed. The phage particles adsorb normally to the mutant bacteria, and the infected bacteria lyse after the usual latent period. They also liberate phage particles which, however, cannot multiply further. After considerable search it was found that strain Sh of *Sh. dysenteriae* was a suitable indicator for the phage particles liberated on lysis of B/3,4,7(2,6). After passage through strain Sh the phage progeny had the properties of normal T2 or T6 phage.

In summary, phage T2 infects bacterial strain B/3,4,7(2,6) to produce a phenotypically modified phage progeny symbolized as T2*. Phage T2* does not produce plaques on B/3,4,7(2,6), or on B, but does produce plaques on strain Sh. Phage T2* after passage through strain Sh reverts to phage T2. Phage T2* adsorbs to strains B, B/4, and B/6 and kills them, but the infection is abortive.

These experiments indicate that the phenotypic change in T2* is different from that found in the phage liberated from the bacteria mixedly infected with T2 and T4. In the latter case the modification is in the specificity of adsorption. In the case of T2* the adsorption specificity is the same as that of T2, so the phenotypic modification must involve some stage in multiplication subsequent to adsorption. It may be noted that the changes in this instance are not adaptive.

An adaptive type of host-induced modification was reported by E. S. Anderson and Felix (1952), involving the Vi typing phages of *S. typhi*. The original Vi II phage strain, phage A, when tested at the limiting test dilution gives confluent lysis with Type A typhoid strains only. When tested at higher concentrations with a bacterial lawn of a Type C strain, a few plaques may be found. When these plaques are picked and subcultured on Type C bacteria, an "adapted" typing strain is obtained, which at the limiting test dilution will give confluent lysis with both Type C and Type A typhoid strains but only partial or no lysis with all other strains of typhoid bacteria. So far, the behavior is typical of that of host range mutants and these adapted typing phage strains were referred to as mutants by Craigie (1946).

The significant observation of Anderson and Felix is that when the "adapted" phage C is plated on a lawn of Type A typhoid, it reverts completely to the characteristics of phage A. For this and other reasons, Anderson and Felix designated this adaptive response "phenotypic modification of host range." The general phenomenon is very common and exhibits other remarkable features that are discussed in Chapters XVI and XXI.

9. Summary

Most taxonomic groups of bacteria include strains which are susceptible to some bacteriophage. The host range of a given phage is often restricted to a single bacterial genus but exceptions to this rule are common. Changes in the surface of a bacterium may block the adsorption of a phage otherwise able to multiply in such a host. These changes may occur by mutation, and are often associated with antigenic changes. Multiplication of a phage in a given host may be blocked at a stage past adsorption. This is often a consequence of the lysogenic condition of the host. Both types of blocks may be overcome by mutation of the phage. The host range of the phage may be affected by the conditions of its growth in a way not involving mutation and selection. One class of such effects is called phenotypic mixing. It is observed when two closely related phages differing in adsorption-specificity multiply in the same bacterium, and affects primarily adsorption-specificity. The effects are promptly reversed when the phage multiplies in pure culture. A second class of such effects is called host-induced modification, and affects host range independently of adsorption-specificity. It is conditioned by the genotype (including carried prophages) of the bacterial host. This class of effects is likewise reversed by transfer of the phage to another host.

CHAPTER X

ADSORPTION OF PHAGE TO HOST CELL

The first step in the infectious cycle is the adsorption of the phage particle to the host cell. Adsorption may be defined as attachment of phage particles to bacterial surfaces so that phage and bacteria will sediment together. As described in Chapter IV, phages adsorb to their host cells by the tips of their tails. The attachment is made to specific receptor substances on the cell surface, often parts of the cell wall (Chapter IX).

Adsorption is usually measured by centrifuging a mixture of bacteria and phage, and counting the phage in sediment or supernatant fractions, or both, by means of plaque counts. The reduction in plaque count in the supernatant fluid can be used to measure adsorption in excess of 30 per cent; for smaller fractions the measurement by difference is too inaccurate, and the sedimented phage must be counted directly. If the fraction adsorbed is very small, antiserum must be used as well (Hershey and Davidson, 1951). Other methods of measurement do not require centrifugation. One such method depends on the fact that infected bacteria can be destroyed by agents such as chloroform that do not inactivate free phage particles (Frédéricq, 1952a). Another makes use of antiserum to inactivate unadsorbed phage (Delbrück, 1945b). Adsorption can also be measured in terms of the fraction of bacteria killed by the phage. Many of these methods, however, depend on steps in the infective cycle taking place subsequent to adsorption as defined above. It cannot be assumed, without test, that any other measurement will yield information equivalent to the reduction in plaque count of the supernatant fluid on centrifugation of the adsorption mixture. Moreover, the results of this measurement may vary, under conditions in which adsorption is reversible, depending on whether the mixture is diluted or not before centrifugation.

1. Kinetics of Adsorption

Krueger (1931) investigated the adsorption of a phage to living and heat-killed staphylococci. He found that with an excess of bacteria, the adsorption follows the kinetics of a first-order reaction. The rate of adsorption is

$$-dP/dt = kBP \tag{1}$$

in which k is the velocity constant, B is the bacterial concentration, and P is the phage concentration. The appropriate solution yields

$$k = \frac{2.3}{Bt} \log \frac{P_0}{P} \tag{2}$$

in which P_0 is the concentration of unadsorbed phage at the beginning, and P at the end, of the time interval t.

Krueger found k to be 2.4×10^{-10} ml. per minute either with living or heat-killed bacteria.

Equations (1) and (2) are generally applicable to adsorption of phage, as indicated by further work described below. In them B can be considered constant provided the ratio of phage to bacteria is kept sufficiently low so that the bacterial surfaces remain effectively unaltered. This explains why the two-body interaction can be described by first-order kinetics.

Krueger (1931) also attempted to study adsorption-equilibrium with results that are not now interpretable owing to ambiguities of his assay method (Chapter III).

A very extensive study of phage adsorption was made by Schlesinger (1932a) using coliphage WLL. This phage was reported by Burnet (1934a) to be related to phage C16 and hence is also related to T2. The bacterium used was *E. coli* 88, either as a broth culture of living cells, or as a cell suspension killed by heating at 70° C. for one hour. Adsorption was carried out at 37° C. In these experiments the amount of unadsorbed phage decreases as an exponential function of time until about 95 per cent of the phage is adsorbed. The adsorption rate then decreases and, when killed bacteria are used, an unadsorbed residue is obtained amounting to 10^{-4} of the initial phage population. This unadsorbed fraction does not adsorb if additional heat-killed bacteria are added, indicating that failure of adsorption is not due to saturation of bacterial receptors, nor to a reversible equilibrium. The unadsorbed fraction adsorbs slowly to living bacteria.

After adsorption of 90 to 99 per cent of the phage to heat-killed bacteria, the residual phage was titrated before and after removal of the bacteria by centrifugation. The plaque counts are the same in either case, indicating that adsorption is essentially irreversible. However, after prolonged periods of adsorption it is found that a small fraction (10^{-3}) of the phage population can be eluted by washing. The phage population therefore consists of three kinds of phage particles: those that adsorb irreversibly, those that adsorb reversibly, and those that do not adsorb at all to heat-killed bacteria.

In his next paper Schlesinger (1932b) demonstrated that the adsorption of at least 95 per cent of the phage population obeys the kinetics described by equations (1) and (2) above. The observed velocity constant k is independent of B, P, and t over ranges of B from 3×10^6 per ml. to 7×10^8 per ml., of P_0 from 6×10^3 per ml. to 6×10^5 per ml., and of t from 2 minutes to 12 hours. The adsorption rate on living bacteria is 2.6 times faster than on heat-killed bacteria. Schlesinger interpreted this difference as being due to destruction of somewhat more than half of the receptor sites during the heat-killing of the bacterial culture.

Schlesinger determined the adsorption capacity of heat-killed bacteria for phage by increasing the phage to bacterium ratio to several hundred. The maximum adsorption capacity is 140 phage particles per bacterium. If Schlesinger's explanation for the reduced adsorption rate is correct, the adsorption capacity of living bacteria might be 140×2.6 or 360 phage per bacterium.   Delbrück (1940a) using a different coliphage and a different strain of *E. coli* found that the saturation value for a culture in the logarithmic growth phase was 250 phage per bacterium, and Watson (1950) found a maximum value of 300 phage per bacterium for the adsorption of T2 to heat-killed *E. coli* strain B.

Schlesinger (1932c) adapted the coagulation theory of von Smoluchowski to the kinetics of phage adsorption, and derived the equation:

$$-dP/dt = 4\pi \, DRBP \qquad (3)$$

in which $-dP/dt$ is the rate of adsorption, D is the diffusion constant of the phage particle, R is the radius of a sphere of the same surface area as the bacterium, and the other symbols are as in equation (1).   By combining equations (1) and (3) he obtained the equation

$$k = 4\pi \, DR \qquad (4)$$

Equation (4) contains the assumptions that every collision between phage and bacterium results in irreversible adsorption, that the bacteria and surrounding fluid are stationary, and that the phage particle itself is dimensionless.   In spite of obvious defects, it gives a rough estimate of what the maximum possible rate of adsorption ought to be.

Schlesinger calculated the diffusion constant from his observed adsorption-rate constant by means of equation (4):

$$D = \frac{3.4 \times 10^{-11}}{4\pi \times 4.3 \times 10^{-5}} = 6.3 \times 10^{-8} \text{ cm.}^2 \text{ sec.}^{-1}$$

According to Taylor, Epstein, and Lauffer (1955), the diffusion coefficient of phages T2 and T6, related to WLL, is about 3.5×10^{-8} cm.^{2} sec.$^{-1}$ at 20° C., in reasonable agreement with Schlesinger's indirect measurement at 37° C.   This means that the observed adsorption-rate constant of equation (2) is in agreement with the theory represented by equation (4), as found also by Delbrück (1940a), Puck, Garen, and Cline (1951), and Stent and Wollman (1952). These results seem to show that a large fraction of the collisions between phage and bacterium lead to successful attachment. Tolmach (1957) and Hershey (1957) question this interpretation, and we conclude here only that adsorption-rate constants in the range 10^{-8} to 10^{-9} per minute can be expected under optimal conditions. The optimal conditions depend on size and condition of the bacterial cells (Delbrück, 1940a; Hershey and Davidson, 1951), and numerous environmental factors to be discussed below.

2. The Ionic Environment

Many reports in the early literature of the effect of salts on phage lysis have been summarized by d'Herelle (1926) and by Sertic (1937). For example, da Costa Cruz (1923) reported that bacteria grown in salt-free Witte's peptone were not lysed by phage, but that the addition of sodium chloride or calcium chloride resulted in lysis. Lisbonne and Carrere (1923) confirmed this salt effect with three different phages. The addition of sugars had no effect. These authors demonstrated that the effect of the electrolytes was on the adsorption of phage to host cell; if phage and bacteria were mixed in salt-free peptone, they could be readily separated by centrifugation. In the presence of salts, the phage speedily became attached to the bacteria and could not be separated by centrifugation.

An interesting paper by Hershey, Kalmanson, and Bronfenbrenner (1944) gave a preview of later developments in this field. These authors found that the relative efficiency of plating (EOP) of phage T2 varies markedly with the concentration of electrolyte added to the agar medium. The EOP is 0.001 or less in the absence of added electrolyte, 0.1 in 0.03 M sodium ion, and 1.0 in 0.2 M sodium ion. Similar results were obtained with potassium, lithium, and ammonium ions. Divalent cations were not tested at comparable concentrations. The EOP was independent of the nature of the anions present.

In an attempt to determine whether the cation effect was on adsorption, phage adsorption was studied with and without added salt, by means of the centrifugation technique. The sediments and supernatants were assayed on both salt-free agar and on agar containing the optimal amount of salt. The fraction of phage adsorbed was calculated from the plaque counts on agar containing salt. It was found that appreciable adsorption of phage occurs in salt-free tryptose broth. The striking observation is that phage adsorbed to its host cell in the presence of salt has a high efficiency of plating on salt-free agar, while phage absorbed in the absence of salt has a very low EOP on salt-free agar, as does unadsorbed phage. It would appear from these experiments that phage adsorbed in salt-free broth does not initiate infection of the host cell and may be reversibly adsorbed.

The possibility of reversing adsorption was tested by adsorbing the phage in the absence of salt, sedimenting the bacteria, and washing the sediment with broth to remove free phage. The sediment was then diluted in salt-free broth, incubated for 20 minutes, and centrifuged again. Assays on both supernatant and sediment indicated that about 50 per cent of the adsorbed phage had been eluted. Phage adsorption in salt-free broth is partly reversible and infection of the host cell by the adsorbed phage does not occur in the absence of salt.

Hershey, Kalmonson, and Bronfenbrenner (1944) also found that phage T2 treated in the presence of salt with very dilute anti-T2 serum showed an increased rate of adsorption under suboptimal conditions, and a greatly increased EOP on low-salt agar. This effect may be related to the activation of cofactor-requiring strains of T4 by one of the anti-T4 antibodies (Jerne, 1956). The observations with T2 might be well worth reinvestigating but are now of doubtful meaning owing to possible complications caused by inhibitors of adsorption often present in phage stocks (Sagik, 1954). The same could be said, in fact, of much of the work reported in this chapter.

The experiments on reversible adsorption described above were abandoned by the authors because it appeared that the transition from reversible to irreversible adsorption could not occur on addition of salt, and therefore that reversible adsorption could not be a step in the infective process (Hershey, personal communication). Further work described below has led to the contrary interpretation.

There were no further quantitative studies of the effect of salts on phage adsorption until the work of Puck, Garen, and Cline (1951). These authors studied the rates of adsorption of various phages to *E. coli* under a variety of environmental conditions, and reached the conclusion that the initial step in phage adsorption is the establishment of electrostatic bonds between appropriate configurations of ionic charges on the two bodies.

In these studies the first-order velocity constants are used to characterize the adsorption rates as the environmental conditions are changed. With phage T1 in buffered salt solutions at 37° C. the optimum salt concentration for phage adsorption is about 0.01 M for salts of univalent cations and 0.001 M for salts of divalent cations. The rate of adsorption is depressed markedly by higher or lower concentrations. The maximum velocity constant is the same in simple salt solutions and in broth, suggesting that no cofactors other than salts are required. Puck, Garen, and Cline (1951) adopted the hypothesis, consistent with their results, that the efficiency with which collisions between phage particles and cells lead to attachment is controlled by electrostatic charges on the colliding bodies, and that cations in the medium affect adsorption by influencing these charges.

3. Organic Cofactors

T. F. Anderson (1945a) discovered that some phages are unable to adsorb to their host cells unless certain organic compounds are present in the environment. He compared plaque counts of phage stocks on the usual nutrient broth agar with counts on agar prepared from ammonium lactate and other salts. Coliphage T2 gives the same counts on the two media, whereas counts of T4 and T6 are much lower on lactate agar than on broth agar. By testing various substances that might be present in broth he found that the addition of tryptophan or phenylanlaine to the synthetic medium results in a large increase in the efficiency of plating. Tryptophan is more effective. Anthranilic acid, indole, and indole-3-propionic acid are inactive. Anderson showed that the role of cofactor is to allow adsorption to occur.

In a later paper T. F. Anderson (1945b) reported that Bz-3-methyl tryptophan, which inhibits growth of bacteria and phage, can substitute very efficiently for tryptophan as an adsorption cofactor. T. F. Anderson (1946) listed a number of organic substances which had varying degrees of cofactor activity. Substitutions or changes in the amino or carboxyl groups of tryptophan destroy all cofactor activity, whereas quite extensive changes are permissible in the remainder of the molecule. Replacement of the indole structure by pyridine, benzene, or thiophene results in a cofactor activity about 1 per cent of that of tryptophan. Delbrück (1948) reported that DL-norleucine had about 0.3 per cent of the activity of L-tryptophan. The remarkable structural specificity of the cofactor is indicated by the fact that L-tryptophan is the most highly active substance yet tested but D-tryptophan is inactive.

By kinetic methods, T. F. Anderson (1948a) showed that cofactor reacts with the phage particles rather than with the host bacteria. This process is termed "activation." Anderson estimated that about six molecules of tryptophan are involved in the activation of each phage particle. There is a rather high temperature coefficient for activation with a temperature optimum at about 35° C. When activated T4 is diluted in a tryptophan-free medium, the phage very rapidly become "deactivated." It is evident that phage T4 reacts in a reversible manner with tryptophan to form an activated complex capable of adsorbing to the host cell.

A small portion of the particles of phage T4 in certain stocks are able to form plaques when plated on tryptophan-free agar. When these plaques are picked and subcultured they give rise to strains which can adsorb in the absence of tryptophan. Thus the ability to adsorb to the host cell in the absence of cofactors is a genetically determined characteristic of the phage (T. F. Anderson, 1948b).

Delbrück (1948) isolated additional cofactor-requiring variants of T4. One of these requires calcium ion in addition to tryptophan for adsorption to take place. The calcium requirement can not be met by magnesium ion. A second strain adsorbs well in the presence of tryptophan without either Mg or Ca ions. The adsorption of both tryptophan-requiring strains is inhibited by the presence of indole in the medium. Anderson's tryptophan-requiring stock, however, is indifferent to indole. The sensitivity to indole also varies among different lines of T2, none of which requires tryptophan.

The reversible activation of phage T4 by tryptophan and the adsorption of the activated complex to the host cell make an interesting kinetic problem which was analyzed in a series of beautiful papers by Wollman and Stent (1950) and Stent and Wollman (1950, 1951), confirming and extending the previous work of T. F. Anderson. The deactivation of the T4-tryptophan complex is a first-order reaction. The rate of activation by tryptophan is proportional to the fifth power of the tryptophan concentration at low concentrations, but is independent of tryptophan concentration at high concentrations. This indicates that five tryptophan molecules must react at a single site to form an activated phage particle. The limiting rate of activation at high concentrations is attributed to a step involving rearrangement of the five adsorbed tryptophan molecules into a specific and relatively stable configuration.

The rate of deactivation is markedly sensitive to tryptophan concentrations below the level at which measurable activation occurs. This is explained by the assumption that deactivation involves loss of a single tryptophan molecule from the organized site leaving the remaining four molecules in a specific configuration. The active configuration can then be restored by the addition of a single molecule at a rate much faster than that characteristic of the primary activation.

The fraction of the phage population activated by a given concentration of tryptophan decreases very rapidly with decreasing temperature. This effect can be overcome by increasing the tryptophan concentration, so that all phage particles are activated by concentrations above 100 μg. per ml. independently of temperature. The rate of activation is also markedly temperature-dependent at low tryptophan concentrations but not at high concentrations. These temperature characteristics are consistent with the model proposed.

The work of Stent and Wollman yielded a satisfactory kinetic model for activation by tryptophan but failed to clarify the nature of the activation process in relation to adsorption. Sato (1956) found that activation could also be brought about by urea under circumstances suggesting that the underlying process resembled protein denaturation. By extension of his idea it might be guessed that all or many phages require a similar activation, differing only with respect to the nature of the requisite cofactors, organic and inorganic. Williams and Fraser (1956) showed that the cementing substance for adsorption is composed of a number of fibrillar structures in the tail of T2, which can be induced to "unwind" under conditions not yet clarified. Possibly activation involves a reversible orientation of these fibrils, and possibly the pH-dependent transformation of T2 described by Taylor, Epstein, and Lauffer (1955) (Chapter IV) is a related phenomenon.

Jerne (1956) found that one of several antibodies produced in response to immunization with T4 can permanently activate cofactor-requiring strains of this phage. His discussion of this phenomenon is very suggestive in connection with the ideas discussed above. Probably a little more work on requirements for adsorption will elucidate the nature of the activation of T2 and related phages by salts and other cofactors.

A paradoxical fact discovered by Anderson (1945a), that infected bacteria form plaques on synthetic agar although the free phage T4 particles do not, was explained by Wollman and Stent (1952). They found that T4, immediately after release from lysed bacteria, is able to adsorb to bacteria without added cofactor. This activated state is transient but deactivation is slow. The natural cofactor responsible for "nascent" activity has not been identified.

In studying the adsorption of various phages to sintered-glass filters, Puck, Garen, and Cline (1951) noted that cofactor-requiring strains of phage T4 adsorb to glass in the presence but not in the absence of tryptophan. A variant of T4 which does not require cofactors for adsorption to cells adsorbs to glass in the absence of tryptophan. This observation discouraged the view that tryptophan might serve to activate an enzyme responsible for adsorption.

4. The Stepwise Nature of Adsorption

Some experiments by Hershey, Kalmanson, and Bronfenbrenner (1944) discussed above demonstrate that phage T2 can adsorb to its host cell in salt-free broth, but that under these conditions it fails to infect. On dilution in salt-free broth some of the adsorbed phage elutes. These experiments demonstrate that adsorption of phage to susceptible bacteria is not equivalent to infection. A similar experiment was performed by Puck, Garen, and Cline (1951) with phage T2. They also obtained clear-cut evidence for the reversibility of phage adsorption under certain environmental conditions.

Under other conditions, adsorption is irreversible and Garen and Puck (1951) investigated the hypothesis that irreversible adsorption is a two-step reaction passing through a reversible phase. Several methods were devised for separating the steps, mostly in experiments with phage T1. One method depends on effects of temperature. The rate of attachment of T1 to its host cell was determined by centrifuging the undiluted adsorption-mixture (so that elution would not occur) and assaying the supernatant fluid for unadsorbed phage after various periods of adsorption. Under these conditions, the first-order velocity constants were 2.7×10^{-9} ml. per minute at $2°$ C. This result showed that the rate of adsorption was indifferent to temperature except for small effects that might be attributed to the change in viscosity. This result was unexpected since Puck, Garen, and Cline (1951) had previously reported a 40-fold increase in rate of adsorption with a rise in temperature from 0 to $37°$ C. However, in the earlier experiments the adsorption mixture had been diluted 100-fold before centrifugation, thus permitting elution of any reversibly adsorbed phage.   That this accounts for the discrepancy was demonstrated by Garen and Puck (1951) who showed that phage T1 adsorbed at 3 ° C. could be largely eluted on dilution into cold broth, but that phage adsorbed at 37 ° C. could not.   Thus the temperature coefficient is low for reversible adsorption and high for irreversible adsorption.

Other methods devised for separating the two kinds of adsorption are the following:

1.   Zinc ions specifically prevent irreversible adsorption of T1 (but not of T2).   Phage T1 adsorbed to B at 37 ° C. in the presence of zinc ions is largely eluted on dilution, whereas T1 adsorbed in the presence of calcium ions is not.   Zinc competes with calcium and magnesium ions for sites on the surface of the bacterial cell, thereby protecting the bacterium against invasion by phage T1.

2.   Suspensions of bacteria heavily irradiated with ultraviolet light still adsorb phage T1 quite rapidly at 37 ° C., but on dilution into cold broth all the phage is eluted.   With unirradiated bacteria, the adsorption is irreversible under the same conditions.   Irradiation must destroy some bacterial substance essential for irreversible adsorption.

3.   Strain B of *E. coli* has at least two different spontaneous mutants that are resistant to phage T1, B/1,5 resistant to both T1 and T5, and B/1 resistant to T1 only.   Phage T1 fails to adsorb to B/1,5 under any condition tested, but adsorbs reversibly to B/1.   Thus, mutation to B/1 results in loss of some factor essential for irreversible adsorption without seriously affecting reversible adsorption.   In B/1,5 both kinds of adsorption fail.   Similarly, B/2 does not adsorb T2.   There is also no reversible adsorption of T4 to B/4 (Stent and Wollman, 1952).

Similar experiments on the adsorption of phage T4 to its host cells in the presence and absence of tryptophan show that no attachment of the phage to the host cell takes place unless tryptophan is present.   This indicates that trytophan is essential for the reversible adsorption to host cells (Garen and Puck, 1951). As mentioned previously, the same is true of the adsorption to glass.

Stent and Wollman (1952) found that the rate of irreversible adsorption of T4 decreases with decreasing temperature in the range from 25 to 5° C. The rate constant also depends on bacterial concentration, decreasing at concentrations in excess of 10^8 per ml. They considered three hypotheses to account for these characteristics.

1. A reversible equilibrium exists between two states of the phage particle, an active state capable of adsorption, and an inactive state which cannot adsorb. The equilibrium would be temperature dependent.

2. Adsorption may occur by two competing reactions, reversible and irreversible. At high bacterial concentrations, most of the phage is adsorbed reversibly and the rate of desorption controls the rate of irreversible adsorption.

3. Adsorption necessarily involves an initial, reversible attachment. Reversibly adsorbed phage may desorb, or become irreversibly attached, by competing reactions. At high bacterial concentrations and especially at low temperatures the conversion from reversible to irreversible attachment, dependent on temperature, becomes rate-limiting.

The third hypothesis is the same as that of Garen and Puck (1951). The infection of host cell (B) by phage (P) may be expressed as:

$$P + B \underset{k_2}{\overset{k_1}{\rightleftharpoons}} PB \xrightarrow{k_3} X$$

where X represents the irreversibly infected host cell. The velocity constant k_1 is the rate of primary attachment and has a low temperature coefficient. The constant k_3 is the rate at which reversibly attached phage becomes irreversibly fixed to the host cell. This rate has the relatively high temperature coefficient discussed above. The constant k_2 is the rate at which reversibly attached phage is liberated again into the medium. Stent and Wollman using T4, and Garen (1954) using T1, demonstrated that k_2 must have a low temperature coefficient, as might be expected for the rupture of ionic bonds. Garen and Puck (1951) have reported evidence suggesting that k_3 may be an enzymically catalyzed reaction. Garen (1954) made a detailed study of the reversible interaction between T1 and B/1, showing that the rate of primary attachment of T1 to B and to B/1 is about the same.

This relatively simple conception of a two-step mechanism of adsorption has been widely accepted and seems to be the most reasonable explanation for the kinetics of adsorption of phages T1, T2, and T4 to their host cells. Tolmach (1957) thoroughly reviewed the evidence for this view. Hershey (1957), however, pointed out that the experimental evidence leaves much to be desired, notably because no test has been made of the postulate that the transition from reversible to irreversible attachment is possible and rapid.

5. Chemical Nature of Receptor Sites

There have been two principal approaches to the problem of the chemical nature of the bacterial receptor sites for phage adsorption. One approach involves a study of the kinetics of phage adsorption to bacterial cells treated with various agents which might alter the cell surface. The second approach involves a study of the chemical properties of the receptor substances after their isolation from the bacterial cells.

The dominant role of salt concentration in the adsorption process led Puck, Garen, and Cline (1951) to postulate that the primary attachment of phage particle to host cell is by electrostatic bonds. The chemical nature of the charged groups involved in adsorption was studied by Tolmach and Puck (1952) and Puck and Tolmach (1954). They used phage labeled with P^{32} and studied the distribution of radioactivity between supernatant and sediment in centrifuged samples of adsorption mixtures. This technique permits the study of adsorption under environmental conditions which would destroy the viability of phage or host cell. The effect of pH was studied over the range from 5 to 12 using phage T2 and *E. coli* B. Maximum adsorption occurred at pH 6 to 8. The pH dependence suggested to Tolmach and Puck that carboxyl and amino groups are primarily involved in phage T2 adsorption and that phosphoric, sulfhydryl, and phenolic groups are unimportant.

This notion was tested by studying the adsorption of phage to host cells which had been treated with various reagents designed to eliminate specific chemical groupings. The results are given in Table XIII. They were interpreted by the authors as indicating that adsorption of phage T2 involved primarily carboxyl groups of the bacterial surface while adsorption of T1 involved amino groups.

TABLE XIII

The Binding of Phages T1 and T2 to Chemically Modified Host Cells[a]

	Adsorption to modified cells[b]	
Reagent used to modify bacteria	T2 phage	T1 phage
Carboxyl reagents		
Propylene oxide (sat'd.)	0	+
CH_3OH (80%) + HCl (0.1 M)	0	+++
Amino reagents		
Nitrous acid (0.5 M, pH 4)	++++	0
Formaldehyde (1.2 M)	++++	+
Acetic anhydride (0.3 M)	+++	++
Other reagents		
I_2 (5 $\times$ 10^{-3} M) + 0.5 M KI	++++	++++
p-Chloromercuribenzoate (5 $\times$ 10^{-4} M)	++++	++++
HCl (0.1 M)	++++	++++
CH_3OH (80%)	++++	++++

[a] From L. J. Tolmach and T. T. Puck, *J. Am. Chem. Soc.*, 74, 5552 (1952).
[b] 0 signifies 0–30% adsorption; +, 30–45%; ++, 45–60%; +++, 60–80%; ++++, 80–100%.

Barry and Goebel (1951) studied the adsorption of phage to cultures of phase II *Sh. sonnei* which had been treated in various ways. The untreated bacteria adsorb T3, T4, and T7 at similar rates. Different culture samples were treated with phenol, formaldehyde, ethylene oxide, ethanol, periodate, thymol, chloroform, heat, sonic vibration, and osmotic shock, and were then tested for their ability to adsorb phage. In all cases the adsorption of phage T3 is very quickly lost whereas the ability to adsorb T7 is scarcely impaired. The adsorption of T4 is markedly decreased following treatment with heat and ethylene oxide. Killing of the bacteria with moderate doses of ultra-violet light does not affect the adsorption of any of the phages but heavier doses selectively inactivate the T3 receptors. It is evident that the receptor for T3 is markedly labile to all the agents tested and that these experiments give no clue to the chemical nature of the receptor sites other than to emphasize that the sites for various phages are different.

Similar experiments on strain B of *E. coli* were performed by Weidel (1953a). Formaldehyde decreases the activity of the receptors for T1, T3, T5, and T7 but not for T2, T4, and T6. Periodic, nitrous, and other weak acids destroy the receptors for T1, T3, T4, T5, and T7 but not for T2. Sodium hydroxide ($N/60$) removed the T5 receptor from the bacterial surface without affecting the T2 receptor. Weidel notes the unusual stability of the T2 receptor; "means to destroy it specifically have not yet been found." However, Tolmach and Puck found that T2 receptors are destroyed by $CH_3OH + HCl$ without inactivation of the T1 receptors. Further work along these lines with more specific chemical reagents may be well worth while.

If phage particles attach to antigenic substances on the bacterial surface (Chapter IX), one might expect that bacterial extracts containing soluble antigens should react with the phage particles to interfere with adsorption. Early attempts to test this possibility met with failure because of faulty concepts of the nature of the bacterial antigens. Because in many cases the immunological specificity is due to a polysaccharide hapten, the efforts of immunochemists were devoted to the isolation of the polysaccharides in pure form. When these were tested for phage neutralizing activity they were usually found to be inert (Burnet, 1934b). It was later found that the phage-inactivating

activity was dependent in many cases on the intact structure of
the bacterial antigen, and could be destroyed by relatively mild
reagents.

Apparently the first demonstration of the inactivation of
bacteriophages by bacterial extracts was made by Levine and
Frisch (1934). Saline extracts of salmonella and shigella
species were found to protect the homologous organisms from
attack by phage. The active substance could be precipitated
by alcohol and partially purified. These results were confirmed
and extended by Burnet (1934b) who referred to the active substance as "phage-inhibiting agent" (PIA). The PIA was prepared by autolyzing the bacteria for two days at 55° C., after
which bacterial debris was removed by centrifugation and the
solution filtered through gradacol membranes of one micron
pore size. Filtration through Seitz or Berkefeld filters resulted
in loss of activity. The activity was measured by incubating
appropriate dilutions of PIA with diluted phage preparations and
determining the surviving phage by plaque count assays. Extracts were prepared from five variant strains of Flexner Y dysentery bacilli, and tested for inhibiting activity against eight different phages. In general it was found that phages attacking a
given bacterial strain were inhibited by extracts from that strain,
while these extracts had no effect on phages to which the bacterial strain was resistant. Occasional extracts that failed to
inactivate the expected phages are not surprising in view of the
lability of many receptor substances.

The active extracts invariably gave precipitates when mixed
with homologous antibacterial serum, the amount of precipitate
being proportional to the phage inhibiting activity. After removal of the specific precipitate, the supernatant fluid was devoid
of phage-inhibiting activity. The neutralization of PIA by antibacterial sera is parallel to the agglutination by these sera of the
bacteria from which the extracts were prepared. An antiserum
which agglutinated several bacterial strains also neutralized the
PIA extracted from these strains.

The action of the most potent preparation of PIA was studied kinetically, and it was found that phage inactivation by this bacterial extract was remarkably similar to phage neutralization by antiphage serum. The inactivation rate was initially first order and later decreased. The fraction of the phage inactivated was independent of the initial phage concentration. The rate was directly proportional to the PIA concentration and had a temperature optimum at about 37 ° C. The phage particles which survived incubation with PIA produced plaques which were smaller than normal and widely variable in size suggesting a decreased rate of adsorption to the host cell.

Burnet concluded that PIA is intimately associated with the somatic bacterial antigen, and that this substance blocks phage infection by combining with receptor sites on the phage particle which in the normal course of events make contact with the bacterial surface.

Further interesting experiments were reported by Burnet and Freeman (1937) using phage H (related to T2) and PIA from a Flexner Y strain of shigella. A variant of phage H was isolated which adsorbed at a slower rate to its host cell. The variant also differed from its parent in a number of other characteristics: larger plaque size, higher titer stocks, greater susceptibility to heat inactivation, and more rapid inactivation by antiphage serum. The variant was also extremely resistant to a preparation of PIA which rapidly inactivated the parent phage stock. A similar variant was isolated from stocks of phage C16.

Successive interaction of antiphage serum and PIA with phage H was also examined. Phage which had been treated with dilute antiphage serum to a survival of 50 per cent proved to be a great deal more resistant to inactivation by PIA than was untreated phage. In contrast treatment of phage with PIA had no effect on its subsequent neutralization with antiphage serum. These facts suggest that combination of phage with PIA is different from combination of phage with antiphage serum or with host cells.

Phage H which had been inactivated to better than 95 per cent by PIA was still able to adsorb to the host cell as judged by the fact that the host cells became agglutinable by antiphage serum. PIA did not prevent adsorption of phage to host cell but did interfere with the next step in the infectious process. As we have seen in Chapter VIII phage particles treated with antiphage serum are also able to adsorb to the host cell although they are noninfectious. Burnet and Freeman concluded from these experiments that phage antibodies and PIA probably do not react with the same site on the phage surface but rather at adjacent sites.

The interaction of phage, PIA, antiphage serum, and host cell is discussed further by Burnet, Keogh, and Lush (1937):

> The first stage in the lysis of susceptible bacteria requires the mutual specific union of certain elements of complementary molecular configuration on the surfaces of the phage particle and bacterium respectively. The specific element on the bacterial surface is intimately related to the polysaccharide hapten which determines the antigenic character of the bacterium. The hapten, as finally isolated by chemical methods, is not present as such in the living bacterial surface, but forms an essential part of a more complex molecular pattern. It is to certain aspects of this pattern, not necessarily the same for each phage lysing the organism, that specific phage adsorption occurs.

Any process by which the bacterial surface components are brought into solution necessarily destroys to some extent their specific molecular pattern. The fact that reaction of phage with its antibody makes the phage resistant to inactivation by PIA must mean that neutralizing antibody and PIA react with receptors that are spatially contiguous and parts of a single complex. These detailed suggestions have been shown by later work to be remarkably accurate.

The kinetic experiments of Burnet were confirmed by Ellis and Spizizen (1941) using coliphage P1. The inactivation by PIA was markedly influenced by salt concentration, being optimal at 0.5 per cent NaCl and negligible in 25 per cent NaCl or in the absence of salt. Phage inactivated by PIA could not be reactivated by changing the salt concentration. About 5 per cent of the phage population was very resistant to inactivation.

Similar observations were made by Goebel (1950) using phage T3 and the purified somatic antigen of phase II *Sh. sonnei*. Phage T3 was rather slowly inactivated by the somatic antigen and a residue of the population, about 1 in 10^4, proved to be completely resistant to inactivation. The original T3 phage population plated with equal efficiency on *E. coli* strain B and on *Sh. sonnei*, phase II. However, the PIA-resistant survivors showed a 40 times greater plaque count on *E. coli* than on *Sh. sonnei*. PIA-resistance and the property of plating only on *E. coli* were not hereditary.

There are many references to qualitative observations on the phage-inhibiting activities of bacterial extracts among which are Freeman (1937), Rountree (1947b), Beumer (1947, 1953), Weidel (1953a, b), and Mondolfo and Hounie (1948).

There have not been many experimental studies of the physical and chemical properties of the phage-inhibiting agents of bacterial extracts. Gough and Burnet (1934) reported on the properties of PIA isolated from *Sh. flexneri*. The material was soluble in half-saturated ammonium sulfate but was precipitated by saturated ammonium sulfate, and by 2.5 volumes of alcohol. Material repeatedly precipitated by these agents was active serologically and as PIA. It gave a strong Molisch test for carbohydrate, a weak biuret test, and no pentose color reaction. Treatment with hot one per cent NaOH liberated the polysaccharide hapten which was serologically active but had no phage-inhibiting activity. Heat treatment at 90° C. and pH 9 caused a rapid loss of PIA with no change in serological activity. The inhibitory activity toward different phages was lost at widely different rates suggesting that not all phages reacted with the same part of the PIA. Attempts at further purification invariably resulted in decreased PIA activity.

Meanwhile a great deal of chemical work on the somatic antigens of the enteric pathogens demonstrated that these antigens are not simple polysaccharides, but are, rather, a complex association of polysaccharide, phospholipid, and protein. The phospholipid can be separated by use of polar solvents without affecting the antigenicity of the mucoprotein, but the polysaccharide and protein separately are nonantigenic.

The most intensive study of the phage-inhibiting activity of purified bacterial antigens was made by Goebel and collaborators using *Sh. sonnei* and the T series of coli-dysentery phages. Phase I of *Sh. sonnei* is susceptible to phages T2 and T6 but resistant to the other T phages. Phase I organisms mutate to phase II, which is serologically distinct from phase I, and concomitantly become susceptible to phages T3, T4, and T7 in addition to T2 and T6. The somatic antigens of phase I and phase II cultures have been shown to be lipocarbohydrate-protein complexes (Baker, Goebel, and Perlman, 1949). The highly purified and electrophoretically homogeneous antigens were tested for phage-inhibiting activity by Miller and Goebel (1949). Phages T2 and T6 were inhibited by neither antigen, and phages T3, T4, and T7 were inhibited by the phase II antigen only. The diluent used had a marked effect on the extent of inhibition. T3 and T7 were strongly inhibited in broth but not in buffer. A tryptophan-requiring strain of T4 was inhibited in broth but not in buffer unless tryptophan was added. A variant of T4 which did not require tryptophan was inhibited equally well in buffer and broth. These results again suggest that the role of tryptophan is in the attachment of phage T4 to the bacterial receptor substance. They also suggest the possibility of a cofactor requirement for T3 and T7.

Heat treatment of the phase II antigen resulted in rapid loss of phage-inhibitory activity. Digestion with pancreatin followed by dialysis and deproteinization by shaking with $CHCl_3$ and octyl alcohol yielded a lipocarbohydrate with negative tests for protein. This material was fully active serologically and essentially as active as the undegraded somatic antigen in its ability to inhibit plaque formation with phage T4. The material is similar to that isolated by Gough and Burnet (1934) from autolyzed cultures of *Sh. flexneri*.

By using somewhat different isolation procedures, Jesaitis and Goebel (1952) isolated a phase II antigen which inactivated phages T2, T3, T4, T6, and T7. The difference between this antigen and that described above which inactivated only T3, T4, and T7 was traced to the use of pyridine in the extraction procedure. Incubation in 50 per cent pyridine at 37 ° C. resulted in a rapid destruction of the T2 and T6 neutralizing activity of the purified antigen without affecting its activity against T3, T4, and T7. The purified antigen was an electrophoretically homogeneous complex of protein, lipid, and polysaccharide.

Digestion with pancreatin resulted in removal of most of the protein, with a concomitant increase in serological activity and in phage-neutralizing activity. Extraction with phenol, which removed all detectable protein, resulted in loss of T2 and T6 activity. This lipocarbohydrate contained glucose, galactose, glucosamine, and heptose. Its composition was 45 per cent reducing sugars, 29 per cent lipids, 4 per cent acetyl, 4 per cent phosphorus, and 13 per cent ash.

In an extension of this work, Goebel and Jesaitis (1953) studied the properties of a somatic antigen isolated from a phage-resistant variant of phase II *Sh. sonnei*, designated as II/3,4,7, susceptible only to T2 and T6. The somatic antigen was isolated from strain II/3,4,7 and its chemical, serological, and antiviral properties were examined. The purified lipocarbohydrate protein antigen inhibited T2 but had no inhibiting effect on T3, T4, T7, or T6. The purified antigen was digested with pancreatin to remove much of the protein. This degraded antigen was much more active against T2 but still was without effect on the remaining T phages. The variant antigen is serologically distinct from the parent phase II antigen, but is related to it. The enzymatically degraded antigen of the variant differs from the corresponding antigen of the parent in electrophoretic mobility, optical activity, and chemical composition. The lipocarbohydrate was separated from the protein by treatment of the degraded antigen with phenol. Paper chromatography of the hydrolyzed lipocarbohydrate revealed only one saccharide, an amino sugar which was neither glucosamine nor chondrosamine. In the case of phase II *Sh. sonnei*, mutation to phage resistance is marked by a change in the chemical constitution of the polysaccharide moiety of the lipocarbohydrate-protein antigen of the organism.   Whether changes occur also in lipid or protein portions is not known.

The mechanism of phage inactivation by PIA is in most cases unknown.   However, Jesaitis and Goebel (1955) studied the inactivation of phage T4 by the specific lipocarbohydrate which had been isolated from the antigenic complex of phase II *Sh. sonnei*.   The addition of this lipocarbohydrate to a concentrated suspension of T4 phage results in an immediate large increase in viscosity (see also Jesaitis and Goebel, 1953).   Electron microscope examination reveals phage ghosts and long filaments, probably of deoxyribonucleic acid (DNA).   The phage DNA is susceptible to degradation by deoxyribonuclease. These results show that attachment of T4 to bacterial receptor substance causes the release of DNA from the phage particles.

Weidel and his collaborators studied receptor substance for T5, isolated from *E. coli* B, with results paralleling those described above in many respects (Weidel, Koch, and Bobosch, 1954; Weidel and Koch, 1955; Weidel and Kellenberger, 1955; Koch and Weidel, 1956a).

6. Summary

Adsorption is defined as attachment of the phage particle to the host cell surface.   The particles attach by the tips of their tails.   The kinetics of adsorption is that of a first-order reaction, the rate being proportional to the varying phage concentration and to the constant amount of bacterial surface.   The adsorption rate is markedly affected by environmental conditions such as salt concentration, pH, and temperature.   Some phages require the presence of organic molecules which must become fixed to the phage before adsorption occurs.   This cofactor requirement for adsorption is subject to modification by mutations of the phage.   Adsorption probably involves at least two successive steps, the first of which is reversible.   The rate of the first step is little affected by temperature, whereas the rate of the second step is temperature-dependent. The first step involves the formation of salt linkages between charged groups on the phage and host cell surfaces. Carboxyl and amino groups play the principal role in a few systems which have been studied. In some cases the phage receptor substance on the bacterial surface is a major bacterial antigen. Bacterial extracts containing the somatic antigen have the property of inactivating some phages. Highly purified antigens in the form of complexes of lipid, protein, and polysaccharide retain this property. Treatment with various chemical reagents has a differential effect on the inhibitory activity toward various phages.

CHAPTER XI

STAGES IN PHAGE MULTIPLICATION

An over-all view of the lytic cycle of phage reproduction was given in Chapter II. In this chapter we shall examine in more detail some of the biological and physical methods used to elucidate the sequence of events. Strictly chemical experiments will be discussed in Chapter XIV.

1. Initiation of Infection

a. Penetration

The electron microscope furnished convincing evidence that phage multiplies within the host cell and is liberated by rupture of the cell membrane (DeMars, Luria, Fisher, and Levinthal, 1953). A section of an infected bacterium illustrating intracellular particles of phage T2 is shown in Figure 2 (Chapter IV). Evidently the infecting phage particle must penetrate through the cell wall to reach the interior. Chemical evidence of penetration was furnished by the observation that phosphorus and nitrogen from the infecting phage were contained in the phage progeny (Chapter XIII). However, these observations did not at first yield information about the chemical composition or biological organization of the phage material which penetrated the host cell wall.

A direct attack on this problem was made by Hershey and Chase (1952) by using isotopic labels. The proteins of phage T2 were labeled with S^{35} and the nucleic acid was labeled with P^{32}. The labeled phage was purified by differential centrifugation and its properties studied by following its radioactivity. Neither the phosphorus nor sulfur was acid-soluble and neither became soluble on exposure of the phage particles to deoxyribonuclease. About 90 per cent of both the phosphorus and sulfur was specifically adsorbable to sensitive bacteria and precipitable by anti-T2 serum, suggesting that the phage was relatively free of extraneous protein and nucleic acid. The labeled phage was subjected to osmotic shock, which separates the phage nucleic acid from the phage membrane or ghost (Chapter V). In the resulting shocked phage neither the phosphorus nor the sulfur was acid-soluble. However, treatment with deoxyribonuclease made 80 per cent of the phosphorus acid-soluble, the sulfur remaining insoluble. About 90 per cent of the sulfur was still adsorbable to sensitive bacteria but only 2 per cent of the phosphorus could be adsorbed. About 97 per cent of the sulfur was precipitable by anti-T2 serum but only 5 per cent of the phosphorus. These results confirm the previous observations of Anderson and Herriott that osmotic shock permits the separation of phage T2 into a protein membrane and soluble DNA. They indicate further that almost all of the phage sulfur and almost none of the phage phosphorus is in the membrane which adsorbs to the host cell and precipitates with antiserum. Conversely, most of the phosphorus and little of the sulfur is in the DNA which is liberated from the membrane and thereby made susceptible to attack by deoxyribonuclease.

Electron micrographs of infected bacteria had demonstrated that phage T2 adsorbs to its host cell by the tip of its tail (Chapter IV). This suggested the possibility that the adsorbed phage might be broken off from the bacterial surface by the strong shearing forces in a Waring Blendor. In fact, Anderson (1949) had found that phage does not adsorb to the host cell while the adsorption mixture is agitated in the Blendor. Hershey and Chase (1952) performed the appropriate experiments using isotope-labeled phage. The phage was adsorbed to the host cell at low multiplicity of infection and unadsorbed phage was eliminated by centrifugation. The infected bacteria were agitated in the Blendor for various times and the distributions of sulfur and phosphorus between bacteria and extracellular fluid were determined by centrifugation. The results of this significant experiment are as follows.

1. The plaque-forming potentiality of infected bacteria is not affected by agitation in the Waring Blendor.

2. Seventy-five to 80 per cent of the phage sulfur can be stripped from the infected cells in the Blendor. This liberated sulfur is precipitable by antiphage serum.

3. Only 20 to 35 per cent of the phage phosphorus is liberated into the medium, half of it without any agitation.

These results demonstrate that, following adsorption of phage T2, the phage membrane remains on the bacterial surface, from which it can be stripped in the blendor without affecting the course of infection. In contrast, most of the phage DNA enters the host cell soon after phage adsorption. A similar situation holds for the T5 serological group of phages. T5 injects its DNA into the host cell, while the complement-fixing antigen remains on the host cell surface and can be liberated in the Waring Blendor (Y. T. Lanni, 1954).

Considered as "injection" of DNA, the penetration mechanism presents at least three problems: the opening of a hole in the tail of the phage particle, the opening of a hole in the cell wall, and the passage of DNA through these holes. Ore and Pollard (1956) suggested that the passage of DNA into the cell can be explained by purely physical mechanisms. The other two problems have been partly clarified by several types of experiments summarized below.

b. Release of DNA from the Phage Particle

Hershey and Chase (1952) noted that partial release of DNA into solution, and complete exposure of viral DNA to deoxyribonuclease, followed the attachment of T2 to the bacterial debris left after lysis of infected cells. They also confirmed important experiments by Graham (1953), showing that adsorption of T2 to heat-killed (but not living) bacteria resulted in exposure of the viral DNA to enzyme action. These findings were extended to the interaction between phage and isolated receptor substances, for T4 by Jesaitis and Goebel (1953, 1955) and for T5 by Weidel, Koch, and Bobosch (1954). These results seem to show that the opening of a hole in the phage particle and release of DNA does not call for the action of a bacterial enzyme.

DNA can also be released from phage T2 following interaction with ion exchange resins (Puck and Sagik, 1953) or with cadmium cyanide (Kozloff and Henderson, 1955), and from T5 by interaction with citrate or merely by removal of calcium (Lark and Adams, 1953). In the last two cases, the reaction is accompanied by loss of adsorbability of the phage ghosts and alterations at the tip of the tail of the phage particle. The relation of these facts to normal injection is obscure, however, especially since the injection by T5 requires calcium and is presumably inhibited by citrate (Luria and Steiner, 1954). If a phage enzyme is involved in the release of DNA, it remains to be demonstrated.

The morphological aspects of penetration by T2 were clarified by Kellenberger and Arber (1955) and Williams and Fraser (1956)(Chapter IV). Fibers at the tail-tip of the phage particle attach to the bacterial surface, exposing the central pin which actually penetrates the cell wall. This penetration could be purely mechanical (Williams and Fraser, 1956) or might be aided by enzymic processes.

Phage T2 inactivated by formaldehyde still adsorbs to the host cell, and kills it with low efficiency. However, the DNA of the inactivated particles is not injected into the bacteria but remains within the phage membrane in a form resistant to deoxyribonuclease. It could be supposed that formaldehyde inactivates an enzyme in the phage particle but in view of the complicated nature of the penetration process, the action of formaldehyde can be explained in other ways.

c. Puncture of the Bacterium

Infection of bacteria by T2 initiates a complex series of cellular reactions many of which have to be considered in any discussion of mechanisms of penetration, especially because no satisfactory conclusions can be reached at this time.

It will be recalled that infection with large numbers of T2 (but not of many other phages) is abortive and causes prompt "lysis from without." Smaller numbers of T2 ghosts (Barlow and Herriott, 1954) or of phage particles inactivated by ultraviolet light (Watson, 1950) produce the same effect, as do also phage particles inactivated by X-rays until bacteria-killing ability is lost (Watson, 1950). These facts may be summarized by saying that phage particles can damage cells severely at the time of infection, and that this damage is independent of injection of DNA, appearing, in fact, to be especially severe when one or another early step in the normal sequence of events is blocked. Thus sensitivity to lysis from without is also increased in the presence of metabolic inhibitors or by deprivation of food (Heagy, 1950; Watson, 1950), but is greatly reduced in the presence of high concentrations of magnesium that do not prevent infection (Barlow and Herriott, 1954). Many of these facts can now be partly understood in terms of two competing processes, one lytic and one antilytic, set in train by the normal process of infection.

Doermann (1948a) first noticed that normal infection produces a rapid change in cellular properties. He observed a sudden fall in turbidity of bacterial cultures following infection. The turbidity passed through a minimum at about 10 minutes after infection, and then rose again. The initial drop was caused by T2, T4, T6, and T5, but not by T1, T3, or T7. It was seen also following infection with T5 in the absence of calcium (no injection), in which case there was no subsequent rise. The effect was independent of multiplicity of infection in the range between 3 and 10 or 15, above which lysis from without was observed. Doermann suggested a spreading alteration of the bacterial surface followed by "recovery." Subsequent experiments confirm his interpretation, except that his "recovery" is much too slow to reflect the development of resistance to superinfection and probably should be ascribed to the general biosyntheses accompanying phage growth.

Two phenomena, the chemical breakdown of superinfecting

phage and their genetic exclusion, led to the recognition that infected cells rapidly develop refractoriness to penetration by phage in a reaction completed after about two minutes (Chapter XVII). Visconti (1953) showed that a reaction of similar swiftness produces almost complete resistance to lysis from without by superinfecting phage. The resistance to lysis cannot reflect merely the failure of normal penetration, because cells infected at multiplicities sufficient to cause lysis in the presence of cyanide do not lyse if the cyanide is added a few minutes later. Evidently the properties of the cell surface as a whole are very quickly altered by metabolic processes occurring after infection. This alteration must account for faulty penetration, genetic exclusion, and breakdown of superinfecting phage, as well as resistance to lysis by numerous agencies.

Puck and Lee (1954, 1955) described important experiments that clarified considerably the nature of these processes. They measured leakage of cell constituents, labeled with radioactive phosphorus or sulfur, into the culture fluid during the first few minutes following infection. Most of the experiments were performed with T2, although a slight leakage occurred also with several other phages tested. Like lysis from without, leakage is prevented by magnesium ions and, unexpectedly, also by potassium ions.

The chief difficulty in these experiments is to discriminate between leakage accompanying normal infection, and frank lysis from without. The difficulty is increased because in most of the experiments of Puck and Lee infection was allowed to occur at low temperatures, which causes abortive infection (Chapter XV).

In one experiment (Figure 3 of Puck and Lee, 1955) infection at moderate multiplicities liberated considerable amounts of acid-soluble phosphorus but practically no ribonucleic acid or galactosidase. Since all these substances are released during lysis from without, it seems clear that the leakage of acid-soluble phosphorus is something different. In other experiments galactosidase was released at moderate multiplicities and the authors draw conclusions from these experiments based on the assumption that there was no lysis from without, but this seems doubtful.

In still other experiments it appears that homologous super-infecting phage does not cause a second leakage. This could be explained by exhaustion of acid-soluble phosphorus during the first leakage coupled with resistance to lysis from without. The authors postulate instead a "resealing reaction." Since this reaction is supposed to explain resistance to lysis from without and, in fact, faulty penetration by superinfecting phage, the two interpretations are not very different.

It seems reasonable to conclude, in agreement with Puck and Lee, that normal infection causes leakage of some cellular constituents, incidentally to penetration of the cell wall by phage, and that the holes have to be repaired before viral growth can proceed. All of the facts discussed above show that the repair does not merely restore the cell surface to its initial condition, but confers on it several new properties.

The ideas of Puck and Lee serve to unify numerous observations, as already discussed. Penetration of the cell wall causes damage detected as leakage of low molecular weight constituents and possibly others, and causes a slight fall in the turbidity of the bacterial suspension. This damage is limited in some way, since it is independent of multiplicity of infection in the absence of lysis from without. The damage is accompanied by an overcompensating repair process that explains resistance to lysis from without and exclusion of superinfecting phage. The two processes are in competition: lysis from without results when the repair mechanism is overwhelmed by excessive damage. The repair mechanism, at least, depends on cellular metabolism. Metabolic inhibitors favor lysis and magnesium ions oppose it.

Puck and Lee (1954) attributed leakage to holes produced by bacterial enzymes, largely by analogy between lysis from without and effects of certain synthetic polyamino compounds that cause lysis. The following work does not contradict this view but suggests the participation of phage enzymes as well.

Barrington and Kozloff (1956) and Koch and Weidel (1956b)

described rather similar experiments in which solubilization of nitrogenous constituents of isolated cell walls by adsorbed phage is measured. The effect is seen with phages T2, T4, T6, and T5, but not with T7. Their results may be summarized as follows.

The amount of material solubilized corresponds to about 1 per cent of the cell wall nitrogen per phage, increasing linearly with multiplicity of adsorption up to about 15 per cent solubilization, after which attachment of additional phage particles has no effect. This maximal solubilization can also be achieved with fewer phage particles if the mixture is repeatedly centrifuged, an effect attributed to an increased opportunity of contacts between insoluble phage enzyme and insoluble substrate. In either case, the maximum solubilization produced by T2 is not increased by adsorption of additional particles of either T2 or T4. This result shows clearly that the materials solubilized are not the phage-specific receptor substances. Phosphorus and amino acids are both solubilized. The reaction fails at low temperatures, but is not inhibited by pretreatment of the cell walls with heat or with phenol. The role of this reaction in penetration is not clear, especially because of the limited effects observed, but an important role in infection may be surmised. It seems very likely that it prepares the cell for the leakage of cell constituents observed by Puck and Lee. It also helps to explain their "sealing reaction," since cell wall materials are very rapidly synthesized after infection (Hershey, Garen, Fraser, and Hudis, 1954).

Park (1956) and Adams and Park (1956) described an enzyme present in phage lysates of *Klebsiella pneumoniae* that acts on the capsular material of these bacteria. The enzyme is found both free in the lysate and attached to phage particles, and the amount produced seems to depend on the hereditary constitution of both bacterium and phage. It is not found in uninfected cells. The role of the enzyme in adsorption and penetration has not yet been studied.

2. The Latent Period

After adsorption of phage to the host cell, a period of time elapses before the cell lyses, liberating phage progeny. This time interval is known as the *latent period* and is measured by a *one-step growth experiment* (Chapter II). In such an experiment, not all the infected cells lyse at the same time. However, if the plaque count is plotted on a logarithmic scale as a function of the time of sampling, the rising portion of the curve is linear (Adams, 1949b; Maaløe, 1950; Barry and Goebel, 1951; Doermann, 1952; Bentzon, Maaløe, and Rasch, 1952). On such a plot, the intersection of the line with the baseline count of infected bacteria provides a suitable working definition of the minimum latent period.

The latent period depends on the phage and host strains, and also on the environmental conditions. Different phages growing on the same bacterial strain may have widely different latent periods (Delbrück, 1946b). Even closely related phages such as T2, T4, and T6 (Delbrück, 1946b) and T5 and PB (Adams, 1951b), may have quite distinct latent periods on the same host. In the case of T5 and PB, Adams (1951b) showed that the latent period of each phage may be separated from other characteristics by genetic recombination. The influence of different hosts on the latent period of the same phage has been reported by Barry and Goebel (1951). The latent period is strongly affected by the physiological state of the host cell, as demonstrated by Delbrück (1940a) and by Hedén (1951). Delbrück (1946b) reported that the latent periods for phages T1, T2, and T7 were the same in a synthetic medium as in broth, even though the bacterial growth was much slower in the synthetic medium. This is not true of all phage-host systems; Adams (1949b) found a latent period for phage T5 of 55 minutes in synthetic medium as compared with 40 minutes in broth.

Temperature generally affects the latent period in a similar manner to its effect on the generation time of the bacteria (Ellis and Delbrück, 1939); at lower temperatures, both increase.

Metabolic poisons are known to alter the latent period. For

example, the addition of penicillin (Krueger, Cohn, Smith, and McGuire, 1948) or aureomycin (Altenbern, 1953) shortens the latent period. Damage to phage particles caused by ultraviolet light can result in a prolonged latent period for those phage particles surviving the irradiation (Luria, 1944).

A phenomenon which has a marked effect on the duration of the latent period is *lysis inhibition* (Doermann, 1948a), which occurs with phages in the T2-C16 serological group. If, throughout the latent period, an infected bacterium is continuously reinfected with phage, bacterial lysis may be delayed for an hour or longer. The mechanism of lysis inhibition is not known. The ability to produce this phenomenon may be lost by mutation of the phage to the so-called *r* (rapid lysis) form. However, a mutant which is *r* type on one host may still produce lysis inhibition on a different host (Benzer, 1957). Thus, lysis inhibition is controlled by both phage and host.

The latent period is insensitive to the number of phage particles with which the host cell has been infected (Delbrück and Luria, 1942). This result was originally interpreted as indicating that only one of the adsorbed phage particles participated in the infectious process. However, later work with genetically marked phage particles indicated that as many as 10 particles might successfully infect a single bacterial cell (Dulbecco, 1949b).

Although the minimum latent period is a reproducible characteristic of a given phage-host system, the precise times of lysis of the individual cells are far from identical. There may be a twofold difference between the latent periods of individual cells.

Adams and Wasserman (1956) described a probit method for analyzing the variation in latent periods for individual cells. They show that the method permits one to recognize heterogeneous populations of bacteria or phage arising from experimental treatments of either one.

3. Burst Size

The burst size is the number of phage particles released per infected bacterium. Its average value is determined by the one step growth experiment.   The average burst size depends on the phage strain, the host cell, and the environmental conditions. Different phages growing in the same host strain may have quite different burst sizes (Delbrück, 1946b).   The same phage growing in different host strains may also have different burst sizes (Barry and Goebel, 1951).   An effect of the physiological state of the host cells was demonstrated by Delbrück (1940b) who obtained an average burst size of 20 with resting bacteria and 170 with growing bacteria.   Hedén (1951) studied the burst size during the period of transition from the resting phase to the phase of logarithmic growth of the host cell.   He found the maximum yield per cell at about the time of onset of bacterial division. This was also the time when the bacterial cell size and the content of ribonucleic acid per cell were maximal.   This applied to bacteria grown in broth or in synthetic medium.   The burst size is generally much larger in media such as nutrient broth than it is in synthetic media.

Under conditions of lysis inhibition, where the time of lysis is delayed, the burst size may be more than doubled (Doermann, 1948a).   Since delaying lysis of the cell permits more phage particles to be produced, it would appear that lysis rather than exhaustion of materials interrupts phage growth.

The phage yield from individual bacteria can be determined by the single burst technique.   A suspension of infected bacteria is diluted sufficiently so that, when samples are distributed into separate tubes, only a small proportion of the tubes will contain infected cells, mostly only one.   The samples are incubated until the bacteria have lysed, and then each is plated to determine its phage content.   In experiments of this type with phage Tl, Delbrück (1945a) found that burst sizes ranged from below 20 to over 1,000.   Since the distribution of burst sizes was much broader than either the distribution of host cell dimensions or the distribution of latent periods, the enormous range in burst sizes was probably not due to either of these factors.   Similar observations have been reported by Delbrück (1945c) and by Hershey and Rotman (1949).   There is no adequate explanation at present for the wide range of burst sizes in a culture.

4. Premature Lysis

The one-step growth experiment reveals nothing about the important intracellular events during the latent period. In order to penetrate behind the scenes, various methods for rupturing the host cell before the end of the normal latent period have been

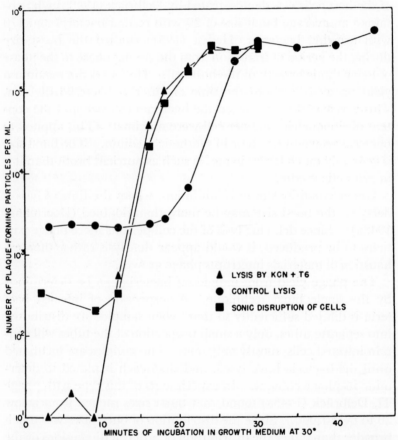

Figure 4. Maturation of phage T3 in infected bacteria. The curve marked "control lysis" is the ordinary one-step growth of this phage. The other two curves show the yields of infective particles released by two different methods of artificial lysis. Reproduced from T. F. Anderson and A. H. Doermann, 1952a, *J. Gen. Physiol.*, **35,** 657, with permission.

devised. Several methods for inducing "premature lysis" are described below.

One method utilizes intense sonic vibration to disrupt the host cell and liberate its contents (Anderson and Doermann, 1952a). This method is limited to phages that are more resistant to sonic vibrations than are their host cells. Phage T3 is suitable for this purpose. The results of a typical experiment are presented in Figure 4. The curve marked "control lysis" is an ordinary one-step growth curve for phage T3; the latent period is 20 minutes at 30° C. and the period of lysis covers the next 10 minutes. The curve marked "sonic disruption of cells" gives the number of infective centers found after sonic treatment of the samples. The count of infective centers remains constant at about 10 per cent of the number of infected bacteria until the 12th minute. This count probably represents infected bacteria which were not disrupted. The samples taken near the end of the latent period (at 16 and 18 minutes) show a marked rise in phage count due to the premature release of mature phage particles. Sonic treatment at 24 minutes or later liberates the normal yield of phage particles.

A second method of premature lysis developed by Doermann (1952) is based on the phenomenon of "lysis from without" described by Delbrück (1940b). If bacteria are attacked by a very large number of phage particles of the T2 species, they may respond by lysing without liberating phage progeny. The phenomenon is due to damage to the host cell membrane by the phage particles rather than to infection in the usual sense. In some cases, as with phage T2 itself, single infection may confer resistance to lysis from without by a secondary challenge with many T2 particles (Visconti, 1953).

In the experiments of Anderson and Doermann (1952a), cells infected with T3 were "lysed from without" by exposure to large concentrations of phage T6 (plus cyanide added to "freeze" the metabolism). By using B/6 as the plating bacterium, it is possible to assay T3 without interference from the T6 present. In Figure 4 the curve marked "lysis by KCN plus T6" gives the results of such an experiment using the same culture of *E. coli* infected with phage T3 that was used for the other two curves in the figure. The base line for the cyanide-T6 lysis curve is very low, corresponding to less than one per cent of the infected bacteria, showing that this method of lysis is very efficient. Otherwise the two methods of premature lysis yield remarkably similar curves. This suggests that either method accurately measures the intracellular content of infective phage particles at the time of sampling.

Two important conclusions about the multiplication of phage T3 may be drawn from these results: (*1*) during the first half of the latent period there are *no* mature phage particles inside the infected cell (this interval is called the "eclipse period"), and (*2*) during the second half of the latent period the number of mature phage particles increases rapidly, reaching an average of about 50 per infected bacterium at the time when spontaneous lysis begins.

Doermann (1948b, 1952) also studied the growth of phage T4 by premature lysis, and many other phages have been studied since with similar results. Doermann also noted that cyanide or 5-methyltryptophan alone could cause premature lysis when added after the end of the eclipse period. Other lysing agents have since been used, notably proflavine (Foster, 1948; De-Mars, 1955), dinitrophenol (Heagy, 1950), shaking with glass beads (Joklik, 1952), decompression under nitrous oxide (Fraser, 1951b; Levinthal and Fisher, 1952), glycine at high concentrations (Kay, 1952; DeMars, 1955), chloroform (Séchaud and Kellenberger, 1956), and chloramphenicol (Tomizawa and Sunakawa, 1956) (see also Chapter XV).

In all of these methods some means must be used to prevent loss of the liberated phage by adsorption to bacterial debris. One may use dilution as in the usual one-step growth experiment, a culture medium unfavorable to adsorption, an inhibitor of adsorption (French, Graham, Lesley, and Van Rooyen, 1952), or addition of a large excess of homologous irradiated phage (Maaløe and Watson, 1951). In the latter case the irradiated phage serves both as a lysing agent and as an inhibitor of adsorption but the specificities are different: T2, T4, and T6 cause lysis from without but only T2 can compete with the adsorption of T2 (Hershey and Chase, 1952).

The lysing agents mentioned above doubtless act in many different ways. Two extremes may be noted. Cyanide promptly stops biosynthesis generally by blocking certain steps in respiratory metabolism, and lysis ensues shortly. Proflavine does not stop synthesis of phage-specific materials, but blocks some final step in maturation of phage particles (DeMars, 1955). Lysis follows only at the end of the normal latent period.

Cyanide and chloroform are perhaps the most generally useful lysing agents.

To summarize, premature lysis of infected cells may be induced by various means. During an eclipse period lasting half way through the latent period no intact phage particles can be detected within the cell. The noninfective form of the phage believed to multiply in the cells during this time is called" vegetative phage" (Doermann, 1953). Its nature was a mystery until the discoveries of Hershey and Chase (1952) and subsequent work pointing to the identity of vegetative phage and phage-precursor DNA (Chapter XIV).

5. Phage Multiplication Studied by Irradiation of Infected Bacteria

The theoretical basis for this method of studying phage multiplication is quite simple, but as often happens in biological systems the interpretation of the experiments is unexpectedly complicated. The inactivation of a suspension of phage particles by ultraviolet light or X-rays is a close approximation to a "one-hit" phenomenon, that is, the surviving fraction is an exponential function of the dose of radiation (Chapter VI). The survival fraction y equals e^{-kD} where D is the dose of radiation and the coefficient k depends on the dosage unit and on the sensitivity of the phage. If a bacterium contains n phage particles and the survival of any one of these is sufficient for survival of the plaque-

forming potential of the infected bacterium, the survival should
be given by the expression

$$y = 1 - (1 - e^{-kD})^n$$

Such theoretical survival curves for bacteria containing various
numbers of phage particles are given in Figure 5, taken from the
paper of Luria and Latarjet (1947).

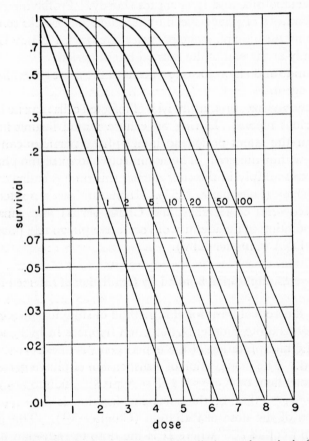

Figure 5. The relation between dose of irradiation and survival of infected
bacteria according to the target theory. The numbers on the curves correspond to different numbers of identical targets per bacterium. Reproduced
from S. E. Luria and R. Latarjet, 1947, *J. Bacteriol.*, **53**, 149, with permission.

In these curves the length of the initial plateau is related to the number of particles per cell, and the ultimate slope of the linear portion is determined by k, characterizing the sensitivity of the individual particles to the radiation. Therefore the survival curves obtained at various times during the latent period should give a clue to the kinetics of phage reproduction. This approach to the study of phage multiplication was made by a number of investigators including T. F. Anderson (1944), Luria and Latarjet (1947), Latarjet (1948), Benzer (1952), and Benzer and Jacob (1953). The subject has been reviewed by Latarjet (1953).

An assumption underlying this method is that the loss of the plaque-forming ability of infected bacteria is due to the effect of the radiation on the intracellular phage particles, rather than on the host cell mechanisms required for phage multiplication. Anderson (1944, 1948d) and Benzer (1952) demonstrated that *E. coli* B treated with many lethal doses of ultraviolet light retained the capacity to support multiplication of bacteriophage T2. The same result for bacteria killed by X-rays was observed by Rouyer and Latarjet (1946) and Labaw, Mosley, and Wyckoff (1953). Very heavy doses could render bacteria incapable of serving as hosts for phage growth, but such doses were much larger than those used in the inactivation of intracellular phage. In the case of some phage-bacterium systems, however, the "capacity" may be very sensitive (Benzer and Jacob, 1953). The essential steps in a so-called "Luria-Latarjet experiment" are the following: (*1*) phage is mixed with bacteria and adsorption permitted to occur for a short period of time; (*2*) unadsorbed phage is eliminated, and the number of infected bacteria is determined; (*3*) phage multiplication is permitted to take place, and samples are removed at intervals during the latent period; (*4*) each sample is exposed to several doses of radiation; and (*5*) the surviving fraction of infective centers is determined for each dose of radiation, and a survival curve is constructed for each time of sampling.

In experiments of this type it is important to have phage

growth in the population of infected bacteria synchronized as
much as possible, and to be able to arrest phage development
during the irradiation.   Benzer (1952) devised techniques which
solved these problems for T2 and T7.   The bacteria were grown
in broth, then aerated in buffer at 37 ° C. for one hour to starve
them.   Adsorption of phage added to such bacteria is rapid but
the infective process is arrested at a very early stage.   If broth
at 37 ° C. is subsequently added, phage growth starts and pro-
gresses normally.   This technique permits the separation of
adsorption from growth, and presumably phage growth starts in
all bacteria simultaneously when broth is added.   A defect of
this method is that a considerable proportion of the adsorbed
phage particles may be inactivated during the adsorption period,
a phenomenon known as "abortive infection."   Another technique for arresting development without interfering with adsorption is the use of cyanide.   When the cyanide is removed by dilution, development starts promptly (Benzer and Jacob, 1953).

Phage growth can be stopped at chosen times during the latent
period by dilution in chilled buffer.   Chilling halts phage development and the samples can then be irradiated at convenience; dilution serves to reduce the ultraviolet absorptivity of the
medium, which is prohibitive with broth.   The results for phage
T7 (Benzer, 1952) come close to the theoretical expectations as
may be seen in Figure 6.   For the first 3 minutes of the latent
period the survival curves are similar to that for free phage T7.
At later times, the curves become multiple hit in character, indicating that phage multiplication has started.   By the sixth
minute, the curve indicates a relatively high multiplicity but the
ultimate slope is only slightly less steep than for free phage.
For the remainder of the latent period the multiplicity increases
further and the ultimate slope decreases somewhat.   These survival curves do not have the flat initial plateau seen in the
theoretical curves of Figure 6, but have a steeper initial gradient.
Benzer (1952) suggested that this may reflect lack of synchroni-
zation of phage growth in different bacterial cells.

Similar experiments with T2-infected bacteria were carried

out by Luria and Latarjet (1947) and by Benzer (1952). The results with this phage are strikingly different from those obtained with T7. Immediately after infection, the infective centers have the same sensitivity to ultraviolet inactivation as free phage, but there follows an increase in resistance to inactivation until, at 5 or 6 minutes after infection, the resistance has doubled.

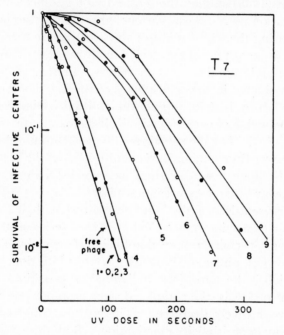

Figure 6. Survival of phage-producing capacity of bacteria infected with T7. The bacteria were irradiated at times after infection indicated on the curves in minutes. Latent period (at 37° C.) 12 minutes. Reproduced from S. Benzer, 1952, *J. Bacteriol.*, **63**, 59, with permission.

Thereafter the resistance increases with great rapidity until maximum resistance, 20-fold greater than that of free phage, is reached at about 10 minutes after infection. At this time the inactivation curves become definitely multiple hit in character. From 10 minutes to the end of the latent period the multiplicity of the inactivation curves increases while the slope of the curve

becomes steeper, the sensitivity approaching again that of free
phage. This remarkable change in sensitivity to ultraviolet inactivation during the first half of the latent period was completely unexpected and entirely different from the behavior of
phage T7. It cannot be explained on the basis of screening by
ultraviolet absorbing materials (Benzer, 1952).

Latarjet (1948) studied the sensitivity of T2-infected bacteria
to inactivation by X-rays at various times during the latent period. During the first 7 minutes, the sensitivity remained essentially the same as that of extracellular virus. Then, during the
8th and 9th minutes there was an increase in resistance to X-rays
without a change in the multiplicity of the inactivation curves.
From the 9th to the 13th minute the multiplicity increased very
rapidly to a value of over 100 with little change in the sensitivity
to inactivation. For the remainder of the 21-minute latent period there was little change in the multiplicity of the inactivation
curves, but there was a gradual increase in X-ray sensitivity,
tending toward that of extracellular phage.

An interpretation of the results obtained with T2 (Benzer,
1952) is that infection may be followed by a series of steps, each
step having a certain cross section for interference by ultraviolet
light. For free phage, or immediately after infection, the total
cross section is the sum of the individual cross sections. As development proceeds, the completed steps drop out and the cross
section progressively decreases. This process could be related
in some way to multiplicity reactivation. Both the rapid change
in ultraviolet sensitivity during the latent period and the phenomenon of multiplicity reactivation occur with phages of the T2
serological group; neither effect occurs in the T7 serological
group.

The remarkable resistance of the phage-producing mechanism
to agents supposedly acting on the intrabacterial DNA can be
shown in another way. Phage particles containing P^{32} of high
specific radioactivity are subject to "suicide" owing to the decay
of radiophosphorus, which presumably produces local damage in
the viral DNA. Stent (1955) applied this principle in experi-

ments designed to explore the role of DNA during infection. He infected bacteria with phage in various combinations such that the parental phage DNA, the newly synthesized intrabacterial DNA, or both, contained P^{32} of high specific radioactivity. Phage growth was allowed to proceed for varying time intervals, and samples of the infected culture were frozen. Decay of radiophosphorus occurred for various times in the frozen state, after which the samples were thawed and titrated to measure the number of infected bacteria still capable of producing phage. The results may be summarized as follows.

1. When only the parental viral DNA contained P^{32}, the ability of the infected cells to produce phage was initially about as sensitive to radioactive decay as are free phage particles. As phage development progressed, however, this sensitivity was gradually lost. By the ninth minute it had disappeared completely.

2. When the newly synthesized viral DNA (and indeed all the intrabacterial phosphorus excepting the parental viral DNA) contained P^{32}, the ability of the infected cells did not at any time reach a stage at which the ability to produce phage was appreciably sensitive to radioactive decay.

3. When all the intrabacterial DNA contained P^{32}, the results were virtually the same as when only the parental viral DNA contained P^{32}.

These results show in an interesting way the dependence of viral growth during its early stages on the integrity of the parental viral DNA. Otherwise they show the same remarkable fact revealed by the experiments with ultraviolet light, namely, that the T2 phage-producing mechanism becomes highly resistant to damage to intrabacterial DNA near the mid-point of the latent period. Stent suggests three ways in which such stabilization might be brought about: (*1*) a stage in viral growth may be reached after which damage to DNA can be *repaired*, as in the phenomenon of multiplicity reactivation (Chapter XVIII); (*2*) a stage may be reached in which some or all the intrabacterial DNA becomes *insensitive* to radiochemical damage; or

(*3*) a stage may be reached after which the intrabacterial DNA is *dispensable*, presumably owing to a transfer of DNA function to other substances not containing phosphorus.

The third alternative was also suggested by Tomizawa and Sunakawa (1956) on the basis of experiments showing that chloramphenicol, added to cultures infected with phage T2 under conditions permitting synthesis of DNA but not protein, blocked those processes resulting in stabilization of the infected bacteria toward the destructive effects of ultraviolet light.

At the present time no decisive choice can be made among the three hypotheses suggested by Stent. It should be recalled, however, that the experiments with T7 do not show the same phenomenon, and one can ask which result reflects basic features of viral growth least complicated by side effects. These and other related experiments are discussed in somewhat different contexts by Hershey (1957) and Stent (1958).

6. Morphological Stages in Phage Development

Objects the size of bacteriophages can be studied by means of the electron microscope, which has revealed structures that may be intermediate stages in the maturation of infective particles. One of these is known by the colloquial name "doughnut." It is a crumpled disk with a central depression which makes it look like a torus in shadowed electron micrographs. Beautiful pictures of doughnuts were published by Wyckoff (1949b). They are also illustrated in papers by Herčík (1955), Hedén (1951), Levinthal and Fisher (1952), DeMars, Luria, Fisher, and Levinthal (1953), and T. F. Anderson, Rappaport, and Muscatine (1953). The latter authors prepared specimens by the critical point method and show that doughnuts are really empty membranes of the same size and shape as the phage head but without any tail. They have been found in association with the large, tailed phage particles T2, T4, T6, and T5.

The size, shape, and occurrence of these particles suggested that they might be an intermediate stage in reproduction. Evidence in support of this view was obtained by Levinthal and

Fisher (1952) in quantitative studies of T2-infected bacteria which were prematurely lysed by the decompression technique at different times during the latent period. The lysates were mixed with polystyrene latex particles and sprayed on collodion films for electron micrography, thus permitting counts of the number of particles per infected bacterium. Doughnuts are first detected at about the 9th minute of the latent period. By the 12th minute, when mature phage first appears, the doughnuts number about 15 per bacterium. At the 21st minute their number reaches a maximum of 30 per cell, while mature phage particles continue to increase, numbering 60 per cell at 25 minutes. It seems reasonable to conclude that the doughnut represents a stage in the assembly of phage particles. The relationship of phage nucleic acid to these structures is not clear. It is possible that the incomplete forms contain nucleic acid that is lost during the preparative manipulations.

Relatively pure preparations of doughnuts can be obtained by the use of proflavine, which specifically inhibits final steps in the maturation of phage particles (DeMars, Luria, Fisher, and Levinthal, 1953). The incomplete particles can be readily concentrated and purified by high speed centrifugation. On examination in the electron microscope they are indistinguishable from doughnuts observed by other means and are essentially free of tailed particles. The formation of doughnuts during early stages of viral growth occurs at the same rate with or without proflavine.

The preparation of purified concentrates of doughnuts obtained by the proflavine technique permitted a study of their serological properties. They fix complement with antiphage serum with about half the efficiency per particle of mature phage. They are precipitated by antiphage serum but do not adsorb phage-neutralizing antibodies from the serum. Purified doughnuts were used for the immunization of rabbits by Lanni and Lanni (1953). The resulting sera gave very strong complement fixation reactions with both doughnuts and mature phage particles, but contained very little neutralizing antibody. From

this and other evidence these authors concluded that the doughnuts are serologically equivalent to the heads of phage particles
(Chapter VIII).

Proflavine lysates were prepared from T2-infected bacteria
labeled with either P^{32} or S^{35}.   The isolated doughnuts were
found to contain about $^2/_3$ as much sulfur per particle as mature
phage, but less than $^1/_6$ as much phosphorus.   These observations are in agreement with the electron microscope studies in
suggesting that the doughnuts are empty phage heads, made of
protein and containing little or no nucleic acid.   The doughnuts do not adsorb to bacteria, which is consistent with the
absence of tails.

Further morphological study was facilitated by the development of the "agar filtration method" of quantitative electron
microscopy (Kellenberger and Kellenberger, 1952; Kellenberger and Arber, 1957).   In this method a sample of crude lysate
is placed on a collodian membrane supported on a specially prepared agar surface.   Water and crystalloids pass into the agar,
while larger particles are deposited on the membrane.   The
material is fixed with formaldehyde vapor and the membrane is
transferred to a specimen grid for electron microscopy.   Counting of particles per unit volume of lysate is achieved by calibration with latex spheres.   The advantage of this method over
others is that no fractionation of the lysate is necessary before
preparation of specimens.

Kellenberger and Séchaud (1957) applied this method to premature lysates of both normal and proflavine cultures of bacteria infected with T2 and T4.   They found, in confirmation of
earlier work, that doughnuts appeared a few minutes before
phage particles in the lysates, and soon reached a constant number of about 50 per bacterium, whereas phage particles increased
for a longer period, to 150 per bacterium.   Proflavine greatly
suppressed the formation of phage particles but did not affect the
formation of doughnuts.   This result is unexpected, because, if
proflavine acts mainly to prevent the conversion of doughnuts
into phage particles, some additional mechanism must be invoked

to explain the failure of doughnuts to accumulate in response to the drug. However, the effect of proflavine may be more complicated (Chapter XV).

Kellenberger and Séchaud were able to count tail pins as well as doughnuts (Chapter IV). Tail pins did not appear until phage particles had already become very numerous, and finally

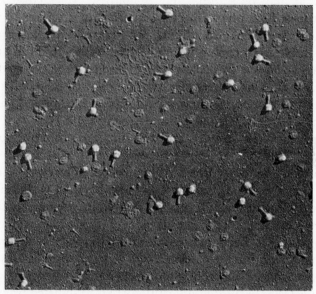

Figure 7. Products of lysis by T2 in the presence of proflavine. Intact phage particles, empty heads, tail pins and, in the upper part of the micrograph, fibrils that may be DNA. ×22,125. Reproduced from E. Kellenberger and J. Séchaud, 1957, *Virology*, **3,** 256, with permission.

numbered about 30 per bacterium. Their formation was not affected by proflavine. The delayed appearance of tail pins might suggest that they are products of defective synthesis or breakdown of phage particles, rather than precursors, in which case some of the doughnuts might originate in a similar way.

Kellenberger and Séchaud found that tail pins of T2 adsorb incompletely and mostly reversibly to bacteria. They do not react with the neutralizing antibody of antiphage serum.

Figure 7 shows an electron micrograph of the products released by lysis of bacteria infected with T2 in the presence of proflavine.

The same and other intermediate structures related to viral
growth have been detected by serological methods (Chapter
VIII) and by chemical methods (Chapter XIV). The total information may be summarized as follows. Infected cells contain at least four phage-specific materials in addition to phage
particles: free DNA, doughnuts, tail pins, and free tail antigen,
all separable from each other in lysates. Only free tail antigen
and free DNA are caused to accumulate by proflavine, that is,
proflavine does not affect the total amount of these substances
formed, but suppresses their incorporation into phage particles
(DeMars, 1955; Kellenberger and Séchaud, 1957).

Doughnuts, tail antigen, and tail pins are probably made of
protein. Tail antigen might be expected to correspond to the
tail fibers of phage particles. When prepared by degradation of
phage particles, the fibers can adsorb to bacteria (Williams and
Fraser, 1956). Free tail antigen found in premature lysates,
however, cannot. The significance of this difference cannot
now be assessed, because present information about the adsorption characteristics of materials found in premature lysates seems
to be unreliable. Thus doughnuts never adsorb, but Maaløe and
Symonds (1953) reported adsorption of an S^{35}-labeled fraction in
T4 lysates that should have been chiefly doughnuts. Kellenberger and Séchaud (1957) observed adsorption of tail pins
found in T2 lysates, but none of the materials, including phage
particles, found in their T4 lysates would adsorb. Unfortunately little of the work with premature lysates has been carried
out with adequate precautions to prevent interactions between
phage-specific materials and bacterial debris in the lysates,
partly because these interactions are not themselves understood
(Sagik, 1954)(Chapter XVI).

The free DNA found in premature lysates undoubtedly is a
phage precursor (Hershey, 1953a). Some of the antigenic protein is, too (Maaløe and Symonds, 1953; Hershey, 1956b).

The phage-specific protein precursors include materials that sediment like doughnuts as well as smaller fragments, in approximately equal amounts as measured by sulfur content (Hershey, 1956b).

7. Conclusion

Phage growth is initiated by the injection of the viral DNA into the cell. Completed phage particles do not reappear until the mid-point of the latent period. Morphologically recognizable elements are formed somewhat earlier. Radiobiological analysis of phage growth also shows that important processes occur during the eclipse period of viral growth. These and other lines of evidence suggest that noninfective phage particles, called vegetative phage, are multiplying during the period of eclipse.

Attempts to enumerate vegetative phage particles in infected cells by radiobiological methods have generally failed. Instead the experiments show that vegetative phage T2 is remarkably resistant to ultraviolet light, X-rays, and decay of constituent radiophosphorus. Vegetative phage T7 does not show this property. For this and other reasons the proper interpretation of the radiobiological experiments is not clear.

CHAPTER XII

CYTOLOGICAL CHANGES IN THE INFECTED HOST CELL

This chapter is devoted to studies of visible changes in bacteria caused by phage infection, and to the sequence of cytological events during the latent period of intracellular phage multiplication. These studies may be conveniently classified into categories on the basis of the technical methods used: (*1*) direct observation of living cells by dark field, ultraviolet, and phase contrast microscopy; (*2*) observation of fixed and stained preparations to determine the succession of cytochemical changes; and (*3*) observation in the electron microscope of fixed and dried whole cells and of embedded and sectioned preparations to obtain higher resolution than is possible in the first two techniques.

All methods agree in demonstrating that marked changes occur in bacterial cells as a result of phage infection. A major problem is the correlation in time of the events observed by the various techniques, and almost as difficult is the elimination or control of artefacts caused by the technical methods employed in the preparation of specimens for observation. Other complicating factors include variation in the sequence of events with different phages attacking the same host strain, and variation in the time required for intracellular virus growth under different environmental conditions, which make it more difficult to compare the experiments of different investigators. These technical hurdles as well as the highly developed imaginations of the investigators are responsible for the great diversity of interpretations which have been published.

1. Observations on Living Cells

The lysis of bacteria by phage may be readily observed under the ordinary light microscope.   For such studies a culture of the susceptible bacterium in the logarithmic growth phase is exposed to an excess of bacteriophage under conditions in which at least 90 per cent of the bacteria are infected within a few minutes. The infected bacteria may then be observed under oil immersion by hanging drop methods or on the surface of agar under a cover glass.   Bacterial lysis begins after the usual latent period for the conditions of temperature and bacterial nutrition used.   The time course for the number of bacteria lysed corresponds to that for phage liberation as observed in the one-step growth experiment, which suggests that the lysis of a bacterium coincides with the liberation of the mature phage particles contained in that bacterium.

With most of the phage-host cell systems studied, infection inhibits further cell division.   An exception occurs with certain temperate phages studied by Lwoff, Siminovitch, and Kjeldgaard (1950) in which the infected cell undergoes one or two divisions before lysis.   In many cases no gross change in cell morphology occurs up to the moment of lysis, at which time the refractive index of the cell suddenly changes, the cell bursts and becomes invisible.   Studies of this event by cinematography have demonstrated that cell disappearance can occur within 3 seconds, the time interval between successive photographs (Bronfenbrenner, Muckenfuss, and Hetler, 1927; Bayne-Jones and Sandholzer, 1933).

Many observers have reported morphological changes occurring in cells after infection.   In some cases the cells swelled markedly and became nearly spherical in shape before bursting. In other cases greatly elongated, filamentous forms developed which might or might not lyse (Burnet, 1925; Bronfenbrenner, 1928).   This variety of changes in cell morphology gave rise to some controversy in the early literature (see Bronfenbrenner, 1928) and may have been due to differences in phage and host strains or differences in environmental conditions in use in different laboratories. An important development was the demonstration by Delbrück (1940b) that two distinct types of lysis could be observed with the same phage-host system depending on the multiplicity of infection. Under conditions of normal infection there was no change in cell shape up to the moment of lysis. In contrast, when the multiplicity of infection was of the order of 200 phage particles per cell, there was a relatively rapid swelling of the rod-shaped bacteria into an oval or spherical shape which then slowly faded out. The latter process, termed "lysis from without," was never accompanied by liberation of viable phage particles. At intermediate multiplicities of infection part of the bacterial population would lyse by the normal, productive bursting, while the remainder of the population would suffer the unproductive "lysis from without." There has been relatively little study in recent years of modes of lysis during bacteriophagy and a comparative study of various phage-host cell systems might well be rewarding.

Observations of the lytic process in the dark field microscope were first reported by d'Herelle (1921, 1926). "Au debut, l'aspect des bacilles est normal; aprés quarante-cinq à soixante minutes on voit des fins granules, de plus en plus nombreux, dans l'intérieur des bacilles, le nombre des bacilles avec granules inclus augmente rapidement avec diminution paralléle du nombre des bacilles normaux." As the number of intracellular granules increased the bacteria swelled, became spherical, and burst, liberating the granules into the medium. The bacterial debris, however, quickly became invisible in the ultramicroscope. D'Herelle concluded that the highly refractile granules that he observed inside the infected bacteria were actually the bacteriophage particles. He based this conclusion on two kinds of evidence: there was always a parallelism in lysates between the number of granules seen in the ultramicroscope and the number of phage corpuscles determined by plaque count; and the number of refractile bodies counted per bacterium infected with the Shiga phage under study varied from 15 to 25, corresponding to an average yield of 18 phage corpuscles for one particle inoculated as determined by plaque counts. The quantitative relationship between the number of highly refractile particles seen in the dark field microscope and the number of infectious particles determined by plaque count was confirmed much later by Schlesinger (1933b).

Dark field observations of phage lysis of *E. coli* in hanging drop cultures, made by Merling-Eisenberg (1938), may be summarized as follows. He found that the motile organisms became motionless following infection. Then fine internal granules began to appear, which were in motion in some cases, while the bacterium increased in size. After a variable period of time lysis occurred. The disruption might occur without any further change in the size or shape of the bacillus as if the whole cell membrane suddenly became permeable. On other occasions an opening appeared at one end or at the side of the bacterium, through which the granules were spewed. The explosion released a very distinct cloud of particles with a blue diffraction color showing marked Brownian movement and soon leaving their "birthplace." They could be readily distinguished from bacterial debris and unspecific particles by this blue color and their fairly uniform size. The phage bodies (150 to 350 per cell) were expelled by the force of the explosion to a distance estimated at 5 to 6 times the length of the bacterium. During lysis the number of phage bodies free in the medium soon reached astronomical figures. This very interesting description of lysis is illustrated with photographs which clearly demonstrate the refractile granules, both inside the bacteria and in the medium. Merling-Eisenberg (1941) made similar observations of phage lysis of staphylococci, in which 1 to 4 granules per cell were released. Very nice motion pictures of phage lysis were made with dark field illumination by Pijper (1945), which are in agreement with the earlier observations described above. Similar dark field observations were reported again by Weigle (see Benzer, Delbrück, Dulbecco, Hudson, Stent, Watson, Weidel, Weigle, and Wollman, 1950).

The possible use of the dark field ultraviolet microscope for studying phage multiplication was suggested by the work of Barnard who published very fine pictures of some of the larger viruses. Pictures of phage C16 before and after agglutination by anti-phage serum were taken by Barnard and published by Burnet (1933c). The phage particles were very easily visible, could be counted, and were barely below the limits of resolution of the microscope. This beautiful optical system does not seem to have been applied to the study of phage-infected bacteria.

The use of the light field ultraviolet microscope for photography of phage infected bacteria by F. L. Gates was described by Bronfenbrenner (1928). He wrote: "In unstained cells photographed at this stage (swollen but not lysed) by means of ultraviolet light, the cytoplasm appears to be of uneven density, quite unlike that of normal bacteria."

Studies of *E. coli* infected with phage T2 were made by ultraviolet microscopy by Heden (1951) and compared with observations by phase contrast microscopy, electron microscopy, and light microscopy of stained preparations. This permitted a direct comparison of developmental changes in unfixed and living cells (ultraviolet and phase contrast observations) with corresponding stages in fixed cells (electron microscope and stained preparations). Uninfected cultures of *E. coli* in the logarithmic growth phase were uniformly opaque in the ultraviolet microscope, presumably because of the cytoplasmic RNA which obscured the DNA-containing bodies, which are so prominent in Feulgen stained cells. After infection with T2 and incubation the bacterial poles gradually became much more light-absorbent at 2,570 A than the equatorial region. After several hours of incubation under conditions of lysis inhibition the polar bodies contained several times more light-absorbing material than did the rest of the cytoplasm. This contrast between polar and equatorial regions was not evident at a wave length of 3,300 A, suggesting that nucleic acid is in reality the light-absorbing material.

In phase contrast studies of living bacteria, the cells appeared uniform until infected. Within 15 minutes after infection the bipolar appearance became evident, and the contrast between polar and equatorial regions increased until lysis. In dried preparations fixed with osmium the bipolar arrangement had disappeared. Polar bodies were not seen in fixed and stained preparations, which suggests that the procedures of fixation and dehydration may create artefacts having little resemblance to the situation in living infected cells.

Similar phase contrast observations of living, phage-infected cultures were made with *Salmonella typhimurium* (Boyd, 1949a) and *E. coli* (Boyd, 1949b). Again the uniformly dense appearance of the uninfected bacteria quickly changed after infection to a bipolar distribution of dense areas. For reasons that are not clear, Boyd assumed that the less dense areas are due to bacteriophage and the darker polar areas are due to bacterial cytoplasm displaced toward the poles by the developing phage. The observations of Hedén with the ultraviolet microscope, referred to above, suggest that it is the DNA and, presumably, bacteriophage synthesis which is concentrated at the poles rather than the bacterial cytoplasm. This suggestion of Hedén's is further supported by the dark field photographs of phage-infected bacteria taken by Merling-Eisenberg (1938) which clearly show a polar distribution of the phage particles.

Boyd (1949b) studied all seven T phages by phase contrast microscopy using strain B of *E. coli* as host. He found characteristic changes in cellular appearance which were similar for serologically related phages but differed from one serological group to another. These observations are significant in demonstrating that the physiological response of the bacterium to infection depends on the genetic constitution of the phage and suggest a rather remarkable control by the phage of enzymatic processes in the bacterium. Such characteristic phage-specific changes in morphology have been defined with greater clarity in stained preparations as we will see. Other observations of phage action using phase contrast have been reported by Hofer (1947), Delaporte (1949), Rice, McCoy, and Knight (1954), and Murray and Whitfield (1953).

2. Observations on Fixed and Stained Preparations

Stained smears, made after the fashion of diagnostic bacteriology, were the basis of the earlier observations and they were not very informative. More recently, however, cytological methods appropriate for the study of bacteria have been devised and these have provided a more rewarding approach to the study of the effects of phage infection on the structure of the host cell. These involve the fixation *in situ* of the cells in or on the culture medium with cytological fixatives (such as osmium tetroxide and other, more complex, solutions); the application of selective staining methods allowing the differentiation of the nuclear chromatin bodies and the cytoplasm, which is strongly basophilic due in large part to RNA (see Murray, Gillen, and Heagy, 1950); and suitable mounting of the preparation to minimize distortion of the cell and to provide for optical needs.

D'Herelle (1926) described briefly the effects of phage infection on the staining properties of the bacterial host. The affinity of the infected bacteria for basic dyes gradually decreased. Weakly staining, amorphous debris gradually increased in amount as the number of intact bacteria decreased. He never saw corroded or broken bacterial cells. The intact cells often became spherical and then burst, becoming amorphous immediately. The spherical forms were extremely fragile and were always less numerous in stained specimens than in dark field preparations made at the same time. The phage particles themselves were below the limits of visibility in the stained preparations.

Rather similar observations were recorded by Bronfenbrenner (1928). The cytoplasm showed marked changes during the swelling of the bacteria, staining less intensely and more unevenly so that the bacteria appeared segmented or beaded. In highly swollen bacteria the chromatin was distributed throughout the bacteria in the form of dustlike particles.

Borrel (1928, 1932) used an iron-tannate-fuchsin mordant which was effective in making visible bacterial flagellae and the larger animal viruses such as vaccinia and molluscum contagiosum. When applied to phage-infected bacterial cultures during lysis it enabled him to see a halo of adsorbed phage particles surrounding the yet unlysed bacteria. Although this procedure may have permitted visualization of extracellular phage particles, it did not contribute to knowledge of the infectious process. Hofer (1947) also used a flagellum stain and the Ziehl-Nielsen stain in an attempt to color extracellular phage particles but again without yielding much information about phage multiplication. His claim to have seen phage particles under these conditions is not convincing.

A remarkable paper by MacNeal, Frisbee, and Krumwiede (1937) described the application of the Casteneda rickettsial stain to the study of the lysis of the cholera vibrio by phage and by antiserum plus complement. The phage-infected bacteria were pleomorphic, enlarged and distorted, and filled with as many as 50 tiny blue-staining granules per cell. Such granules were never seen in normal bacteria, nor in bacteria undergoing lysis by complement and antibody. It seems very probable that the granules were intracellular phage particles. This work does not seem to have been followed up nor to have attracted much notice.

The first applications of chromatin-staining procedures to the study of phage-infected bacteria seem to have been made by Luria and Palmer (1946) and by Beumer and Quersin (1947). Luria and Palmer used Feulgen and Giemsa stains following the general procedures of Robinow (1944). Infection with phage T2 resulted in the disorganization of the nuclear bodies and migration of the chromatin to the periphery of the cell. The cells then gradually filled up with granular chromatin. Phage T1 caused relatively little change in the appearance of most cells. Infection with phage T7 caused great swelling of some nuclear bodies and shrinking of others. The different phages caused characteristically distinct cytological changes in appearance of the host cell nuclear apparatus.

Beumer and Quersin (1947) and Quersin (1948) used Robinow's staining techniques to study the cytological changes produced by several different phage strains on a number of different host bacteria.   They found that in general the bacterial nucleus was distorted or destroyed and replaced with a mass of chromatinic material, and the bacterium swelled.   The type of lesion produced was characteristic of the phage and not of the host cell because the same phage produced essentially the same sequence of changes in different bacteria, whereas different phages acting on the same bacterial strain produced characteristically different lesions.   Delaporte (1949), using similar methods, studied the action of phage T4 on normal *E. coli* cells and on ultraviolet-treated bacteria.   Lysing cells liberated large numbers of tiny, stained particles which may have been the phage particles.   The action of a phage on *B. cereus* was also described briefly.   Rita and Silvestri (1950) gave a brief description of modifications in the host cell nucleus resulting from infection of *E. coli* with phages of the T series, including T5.

P'an, Tchan, and Pochon (1949) studied the action of phage on *Pasteurella pestis*.   The cell and its nuclei increased in size after infection, and the nuclei fused into a convoluted axial filament. At lysis the cell outline became less distinct and the axial filament disappeared.

A rather detailed description of progressive cytological changes produced in *E. coli* following infection with phages T1, T2, T4, T6, and T7 was published by Luria and Human (1950).   Samples of the infected bacteria were taken at intervals during the latent period and added to a formalin-dichromate fixative.   After fixing the bacteria were washed, and spread on agar, and impression films were stained by the Robinow technique.   Again the sequence of cytological changes was found to be characteristic of the phage type; the effect of the closely related phages T2, T4, and T6 being very similar but quite distinct from the changes caused by T1 and T7.   With ultraviolet-inactivated T2 phage, infection was followed by the same initial destruction of the bacterial nucleus as occurs with active T2 phage.   However, these cells did not subsequently fill up with granular chromatin as do cells infected with active phage.   With inactivated T1 phage the cytological changes were the same as those observed with active T1 except that lysis did not occur. With inactivated T7 phage the initial changes were the same as with active T7 phage, but then the cells filled up with chromatin like T1-infected cells instead of forming a large central chromatinic body as was seen with active T7 phage. In the case of infection with irradiated T1 phage, synthesis of material absorbing at 2,600 A proceeded at the same rate as with active phage, but with irradiated T2 phage the synthesis of light-absorbing material proceeded at a relatively slow rate compared with synthesis in bacteria infected with active phage T2. Hedén (1951) reported that his cytological studies with T2-infected *E. coli* cells were in essential agreement with the results of Luria and Human.

An intensive study of the cytological changes produced in *E. coli* by infection with phage T2 was made by Murray, Gillen, and Heagy (1950). The staining methods of Robinow were used, and replicate samples of infected bacteria taken at intervals during the latent period were stained with Giemsa (after treatment with HCl) for chromatin, with thionine for cytoplasm, and with tannic acid and gentian violet for cell walls. The Giemsa and thionine staining methods complemented each other and the cell wall stain permitted the visualization of bacterial "ghosts" after lysis had occurred. The observations with the Giemsa stain were in agreement with those of Luria and Human (1950). During the first few minutes the bacterial nucleus disintegrated and the chromatin migrated to the periphery of the cell forming "marginated cells." Then during the second half of the latent period, this chromatin became granular. In lysis-inhibited cells the granules increased in size and coalesced, giving a banded appearance. The staining capacity of the cytoplasm with thionine decreased and was almost lost at the time of lysis. The authors suggested that late in the latent period the chromatin is distributed cylindrically near the cell wall. This paper is illustrated with beautifully reproduced photographs of stained preparations. Studies of T2-infected bacteria by Beutner, Hartman, Mudd, and Hillier (1953) using DeLamater's staining technique are in agreement with the results obtained by the previous investigators.

Murray and Whitfield (1953) made a detailed study of the effects of phage strains of the T5 species on various host cells. Again it was found that the cytological changes were characteristic of the phage and independent of the particular host strain, whether *Escherichia*, *Shigella*, or *Salmonella*. The sequence of changes was similar to that observed with the T-even phages: cessation of cell division, loss of stainable nuclear chromatin and disruption of nuclear sites, followed during the second half of the latent period by a new synthesis of finely granular chromatin. However, unlike the T-even phage infections, the loss of stainable chromatin was virtually complete and was not accompanied by migration to the periphery of the cell.   In the case of three of the phages (T5, BG3, and 29 alpha) lysis occurred at this stage; with three other strains (PB, PB1, and poona) there was an accumulation of spherical masses of chromatin during the last 10 minutes of the latent period preceding lysis.   Five hybrids of T5 with PB isolated and characterized by Adams (1951b) were studied by Murray and Whitfield.   Three were found to behave like the T5 parent and two like the PB parent.   The cytological pattern segregated independently of host range, latent period, and heat resistance, and thus behaved as an additional genetic marker for this group of phages.   Adsorption of ultraviolet-inactivated phage to the host cell caused the initial nuclear disintegration, but the secondary synthesis of granular chromatin did not occur.   Adams (1949b) had previously demonstrated that calcium ion was essential for some step in the reproduction of phage T5 subsequent to adsorption.   Murray and Whitfield found that when infection occurred in the absence of calcium ion there was nuclear disintegration as usual, but the new synthesis of granular chromatin did not follow.   Later Luria and Steiner (1954) demonstrated that calcium was essential for the penetration of phage T5 nucleic acid into the host cell.   These results show that adsorption of phage T5 to the host cell is of itself enough to cause nuclear disintegration, even though the phage nucleic acid does not penetrate to initiate phage replication.   Adsorption of phage T5 in the absence of calcium may be analogous in its effects to the adsorption of ghosts of phage T2 (Herriott, 1951a).

Bonifas and Kellenberger (1955) observed that adsorption of ghosts of phage T2 caused an aggregation of the host cell chromatin rather than the peripheral migration observed when either active or ultraviolet-inactivated phage was adsorbed. This was confirmed by Whitfield and Murray (1957) who further observed that if the multiplicity of infection with the active phage was increased to 70 or 100 phage per cell chromatin aggregation preceded the premature "lysis from without." Multiple infection with T5 phage likewise caused aggregation to precede the usual loss of stainable chromatin. The above observations suggest that alterations of the cell boundary, more severe following infection with ghosts than with phage, contribute to cytological effects.

Puck and Lee (1954, 1955) suggested that infection with any of the T phages initiates a cycle of permeability changes in the cell boundary during the period following the attachment of the phage to the cell. Direct evidence of visible as well as chemical disorganization of cell membranes by phage adsorption has also been noted (Chapter XI). The studies of Whitfield and Murray (1956, 1957) showed that some of the cytological effects of infection may be secondary to permeability changes. They found that the chromatin aggregation, so commonly observed as a first cytological stage of infection (e.g., with phage T7), occurred at low multiplicities of infection if a sufficient quantity of sodium chloride was present in the medium; on salt-deficient medium this effect was replaced by chromatin fragmentation. With phages T2 and T5 the same was true, provided that there was a sufficient multiplicity of infection. The results suggest that the conformation of chromatin is dependent on the ionic balance maintained in the living cell; disturbance of this balance, whether by phage adsorption to the cell surface or by metabolic interference, is reflected in the subsequent behavior of chromatin, which varies according to the cationic environment provided for the experiment. These considerations underline the cautions expressed at the beginning of this chapter.

Lysogenic systems have not been subjected to much cytological study.   Observations of cultures of lysogenic *B. megaterium* 899 after induction by ultraviolet light have been reported by Delaporte and Siminovitch (1952).   For the first 17 minutes after irradiation the bacterial cells continue to grow and divide in a manner that is not distinguishable from nonirradiated cultures. After this time the nucleus is disposed as an axial filament nearly as long as the cell.   This then begins to swell at some points and the chromatin seems to move to form the surface of a cylinder, considerably larger in diameter than the original filament.   During this time the bacterial cell increases in both length and diameter.   The central nuclear cylinder is about $^1/_3$ the diameter of the bacterium at the end of the latent period.   At the time of lysis the bacterial membrane loses its rigidity and the cytoplasm disperses, followed immediately by the disappearance of the axial cylinder.   This sequence of events differs from that seen with previously studied lytic systems.   The authors suggest that the phage particles are synthesized at the surface of the hypertrophied nuclear filament.

Whitfield and Murray (1954) studied the sequence of cytological events during the lysogenization of *Shigella dysenteriae* with the temperate phages P1 and P2.   The first stage of infection with both phages consisted of the condensation of the chromatin into annular aggregates which tended to fuse and form into an axial filament.   In P1 infections this stage occupied about half of the latent period.   The axial filament then expanded within the cell to form a complex reticulum which, in the case of lysogenization, separated into discrete normal nuclear elements. The resulting cells were indistinguishable from those of the sensitive strain.   The same stages were observed when a virulent mutant of P1 was used, but lysis occurred while the chromatin was in the stage of expansion.   In P2 infections, on the other hand, the axial filament of chromatin persisted up to lysis or, in the event of lysogenization, the chromatinic filament showed expansion and separation into discrete normal elements, starting from the poles of the growing elongating cells.   The first normal-appearing cells were nipped off from the terminal portion of the cell and division was not equatorial.

As an interesting comparison with the previous studies, Delaporte (1952) described the cytological changes in an induced colicinogenic strain of *E. coli*. Strain ML after ultraviolet induction was incubated at 37° C. and sampled at intervals. Intracellular colicin is detectable within 15 minutes, and appears in the medium after 75 minutes, increasing in amount until about 2 hours after irradiation. During this time the bacteria swell and gradually fill up with Feulgen positive chromatin which seems to have no definite arrangement in the cells. The lysis which liberates the colicin is accompanied by a gradual decrease in cell size and amount of chromatin per cell. However, it should be mentioned that Kellenberger and Kellenberger (1956) published an electron microscope study of lysates of colicinogenic strains (including ML). They were unable to identify a colicin particle, possibly because the size of these would be of the same order as the many granules liberated from normal bacteria. In any case, the colicins may not correspond in structure to the phages and there are not enough studies to allow a clear statement of cytological events.

3. Electron Microscope Observations

There is a very extensive literature dealing with electron microscope studies of phage-infected bacteria. The pertinent references have been listed by Beutner, Hartman, Mudd, and Hillier (1953). There are a number of defects which severely limit the value of much of this work. The ability to distinguish phage particles and other minute structures within the relatively large, whole bacteria is limited by electron scattering and by lack of contrast, and the situation is made worse by shadowing. It is unlikely that studies of whole bacteria by electron microscopy can be very rewarding; however, various means of circumventing the difficulty have been devised and these will be discussed. The techniques of studying biological materials with the electron microscope are still in embryonic state.

One approach is breaking open the bacteria at intervals during the latent period and studying the liberated material. The rapid decompression technique of Fraser (1951b) was used by Levinthal and Fisher (1952, 1953) (Chapter XI). Phage-infected bacteria are unusually fragile and may be easily ruptured (Levinthal and Visconti, 1953). This undoubtedly accounts for the claim by Wyckoff (1949a) that phage-infected bacteria lyse, in the sense of cell rupture, within 5 minutes after infection. Wyckoff concluded "that the membranes of young bacteria rupture soon after contact with phage which then proliferates in and at the expense of the bacterial protoplasm by a process that resembles the division shown by bacteria and other microorganisms." This conclusion is at variance with all other evidence about phage multiplication.

Useful information can be obtained from experiments with isolated host cell components, as was the case in Weidel's (1951) study of the effect of the T-even phages upon isolated cell membranes of *E. coli* B (see also Chapter XI). He showed that a local damage to the cell wall occurred after adsorption had taken place. The local loosening of the wall fabric was recognizable as visibly altered patches of the wall and, if a sufficient number of particles were adsorbed, could result in complete destruction. His description of the phases of destruction is very reminiscent of the previously noted descriptions of "lysis from without."

Another method for studying whole phage-infected bacteria in the electron microscope employs a high contrast lens system, which permits some differentiation of structure to be observed even in uninfected cells (Mudd, Hillier, Beutner, and Hartman, 1953). In cultures of *E. coli* typical cells have three opaque areas, at the two poles and in the center of the cell. These opaque, cytoplasmic regions are separated by areas of lesser density corresponding to the two nuclear bodies as seen in stained cells and to the "vacuoles" seen in sectioned bacteria by Birch-Andersen, Maaløe, and Sjostrand (1953). Some minutes after infection with phage T2, the less dense areas move to the margins of the cells, much as does the chromatin seen in stained preparations. For the first half of the latent period there is no evidence of any intracellular objects resembling mature phage. During the second half of the latent period there is a decrease in the opacity of the bacteria and they become markedly granular. Mature phage particles appear within the bacterial cell, more numerous as time goes on. Also one may see objects, slightly larger and less opaque than mature phage, which are probably homologous to the "doughnuts" described by Levinthal and Fisher (1952). At a still later time the infected bacteria are disrupted and exhibit a ruptured membrane, a dense pile of phage particles, and relatively little other bacterial substance. Prominent features of the cells throughout this course of events are large, opaque bodies, several hundred $m\mu$ in diameter, which are referred to by the authors as bacterial mitochondria. The properties of these large granules were reported by Hartman, Mudd, Hillier, and Beutner (1953). When triphenyltetrazolium chloride was added to a growing culture of *E. coli*, it was reduced to formazan which stained these granules red. They remained stainable and unchanged in location or size throughout the period of phage multiplication, even while the bacterial nuclei were disintegrating and the bacterial cells were filling up with phage particles. Quantitative studies indicated that the tetrazolium-reducing activity of an infected bacterial culture remained constant throughout the latent period and only decreased when lysis began. Even after the bacterial cells had lysed, the red-stained granules were readily visible in the microscope. These granules are, according to these workers, functionally analogous to mitochondria in the cells of higher organisms, and much circumstantial evidence suggests that they play an essential role in phage multiplication.

A technique likely to have extensive and useful application in the future is the sectioning of fixed bacteria embedded in methacrylate (Birch-Andersen, Maaløe and Sjöstrand, 1953; Kellenberger, Ryter, and Schwab, 1956). Preliminary results with T4 and *E. coli* B indicate that this may become a powerful tool for following the course of intracellular events in infected bacteria (Maaløe, Birch-Andersen, and Sjöstrand, 1954). Log phase cells of *E. coli* contain two or more large vacuoles, each

vacuole in turn containing a dense central object which is interpreted to be a coil of tightly wound threads.   The vacuoles occupy positions in the cell corresponding to the nuclear bodies
seen in stained cells.   Cells fixed 4 to 8 minutes after infection
showed considerable rearrangement.   The nuclear areas, in
particular, were replaced by similar foci (containing elongated
dark bodies) at the periphery of the cells.   The uncertainties of
fixation and damage during polymerization of the embedding
plastic must be considered as major difficulties to be solved before really useful preparations and interpretations can be expected (see Maaløe and Birch-Andersen, 1956).

A defect in the interpretation of much of the work with the
electron microscope is the tendency of the technologist to arrange
his photographs in what seems to him to be a logical sequence.
Even when samples for examination are taken serially during the
latent period, it may be impossible to arrange them in true tem-
poral order.   This is in part due to difficulties in starting and
stopping the infectious process simultaneously in all cells and in
part because, even when trouble is taken to synchronize phage
development in the population of infected bacteria, the developmental process soon gets out of phase in the individual cells
(Benzer, 1952).   However, probably none of the difficulties is
insuperable, and current technical developments lead one to
hope that micrographic work will contribute greatly toward an
understanding of viral growth.

4. Summary

Phage multiplication is accompanied by major changes in the
cytology of the host bacteria.   Bacterial multiplication stops, in
some cases immediately after phage adsorption but in other systems only after one or two cell divisions.   In most systems there
is an enlargement of the bacterial cells during the latent period.
The release of phage which terminates the latent period is usually
accompanied by an abrupt disintegration of the cells.   In a few
cases where the bacterial cell walls seem to be unusually sturdy,
lysis involves a slow collapse of the cell with leakage of the cyto-

plasm through a hole in the wall. Phage multiplication invariably involves marked changes in the appearance of the bacterial nucleus and, usually, a marked decrease in the stainability of the cytoplasm; however, the sequence of changes varies greatly from one phage to another. The cytological changes observed are characteristic of the phage rather than of the host cell, are under genetic control, and are of taxonomic significance because phylogenetically related phages produce similar cytological patterns.

A careful comparison of the appearance of living cells by dark field or phase contrast microscopy with the appearance of fixed and dried cells by electron microscopy or in stained preparations suggests that the procedures of fixing and drying are likely to result in the production of artefacts. This places limitations on the interpretation of some of the cytological evidence that have not always been evident to workers in this field. Any interpretation should take into consideration the large amount of information about the mechanisms of phage multiplication which has been obtained by other means.

Up to the present the nuclear staining techniques have been the most productive of new information about the response of the host cell to invasion by bacteriophage. However, it is probable that recent improvements in electron microscope technology will permit studies of the phage-infected bacterium at an order of resolution approaching that of biochemical techniques.

As is true of most recent phage research, a tremendous amount of effort has been devoted to the cytological examination of a very few phage strains. It would be desirable to apply the techniques now available to a broader range of phages and host strains and conditions.

CHAPTER XIII

ISOTOPIC STUDIES ON THE FATE OF THE INFECTING PHAGE PARTICLES

The first use of the expression, "fate of the infecting virus particle," occurs in the title of a paper by Putnam and Kozloff (1950). The expression is usually understood in the sense of the fate of the chemical constituents of which the infecting virus particle is composed. However it could with equal justification be used to mean the fate of the genetic factors with which the infecting virus particle is endowed. In the present chapter we will be concerned primarily with the fate of the material substance.

The principal experimental approach to this problem calls for the use of isotopes, because it is only by the use of such specific labels that one is able to distinguish phage material from host material. By using appropriate differential labels it is possible to trace phage protein and phage nucleic acid during the infectious process. The bacteriophage particles are labeled by growing the host bacteria in a nutrient medium containing the appropriate labeled ingredient, infecting with phage, and permitting lysis to take place in the labeled medium. The phage is then isolated and purified by differential centrifugation until the isotope content becomes constant. Putnam and Kozloff (1950) found no evidence that extracellular phage can exchange isotope labeled compounds with the environment. This is in agreement with the generally accepted principle that bacteriophages have no metabolic activity of their own. The isotope composition of a labeled phage preparation which has been properly purified remains constant until infection, except for changes due to radioactive decay.

1. Morphological, Functional, and Chemical Differentiation of the Phage Particle

A most important discovery relative to the fate of the infecting phage particle was reported by Hershey and Chase (1952) and further elaborated by Hershey (1955). These experiments have been described in detail in Chapter XI. The essential features together with other relevant details will be briefly summarized here. Most of the information has been obtained with the T2 serological group and with T5, and it may be unwise to extrapolate at present to other kinds of phage.

a. Chemical Composition

Phage T2 consists almost exclusively of protein and deoxy-pentose nucleic acid (DNA). Few attempts have been made as yet to fractionate the proteins of phage but serological evidence suggests that at least two different proteins are present, one in the phage head and a second in the phage tail. The protein contains a considerable amount of methionine and so can be conveniently labeled with S^{35}. The DNA may be labeled with P^{32} and both protein and DNA can be labeled with C and N isotopes.

b. Physical Fractionation — Osmotic Shock

Phage T2 consists of a protein membrane and a DNA core. By means of osmotic shock followed by high speed centrifugation it is possible to separate the sedimentable membranes from the DNA in the supernatant fluid. Not more than 5 per cent of the total phage protein remains with the DNA fraction. Even this protein has the same amino acid composition as the sediment. About 3 per cent of the total sulfur-containing protein of the phage may enter the host cell with the phage DNA. The function of this protein is not known. This does not leave much room for a hypothetical, sulfur-free, basic protein which might be in intimate association with the liberated DNA. If such a protein exists it must amount to less than 5 per cent by weight of the phage DNA (Hershey, 1953c). Therefore phage T2 must consist almost exclusively of a sulfur-containing protein membrane and a DNA core, which can be separated from each other by osmotic shock. The membrane is undamaged by this procedure as far as can be observed in the electron microscope and retains important physiological properties (Chapter V).

c. Physiological Fractionation — the Blendor Experiment

Phage T2, differentially labeled with S^{35} and P^{32}, is adsorbed to the host cells in a salt medium which insures a high efficiency of attachment. The infected bacteria are freed of unadsorbed isotopic material by centrifugation and resuspension in an appropriate diluent. The infected bacteria are now vigorously agitated in a Waring Blendor, centrifuged, and both bacteria and supernatant fluid assayed for S^{35} and P^{32}. The stirring in the Blendor has essentially no effect on the plaque-forming potential of the infected bacteria. After this treatment about 80 per cent of the phage S^{35} is found in the supernatant in the form of protein which is sedimentable after two hours at $12,000 \times g$ and is precipitable by anti-T2 serum. From 20 to 35 per cent of the phage P^{32} is left in the supernatant, the rest being sedimented with the bacteria. This means that 80 per cent of the phage protein can be separated from 65 to 80 per cent of the phage DNA phosphorus by the physiological procedure of infection of the host cells. The Blendor serves to tear the phage membranes loose from the bacterial surface, but the separation of phage DNA from phage protein has already occurred as a stage of infection.

d. Functional Differentiation of Phage Protein and Phage DNA

These experiments demonstrate that at least 80 per cent of the sulfur-containing proteins of the phage remain on the surface of the infected bacteria, from which they can be detached by agitation in the Blendor. Because this treatment has no effect on the course of the infection, it may be concluded that the bulk of the phage protein is expendable after infection and plays no role in the intracellular multiplication of phage. Similar conclusions were reached in the case of T5-infected bacteria by Y. T. Lanni (1954) who found that the complement-fixing antigens of the infecting phage could be removed from the bacterial surface by treatment in the Blendor.

Conversely 65 to 80 per cent of phage P^{32} is not removable by treatment in the Blendor, presumably because the phage DNA has penetrated into the interior of the bacterial cell where it is involved in intracellular phage multiplication. The general conclusion from these experiments is that following adsorption the protein membrane of the phage serves as a syringe to "inject" the phage DNA into the host bacterium.

It may be assumed, but it has not yet been proved conclusively, that nucleic acid is the sole agent of genetic continuity during multiplication of the phage (Hershey, 1956a) and that the phage protein, after injection of the DNA has been completed, plays no further role in phage replication. If these assumptions are correct it greatly simplifies the problem of the fate of the infecting phage particle. The phage protein after infection is discarded, and so the fate of the phage DNA is all that remains to be considered. Remembering that these are tentative assumptions rather than proved conclusions we can see what other evidence can be brought to bear on this problem.

2. The Breakdown of the Infecting Virus Particle

We have seen that the infection of the host cell results in a physiological fractionation of the phage particle into an external protein portion and an internal nucleic acid portion. We may now consider whether these two major segments remain intact during infection, or whether there is a chemical degradation of either portion into smaller fragments. The evidence in the case of the phage protein seems to be more clear cut and will be presented first.

a. Absence of Breakdown of Phage Proteins

In the experiments of Hershey and Chase (1952) with S^{35}-labeled phage T2, about 80 per cent of the phage methionine could be liberated from the infected bacteria by violent agitation, together with about 80 per cent of the carbon of other amino acids (Hershey, 1955). All of the liberated S^{35} is sedimentable at high speed and specifically precipitable by antiphage serum, which indicates that the fragments must be more or less intact phage membranes. Examination of the liberated phage membranes in the electron microscope shows them to have damaged tails, suggesting that part of the missing 20 per cent of phage S^{35} may consist of phage tail tips which remain fixed to the bacterial surface when the remainder of the phage is torn away in the Blendor. Much of the residual S^{35} remains attached to the bacterial debris after bacterial lysis and when the final phage lysate is analyzed only about 2 per cent of the initial phage S^{35} is found in the supernatant after centrifugation at 12,000 $\times$ g for 30 minutes (Hershey and Chase, 1952). These experiments indicate that essentially none of the proteins of the infecting T2 phage are converted into low molecular weight fragments during the infectious process. This is in agreement with the basic assumption that once the injection of phage DNA into the host cell has been completed, the phage protein plays no further role in the infectious process, but remains physiologically inert, outside of the bacterial cell wall.

Experiments by French (1954) are in essential agreement with these conclusions. French prepared stocks of phage T2 which were labeled with 2-C^{14} lysine. He was able to demonstrate by fractionation procedures that in the purified phage more than 90 per cent of the C^{14} label was in the lysine of the phage protein. This labeled phage was then used to infect host bacteria at a multiplicity of 10 and after lysis the lysate was fractionated by centrifugation and the distribution of the C^{14} label was determined. The bacterial debris, sedimented at 5000 $\times$ g, contained 83 per cent of the C^{14}, and the high speed supernatant contained 11 per cent. Unfortunately this nonsedimentable material was not further investigated so it is not known whether it consisted of phage protein or of smaller breakdown products. Only 1.2 per cent of the label was found in the final yield of purified phage. One may conclude from these experiments that there is little or no degradation of the protein of infecting phage particles during the infectious process.

In contrast to these conclusions are those of Kozloff (1952a,b) which are based on experiments with N^{15}-labeled T2 phage. Kozloff concluded that "up to 80 per cent of the parent virus DNA and protein was extensively broken down to a variety of small fragments during virus reproduction." Actually these papers give no experimental evidence that the virus *protein* was broken down.

b. Breakdown of Phage Nucleic Acid Following Superinfection

The work of Hershey and Chase (1952) demonstrated that shortly after phage adsorption the bulk of the phage nucleic acid enters the bacterial cell. There seems to be general agreement that some of this nucleic acid is broken down to very small fragments during intracellular phage growth. The first indication of the extent of this degradation is in a paper of Putnam and Kozloff (1950). Purified labeled T6 phage was used to infect bacteria at a multiplicity of 3, and after bacterial lysis the lysate was fractionated to determine the distribution of the P^{32} label. About 10 per cent of the P^{32} was found in the bacterial debris, 40 per cent in the purified phage progeny, and 50 per cent failed to sediment at $20,000 \times g$ for 2 hours. In another experiment in which the lysate was fractionated by means of a Sharples supercentrifuge 57 per cent of the P^{32} was found in the effluent. On further fractionation of the effluent, 26 per cent of the initial phage P^{32} was recovered in acid-soluble form. Of this about half, or 13 per cent of the initial phage P^{32}, was inorganic phosphate. Essentially the same distribution of P^{32} was found whether the multiplicity of infection with labeled phage was 1 or 3.

The next important development was the investigation of the kinetics of release from infected bacteria of trichloroacetic acid–soluble phosphorus derived from the infecting phage. This work led to the discovery that a considerable part of the P^{32} of phage T2 may be liberated within a few minutes of the time of adsorption, and that the amount liberated depended on the multiplicity and timing of the infection (Lesley, French, and Graham, 1950). This phenomenon, which is called "superinfection breakdown," has been studied further with results summarized by Graham (1953). The essential features of the phenomenon may be summarized as follows.

1. At a multiplicity of 0.2 $T2r^+$ phage particles per bacterium, about 5 per cent of the phage P^{32} is liberated within 10 minutes of adsorption. No more P^{32} is liberated until bacterial lysis when readsorption of the first phage liberated occuis. During the ensuing period of lysis inhibition about 20 per cent more of the phage P^{32} is liberated.

2. At multiplicities of 3 to 10, about 15 per cent of the P^{32} is liberated in the first 10 minutes, followed by a slow liberation of P^{32} starting at 30 minutes.

3. If bacteria are infected with unlabeled phage, followed 5 minutes later by labeled phage, about 50 per cent of the P^{32} of the superinfecting phage is liberated within the next 10 minutes. This phenomenon of *superinfection breakdown* is in part responsible for the small amount of P^{32} released after primary infection at low multiplicity.

4. If the time interval between primary infection and superinfection is varied, it is found that the amount of P^{32} liberated is 30 per cent after a 1 minute interval and nearly maximal after a 2 minute interval. The physiological condition responsible for superinfection breakdown is established within 2 minutes after primary infection.

5. Primary infection with one phage particle per cell is enough to establish the conditions for superinfection breakdown and increasing the multiplicity to 10 has no further effect.

6. The multiplicity of the superinfecting phage is also without effect.

7. The phenomenon can be demonstrated repeatedly with the same batch of infected bacteria under conditions of lysis inhibition. Superinfection with a multiplicity of 3 labeled phage at 5 minutes, 23 minutes, and 43 minutes after primary infection re-

sulted in liberation of 56 per cent, 53 per cent, and 74 per cent, respectively, of the added P^{32}.

8. Superinfection breakdown of $T2r^+$ phage occurs after primary infection with T2, T4, and T6 phage, r or r^+, and with T5 but does not occur after primary infection with T1, T3, or T7. Superinfection with r phages follows the same pattern as with r^+ phages but the amount of breakdown is less (30 per cent). Primary infection with T3 followed by superinfection with $T2r^+$, followed still later by superinfection with labeled $T2r^+$ does not lead to superinfection breakdown. Primary infection with T2 or T7 does not result in breakdown of superinfecting T7.

9. Superinfection breakdown does not occur in heat-killed bacteria but does occur in bacteria killed by ultraviolet light. Superinfection breakdown is prevented if cyanide is added to the bacteria before the primary infection, but is not prevented if cyanide is added 5 minutes after primary infection and before superinfection. One may recall that in cyanide-poisoned bacteria the development of phage T2 is arrested at an early stage (Benzer and Jacob, 1953). Streptomycin added either before or after primary infection prevents superinfection breakdown, even in streptomycin-resistant bacteria in which phage development is normal. Deoxyribonuclease isolated from *E. coli* is inhibited by streptomycin.

10. Heat-killed phage T2 is inactive both in primary infection and superinfection, whereas ultraviolet-inactivated T2 performs either role in superinfection breakdown.

11. In all experiments recorded above the bacteria were grown in tryptose broth. Kozloff (1952a) records a personal communication from Graham that superinfection breakdown does not occur with bacteria which have been grown in ammonium lactate medium. It likewise does not occur when magnesium is deficient. Hershey, Garen, Fraser, and Hudis (1954) report that reduction of the magnesium level in their cultures to 10^{-5} M blocks superinfection breakdown, presumably by inhibiting bacterial deoxyribonuclease. They also state that the limitation of breakdown at about 50 per cent is due to incomplete injection by superinfecting phage.

As discussed in Chapter XVII, superinfection breakdown is probably related to but does not cause genetic exclusion of superinfecting phage. Similarly, it seems clear that superinfection breakdown results from the action of bacterial deoxyribonuclease, but it is not likely that it depends simply on the activation of this enzyme after infection, because T3 activates enzyme but does not activate the breakdown mechanism.

Pardee and Williams (1952, 1953) found that the activity of bacterial deoxyribonuclease increases after infection with T2 and T3. Kozloff (1953) showed that the effect is due to the destruction of a specific inhibitor of the enzyme, probably part of the bacterial ribonucleic acid.

The role of the enzyme in superinfection breakdown is indicated by the fact that streptomycin and low magnesium concentrations interfere with breakdown and with the action of the enzyme (Graham, 1953).

Superinfecting phage is treated differently from the primary infecting phage in three ways. The superinfecting phage, only, is subject to a powerful genetic exclusion, to partial interference with injection, and to complete breakdown of the injected DNA. Inhibition of deoxyribonuclease prevents breakdown but does not affect exclusion or injection. The exclusion may mean that injection is not only incomplete but also abnormal in other, unknown, ways. The fact that the breakdown products do not remain in the cells also suggests this conclusion. If so breakdown, though requiring active deoxyribonuclease, probably depends primarily on the hypothetical, abnormal kind of injection. In any case the breakdown as such does not influence the outcome of the infection in any discernible way (Graham, 1953; Hershey, Garen, Fraser, and Hudis, 1954).

Also following primary infection, a small amount of the phage DNA, not exceeding 5 per cent under optimal conditions, is broken down to low molecular weight material by the intrabacterial deoxyribonuclease. This may reflect some side reaction to which only a few of the phage particles are subject, rather than a necessary consequence of the infectious process itself. Further investigation might show that the breakdown of both primary and secondary infecting phage is the result of a similar failure at some early step in the infectious process, differing only with respect to the proportion of particles involved.   In general, some particles are excluded from participation in viral growth by failure to inject, and some by subsequent unspecified failures, under all conditions (Chapter XVII).   Genetic exclusion of superinfecting phage is thus the consequence of two distinct but probably related kinds of physical exclusion, one measurable by the Blendor experiment, the other by the breakdown effect.   Both may be regarded as consequences of a pathological exaggeration of a normally inefficient excluding mechanism.

3. Material Transfer from Infecting Phage to Progeny

An interesting aspect of the fate of the infecting phage particle is the transfer of its chemical substance to the phage progeny. One may propose such questions as: Does the DNA of the infecting phage particle or a major portion of it appear as a unit in the phage progeny? Is the entire phage particle expendable once it has served its function as a pattern for the synthesis of new phage? Answers to these questions have been sought by the use of isotopic labels with a detailed analysis of the distribution of the isotope in the various fractions of the lysate.   The most interesting information has been derived from experiments in which the infecting phage has been labeled with different isotopes so that differential transfer of the various parts of the infecting phage can be detected.   This type of experiment has already yielded much information which in relation to genetic experiments has suggested mechanisms of phage replication.

a. Lack of Transfer of Phage Protein to Progeny

As discussed previously, the protein membranes of the infecting phage particles do not participate in the intracellular replication of phage.   Once penetration of the phage nucleic acid into the host cell is accomplished, the membranes can be detached from the infected bacteria by vigorous shaking without affecting phage development. These facts in themselves imply that little or no transfer of phage protein from parent to progeny should be expected. However, prior to this discovery there were several papers which indicated that phage protein was indeed transferred to progeny. It is worth while to discuss these experiments briefly as an indication of the type of technical error which can result in false conclusions. In a brief report Hershey, Roesel, Chase, and Forman (1951) stated that about 35 per cent of the sulfur of infecting T2 phage was found in the phage progeny, and that when this phage progeny was used in a second cycle of infection, 40 per cent of its sulfur was found in the second cycle progeny. Since only the phage protein is labeled in sulfur, these experiments were interpreted as transfer of parental protein to progeny. The transfer of about 18 per cent of parental T6 phage N^{15} to progeny was reported by Kozloff (1952b). The apparent transfer of protein N was not equal to the transfer of nucleic acid N, and the ratio of the two was not constant from one experiment to another, varying from 0.4 to 0.9. Kozloff (1952c) concluded that nucleoprotein was not transferred from parent to progeny as a unit, but that there was extensive rearrangement of the contributed parental material which suggested the use of breakdown products of the infecting virus for synthesis of protein and DNA of the progeny virus.

The earlier reports of the transfer of parental protein to progeny were demonstrated by Hershey and Chase (1952) to be the result of unsuspected contamination of progeny phage with protein remnants of the infecting phage. If, after infection with sulfur-labeled phage, the bacteria were agitated in the Waring Blendor, centrifuged to eliminate the dislodged membranes, and then permitted to lyse in a fresh medium, the isolated phage progeny was found to contain only one per cent of parental sulfur. Therefore there is no obligatory transfer of sulfur-containing proteins from parent to offspring. Under the usual conditions of multiple infection there is a considerable spontaneous elution of phage membranes which cannot be distinguished from or separated from the phage progeny and which therefore simulate a material transfer from parent to progeny. The treatment of the infected bacteria in the Waring Blendor followed by centrifugation seems to be a useful way of preventing this contamination. These conclusions were confirmed by Kozloff (1953) and by French (1954).

Experiments by Volkin (1954a) suggested that phage T4 contains about 30 per cent of its total protein content in the form of a nucleoprotein. Hershey (1955) failed to confirm this in careful studies of phage T2 labeled with either S^{35} or C^{14}. He did find evidence for a "nonsedimentable" protein fraction in osmotically shocked T2 preparations, amounting to about 3 per cent of the total protein. This nonsedimentable protein was chemically similar to phage ghosts but serologically distinct and apparently was injected into the host cell along with the phage DNA. There was no evidence that this protein contributed materials to the phage progeny.

b. Transfer of Phage Nucleic Acid to Progeny

In marked contrast to the situation with phage protein, there is conclusive evidence that substances from the infecting phage contribute to the nucleic acid of phage progeny. In experiments of Hershey and Chase (1952) with P^{32}-labeled phage T2 there was a transfer of 30 per cent of the parental phosphorus to the progeny phage after treatment of the infected bacteria in the Blendor. Therefore this cannot be due to residual DNA in contaminating phage membranes. The results of a number of other transfer experiments are recorded in Table XIV. The transfer of parental nucleic acid substance to progeny varies from 15 to 60 per cent in different experiments, the efficiency of transfer depending largely on experimental conditions. The percentage transfer is of the same order of magnitude for T2, T3, T4, T6, and T7; for P^{32}, for DNA-N^{15}, and for C^{14}-purines and pyrimidines. Much of this work has been briefly summarized by Kozloff (1953), and more recent work by Hershey and

Burgi (1956). Some of the factors which affect the efficiency of transfer will now be considered.

TABLE XIV

Transfer of DNA from Parent to Progeny Phage

Phage	Isotopic marker	Per cent transfer	Reference
T6	P^{32}	22–42	Putnam and Kozloff (1950)
T2	P^{32}	15–25	Lesley, French, Graham, and van Rooyen (1951)
T2	P^{32}	20–40	Maaløe and Watson (1951)
T2	P^{32}	35	French, Graham, Lesley, and van Rooyen (1952)
T6	P^{32}	44	Kozloff (1952b)
T6	N^{15}	27	Kozloff (1952b)
T2	P^{32}	30	Hershey and Chase (1952)
T7	P^{32}	20–30	Mackal and Kozloff (1954)
T3	P^{32}	38–46	Watson and Maaløe (1953)
T4	P^{32}	40–50	Watson and Maaløe (1953)
T2	C^{14}-purine	48–55	Watson and Maaløe (1953)
T3	C^{14}-purine	32–38	Watson and Maaløe (1953)
T4	C^{14}-purine	40–44	Watson and Maaløe (1953)
T2	P^{32}	40–45	Hershey (1953a)
T2	P^{32}	28	French (1954)

1. Superinfection breakdown. In view of the phenomenon of superinfection breakdown described above, one might anticipate that transfer of P^{32} from superinfecting phage to progeny would fail. This point was checked by French, Graham, Lesley, and van Rooyen (1952) who infected bacteria with unlabeled T2 phage and then superinfected with P^{32}-labeled T2 phage after various time intervals. The transfer of P^{32} decreased from 30 per cent for simultaneous infection to 18 per cent after one minute, 7 per cent after 2 minutes, and 2 per cent after 5 minutes. This experiment indicates quite clearly that superinfection breakdown will decrease the efficiency of transfer under conditions of multiple infection unless the adsorption period is made very short. These experiments were independently confirmed with P^{32}-labeled phage T4 by Watson and Maaløe (1953). This cause of reduced efficiency of transfer can be eliminated by making the adsorption period less than one minute.

2. *Readsorption of progeny phage.* If some of the labeled progeny phage is lost either by readsorption to yet unlysed bacteria or to bacterial debris, this fraction of the transferred label will be lost from the progeny. This will cause an apparent decrease in the efficiency of transfer of parental materials to progeny phage. This loss of daughter phage was prevented in the experiments of Watson and Maaløe (1953) by treating the infected bacteria with antibacterial serum toward the end of the latent period. Antibacterial serum effectively prevents adsorption of phage to otherwise susceptible bacteria (Delbrück, 1945b). In earlier studies Maaløe and Watson (1951) prevented loss of progeny T2 phage by saturating the bacterial receptors with ultraviolet-killed, unlabeled T2 phage. These or similar devices have been used in most subsequent experiments.

3. *Latent period and burst size.* In infections with P^{32}-labeled T4r phage, lysis occurs at the end of the usual latent period with a burst size of about 140 and a transfer of P^{32} to progeny of 40 to 50 per cent (Watson and Maaløe, 1953). About half of the parental P^{32} is liberated into the medium in a nonsedimentable form. A natural question is whether or not some of this wasted P^{32} would be converted into mature phage if the infectious process had not been interrupted by lysis. To answer this question Watson and Maaløe (1953) infected bacteria with labeled T4r$^+$ and then produced lysis inhibition by reinfection with unlabeled phage. Although the burst size was increased to 350 the transfer of parental P^{32} was still only 50 per cent indicating that essentially no parental P^{32} was transferred to phage particles formed after the end of the normal latent period.

The converse experiment, shortening the latent period by premature lysis, has been done several times. Maaløe and Watson (1951) using P^{32}-labeled T2r$^+$ for infection, lysed the infected culture prematurely at 11 minutes, before there was one mature phage per cell. With an excess of ultraviolet-inactivated T2

phage as a carrier, the lysate was fractionated in the usual way
and only 1.6 per cent of the parental P^{32} was found in the phage
fraction. In a second sample lysed at 34 minutes, the burst size

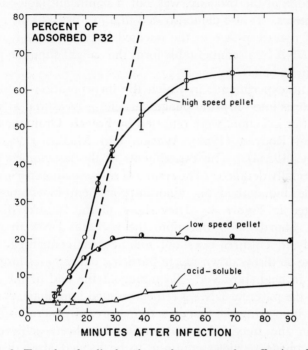

Figure 8. Transfer of radiophosphorus from parental to offspring phage T2.
The curves show distributions of P^{32} measured by centrifugal fractionation of
lysates prepared at different times after infection with 3 labeled phage particles
per bacterium. The vertical lines span the observed range of variation in
three independent experiments. Acid-soluble P^{32} is measured from separate
aliquots of unlysed culture. P^{32} not accounted for is DNA nonsedimentable
after lysis. The dashed line shows infective phage particles per bacterium
released during lysis. These are distributed, independently of time of lysis,
in the ratio 14 : 86 between low and high speed pellets, and account for the
rise in both fractions after 10 minutes. The observed efficiency of transfer
is therefore about $60/0.86 = 70\%$. The rise in acid-soluble P^{32} is probably
the combined result of superinfection breakdown of readsorbed offspring
particles and enzymatic destruction of phage-precursor DNA, both occurring
after lysis of some bacteria at about 25 minutes. Experiments by A. D. Hershey, unpublished.

was 248 and the P³² transfer was 29 per cent. This experiment served two purposes: it demonstrated that contamination of the progeny with parental P³², as contrasted with incorporation of the isotope in the progeny, was not a significant factor in such experiments. It also demonstrated that just prior to the appearance of mature phage in the infected bacteria there is no precursor DNA in a sedimentable form that might simulate mature phage in its behavior.

Kinetic experiments, in which the incorporation of parental phosphorus into offspring phage particles is measured at various times after infection, were reported by French, Graham, Lesley, and van Rooyen (1952), Watson and Maaløe (1953), and Hershey (1953a). The experiments of the last-named author are especially detailed. The results of subsequent experiments of the same kind, embodying minor improvements in technique, are illustrated in Figure 8. They show all the features discussed above. Shortly after infection, the parental DNA in prematurely lysed cultures does not sediment at centrifugal speeds sufficient to throw down phage particles. It remains largely insoluble in acid, however. Beginning at the end of the eclipse period, the parental DNA is reincorporated into phage particles, most of it entering the first ones to mature. By 50 minutes after infection the maximal incorporation has been achieved, although phage particles continue to be formed after this time. The observed transfer is about 70 per cent.

c. Material Transfer Without Genetic Transfer

In previous sections of this chapter we have considered the fate of the substance of the infecting phage particles when these were the direct ancestors of the final phage yield. We will now consider the available evidence with respect to transfer of substance from phage particles which are not the parents in a genetic sense of the final phage yield. These experiments call for mixed infection with two phages in which matters are arranged so that only one of them is capable of multiplying.

1. Material transfer between unrelated phage strains. The first experiment of this type was performed by Kozloff (1952b). Host bacteria were infected with unlabeled T7 at a multiplicity of 6 and after incubation for 3 minutes were infected with P^{32}-labeled T6 at a multiplicity of 1.5. The infected bacteria were centrifuged to remove unadsorbed phage and then permitted to lyse. The final yields of the phages were 4.4×10^9 T7 and 3.3×10^9 T6 per ml. The T6 and T7 phages were liberated from different bacteria because plating on mixed indicators gave no clear plaques, confirming the occurrence of mutual exclusion between this pair of phages. The phage yield was purified in the usual way by differential centrifugation and the T6 progeny were then removed by repeated absorption of the phage mixture with B/3,4,7. Of the original P^{32} present in the parent T6 phage, 37 per cent was found in the T6 progeny and 4.6 per cent in the T7 phage. This experiment suggests the transfer of P^{32} from T6 to T7 in mixedly infected cells, although the amount transferred is far less than in the homologous system. Unfortunately the incorporation of the P^{32} into the T7 phage was not further checked by determining the distribution of the isotope after adsorption of the T7 phage to B/6, for instance, or after precipitation with anti-T7 serum, so that the transfer cannot be accepted as proved by these experiments.

In experiments by French, Graham, Lesley, and van Rooyen (1952) the transfer of P^{32} from T2 to T7 and to T1 was tested. The experimental conditions were such that T2 was almost completely excluded, the T2 yield being at the most 10 per cent of the total phage. The amount of P^{32} which was found in the isolated phage progeny varied from 3 to 6 per cent. However this represents maximum possible transfer values to heterologous phage rather than actual transfer values, because in these experiments neither parental labeled T2 phage which failed to absorb, nor progeny T2 phage which should be relatively rich in P^{32} label, were removed from the phage yield. Therefore these experiments do not demonstrate actual heterologous transfer of phage materials, as was realized by the authors who concluded "that little of the phosphorus of T2 phage is incorporated into T1 or T7 progeny."

A definitive experiment involving heterologous transfer of phage label was reported by Watson and Maaløe (1953). Bacteria were mixedly infected with 5 particles of unlabeled T4r and 1 particle of P^{32}-labeled T3 per bacterium. Under conditions of simultaneous infection with this pair of phages, T3 is excluded from multiplication in essentially all bacteria. In one such experiment 24 per cent of the P^{32} label was in the bacterial debris, 49 per cent was not sedimentable, and 27 per cent was in the purified phage yield. Of the P^{32} in the phage yield only 4 per cent was precipitated by anti-T3 serum, whereas 92 per cent was precipitated by anti-T4 serum. The authors concluded that about 25 per cent of the P^{32} label of the excluded T3 phage was incorporated into the yield of T4. This experiment seems to demonstrate quite conclusively that material transfer can take place between unrelated phages in the absence of genetic transfer and under conditions in which the donor phage does not multiply. The reasonable assumption is that the excluded donor phage was extensively degraded inside the host cell and part of its chemical substance used as raw material for multiplication of the dominant phage. In different experiments, $^{1}/_{2}$ to $^{2}/_{3}$ of the P^{32} of the excluded phage was liberated on host cell lysis in a form not sedimentable at 12,000 $\times$ g, further evidence that extensive degradation of the excluded phage occurs.

2. *Material transfer from inactivated phages.* In the experiments of Kozloff (1952b), N^{15}-labeled T6 was inactivated with various doses of ultraviolet light or X-rays, mixed with unlabeled active T6, and the mixture used to infect bacteria. The T6 progeny was isolated and the amount of label incorporated into progeny nucleic acid and protein determined. Between 5 and 18 per cent of the parental N^{15} was found in the nucleic acid of the phage yield and Kozloff concluded that transfer had occurred. This interpretation, however, is weakened by the parallel finding that from 4 to 15 per cent of the parental N^{15} was found in progeny protein. This is evidence for contamination of progeny

phage with the protein membranes of parental phage as discussed previously and raises the possibility of a similar contamination with parental phage nucleic acid.

Similar experimental findings were reported by French, Graham, Lesley, and van Rooyen (1952) and by Watson and Maaløe (1953) but their results are likewise ambiguous due to the possibility of contamination of progeny particles with damaged parental phage. This danger is well illustrated by the following experiment of Hershey, Garen, Fraser, and Hudis (1954). T2 was suspended in a 2 per cent peptone solution containing P^{32}. When the radiation damage had reduced infectivity to about one per cent of the initial value, the inactivated phage was tested in a Blendor experiment. The damaged phage adsorbed normally but injected less than 20 per cent of its DNA. A mixed infection was made with P^{32}-labeled, β-ray-inactivated phage and unlabeled active phage. The progeny were then examined as in Kozloff's experiment but it proved impossible to interpret the results. A large proportion of the inactivated phage do not inject and at the time of cellular lysis become detached from the bacterial cells. Apparently many particles killed by ionizing radiation not only fail to inject but also make a weak attachment to bacteria.

Ultraviolet radiation has less effect upon injection and here it may be possible to follow the fate of the injected damaged DNA. Hershey and Burgi (1956) studied this question. They repeated Kozloff's experiments in which bacteria are infected with ultraviolet-killed, P^{32}-labeled T2 and unirradiated, unlabeled T2. They confirmed Kozloff's conclusion that there is normal transfer of isotope from the irradiated particles to the issue of the mixed infection. However, by special techniques they could show that about half of the reincorporated P^{32} is in noninfective particles among the offspring. Apparently such particles are noninfective because of the radiation-damaged DNA they receive. If so, the results tend to support the idea of direct transfer of large pieces of DNA from parental to offspring particles—quite the contrary of conclusions suggested by the early experiments of this type.

d. Physical State of Parental Isotope during Transfer

The above experiments demonstrate that constituents of parental nucleic acid appear in progeny particles. They do not directly tell us, however, whether the transfer occurs by way of genetically specific macromolecules or whether the parental DNA is first degraded to low molecular weight nucleic acid precursors. Kozloff favored the latter route, largely because of his observations of transfer unconnected with genetic transfer. Hershey and Burgi's experiments cited above destroy the force of this argument. Another possible way of deciding between these alternatives is to examine the physical state of the parental isotope during various stages of the latent period. This was done by Watanabe, Stent, and Schachman (1954) who broke open infected bacteria by decompression and examined the sensitivity to deoxyribonuclease and sedimentation characteristics of the intracellular isotope. At all times over 50 per cent of the P^{32} was in high molecular weight form, either as fibrous DNA or as part of mature phage particles. In all their experiments some isotope was observed in low molecular weight material, partly owing to suboptimal conditions of viral growth. Their experiments (which had another purpose) thus failed to answer the question asked here. All observations of this type are compatible with breakdown of parental DNA if we allow for the possibility of very rapid resynthesis into genetically specific material.

Hershey, Garen, Fraser, and Hudis (1954) made several attempts to find evidence for possible short-lived intermediates. By growing infected bacteria in the presence of large amounts of nucleic acid precursors, they tried to influence the outcome of transfer experiments with C^{14}-labeled T2. Even though free bases and nucleosides compete efficiently with CO_2 and glucose as a source of viral DNA carbon, they are without effect on parent to progeny transfer when added to cultures infected with labeled phage. The same amount of parental C^{14} is transferred to the progeny irrespective of the amount of precursors added to the infected system. Not only is the total transfer of C^{14} the same, but also its distribution among the four nucleotides. Thus the intermediates must be nucleotides or larger fragments. Kozloff (1953) summarizes early experiments in which unequal transfer of parental phosphorus and DNA nitrogen was observed. This result is inconsistent with all other comparable observations, summarized by Hershey and Burgi (1956). Kozloff's results remain unexplained, but it should be pointed out that the transfer experiments he describes were performed under conditions rather unfavorable to phage growth and efficient transfer.

It must be concluded that there is no decisive evidence for or against the possibility that some of the transfer occurs by way of small, functionally unspecific, fragments of DNA.

e. Distribution of Parental Isotope among Progeny Particles

All the previous work has dealt with populations of virus particles multiplying within a very large number of bacteria. The measured efficiency of transfer is an average summed over very many individual infections. By themselves, the incomplete transfer values are compatible with the assumption that the DNA of the infecting phage remains intact during replication and with a certain probability becomes infective again and reappears among the progeny. This possibility, however, is ruled out by the P^{32}-suicide experiments of Hershey, Kamen, Kennedy, and Gest (1951). In their experiments phage containing P^{32}-labeled DNA loses infectivity upon radioactive decay (Chapter VI). Uniformly P^{32}-labeled bacteria growing in P^{32}-labeled medium were infected with nonradioactive parental T4 particles. Following lysis and the release of about 100 progeny particles per bacterium, the progeny were isolated and all proved to be subject to killing by radioactive decay. The failure to observe any stable progeny indicates that none of them contained the intact DNA from an unlabeled parental particle. It is clear that the phage DNA does not remain in one piece but is dispersed among progeny particles.

The DNA is not randomly dispersed among a large fraction of the progeny particles. This was first suggested by the transfer experiments already discussed which showed that most of the parental isotope is incorporated into the earlier formed progeny. More recently Stent and Jerne (1955) confirmed this point in some remarkable experiments employing the P^{32}-decay principle. In their experiments nonradioactive bacteria were infected with heavily P^{32}-labeled particles of phage T2, and a progeny of early formed particles secured. These particles proved to be stable insofar as repeated plaque-counts could determine, although they contained large amounts of P^{32}. Stent and Jerne realized that this must reflect an extreme concentration of P^{32} in very few particles, so few that their loss by suicide could not be detected by reductions in plaque count. To prove their inference, they performed the following experiment.

Unlabeled bacteria were infected with a highly radioactive *parental* generation of phage particles as before, to obtain a *first generation* of particles that was likewise radioactive, but contained only P^{32} derived from its parents. As a test of viability of the *labeled first generation* particles, they measured the transfer of P^{32} from particles of the first generation to those of a second. They found about 50 per cent transfer as expected. However, if a sample of the first generation progeny was tested again, a few days later, the efficiency of transfer to a second generation had markedly decreased. Thus the first generation progeny must contain much of its P^{32} concentrated in a few particles that are subject to radioactive decay. Other particles also contain P^{32}, but are not subject to decay at appreciable rate. Stent and Jerne concluded that part of the transfer of DNA from parental to offspring particles preserves large pieces of parental DNA among the offspring particles.

Levinthal (1956) developed an autoradiographic method for determining the amount of P^{32} in individual phage particles. This furnishes a powerful technique for investigating the distribution of transferred P^{32} among offspring phage particles. By it he shows that the phage DNA is indeed transmitted to offspring particles partly in the form of large pieces each containing about 20 per cent of the DNA from a single parental particle.

The possible implications of these and other experiments in progress make exciting reading and are discussed by Levinthal (1956), Hershey and Burgi (1956), and Delbrück and Stent (1957). The experimental results and interpretations are still too fluid, however, to discuss here in detail.

f. Efficiency of Transfer

As previously described, the efficiency of transfer of labeled parental DNA to offspring seldom exceeds 50 per cent even under the best attainable experimental conditions. This fact occasionally prompted speculation that the limited transfer signified something fundamental about replication of DNA. One such speculation was testable. Maaløe and Watson (1951) performed the first two-cycle transfer experiment, which had been suggested by S. S. Cohen. They found that the efficiency of transfer during first and second cycles of growth from P^{32}-labeled parents was the same. This result disposed of the possibility that phage particles contain two kinds of DNA, one transferable and one not. Hershey and Burgi (1956) present evidence that the incomplete transfer should be attributed to random losses that have nothing to do with the mechanism of transfer (Figure 8). Other developments support their contention to this extent: it now seems clear that an explanation of the low efficiency of transfer will not contribute much to an understanding of the mechanism of transfer.

The experiments of Levinthal (1956), Hershey and Burgi (1956), and Stent, Jerne, and Sato (1957) revive the idea that the DNA of T2 is composed of functionally distinct parts. The merits of this idea are still debatable. However, it is clear that such parts, if they exist, are transmitted from parents to progeny with similar efficiency and probably without interconversion.

4. Summary

Here we will summarize the contributions which the transfer experiments give to our knowledge of phage reproduction. Almost all these experiments have been done with the T series of coli phages, and most of them with T2 and its relatives. First of all the transfer experiments confirm the differentiation of the phage particle into a DNA core and a protein membrane. The components are structurally different and functionally distinct. Upon adsorption to a host cell, most of the protein membrane remains on the bacterial surface while most if not all the nucleic acid core penetrates to the interior of the bacterium. Accordingly little phage protein, unlike the injected DNA, is incorporated into progeny particles. The Blendor and transfer experiments thus establish the physical basis for the disappearance of the infective virus particle upon infection.

In contrast to the rather static role of phage protein, the nucleic acid is functionally and materially active. The Blendor experiment of Hershey and Chase suggested a primary genetic role for phage DNA and a major aim of present day transfer experiments is to establish a connection between genetic function and material behavior of DNA. Early experiments showed that approximately 50 per cent of the parental DNA reappeared within progeny particles but they left open the question whether the phage DNA remains intact during replication or whether it is dispersed and fragmented. After much early confusion and ambiguity this problem now seems capable of experimental resolution. The entire DNA content of the phage particle certainly does not remain intact during replication. This was shown by the initial P^{32}-suicide experiments. It was not apparent, however, whether this dispersal of DNA involved fragmentation of a single molecule, the distribution of several intact molecules among several progeny particles, or possibly both processes. This question can now be attacked by methods capable of analyzing the isotopic composition of single progeny particles. Independently, Levinthal and Stent and Jerne have achieved this objective, the former by the development of an elegant autoradiographic technique, the latter by subtle manipulation of the P^{32}-suicide experiment. Both agree that the parental isotope is not randomly distributed among progeny particles. Approximately half of it is transmitted as pieces containing perhaps 20 per cent each of the DNA in one particle, the remainder in considerably smaller pieces.

The transfer as large and small pieces without apparent interconversion suggests to Levinthal a functional division into two kinds of DNA which, however, must be transmitted with equal efficiency. The large pieces, at least, may have genetic function since they seem, in the experiments of Hershey and Burgi, to be transmitted in association with radiation damage and authentic genetic markers. At present, however, these ideas are rather precariously based on preliminary results that are by no means free of inconsistencies.

An unexpected finding of the transfer experiments is the phenomenon of superinfection breakdown. Shortly after infection with T2, the receptivity of the cell to virus is changed in several important ways. Superinfecting T2 injects only half its DNA, and this half is quickly broken down to low molecular weight material and excreted into the culture medium. If the cell is superinfected with some other phages no breakdown occurs, but the superinfecting phage particles are nevertheless excluded from participation in growth. It is clear that the cellular deoxyribonuclease brings about the breakdown of superinfecting T2, and that an intracellular inhibitor of this enzyme is partly destroyed shortly after infection. The fact remains, however, that the DNA of the primary infecting phage is subject to little or no breakdown at the time of infection, and remains immune afterwards. It must be protected either by a change in state, or by a favored location in the cell that the DNA of superinfecting phage fails to reach. The second alternative is perhaps favored since injection by superinfecting T2 is clearly abnormal, and may fail entirely for other phages whose DNA is not subject to breakdown. In any case it is clear that the breakdown by deoxyribonuclease is not the primary cause of genetic exclusion of superinfecting phages.

CHAPTER XIV

NUTRITIONAL AND METABOLIC REQUIREMENTS FOR PHAGE PRODUCTION

The nutritional requirements for phage production are considerably more complex than are, for instance, the requirements for bacterial multiplication. How complex they seem depends on our frame of reference and on the operational methods used. The nutritional requirements for phage reproduction will be quite different whether one considers the intracellular vegetative phage, the infected bacterium, or the mixture of free phage and uninfected bacteria to be the reproducing unit. In the latter case one has to consider requirements for adsorption as well as sources of food. If the infected bacterium is the unit under consideration, the nutritional requirements are in general the same as those of the host cell alone in the same environment because the infected cell is synthesizing chemically similar protoplasm using the same enzymes as are used by the uninfected cell. A few exceptions to this generalization will be noted below. If the intracellular phage particle is considered as the reproducing unit, the nutritional environment must include all the chemical elements, amino acids, and nucleotides that go to make up the particle because the phage particle is incompetent to synthesize these substances for itself. If one uses isotopic labels to determine the ultimate source of nutrients, further refinement is possible. One can, for instance, allocate the source of some of the phage phosphorus to the infecting phage particle, some to the bacterial host before infection, and some to the extracellular environment after infection. These various aspects of phage nutrition will be considered in what is hoped will be a logical fashion. Certain points of view with respect to phage nutrition have been presented in reviews by Cohen (1949, 1953b, 1956) and by Putnam (1952) and the topic has been briefly considered in a number of general reviews of phage work such as that by Benzer, Delbrück, Dulbecco, Hudson, Stent, Watson, Weidel, Weigle, and Wollman (1950) and one by Putnam (1953). The role of the enzymatic constitution of the host cell as a factor in the nutritional environment of the reproducing phage has been discussed by Cohen (1952) and by E. A. Evans, Jr. (1954).

1. Requirements for Adsorption and Penetration

The role of the ionic environment in phage adsorption has been discussed extensively in Chapter X and will be briefly summarized here. Adsorption of phage to host cell involves at least two separate steps, the first step being a reversible attachment of phage particle to host cell and the second step being irreversible. The second step involves liberation of phage DNA from the protein membrane and under appropriate conditions this DNA penetrates into the host cell interior. For a particular phage-host cell system there is an optimum salt concentration at which the rate of attachment is maximal. The optimum salt concentration for monovalent cations differs from that for divalent cations in instances where either is effective. The cationic environment also controls the rate of the second step and for some phages the cationic requirement is rather specific. A surprisingly large proportion of the phages which have been examined have a more or less specific requirement for calcium ion. In many cases this requirement is known to involve a step subsequent to adsorption and in the case of phage T5 the step is definitely penetration of the phage DNA into the host cell. In addition to the ionic requirements just mentioned, there is one case of a relatively specific requirement for an organic cofactor for adsorption, the tryptophan-requiring strains of phage T4 which have been discussed in Chapter X. It would be surprising if this were a unique case.

The very extensive literature dealing with the ionic environment required for adsorption or penetration would make pretty

TABLE XV

Salt Effects or Requirements

Phage	Comment	Reference
Megaterium 899	Calcium requirement	Wollman and Wollman (1936a)
Megaterium	Loss of calcium requirement	Wollman and Wollman (1938)
Megaterium 899	Calcium after adsorption	Clarke (1952)
Diphtheria, B and β	Calcium for adsorption	Barksdale and Pappenheimer (1954)
Pasteurella	Calcium requirement	Rifkind and Pickett (1954)
Streptococcus	Citrate inhibition	Cherry and Watson (1949)
Streptococcus	Calcium after adsorption	E. B. Collins, Nelson, and Parmelee (1950)
Streptococcus	Calcium required	Shew (1949)
Streptococcus	Calcium required	Reiter (1949)
Streptococcus	Calcium for penetration	Potter and Nelson (1953)
Streptomyces	Citrate inhibition	Perlman, Langlykke, and Rothberg (1951)
Staphylococcus	Citrate inhibition	Asheshov (1926)
Staphylococcus	Citrate inhibition	Burnet and Lush (1935)
Staphylococcus	Calcium after adsorption	Rountree (1955)
Staphylococcus	Ca or Mg for adsorption	Rountree (1951a)
Coli Lisbonne	Oxalate inhibition	Bordet and Renaux (1928)
Coli Lisbonne	Calcium for adsorption	Beumer and Beumer-Jochmans (1951)
Shiga phage	Citrate inhibition	Stassano and de Beaufort (1925)
Coli phage	Calcium after adsorption	Andrewes and Elford (1932)
Coli phages	Citrate inhibition	Burnet (1933e)
Coli phages	Calcium after adsorption	Wahl (1946a)
Coli phage S13	Calcium requirement and phosphate inhibition	Wahl and Blum-Emerique (1951, 1952b)
Typhoid phage	Calcium after adsorption	Kay and Fildes (1950)
Enterophages	Divalent cations required	Fildes, Kay, and Joklik (1953)
Staphylococcus	Salt effect	Scribner and Krueger (1937)
Coli phages	Salt effects	Gest (1943)
Various phages	Salt effects	Gratia (1940)
Various phages	Salt effects	Sertic (1937)

dull reading. Much of it consists of some such statement as "inhibited by 0.01 M citrate" with no attempt to study the mechanism by which citrate inhibits phage reproduction. Therefore much of this literature is summarized in Table XV. There are undoubtedly many additional references which have been overlooked, but the table does suggest how broad is the range of phage types that require calcium. For a discussion of the more fundamental papers dealing with mechanisms see Chapters X and XI.

2. Metabolic Requirements for Phage Multiplication

Phage multiplication involves the synthesis of about 100 copies of the infecting phage particle in a period of time commensurate with the generation time of the host cell. The total amount of new phage protoplasm synthesized in a single host cell, perhaps 10^{-13} gram, is considerably less than the weight of the host cell which is of the order of 10^{-12} gram, so the effort involved in producing the usual yield of phage is certainly no greater than that required for duplicating the host cell. The raw materials, the energy supply, and the anabolic enzymes required for phage synthesis should be well within the capabilities of the host cell insofar as phage protoplasm contains the same ingredients as the host cell. The only building block so far found in phages but not in the host cell is the hydroxymethylcytosine of the DNA of phages related to T2 (Wyatt and Cohen, 1953). With this single known exception, one might anticipate that the host cell would be able to furnish everything needed for phage multiplication except the unique patterns such as those which control the antigenic specificity of the phage proteins. These patterns are presumably furnished by the DNA of the invading phage particle. Despite this apparent simplicity of the problem of phage nutrition, a considerable amount of effort and ingenuity has been devoted to work which is directly or indirectly related to the requirements for phage multiplication. A question which has often been asked is, does the phage particle contain any enzymes, or is it entirely dependent on the metabolic activity of the host cell?

This question should be divided into two parts, one concerning the mature extracellular phage particle, the other involving the intracellular, vegetative phage. The answer may be quite different in the two cases.

a. Lack of Metabolic Enzymes in Mature Phage

As discussed previously in Chapters X and XI, it is quite possible that phage enzymes are involved in the release of phage nucleic acid from its protein shell, and in the penetration of phage DNA into the host cell. Yet even here there is no certain evidence for the existence of phage enzymes. Far less evidence is available for the participation of phage enzymes in the later stages of phage reproduction. The important work of Hershey and Chase (1952) demonstrated that, following adsorption of phage to the host cell, most of the phage protein remains on the host cell surface while the phage nucleic acid penetrates through the cell wall into the cell interior. Other experiments indicate that about 3 per cent of the total phage protein penetrates into the host cell (Hershey, 1955). The function of this protein is not known but it might be enzymatic. Prior to this work it was commonly assumed that phage infection involved the penetration of the entire phage particle into the host cell where it multiplied in the host cell juices like a miniature bacterium. It is undoubtedly this concept which induced various workers to search for oxidative and fermentative activities in phage preparations.

Much of the earlier work on possible metabolic activities of phage particles was reviewed by Bronfenbrenner (1928) who concluded that although there was no evidence for an independent metabolism of phage, the question was still open. Bronfenbrenner attempted to measure CO_2 production by phage in a microrespirometer using 10^{12} particles (about 1 mg.) of phage. Although the method was sensitive to 5 μl. of CO_2 he was unable to detect any CO_2 production by this relatively large amount of phage.

A very careful study of the respiratory and fermentative activities of a resting phage suspension was made by Schüler (1935)

using phage WLL of Schlesinger, which is related to T2. This
phage was concentrated and purified by high speed centrifugation and contained 2.3×10^{12} particles per mg. dry weight. Its
respiration was measured in the Warburg apparatus in various
nutrient media, including ammonium lactate-phosphate medium and glucose broth, both in the presence and absence
of heat-killed bacteria. With amounts of phage varying from
1 to 17 mg. per vessel the respiration was negligible. For instance, with 17 mg. of phage in glucose broth containing 30 mg.
of boiled *E. coli* cells the uptake of oxygen was 0.28 μl. per mg.
per hour, in contrast to about 100 for bacteria. Glucose fermentation, measured as displacement of CO_2 from a bicarbonate
buffer, was likewise negligible in comparison with the fermentative activities of *E. coli*.

In an attempt to study the respiration of multiplying phage,
Schüler measured the oxygen uptake of living host cells in lactate-phosphate medium in the presence of an excess of active or heat-killed phage. There was no detectable difference
in respiratory activity whether the phage was active or dead.
Schüler also tested 1 mg. amounts of active phage for the presence of the following types of enzymic activity, trypsin, papain,
lipase, amylase, maltase, nucleosidase, catalase, urease, arginase,
and phosphatase. In tests lasting 24 hours, all results were
negative except for phosphatase. The phage preparations were
very active in splitting hexosediphosphate and also in hydrolyzing
hexosemonophosphate, glycerophosphate, and nucleic acid. The
phosphatase activity was inhibited by $M/10$ fluoride. It could
be greatly decreased by washing the phage with distilled water,
and then largely restored by addition of a bacterial filtrate which
had little activity itself, suggesting a requirement for some kind of
cofactor. It is quite possible that this is bacterial phosphatase
which is adsorbed to the phage particles, but if so the adsorption
seems to be rather specific.

A similar study was reported by Ajl (1950) using centrifugally concentrated T2 phage. Measurements in the Warburg
respirometer using 5×10^{12} T2 particles per vessel showed no

detectable oxygen uptake with succinate, fumarate, malate, pyruvate, acetate, or glucose as substrates. An equal amount (4.5 mg. dry weight) of *E. coli* cells catalyzed the uptake of 100 to 200 μl. of oxygen in 2 hours with these substrates under the same conditions. Similar experiments using 8.6 mg. of phage with glutamic or aspartic acids resulted in no detectable oxygen uptake, CO_2 evolution, or NH_3 liberation. Dehydrogenase activity was measured in Thunberg tubes using methylene blue at 1:5,000 to 1:50,000 and phage at 5×10^{12} particles per tube. There was no detectable reduction of the dye in 6 hours using glucose, succinate, malate, or boiled *E. coli* juice as substrates.

No endogenous CO_2 production and no CO_2 evolution from glucose could be detected, but pyruvate and oxalactate as substrates yielded considerable amounts of CO_2. However, this was readily demonstrated to be nonenzymatic in nature because boiled phage was more active than unheated phage. Preliminary experiments indicated that concentrated phage preparations did contain some ATPase activity, but no quantitative results were given and it is not clear whether this is a true property of the phage or due to a contaminating bacterial enzyme. With this single exception, all experiments were in agreement in that they failed to yield evidence for metabolic activity in mature phage particles.

Similar studies on concentrated preparations (5×10^{12} particles/ml.) of staphylococcus phage have been reported by Price (1952) but without details. "Tests for all the reactions in glycolysis and those in the Krebs cycle were negative." Price also stated that there was no oxidation of gluconic acid, amino acids, or fatty acids.

Putnam (1953) reported that Kozloff (private communication) was unable to detect the presence in phage T6 of glycerol phosphatase, phenolphthalein phosphatase, DNAase, ATPase, or protease. These results are in conflict with those of Schüler and Ajl, who used closely related phages.

One may safely conclude that up to the present there is no unequivocal evidence for the existence of any enzymic activity in mature, extracellular phage, and there is strong evidence against the existence of the usual enzymes of intermediary metabolism. This implies that the multiplying phage is dependent on the host cell for energy yielding enzyme systems and for the synthesis of the common organic compounds which are constituents of mature phage. In addition the infected host cell may synthesize certain new enzymes which are required for phage replication and which are found in neither the uninfected host cell nor in mature phage. Such hypothetical enzymes would then be uniquely associated with the vegetative state of bacteriophage.

b. Enzymic Activity Associated with Vegetative Phage

The infected bacterium has a number of physiological properties not shared by the normal bacterium. It synthesizes several antigenically specific proteins that are unique to the phage particle, as well as a unique kind of nucleic acid. These proteins and nucleic acid molecules are assembled into the peculiar morphological structure characterizing the mature phage particle. Nothing is yet known about the enzymes required for the synthesis of proteins and nucleic acids, but if any of the specificity of these substances is dependent on specific enzymes, then vegetative phage must have associated with it some phage-specific enzymes. A search for such enzymes is beyond the reach of present biochemical techniques.

In the meantime, several pieces of evidence suggest the possibility that there may be enzymes of intermediary metabolism specifically associated with vegetative phage. One piece of evidence stems from the discovery of the pyrimidine base 5-(hydroxymethyl)cytosine (HMC) in phages T2, T4, and T6 by Wyatt and Cohen. This base is not present in detectable amounts in the uninfected host bacterium and has not yet been found elsewhere in nature. Infection of the host cell with phage T2 results in a prompt halt in the synthesis of cytosine and initiation of the synthesis of hydroxymethylcytosine (Hershey, Dixon, and Chase, 1953). It has been suggested by Cohen (1953b) that this shift in the synthetic activities of the bacterium following infection with T2 phage is sufficient explanation for the long-recognized fact that the net synthesis of bacterial DNA and RNA stops following infection. If this suggestion is correct there still remains the major problem of the mechanism for the shift from cytosine synthesis to the synthesis of HMC. Various possible mechanisms have been discussed in detail by Cohen (1953b), among them the possibility that the infecting phage supplies the essential enzymes for HMC synthesis.

A possible example of enzymic activity supplied by the infecting phage was reported by Barner and Cohen (1954). A mutant strain of *E. coli*, 15T$^-$, is unable to grow unless thymine or thymidine is supplied. When this strain is infected with phage T2 in the absence of thymine, the phage multiplies and its thymine content ultimately exceeds that of the cells prior to infection. The authors suggested two possible explanations, that the infecting virus supplies an enzyme or coenzyme essential for thymine synthesis, or that virus infection releases an inhibition of an enzyme system already present in the uninfected cell. A later paper furnished further information on the metabolism of strain 15T$^-$ (Cohen and Barner, 1954). The bacteria were grown in uniformly labeled C^{14}-glucose and the nucleic acid bases were isolated and analyzed for C^{14} content. The experiments indicate that strain 15T$^-$ is able to synthesize thymine at about 4 per cent of the normal rate but much too slowly to permit growth of the bacteria. This finding suggests that phage infection releases an inhibition rather than furnishes a lacking enzyme. These studies demonstrate the difficulty in drawing valid conclusions without a thorough investigation of the system.

A purine requiring mutant of *E. coli* strain B which permitted production of phages T1 and T5 in the absence of added purines was reported by Gots in a discussion of the paper of Cohen (1953b). This strain did not permit production of phages T2, T3, and T4 unless a purine was added to the medium.

Similar experiments with amino acid-requiring strains of bacteria yielded different results. The infecting phage does not compensate for the bacterial deficiencies (Cohen, 1949; Gots and Hunt, 1953; Burton, 1955).

Although there is abundant evidence that an infecting bacterial virus can seriously alter the host cell metabolism, there is still no clear cut evidence that the invading bacteriophage introduces metabolically significant enyzme systems into the host cells. Phages can also introduce bacterial genetic substances controlling enzyme synthesis by means of the process known as transduction, and prophages in lysogenic bacteria may have profound effects on the metabolic activities of the host cell (Chapter XIX). Indeed, the evidence furnished by work with temperate phages makes it seem quite probable that enzymatic activities uniquely associated with infection will be demonstrated eventually.

c. Enzymic Activity of the Host Cell

It is now generally accepted that the energy requirement for phage multiplication must be obtained through the functioning of the enzymes of the host cell. Much of this evidence, obtained by the use of enzyme inhibitors, will be described in Chapter XV. However, one piece of evidence derived directly from an interesting property of the phages is worth discussing here. The infection of a susceptible bacterium by certain virulent phages prevents the synthesis of adaptive enzymes which are readily formed in uninfected bacteria (Monod and Wollman, 1947). A strain of E. coli infected with a virulent bacteriophage lysed and liberated mature phage if glucose were present as an energy source. However, in the presence of lactose, phage growth and cell lysis occurred only if the bacteria had been adapted to lactose utilization before infection. Synthesis of the required enzyme took place in uninfected cells within an hour after addition of lactose, but did not occur at all in infected cells. In a further refinement of this technique Benzer (1953) demonstrated that the rate limiting factor in phage multiplication in a lactose medium is the amount of induced enzyme synthesized before phage infection. These experiments show clearly that the lactose-hydrolyzing enzyme is a host cell enzyme and is not replaceable by phage enzymes.

Rather similar evidence is available with respect to the enzymes involved in the synthesis of amino acids. If a culture of *E. coli* is grown in a medium containing ammonium lactate and salts it will support the growth of a number of phage strains without the addition of amino acids or growth factors. However, if broth-grown bacteria are transferred to the chemically defined medium and then infected with T2 phage the latent period is greatly prolonged and the burst size decreased. An appropriate mixture of amino acids and purine and pyrimidine bases restores phage production by broth grown bacteria (Fowler and Cohen, 1948; Cohen and Fowler, 1948). These experiments show that the rates at which the bacterium can synthesize the raw materials for phage protein and nucleic acid depend on the environment in which the bacteria were grown before infection. Very similar results were observed by Gots and Hunt (1953) in studying the requirements for growth of phage lambda after ultraviolet induction of lysogenic cultures. It was found that for lambda production in broth-grown cells, isoleucine, leucine, and valine are essential. Yet when strain K12 is grown in a glucose–ammonium chloride medium, induced lysis and phage production occur without the necessity of added amino acids (Borek, 1952). Again the nutritional requirements for phage production are seen to depend on the synthetic capabilities of the host cells as conditioned by their previous environment. In bacteria genetically incompetent to synthesize certain amino acids, phage production does not occur unless the amino acids required for bacterial growth are included in the medium (Borek, 1952; Burton, 1955). Adsorption and invasion by T2 occurs in the absence of the amino acid required for cellular multiplication. However, no phage DNA synthesis occurs, nor does the complex become resistant to ultraviolet light (see Chapter XI), until the required amino acid is added. A similar block in development is caused by chloramphenicol (Chapter XV).

In washed and starved bacteria unknown physiological

changes take place which interfere with phage production. Such studies were reported by Gross (1954a, b) using phage T2 and strain K12 of *E. coli* grown in a glucose ammonium chloride medium. If such cultures were infected with phage T2, they lysed normally with an average burst size of 10 to 20 phage particles per cell. If the bacteria were washed in buffer, starved by aeration, infected, and then returned to glucose medium there was no phage yield. However, if the starved infected bacteria were incubated in broth there was an average burst size of 20. Results similar to those observed in broth were obtained by re-suspending the bacteria in a mixture of amino acids. No single amino acid would suffice for phage production. Evidently starvation of the bacteria causes some physiological damage which renders the cells unfit for phage production in unsupple-mented media. The effect of the damage can be reversed by a suitable mixture of amino acids.

One may conclude from what information is available that phage production is dependent on the host cell metabolism for energy and for the synthesis of the raw materials of protoplasm such as amino acids and nucleic acid bases if these are not fur-nished in the medium. Therefore, any interference with the energy metabolism or the synthetic enzyme systems of the host cell may be expected to have an effect on phage production. However, it is possible to interfere with bacterial multiplication without affecting phage growth and vice versa, showing that the nutritional requirements for the two processes are not identical.

d. Synthetic and Energetic Machinery of the Host Cell

The immediate effects of infection by the virulent phage T2 are numerous and dramatic. Cell division is halted and the synthesis of new respiratory enzymes is stopped, but the func-tioning of the existing respiratory apparatus remains unim-paired. The net synthesis of ribonucleic acid and of bacterial deoxyribonucleic acid (DNA) stops, and the synthesis of phage DNA soon starts (Cohen, 1949). The bacterial nuclei are de-stroyed (Luria and Human, 1950), but the tetrazolium reductase activity of the infected cells remains unimpaired (Hartman, Mudd, Hillier, and Beutner, 1953). Synthesis of at least one enzyme is abruptly terminated (Benzer, 1953), but protein synthesis as a whole continues unabated (Cohen, 1949; Hershey, Garen, Fraser, and Hudis, 1954).

Cohen (1947a) summed up these metabolic effects as follows: "The virus appears to be synthesized by the cell according to the models (templates) which it provides for the host's enzymes." Luria (1950) refers to "parasitism at the genetic level." Both authors express what is now the common view: after infection with T2 specific bacterial functions, such as synthesis of bacterial DNA and bacterial enzymes, can be dispensed with. Generalized processes, such as formation of amino acids and nucleotides, and doubtless oxidative phosphorylation, remain essential to viral growth. The bacterium, as we have seen, must furnish these generalized working systems out of its past activity; the phage cannot create them and indeed renders the bacterium unfit to do so; it supplies mainly a new detailed plan for coordinated action of existing metabolic systems. The following observations are consistent with this view in showing that deliberate interference with specific bacterial syntheses does not prevent growth of phage.

Bacteria treated with as many as 30 lethal doses of ultraviolet light are still able to support the multiplication of phage T2 (T. F. Anderson, 1944, 1948d; Luria and Latarjet, 1947; Labaw, Mosley, and Wyckoff, 1950a, b). Jacob, Torriani, and Monod (1951) exposed *E. coli* to sufficient ultraviolet light to reduce the survivors by a factor of 10^5. As a result of this treatment the bacteria lost ability to synthesize the inducible enzyme β-galactosidase in detectable amounts, yet still were able to produce T2. Phage can also multiply in bacteria treated with many lethal doses of X-rays, as demonstrated by Rouyer and Latarjet (1946), by Latarjet (1948), and by Labaw, Mosley, and Wyckoff (1953). Similarly, bacteria rendered nonviable by treatment with mustard gas are able to support growth of phage T2 (Herriott, 1951b). Irradiation and mustard treatment probably kill bacteria by specific inhibition of DNA synthesis (Kelner, 1953; Herriott, 1951b). Evidently phage infection reverses this inhibition, which suggests that the original damage was confined to terminal steps in DNA synthesis.

Similar conclusions may be drawn from numerous papers on the induction of phage multiplication in lysogenic bacteria by agents normally lethal for bacteria. For instance, a dose of ultraviolet light that kills 70 per cent of a nonlysogenic variant of K12 gives 95 per cent induction of phage growth in the lysogenic strain (Weigle and Delbrück, 1951).

Penicillin is supposed to interfere specifically with formation of cell wall material in *E. coli* (Hahn and Ciak, 1957). Concentrations of penicillin which prevent bacterial multiplication do not prevent phage growth, although the phage yield is somewhat reduced because of premature lysis (Price, 1947a; Elford, 1948; Krueger, Cohn, Smith, and McGuire, 1948). Such lethal concentrations of penicillin do not interfere with most of the synthetic abilities of the bacteria because the cells increase markedly in size and in content of protoplasm after treatment with penicillin, much as they do after treatment with ultraviolet light, X-rays, or mustard gas.

We may conclude that viability of the host cell is not important to the lytic cycle of phage growth provided generalized metabolic processes continue to function. However, interference with energy metabolism or with the source of supply of building blocks results in failure of phage growth.

These conclusions reached from the study of phage T2 have been informative, but must be regarded as an example of the extreme case. Less severe metabolic effects of infection are seen with other phages (Siminovitch, 1953). Synthesis of DNA and cellular multiplication may be interrupted, but other biosyntheses, including enzymic adaptation, may continue at a reduced rate. Even synthesis of DNA does not stop completely (Lwoff, 1953). Evidently if the bacterium is to survive, as in the event of lysogenization by a temperate phage, practically all metabolic effects of infection would have to be reversible. T1, though little studied from this point of view, may be a case in point. According to Luria and Delbrück (1942), T1 inactivated by ultraviolet light does not kill bacteria. It nevertheless produces striking cytological changes in the cells (Luria and Human, 1950). In no instance is it clear which effects of infection should be ascribed to action localized at the cell surface and which to the injected materials. Thus ultraviolet-inactivated T2 and T5 (and a few other phages, perhaps) kill bacteria with high efficiency. Ghosts of T2 kill with low efficiency, and adsorbed ghosts that fail to kill produce transient cellular changes (French and Siminovitch, 1955). Systematic elucidation of these questions will be a necessary part of the clarification of current ideas about possible phage-host relationship (Stent, 1958).

3. Partial Metabolic Requirements for Vegetative Replication

We have just seen that multiplication of phage T2 is independent of specific bacterial biosyntheses such as that of DNA, certain enzymes, and probably bacterial ribonucleic acid. Even more remarkable is recent evidence that synthesis of phage protein and DNA are to some extent independent.

Watanabe (1957) showed that bacteria heavily irradiated with ultraviolet light some time after infection with phage T2 showed a markedly reduced capacity to synthesize DNA, but continued to form serologically specific phage protein at an appreciable rate. Their results suggest that the role of DNA in protein synthesis is a passive one, as do the corresponding experiments with uninfected bacteria (Kelner, 1953).

Burton (1955) first showed that synthesis of DNA is independent of synthesis of protein in bacteria infected with T2. To test this, he used amino acid–requiring strains of *E. coli*, which were grown in supplemented medium, infected with phage, and transferred to deficient medium at various times after infection. He found that deprivation of an amino acid during the first few minutes after infection could prevent phage DNA synthesis from starting, but had little effect if the transfer to a deficient medium was postponed until a later time. The same phenomenon was discovered independently by Tomizawa and Sunakawa (1956), who used the antibiotic chloramphenicol to inhibit protein synthesis (Wisseman, Smadel, Hahn, and Hopps, 1954).

Hershey and Melechen (1957) made a thorough study of the action of chloramphenicol in T2-infected bacteria. Suitable time schedules of chloramphenicol inhibition and reversal, together with labeling of phage precursors by means of radioactive isotopes, showed that large amounts of typical phage precursor DNA could be accumulated in cells that contained virtually no phage precursor protein. When such cells were transferred to a medium free from chloramphenicol, phage particles were formed that contained principally the phosphorus of DNA formed before, and protein formed after, the removal of the antibiotic. These findings constitute the chief evidence for the view (Hershey, 1953b) expressed frequently in this book, that vegetative reproduction and maturation in phage T2 can be equated, respectively, with synthesis of phage DNA and protein. According to Hershey (1957) the evidence is still incomplete.

Another line of evidence pointing in the same direction may be cited here. Watanabe, Stent, and Schachman (1954) infected bacteria with P^{32}-labeled particles of phage T2 and subsequently broke open the infected cells and measured the sedimentation constant of the P^{32}-labeled DNA in the extracts. Depending on the time of breakage of the cells, the labeled material sedimented like free DNA or like mature phage particles. No evidence was found for phosphorus-containing structures of intermediate complexity. The authors interpreted their results to mean that phage precursor DNA does not form stable attachments to complex particles in the cell until incorporated into a finished phage particle.

4. Sources of Material for Phage Synthesis

Three sources of the raw materials used for the formation of phage particles can be distinguished by the appropriate use of isotopic tracers: the substance of the parental phage particles, the bacterial contents at the time of infection, and the culture medium in which phage growth occurs. Much of the work along this line was done by Putnam, Kozloff, and Evans, summarized in several reviews (E. A. Evans, Jr., 1952; Putnam, 1952; Kozloff, 1953).

a. Materials Derived from the Parental Phage

The infection of one bacterial cell by a single phage particle can result in the production of 100 or more progeny phage particles. It is evident that quantitatively the contribution of parental substance to phage progeny must be small. Nonetheless, this topic has been very actively studied because of the evidence it may furnish about the mechanisms of phage reproduction. This work was discussed in detail in Chapter XIII. It is sufficient here to recall that only constituents of the parental DNA are significantly transferred to the offspring, with an efficiency of about 50 per cent. There is no reason to suppose that this transfer is obligatory in a nutritional sense; indeed, only the first offspring particles to be formed contain measurable amounts of parental phosphorus. In point of fact, however, the transfer cannot be prevented by experimental means.

b. Protein Materials Assimilated before and after Infection

The contributions from these two sources can be measured separately and should add up to the total phage protein. By growing the bacteria in a medium appropriately labeled with isotopes one can label the bacterial proteins, nucleic acids, or both. Then by transferring to an unlabeled growth medium one can measure the bacterial contribution to the phage substance. The dilution suffered by a given isotope in any compound in going from the bacterium to the phage is a measure of the bacterial contribution providing exchange reactions are ruled out. Similarly by growing the phage on unlabeled bacteria in a labeled growth medium one can determine the fractional contribution to phage substance made by the medium. One may study the process kinetically by introducing an appropriate isotopic label at any time before or after bacterial infection and similarly one can dilute out the label at any time. This provides a tremendous flexibility to the experiments and permits one to study the dynamics of phage synthesis.

Relatively less information is available as to the source of phage proteins because the major effort has been expended on the currently more interesting problem of nucleic acid metabolism. Kozloff, Knowlton, Putnam, and Evans (1951) studied the source of phage T6 nitrogen compounds by labeling either the bacterium or the growth medium with N^{15}. They concluded that from 10 to 20 per cent of the phage protein nitrogen is derived from bacterial substances assimilated before infection and the remainder is obtained from the medium after infection. The contribution to phage amounts to about 2 per cent of the bacterial protein indicating that most of the bacterial protein is unavailable for phage synthesis.

The experiments were extended by Siddiqi, Kozloff, Putnam, and Evans (1952). Using bacteria labeled with N^{15} and with C^{14}-lysine, they concluded that about 15 per cent of the phage T6 protein could have been derived from the host cell. The source of this material was host cell proteins rather than acid-soluble metabolites. Only 1 to 2 per cent of the bacterial lysine was available for synthesis of phage protein. Most of the virus protein must be synthesized *de novo* from materials in the growth medium.

Putnam, Miller, Palm, and Evans (1952) isolated the protein from phage T7 grown in bacterial cells labeled with N^{15} and concluded that about 40 per cent of the phage protein nitrogen was derived from bacterial substances assimilated before infection and the remainder was derived from the medium after infection. The increased fraction of host protein in phage T7 as compared with phage T6 is probably a reflection of the smaller size of phage T7, since only a small amount of bacterial substance is utilized in either case.

There is one major difficulty with all these experiments, and that is the difficulty in determining when the phage preparation is adequately pure.   In all of the previous papers the final phage yield used for analysis was purified only by differential centrifugation.   Physical and chemical criteria of purity applied to such preparations are virtually useless as tests of radiochemical purity in experiments of the type under consideration.   This point was tested in experiments by Hershey, Garen, Fraser, and Hudis (1954) using phage T2 grown in bacteria labeled with preassimilated S^{35}.   The radiochemical purity of the centrifugally isolated phage preparations was measured by following the adsorption of the sulfur label to strain B of *E. coli* and failure of adsorption to B/2.   These tests indicated that indeed most of the radioactivity of the final phage yield was due to contaminating bacterial proteins and was not built into the phage particles.   Only 2 to 3 per cent of the total phage protein could have been derived from labeled bacterial protein, the latter contribution amounting to only 0.4 per cent of the total labeled bacterial protein.   Even this small amount may have been derived from bacterial glutathione rather than from bacterial protein.   These experiments demonstrate quite conclusively that the host cell makes a negligible contribution to the proteins of phage T2.   This finding that contaminating bacterial protein is responsible for the host cell isotopic label found in the phage yield is sufficient explanation for the observation by Kozloff, Knowlton, Putnam, and Evans (1951) of an inverse relationship between the phage yield and the apparent host contribution to the phage.   If the amount of contaminating bacterial particles per cell present in the phage yield is approximately constant, as indicated by the results of Hershey, Garen, Fraser, and Hudis (1954), it would constitute a smaller fraction of the yield, as the yield of phage particles per cell increased.   This might also be the explanation for the apparently large host cell contribution made to the small phage T7 as observed by Putnam, Miller, Palm, and Evans (1952).   One may conclude that at present there is no definitive evidence that *any* phage materials are derived from host cell proteins although in the case of phage T2 it is possible that 2 to 3 per cent of the phage protein might be derived from this source.   Evidently most if not all of the phage protein is derived from materials assimilated from the growth medium after phage infection.

The kinetics of protein synthesis in phage-infected bacteria has been investigated in several laboratories. Cohen (1947 a, 1948) found that protein synthesis in T2-infected bacteria proceeded without interruption, although the net synthesis of RNA and DNA was stopped. The protein increment was not characterized to determine whether it was of phage or bacterial specificity. Levinthal and Fisher (1952, 1953), by breaking open T2-infected bacteria at intervals during the latent period, observed toroid-shaped objects ("doughnuts") which appeared before mature phage, increased in number during early stages of phage maturation, and then decreased toward the end of the latent period. These objects were apparently phage precursors, resembling empty phage heads in shape and size and being agglutinated by antibodies to phage heads. They did not adsorb to the host cells because the organ for attachment, the tail, was lacking. A small number of doughnuts with tails were also observed in these premature lysates. Similarly DeMars, Luria, Fisher, and Levinthal (1953) and DeMars (1955) reported the detection of soluble phage antigens in T2-infected bacteria which were not part of either mature phage particles or "doughnuts." These soluble antigens were characterized by their ability to block phage-neutralizing antibodies. These experiments demonstrate that proteins with the specificity of phage but not yet built into mature phage are present in phage-infected bacteria during the latent period. Similar experiments with T5-infected bacteria were reported by Y. T. Lanni (1954).

A different kind of phage precursor was detected in T2-infected bacteria by Maaløe and Symonds (1953) by the use of S^{35} from the medium as a label. These precursors contained protein but no nucleic acid, sedimented more slowly than mature phage, adsorbed to sensitive bacteria but did not kill them, and were agglutinated by antiphage serum. These properties resemble those of "osmotic ghosts" of phage T2. Their number was approximately constant from 15 minutes after infection until lysis and measured 30 to 50 per infected bacterium (assuming the same sulfur content as mature phage). By introducing S^{35}-sulfate into the medium at various times during the latent period it was possible to determine the time required for a newly assimilated S^{35} atom to appear in a mature phage particle. The average elapsed time was found to be 6 to 7 minutes. These kinetic experiments also indicated that the noninfectious S^{35}-containing particles are actually phage precursors and not cast off waste products of phage multiplication.

More elaborate kinetic experiments in which total protein synthesis and specific phage protein synthesis were determined were reported by Hershey, Garen, Fraser, and Hudis (1954). In confirmation of Cohen's work they found that total protein synthesis continued at the same rate after infection as before. Synthesis of specific phage protein began after a delay and gradually accelerated until it was proceeding at about one-half the rate of total protein synthesis. The nature of the remaining half of the protein synthesized after phage infection is obscure but it is probably bacterial protein; at least much of it sediments with the bacterial debris. The intriguing possibility remains that some of it may be associated uniquely with vegetative phage. The experiments suggest that there is a gradual shift from the synthesis of nonphage protein to the synthesis of specific phage protein as the infectious process continues. Inorganic sulfate from the medium is assimilated into acid-insoluble protein in about 2 minutes. Early assimilated S^{35} exists as phage precursor protein for about 11 minutes before appearing in mature phage. Late assimilated sulfur persists as phage-precursor for only 8 minutes. The efficiency with which assimilated sulfur is converted into mature phage is 0 before infection, 5 to 10 per cent during the first 5 minutes after infection, increasing to about 60 per cent toward the end of phage growth. It is desirable to determine the nature of the large amount of protein synthesized in phage infected bacteria which never appears in mature phage. One wonders if this nonphage protein is related in any way to the infectious process. Interest in this question is heightened by the findings of Volkin and Astrachan (1956a, b). They demonstrated that an amount of RNA small relative to the total cellular content is synthesized beginning immediately following infection. This RNA has a base composition unlike that of the RNA in uninfected cells and more nearly like the analogous base composition of the infecting T2 DNA.

c. Nucleic Acid Materials Assimilated before and after Infection

Because of the importance of nucleic acids in heredity a major effort has been expended in numerous laboratories on the study of nucleic acid synthesis in phage-infected bacteria. As indicated in Chapter VII chemical analyses of various phages shows that those studied so far contain only protein and deoxyribose nucleic acid. The work of Hershey and Chase (1952) demonstrated that infection with phage T2 involved penetration of phage nucleic acid into the host cell, leaving most if not all of the phage protein outside of the host cell. This immediately gave phage nucleic acid the dominant position in phage replication. The equally startling discovery by Wyatt and Cohen (1953) of a new pyrimidine, 5(hydroxymethyl)cytosine, in various strains of the T2 species of phage furnished material for speculation as well as an invaluable tool for distinguishing phage nucleic acid from bacterial nucleic acid in bacteria infected with these phage strains. Because of the very large number of papers related to the problem of phage nucleic acid synthesis it would be difficult as well as confusing to follow a chronological development of this field. Instead we shall describe present concepts of the synthesis of phage nucleic acid referring to those papers which relate directly to the problem. Most work has been done with phage strains T2, T4, and T6, and will be described first.

Infection with phage T2 involves injection of phage nucleic acid into the host cell (Hershey and Chase, 1952). Infection prevents further host cell division and stops the synthesis of RNA and of bacterial DNA (Cohen, 1947a) without interrupting bacterial respiration. Infection is soon followed by cytologically evident disintegration of the bacterial nuclei (see Chapter XII).

The infected cell then contains phage DNA derived from the infecting particle and bacterial DNA derived from the degenerate bacterial nuclei. Published work from various laboratories (Cohen, 1947a; Kozloff and Putnam, 1950; Labaw, 1951) demonstrated that phosphorus from the host cell was found in the phage progeny. The utilization of host cell pyrimidines (Weed and Cohen, 1951) and host cell purines (Koch, Putnam, and Evans, 1952) for phage synthesis is consistent with the assumption that the host cell DNA is available as a raw material for phage production. This was proved when Kozloff (1953) reported that host cell thymine appeared in the phage DNA, as confirmed by Hershey, Garen, Fraser, and Hudis (1954). There is general agreement that the conversion of host cell DNA to phage DNA is more or less complete. Hershey, Garen, Fraser, and Hudis (1954) obtained evidence that a small amount of the host cell RNA may be utilized for synthesis of phage DNA as well. The bacteria also contain large amounts of transient intermediates that contribute phosphorus to phage DNA (Hershey and Melechen, 1957).

The general conclusions about the sources of materials for the synthesis of phage T2 DNA may be summarized in tabular form as follows:

Source	Use	Material contribution to yield, %
Phage DNA	Pattern	0.1–1
Host DNA	Raw material	5–40
Host RNA	Raw material	5–10
Transients	Raw material	5–40
Medium	Raw material	60–80

As we shall see in Section 5 of this chapter, these host-cell contributions to the substance of the phage particles are utilized mainly by the first phage particles to be formed. Thus their fractional contribution to the total yield of phage is variable depending on whether the yield is large or small. The efficiency of utilization of various components is in general more interesting and has occasionally been measured. The bacterial DNA (labeled in thymine) is utilized almost completely (Kozloff, 1953; Hershey, Garen, Fraser, and Hudis, 1954), and supplies raw materials sufficient to make about 30 phage particles per bacterium (Hershey and Melechen, 1957). The bacterial RNA, on the other hand, is utilized very inefficiently (Putnam, 1952). A bacterium that contains RNA equivalent in mass to the DNA content of more than 200 phage particles actually furnishes purines and pyrimidines to DNA sufficient to make only about 10 particles (Hershey, Garen, Fraser, and Hudis, 1954). Transient intermediates plus RNA present in the cell at the time of infection furnish phosphorus to DNA sufficient to make about 30 phage particles (Hershey and Melechen, 1957). Thus the bacterial cell at the time of infection contains several forms of phosphorus that is available for incorporation into phage, the total amount being sufficient to make about 60 particles of phage T2 per bacterium. The actual amount found in the isolated phage particles may be as high as 50 phage equivalent units per bacterium (Hershey and Melechen, 1957) or may be much lower, depending on the experimental conditions and techniques.

The chief point of interest in these facts is concerned with the significance of the efficient conversion of bacterial DNA into phage DNA. At the present time all the known facts are consistent with the idea that it serves solely as a source of raw materials. Thus the amount of preassimilated phosphorus per bacterium available for conversion into different phages is about the same, which has the effect, puzzling at first sight, of causing the contribution *per phage* to be about the same for large and small phages (Labaw, 1951; Hershey, 1953b), and also has the effect of causing the contribution from the medium after infection to be very small for small phages like T7 (Putnam, Miller, Palm, and Evans, 1952; Labaw, 1953). The differences in composition between bacterial DNA and the DNA of T2 call for considerable reorganization. Any direct incorporation of bacterial DNA into phages is not consistent with current ideas about the structure and function of DNA, nor with much experimental evidence (Kozloff, 1953, Hershey, Garen, Fraser, and Hudis, 1954).

5. Kinetic Studies of DNA Metabolism

Several investigators have used kinetic methods to follow the course of nucleic acid metabolism in phage-infected bacteria. Cohen (1947a, 1948) demonstrated that in T2-infected bacteria net RNA synthesis stopped and there appeared to be an interruption in DNA synthesis after which DNA was produced even more rapidly than in uninfected cells. In infected cells DNA synthesis was well ahead of phage maturation but the two curves were parallel as if both processes were controlled by the same rate-limiting reaction (Cohen, 1949). The rates and total amounts of DNA synthesis in bacteria infected with T2r^+ and T2r phages were compared by Cohen and Arbogast (1950b). Infected cells of both types formed DNA at the same linear rate, but synthesis continued 2 to 3 times longer in the lysis-inhibited cells. These findings were confirmed by Stent and Maaløe (1953) who determined by use of P^{32}-labeling that assimilation of phosphorus from the medium into phage proceeded at the same rate in lysis-inhibited cultures as in cultures before lysis inhibition, and hence that the phenomenon of lysis inhibition merely delays the lytic reaction without directly affecting phage synthesis.

By the use of isotopic labels Weed and Cohen (1951) showed that T6r^+ phage harvested after premature lysis at 35 minutes after infection contained a much higher proportion of pyrimidines originating in the host than did phage harvested after spontaneous lysis at 5 hours. The quantitative data suggested that essentially all available host pyrimidines had been built into phage which had matured during the first 35 minutes after infection. Contrary conclusions drawn from kinetic experiments by Kozloff, Knowlton, Putnam, and Evans (1951) may be attributable to two causes; the sampling times were 3.5 and 24 hours after infection, long after all host contributions had been assimilated into mature phage, and also after phage synthesis had ceased in the lysis-inhibited cultures.

Experiments by Maaløe and Stent (1952) indicated that during phage maturation there was no stage in which immature phage particles containing DNA could be detected by centrifugation, by precipitation with antiphage serum, or by adsorption to heat-killed bacteria. They concluded that either the incorporation of phage DNA into its membrane was the last stage in maturation or else that the hypothetical immature DNA-containing phage particles were structurally unstable and disintegrated during host cell lysis. Thus there were only two observable forms of phage DNA that could be isolated from infected bacteria; free DNA in solution and DNA in fully infectious, mature phage particles.

Very detailed kinetic studies using P^{32} and phage T4 were published by Stent and Maaløe (1953). They concluded, in agreement with Weed and Cohen (1951), that there was a greater contribution of host cell materials to the earlier produced phage. The first phage particles to mature received about 60 per cent of their phosphorus from materials assimilated before infection. About 70 to 80 per cent of the total available bacterial contribution had been incorporated into mature phage particles during the first 30 minutes. Within a minute or two after infection the rate of assimilation of phage-precursor phosphorus from the medium increased by a factor of eight as compared with the rate before infection. This is probably due in part to the elimination of other uses for phosphorus such as synthesis of RNA (Cohen, 1952). The average time between the assimilation of phosphorus atoms and their incorporation into mature phage was 14 minutes with a minimum of 5 minutes.

Kinetics of phosphorus assimilation in phage T6 were studied by Labaw (1953) by introducing P^{32} into the bacterial culture at various times before or after infection. Most of his results with this phage are similar to those already described. One observation is in disagreement with other findings. The phosphorus contribution of the host cell to the mature phage is a constant value of about 30 per cent of the phage phosphorus regardless of the time of lysis or the mean burst size. This is in direct contradiction to the results of Weed and Cohen (1951), of Stent and Maaløe (1953), and of Hershey to be discussed next. These authors all agree that the host contribution is greater to the phage particles that mature earlier.

The kinetic work has led to the concept of a series of pools of raw materials at different levels of organization which contribute to the substance of the mature phage. For instance, there is a pool of transient intermediates that is fed from the medium and perhaps from the host cell RNA and DNA, and from which phosphorus is withdrawn for the synthesis of phage DNA. There may be, in fact, a pool for each nucleoside and nucleotide involved in phage synthesis, similarly nourished from various sources. Lastly there is the pool of specific phage DNA, nourished from all the other pools and the only one to be drawn upon directly by maturing phage particles. Of these the most interesting is the pool of phage-precursor DNA (Hershey, 1953a).

The infected bacterium contains three operationally distinguishable kinds of DNA: (1) mature phage DNA characterized by its content of hydroxymethylcytosine (HMC) and by its organization into sedimentable particles with the physiological properties of infectivity, adsorbability to host cells, and precipitability by antiphage serum; (2) phage precursor DNA, after cell lysis nonsedimentable, precipitable by trichloroacetic acid, sensitive to deoxyribonuclease, and containing HMC; and (3) bacterial DNA with properties similar to phage-precursor DNA except that it contains cytosine in place of HMC. The absolute amounts of these forms of DNA were determined by Hershey, Dixon, and Chase (1953) at various times after infection with phage T2. The amounts were reported for convenience in terms of units of DNA per bacterium (the unit being the amount of DNA contained in one phage particle), although they might have been measured in terms of phosphorus, diphenylamine color, optical density at 260 mμ, cytosine, or HMC.

In a typical experiment mature phage particles first appear about 10 minutes after infection and increase at a linear rate of about 6 phage per minute per bacterium reaching about 600 phage particles per bacterium in 2 hours. The total DNA increases at the same rate as the phage starting at about 100 units per bacterium at the time of infection and reaching about 700 units in 2 hours. The amount of bacterial DNA per cell decreases approximately linearly from between 50 and 100 units at the time of infection to less than 10 units at 30 minutes. This means that essentially all the bacterial DNA should have entered the pools of raw materials within 30 minutes after infection, a result in agreement with most earlier studies. The phage DNA (containing HMC) has already increased to about 10 units per bacterium at 5 minutes after infection and thereafter increases linearly at a rate of about 7 units per minute per cell. From the time that the first mature phage particles appear there is a constant excess of about 80 units per cell of phage DNA above that incorporated into mature phage. This is the pool of phage precursor DNA.

The properties of the pool of phage-precursor nucleic acid were reported by Hershey (1953a), who investigated the size of the precursor pool, the rate at which raw materials from various sources entered the pool, and the rate at which DNA was withdrawn from the pool by phage maturation. The technique was to label various source materials with P^{32} and then determine the rate at which this label entered the precursor pool and the mature phage. The various experiments involved labeling of phosphorus assimilated before infection, parental phage phosphorus, phosphorus assimilated after infection, and phosphorus assimilated during a few minutes only. The following conclusions were drawn from this study.

During the first 10 minutes of phage growth in T2-infected *E. coli* a pool of DNA is built up that is later to be incorporated into phage. This pool receives phosphorus from bacterial DNA but does not include bacterial DNA. Ten minutes after infection phage maturation starts and DNA synthesis and phage maturation keep pace so that the amount of phage precursor DNA remains constant. The pool of phage precursor contains 50 to 100 phage particle equivalents of DNA per bacterium. Neither the precursor nor the mature phage exchanges phosphorus with the phosphate of the medium. The phosphorus of mature phage does not exchange with the phosphorus of the precursor DNA indicating that maturation is an irreversible process. Maturation is a remarkably efficient process; about 90 per cent of the phosphorus which enters the pool early is later incorporated into phage. Phage DNA is synthesized at the rate of 7 to 8 phage particles per minute per bacterium; this is faster than bacterial DNA but slower than bacterial RNA is produced in uninfected bacteria. The transport of phosphorus from medium to precursor DNA takes an average of 8 or 9 minutes, and from precursor to mature phage an additional 7 or 8 minutes. The usable parental phosphorus enters the precursor DNA pool before 10 minutes. The parental phosphorus is incorporated into mature phage progeny between 10 and 25 minutes after infection. The preassimilated phosphorus from the host cell enters the precursor pool at the same rate as the bacterial DNA disappears. It has essentially all entered the pool by 25 minutes and has been incorporated into mature phage by 40 minutes after infection. Hershey suggests that the rate of phage maturation is determined by the pool size and hence by the rate of synthesis of phage-precursor DNA.

This demonstration of the properties of the pool of phage-precursor DNA is of great interest because of the resemblance of this pool to the vegetative phage pool, or mating pool, discerned in genetic experiments (Chapter XVIII). When a bacterium is infected with two or more genetically distinguishable particles of phage T2, the phage nucleic acids penetrate into the host cell and are then called vegetative phage. The vegetative phage particles multiply, and when the intracellular population becomes high enough for unlike pairs to collide, mating begins. After this time vegetative phage is withdrawn from this mating pool at a linear rate to form mature phage. Mature phage particles play no further role in replication or mating. The mating pool contains a constant number of 30 to 50 vegetative phage particles. It seems reasonable to conclude (Hershey,

1954) that the pool of phage-precursor DNA is the material substance of which the pool of mating vegetative phage is composed.
The reader is referred to reviews by Hershey (1956a, 1957) for
additional discussion.

In contrast with the tremendous amount of research dealing
with the T2 species of phage, there is a dearth of information
about the kinetics of assimilation of nutrients in the case of other
phages. Essentially all the phosphorus of phage T7 is derived
from preassimilated host cell phosphorus, whereas with phage T1
about 70 per cent is derived from the host cells and 30 per cent
from the medium (Labaw, 1953; Putnam, Miller, Palm, and
Evans, 1952).

Experiments with phage T5 reported by Labaw (1953) present certain unique features. Labaw believes that the host contribution to phage phosphorus is not derived from complex bacterial substances such as nucleic acids, but rather is derived
solely from phosphorus assimilated not over two minutes before
infection. The data on this point are not convincing, however,
and the experiments were criticized by Stent and Maaløe (1953).
Labaw also observed that the rapid uptake of phosphorus from
the medium for synthesis of phage T5 did not begin until about 9
minutes after infection. This may be correlated with the fact that
penetration of phage T5 into the host cell is a slow process, as
compared with T2, requiring about 10 minutes (Lanni, 1954;
Luria and Steiner, 1954).

6. Summary

The nutritional requirements for phage production have been
discussed from several points of view considering separately the
extracellular phage particle, the infected cell, and the vegetative
phage within the cell. It has not been possible to demonstrate
metabolic systems in mature phage. The phage is dependent on
host cell enzymes for the energy and the generalized synthetic
reactions required for phage reproduction although a viable host
cell is not required. There is some circumstantial evidence sug-

gesting that certain enzymes may be peculiar to the infected cell but such enzymes are yet to be demonstrated.

The materials for phage synthesis are derived from three sources, the infecting phage particle, host cell substance assimilated before infection, and the growth medium after infection. The contribution from parental phage is quantitatively small, because of the large factor of increase in each growth cycle. About 50 per cent of the parental DNA appears in phage progeny. Less than 3 per cent of the parental protein can be transferred to phage progeny.

The host cell contribution of preassimilated material is quantitatively important. Probably little or no host cell protein is used in synthesis but essentially all the host cell DNA is converted into phage DNA. In the case of phage T2, 20 to 30 per cent of the progeny DNA is derived from host cell DNA, a small amount from host cell RNA, and the remainder from transient intermediates and from the growth medium after infection. The phage protein is derived almost exclusively from materials assimilated from the growth medium after infection.

Kinetic studies reveal that specific phage proteins appear in infected cells before mature phage particles, and that these phage proteins are probably precursors of mature phage. The phage proteins are found in three forms, soluble protein with the antigenic specificity of phage tails, proteins organized as empty phage heads, and perhaps empty phage heads with tails attached. Apparently the only organized structures which contain DNA are the fully mature phage particles. It takes about 2 minutes on the average for sulfate from the medium to be assimilated into protein and about 6 minutes more for this protein to be converted into mature phage particles. A large amount of unidentified protein is synthesized in phage-infected bacteria immediately after infection. The function of this protein is unknown.

Kinetic studies indicate that phage DNA synthesis starts soon after infection and at the same time bacterial DNA is broken down and resynthesized into phage DNA. Phage DNA is produced at a rate sufficient for 6 to 8 phage particles per minute per infected bacterium. There is a precursor pool containing about 80 phage equivalents of DNA which is fed from the medium and from the host-cell nucleic acids and which is drawn upon by maturing phage particles. The transport of phosphorus from the medium to the precursor DNA pool requires on the average 8 to 9 minutes and from the pool into mature phage an additional 7 to 8 minutes. The great interest in this pool of phage-precursor DNA arises from the fact that its size and kinetic properties are similar to those deduced from genetic experiments concerning the mating pool of vegetative phage. This striking similarity in properties leads to the conclusion that the pool of phage-precursor DNA is the material of which the mating pool of vegetative phage is composed.

CHAPTER XV

CHEMICAL INTERFERENCE WITH PHAGE GROWTH*

The effects of chemical agents on phage growth have been touched on in previous chapters, particularly when specific requirements for the various stages of phage development were considered. This chapter will serve to integrate and consider in more detail the varieties of chemical interference which may be imposed upon the phage-reproducing system. In terms of over-all consequences such interference is a form of chemotherapy if we extend the definition of chemotherapy to include chemoprophylaxis of cyclic or subsequent infection. The inhibitors which prevent the growth of phage do not, as a rule, cure the afflicted bacterial host of its phage infection. The inhibitors either prevent the bacteria from becoming infected or they halt the formation of new phage progeny; the infected cells are sacrificed. Therapeutic action can be considered only in terms of freeing a bacterial community of an infectious agent so that the healthy members are spared and the population flourishes. As in all cases of effective chemotherapy, this implies properties of selective toxicity in that one member of the host-parasite complex is destroyed without affecting the other. Though this may be a desirable circumstance in our development and understanding of viral chemotherapy, it need not be the sole prerequisite for consideration. Indeed, investigations with chemical agents which exhibit no selective action in the phage-bacterium system have helped considerably in determining how much of the bacterial metabolism is required to support the growth of phage. Further details covering problems of virus

* Chapter contributed by Joseph S. Gots.

chemotherapy may be found in the reviews by Cohen (1949, 1953a) and by Matthews and Smith (1955).

In this chapter we will deal only with those substances which prevent the establishment of phage infection or prevent the production of active phage progeny. Agents which have a direct phagicidal action were considered in Chapter V and will not be dealt with here unless the treatment which inactivates the free particle has a consequential bearing on some stage of the infectious process. The specific inactivation of phage by receptor substances, which results in loss of adsorbing or penetrating potentials, was described in Chapter X.

To assess the action of a drug on phage production, its action on the growth of uninfected bacteria should also be determined. The results to be expected may be classified as follows.

1. Both bacteria and phage may be inhibited. The majority of the known inhibitors fall into this category. The nonselective action is an obvious expression of the similar requirements for the synthesis of phage and for the synthesis of bacterial protoplasm. The substrates and enzymic processes which are required to supply energy and to permit synthesis of protein and nucleic acid are equally indispensable for phage and bacteria.

2. Bacterial growth may be inhibited without affecting phage production. As indicated in Chapter XIV, viable bacteria are not always essential for phage growth. Agents such as penicillin (Price, 1947a), sulfur mustard (Herriott and Price, 1948), and pentamidine (Boyd and Bradley, 1951; Amos and Vollmayer, 1957) allow phage production at concentrations which completely inhibit the growth of the bacteria. In these cases we must look for a metabolic process which is essential for the survival and growth of the bacteria but which plays no role in the formation of phage. In the case of penicillin, the nature of such a process has been revealed by the reports of Park and Strominger (1957) and J. Lederberg (1957). Penicillin apparently kills bacteria by preventing the synthesis of cell wall material. Since phage growth can occur in bacterial protoplasts, the maintenance of the cell wall is not required for the synthesis of phage.

3. Phage production may be inhibited without affecting bacterial growth. This result is the essence of chemotherapy and hence has received favored attention in the search for inhibitors. A number of screening programs, involving hundreds of compounds, have been undertaken toward this aim. However, the productive yield of promising agents which has come from these heroic surveys has been disappointingly meagre. Often there is only a narrow threshold between the concentrations which inhibit bacteria and phage. Too often little attempt is made to determine whether or not the agents exert a direct inactivation of the phage, or to determine at what stage they may act. Only those which have been more thoroughly studied will be considered in later sections of this chapter.

A variety of methods has been employed in studying the action of chemicals as inhibitors of phage development. The nature and the extent of the method is dictated by the purpose of the analysis. Where the purpose involves a probing analysis of the mechanism of action, all the available techniques must be called upon. For the screening of a large number of compounds simpler methods have been devised which allow for economy of time and effort. Specialized and ingenious techniques are described by Jones and Schatz (1946), Hall, Kavanagh, and Asheshov (1951), Nicolle and Mimica (1947), and Hoshino (1954a). These methods serve only as a convenient device for selecting agents that may deserve further attention. The final evaluation must depend on an analytical dissection of action at all levels of phage multiplication.

1. Prevention of Adsorption

Phage growth can be prevented at the start by preventing adsorption. This can be achieved by a variety of means: by imposing a physical restriction such as viscosity; by the destruction or alteration of that portion of the phage tail which is required for adsorption; by the destruction of the receptor sites on the bacterial surface; by removing or competing with cationic requirements; and by competing with organic cofactors.

The first recognition that chemical agents which inhibit the action of phage can do so by preventing adsorption, may be, attributed to d'Herelle (1926). He explained the inhibition of mass lysis by viscous colloids such as gelatin, agar, egg albumin, and gums as a physical barrier between phage and host. Nonviscous colloids such as colloidal silver and colloidal sulfur had no effect. Though this concept may seem obvious in hindsight, it was not so at the time and indeed the literature of that era contains other more intricate explanations for the inhibitory action of the colloids.

The anatomy of the phage particle has been dissected sufficiently to allow us to assign the function of attachment to a particular structure. This apparently resides, at least in the T series of coliphages, in the distal portion of the tail in the form of protein strands which are wound like the fibers of a rope and held together by disulfide bridges. Manipulations which alter or destroy this portion of the tail will result in an inactivation with respect to phage attachment. Kellenberger and Arber (1955) achieved this with T2 and T4 phages by treatment with hydrogen peroxide and ethanol. With this treatment the rope-like distal sheath unravels and eventually dissolves leaving phage particles with shortened tails. These bobtailed phages may adsorb reversibly but they are unable to proceed to the irreversible step of attachment and hence can neither kill the host nor establish infection. Kozloff and Henderson (1955) obtained a similar distal decaudation of T2, but not of the other T phages, by treating the phage with cyanide complexes of metals of the zinc group, notably the anion $Cd(CN)_3$. The rate of inactivation of the phage correlates directly with the rate of appearance of the bobtailed forms. These forms can neither attach to nor kill the host cells. The modifications obtained by these treatments are of particular interest since the phages undergo similar changes when they normally adsorb to bacteria or even to isolated bacterial cell walls. Brown and Kozloff (1957) demonstrated that the cleavage of the tail upon adsorption is required to expose an enzyme which dissolves the cell wall thus paving the way for the injection of phage DNA.

Chemical agents whose inactivating action may be reversed by simple procedures such as dilution, heating, or prolonged storage apparently act by preventing adsorption.   This may well be due to a reversible interaction with groupings which are essential for attachment.   An inhibitor of this nature may be found in fresh lysates of T2 coliphage (Sagik, 1954).   The presence of such a substance in a lysate containing bacterial products is not too surprising since the same type of transient, reversible inactivation of phage can be obtained with simple aldehydes and aldoses (Kligler and Olenick, 1943) and with a phospholipid (Levin and Lominski, 1936).

Not only is it possible to damage the attachment organ of the phage but it is also possible to destroy the complementary receptor sites on the surface of the bacteria.   Chemical agents that can do this are described in Chapter X.

Chapter X presents an account of the inorganic requirements for adsorption.   It is possible to prevent adsorption by creating a deficiency of cations, such as the removal of calcium ions by citrate, or by adding a nonfunctional cation which may compete with functional ones.   Garen and Puck (1951) showed that the second step of adsorption can be prevented by zinc ions in infections with T1 but not with T2.   This was due to a specific competition with calcium or magnesium ions which are required by T1.   Reversible attachment was not affected by zinc.   In effect, this represents a type of "cure" in that the infectious agent, though adsorbed, is unable to establish infection and can be removed with the restoration of a viable host.   Another case with similar consequences is found in the action of apple pectin on T2 (Reiter, 1956).   Reiter presented convincing evidence that the inhibitory action of pectin on the production of T2 phage is primarily due to a prevention of the irreversible step of adsorption.   The phage which had been adsorbed in the presence of pectin was not inactivated, had not penetrated, and could be recovered in an active form by elution, or by artificial lysis of the bacteria.   Since excess NaCl reversed the inhibition, pectin was considered to act as a polyelectrolyte which can compete for cations. In addition to its ability to interfere with adsorption, pectin may also affect phage multiplication as evidenced by the low burst sizes obtained when pectin was added after adsorption. The inhibition of T2 multiplication by citrus pectin was previously reported by Maurer and Woolley (1948). Their conclusion that the pectin might act by inducing a lysogenic state was not supported by experimental data and can now be explained by the findings of Reiter.

Our final consideration in the prevention of adsorption deals with those agents which can antagonize the organic cofactors for adsorption. Delbrück (1948) found that indole can prevent the adsorption of certain of the T4 strains that require tryptophan as a cofactor. The relation between indole and tryptophan in activation of phages is not clear (Chapter XVI).

2. Prevention of Penetration

Prevention of penetration refers to the ability of a chemical agent to prevent the injection of the phage DNA into the bacterial host. In the case of T5, as discussed in Chapter XI, this process requires calcium ions and can be stopped by the addition of citrate. Other polyvalent cations are also involved, as evidenced by the inhibitory action of the chelating agent Versene on T2 production (Kozloff and Henderson, 1955). When T2 is adsorbed to bacteria in the presence of the chelator, the bacteria are killed but no production of phage ensues. That this is indeed interference with injection is shown by the fact that 90 per cent of the adsorbed phage DNA can be removed from the bacteria by the Blendor technique as compared to 30 per cent in the absence of versene. Kozloff and Henderson interpreted this result to mean that metal complexes participate in the injection of DNA in a manner analogous to the action of cadmium cyanide on T2 particles. Versene presumably acts by combining with metals on the bacterial surface. Other chelating agents may act in the same way. The action of chymotrypsin as an inhibitor of rhizobium phage is suggestive of an interference with penetration. Chymotrypsin does not prevent adsorption but inhibits phage production only when added before the phage (Kleczkowski and Kleczkowski, 1954). Another potent chelating agent, 8-hydroxyquinoline, is also known to inhibit phage production (Wooley, Murphy, Bond, and Perrine, 1952).

Hershey and Chase (1952) have shown that when T2 is treated with formaldehyde, it is rendered incapable of injecting its DNA into the cells to which it attaches. The inactivated phage can still adsorb to and kill the bacteria but this adsorption does not sensitize the phage DNA to deoxyribonuclease. Seventy per cent of the adsorbed phage DNA can be detached from the bacteria in a form which is still resistant to the action of deoxyribonuclease. It is apparent from this experiment that formaldehyde inactivates an ingredient of T2 phage which is required for the injection process. Brown and Kozloff (1957) have shown that a phage enzyme is involved in this step. This enzyme which is located in the tail of the phage and paves the way for injection by dissolving the cell wall might well be the site of inactivation by formaldehyde.

3. Inhibition at the Intracellular Level

Since the two major constituents of the phage particle are protein and DNA, we can largely restrict our discussion of direct interference with phage synthesis to the processes concerned with the synthesis of the two macromolecules. Because the phage itself is devoid of any independent metabolic activity, many reactions which are required for the synthesis of phage protein and phage DNA must be operative in uninfected bacteria. The same conclusion follows from the vast number of agents that suppress phage synthesis and bacterial growth equally. This aspect of the problem is relevant only when the attention of the investigator is focused on differential inhibition and chemotherapeutic response. It becomes irrelevant when the analysis is concerned primarily with the sequence and interdependence of biosynthetic steps.

Agents which prevent the synthesis of protein and nucleic

acids may operate by interfering with nonspecific energy-yielding reactions, by preventing synthesis or polymerization of the essential building blocks, or by interfering with the synthesis or function of specific cofactors. Numerous agents of many types are known to inhibit both phage and bacteria and no attempt will be made to list them here. The effects of literally hundreds of compounds are reported in several heroic surveys (Wooley, Murphy, Bond, and Perrine, 1952; Bourke, Robbins, and Smith, 1952; Graham and Nelson, 1954).

a. Interference with Energy Metabolism

The over-all energy supply of the bacterial cell is furnished through an integration of enzymes involved in the uptake of oxygen and the transport of electrons, the oxidation and fermentation of utilizable carbohydrates, the formation of energy-rich phosphate bonds, and the regeneration of essential co-enzymes. Upon infection with phage, the over-all energy supply remains the same but it is now directed toward the synthesis of phage rather than bacteria (Cohen and Anderson, 1946; Cohen, 1949). The action of enzyme poisons which are known to be inhibitors of energy production further serves to indicate that the energy supply which is essential for phage synthesis is a product of the enzyme activities of the bacteria. The synthesis of a variety of phages can be completely prevented by azide, cyanide, fluoride, arsenite, iodoacetate, and 2,4-dinitrophenol. With few exceptions, the multiplication of the uninfected bacteria is also inhibited. The exceptions are reported in terms such as "little," "not appreciable," "essentially inactive," or "materially unaffected." At any rate, differential action is observed only over a limited and, in some cases, very narrow range of concentrations. Some differential impairment of phage synthesis was obtained with cyanide (Dolby, 1955; Czekalowski, 1952), arsenite (Dolby, 1955; Asheshov, Hall, and Flon, 1955), fluoride (d'Herelle, 1926) and 2,4-dinitrophenol (Fitzgerald and Babbitt, 1946; Czekalowski, 1952).

Under special conditions where uninfected bacteria are unable to grow but can still produce phage when infected, phage production is completely halted by respiratory poisons (Spizizen, 1943b; Price, 1947b). In the system described by Price, the inhibition of phage synthesis in penicillin-inhibited staphylococci by azide, fluoride, and iodoacetate is accompanied by a decrease in ATP synthesis.

Another action of the metabolic poisons is their ability to promote lysis of infected cells (Cohen, 1949; Heagy, 1950; Doermann, 1952; Anderson and Doermann, 1952a). When bacteria are infected with the T2 or its relatives in the presence of cyanide, iodoacetate, or 2,4-dinitrophenol, the adsorption of only a few particles per cell immediately initiates lysis from without with the loss of the adsorbed phage. This does not occur with other phages. In all cases, lysis fails when the inhibitors are added during the early part of the latent period, but the infecting phage is lost and subsequent production does not occur. When added during the second half of the latent period, premature lysis is induced with the liberation of those active phages which have already been formed.

b. Prevention of Protein Synthesis

As indicated in Chapter XIV, bacteria which are unable to synthesize amino acids as a result of either a physiological or genetic impairment will not support the growth of phage unless the medium is supplemented with the required amino acid. Chemical interference with amino acid metabolism, and hence protein synthesis, would be expected to result in a cessation of phage formation. The inhibitors which have been examined are structural analogues of natural amino acids. Analogues of glycine, tryptophan, methionine, glutamic acid, and phenylalanine have been found to inhibit phage production as well as bacterial multiplication.

The first test of an amino acid analogue as an inhibitor of phage synthesis was made by Spizizen (1943a). He found that aminomethane sulfonic acid, a structural analogue of glycine, inhibits the production of a coliphage under special conditions in which phage growth is supported by glycine alone.

A detailed analysis of the effects of the tryptophan analogue, 5-methyltryptophan, on T2 synthesis was made by Cohen and Fowler (1947). When the analogue is added at the time of infection, or even during the first half of the latent period after infection, phage is not formed and the adsorbed phage is eventually lost. When added during the latter part of the latent period it behaves like other metabolic inhibitors by lysing the infected cell and liberating the intracellular phage (Doermann, 1952). Tryptophan reverses the inhibition under conditions which will also reverse the inhibition of bacterial growth. Upon the addition of tryptophan to inhibited infected bacteria, phage formation resumes and lysis occurs after a time which is equal to the difference between the normal latent period and the time interval between infection and addition of the inhibitor.

Similar results were obtained with methionine sulfoxide, an antimetabolite of glutamic acid (Fowler and Cohen, 1948). Lysis and liberation of T2 is prevented by methionine sulfoxide and this effect is reversed by glutamic acid. The inhibition of phage growth in this instance is not complete.

The differential action of sodium salicylate and sodium gentisate, as inhibitors of T2 multiplication, can be reversed by amino acids (Spizizen, Hampil, and Kenney, 1951). Phage production in the presence of salicylate is supported by the addition of tryptophan or its precursors, indole and anthranilic acid. The inhibition of bacterial multiplication requires concentrations of salicylate 6 to 10 times greater than the minimal concentration for phage inhibition. Bacterial inhibition, however, is not reversed by tryptophan but can be reversed by pantothenate which has no effect of the inhibition of phage. This is a unique example of differential action with respect to both inhibition and its reversal.

It is not unusual that natural amino acids may themselves act as inhibitory antimetabolites of other amino acids. Serine and leucine can inhibit the multiplication of T2 and the inhibition by leucine can be reversed by isoleucine, valine, or norleucine (Fowler and Cohen, 1948). Cysteine has been found toxic for phage development and causes an abortive loss of the adsorbed phage (Fowler and Cohen, 1948, Mutsaars, 1950; Tanami and Kawashima, 1953). The inhibition by cysteine has been related to its ability to bind metals (Spizizen, Kenney, and Hampil, 1951), but also to a more specific disorganization of amino acid metabolism, particularly that of threonine (Gots and Hunt, 1953). A lysogenic strain of *E. coli* K12, which is known to be inhibited by valine, will not produce lambda phage in the presence of valine unless isoleucine is added (Gots and Hunt, 1953). An inhibition of T2 growth by methionine has also been reported (Czekalowski, 1952).

c. *Prevention of DNA Synthesis as a Consequence of Protein Deficiency*

Cohen (1948) showed that 5-methyltryptophan inhibits both protein and DNA synthesis in bacteria infected with T2. This suggested that protein formation is an essential prerequisite for DNA synthesis. Further analysis by Burton (1955) showed that if deprivation of amino acids is delayed for 7 minutes after infection with T2, phage and subsequent protein synthesis is still prevented, but DNA of the hydroxymethylcytosine type is formed. Similar results have been obtained independently with another inhibitor of protein synthesis, chloramphenicol (Melechen, 1955; Tomizawa and Sunakawa, 1956, Hershey and Melechen, 1957). This antibiotic had been shown previously to prevent phage formation at some stage (Edlinger, 1951; Bozeman, Wisseman, Hopps, and Danawskas, 1954). The essentials of these findings may be summarized by saying that the synthesis of phage DNA requires an initial synthesis of protein which may be inhibited by 5-methyltryptophan or chloramphenicol. If synthesis of the initial protein is first allowed, continued synthesis of protein is not required for DNA synthesis. Thus, the delayed addition of the inhibitors will permit DNA synthesis but will prevent the formation of further protein which is necessary for phage growth. Hershey and Melechen (1957) employed this principle to demonstrate that synthesis of phage-precursor DNA is independent of synthesis of phage-precursor protein.

d. *Prevention of DNA Synthesis*

Specific attack against the nucleic acid metabolism of phage-infected bacteria has been attempted with a number of structural analogues of the purine and pyrimidine bases.   Inhibitions have been reported in experiments with bacteria and phage, but the effects on DNA synthesis were usually not tested.   The anti-purines whose effects on phage production are significant enough to warrant further analyses include those with triazine or triazole substitutions (Matthews and Smith, 1955; Wooley, Murphy, Bond, and Perrine, 1952) and 2,6-diaminopurine (Asheshov, Hall, and Flon, 1955).   The latter deserves special attention since it is able to eliminate kappa from paramecia (Stock, Jacobson, and Williamson, 1951).

The antipyrimidines of particular interest are those which act as thymine antagonists by virtue of a halogen substitution in the 5 position.   These do not prevent DNA synthesis but may be incorporated into the DNA molecule in place of thymine.   The effects of this incorporation on phage activity will be considered in a later section of this chapter.   The presence of the unique pyrimidine, 5-(hydroxymethyl)cytosine, in the DNA of T2 and related phages should offer a possible target for specific attack. Under special conditions where this pyrimidine can act as a growth factor for bacterial auxotrophs which require the pyrimidine moiety (2-methyl-5-(hydroxymethyl)cytosine) of thiamine for growth, "methioprim" (the 2-methylmercapto derivative) behaves as a competitive inhibitor of 5-(hydroxy-methyl)cytosine. The production of T2, however, is not affected by this analogue (Gots, unpublished observations).

e. *Prevention of Coenzyme Activity*

Structural analogues of the B vitamins are known to act as specific competitive inhibitors of either the synthesis or function of the coenzymes. As inhibitors of phage production, special consideration may be given to the antimetabolites of *p*-aminobenzoic acid, niacin, and pyridoxine.

In the presence of sulfanilamide, *p*-aminobenzoic acid is required for the growth of *E. coli* B. The requirement can be progressively decreased by successive additions of methionine, xanthine, thymine, and valine, all of which are end products whose syntheses require the participation of a coenzyme derived from *p*-aminobenzoic acid. The coenzyme, presumably a folic acid derivative, mediates the transfer of single carbon units. Rutten, Winkler, and DeHaan (1950) looked for a *p*-aminobenzoic acid requirement for phage production by infecting bacteria which, in medium supplemented with the end product metabolites, are permitted to grow in high concentrations of sulfanilamide. Phage production was obtained. However, if the bacteria were first grown in the sulfanilamide-metabolite medium and were then infected, they no longer supported the growth of T2, T4, and T6 coliphages, but could still produce T1, T3, and T7. The inhibition of T2 and its relatives could be relieved by *p*-aminobenzoic acid. This indicates that growth of the T2-like phages requires a metabolite different from those that suffice for growth of bacteria and other phages. This metabolite should differ from others by one carbon atom. A promising candidate is 5-(hydroxymethyl)cytosine. Cohen (1953b) considered this possibility but his results were disappointing since the inhibition of T4 by sulfanilamide could not be reversed by 5-(hydroxymethyl)cytosine or its deoxyriboside, or by 5-(hydroxymethyl)uracil.

Deoxpyridoxine can prevent the liberation of phage under conditions which do not affect bacterial growth (Wooley and Murphy, 1949; Asheshov, Hall, and Flon, 1955). Since its inhibitory effects are reversed by various organic acids as well as pyridoxine, its role as a specific antimetabolite cannot be accurately assessed. Furthermore, sufficient analyses have not been made to determine whether the inhibitory effects are directed against internal metabolism or against some other stage of the infection sequence. The same reservation must be made in evaluating the significance of the differential action of niacin analogues such as 6-amino nicotinic acid (Wooley, Murphy, Bond, and Perrine, 1952) and isonicotinic acid (Bourke, Robbins, and Smith, 1952). In the latter case an interesting observation was made but not pursued. Lysates of T2 obtained in the presence of isonicotinic acid killed bacteria on subsequent infection without the production of new phage progeny.

f. Prevention of Ma.uration

Only one class of substances, the acridine dyes, are known to prevent phage growth while permitting synthesis of phage protein and nucleic acid, but they are of special interest for that reason. When bacteria are infected with T2 in the presence of proflavine, synthesis of protein and DNA occurs and the bacteria lyse as usual, but do not liberate infective particles (DeMars, 1955). Phage-specific elements are found, however, and one can only suppose that some final step in the maturation of the particles is blocked (Foster, 1948).

This example is also exceptional because the effect depends on the genotype of the phage. The growth of many phages is not blocked by low concentrations of the inhibitor, and sensitive phages can mutate to resistant forms (Foster, 1948). In the so-called defective strains of lysogenic bacteria it is also possible to show that phage mutations can affect late steps in maturation (Chapter XIX). Because of their potential value in the study of phage morphogenesis, the effects of the acridines will be discussed in some detail.

The acridines gained prominence in the early days of chemotherapy as drugs which exhibited a remarkable degree of selective inhibition in protozoal diseases. Wolff and Janzen (1922) reported that trypaflavine (acriflavine) and rivanol can inhibit "bacteriophagy" with four different phages at concentrations too low to affect bacterial growth or destroy free phage particles. This observation lay dormant for 24 years until Fitzgerald and Babbitt (1946) found that 8 out of 11 acridines inhibit the mass

TABLE XVI

Inhibition of Phage by Acridines

Acridine	Differential inhibition of phage	No differential effect
Acriflavine	Coli[a,b,c,d] T series[e,f,g,h] Salmonella[a] Shigella[a] Staphylococcus[a,i,e] Actinomyces[j] B. subtilis[i]	Shigella[e]
Proflavine	Coli[b] T2, T4, T5, T6[f,k] Pseudomonas[m] Staphylococcus[o]	T1, T3, T7[k] Salmonella[l] Streptococcus[n]
Rivanol	Coli[a,c,d] Salmonella[a,l] Shigella[a] Staphylococcus[a,o]	
Quinacrine	Coli[b,c] T series[h]	
Phosphine GRN	Coli[b,e] Staphylococcus[o]	Shigella[e] Staphylococcus[e]
5-Aminoacridine	Pseudomonas[m] Staphylococcus[o] Coli[p]	
2,7-Diaminoacridine	Pseudomonas[m]	
3,6-Diaminoacridine	Streptococcus[n]	
Sulfa-acridine	T2, T4, T6[h]	T1, T3, T5, T7[h]

[a] Wolff and Janzen (1922).
[b] Fitzgerald and Babbitt (1946).
[c] Mutsaars (1951a).
[d] Mutsaars (1951b).
[e] Smith (1949)
[f] Bourke, Robbins, and Smith (1952).
[g] Hoshino (1954b).
[h] Bird (1956).
[i] Nicolle and Mimica (1947).

[j] Woodruff, Nunheimer, and Lee (1947).
[k] Foster (1948).
[l] Boyd and Bradley (1951).
[m] Dickinson (1948).
[n] Graham and Nelson (1954).
[o] Hotchin (1951).
[p] Fitzgerald and Lee (1946).

lysis of bacteria infected with a coliphage at a very low multiplicity of infection. The concentrations used were insufficient to prevent the growth of uninfected bacteria. These observations revived interest in the acridines and a flood of reports followed which confirmed the differential action of a variety of acridines against a variety of phages. Table XVI summarizes this work, which shows that not all phages are inhibited selectively relative to their hosts. Mutant phages resistant to acriflavine have been isolated by selection (Foster, 1948; Mutsaars, 1951b; Hoshino, 1954b). Differential inhibition cannot be demonstrated with these mutants since they are now more resistant than the bacterial host.

The stage at which proflavine (2,8-diaminoacridine) prevents the development of phage has been studied extensively. The analysis by Foster (1948) separates phages into those (T2, T4, T5, and T6) whose development is prevented by concentrations which are 0.1 to 0.5 the concentration required to inhibit bacteria, and those (T1, T3, and T7) which are inhibited only at bacteriostatic concentrations. The activity of free phage and its adsorption to bacteria are not affected by proflavine. Lysis occurs after the normal latent period but no infectious particles are found in the lysates. The same result is obtained when the acridine is added at any time during the first half of the latent period. When added later, the bursts yield only those phage particles which had already matured before the addition of proflavine.

DeMars, Luria, Fisher, and Levinthal (1953) examined lysates obtained in the presence of proflavine and found the same "doughnuts" (empty phage heads) that had been seen in premature lysates not containing proflavine (Levinthal and Fisher, 1952). The phage heads contain sulfur and phage-specific complement-fixing antigens but no DNA. The antigen which combines with neutralizing antibody is also present in proflavine lysates but can be separated from the phage heads. DNA containing hydroxymethylcytosine is also found (DeMars, 1955), as well as tail pins (Kellenberger and Sechaud, 1957). Thus the synthesis of at least four macromolecular phage components proceeds unhampered by proflavine. Phage production is arrested at a late stage that may call for the assembly of these several components (Chapter XI).

The mechanism by which proflavine interferes with maturation is unknown. It may act directly on an enzyme required for assembly, or block the synthesis of an unknown phage constituent, or alter the nucleic acid produced. Nucleic acids are known to combine chemically with the acridines and the often reported ability of nucleic acids, both RNA and DNA, to reverse the inhibitory action of acridines may well be an expression of this chemical combination. An indication that the DNA formed by phage-infected bacteria under proflavine inhibition may be different from normal phage DNA was described by Astrachan and Volkin (1957). DNA labeled with P^{32} was isolated from the proflavine-treated system and mixed with 20 times the amount of authentic phage DNA. The nucleotide sequences obtained by degradation of the DNA mixture were then examined for differences in specific activities. Differences could not be detected among the products which were obtained by the action of deoxyribonuclease. However, significant differences were found at higher levels of organization among the larger polynucleotide fragments obtained by heating the DNA mixture.

Final evaluation of the mechanism of action of proflavine must also take into account the reports of Manson (1954, 1957) describing inhibitory effects on DNA synthesis. In a medium containing a low level of inorganic phosphate sufficient for normal growth of T2, proflavine prevents the synthesis of DNA and utilization of glucose and inorganic phosphate. With a high level of phosphate, phage development is still suppressed but DNA synthesis is normal. In T5 infection, high levels of phosphate do not suffice to reverse proflavine inhibition of DNA synthesis.

4. Abortive Infection

The term abortive adsorption (Benzer, 1952) or abortive infection (Benzer and Jacob, 1953; Gross, 1954a) refers to the tendency of bacteria, infected or held under conditions in which growth of phage is arrested, to lose the capacity to produce phage when transferred to normally favorable conditions. To preserve the singularity of the phenomenon one excludes from consideration those conditions, such as high temperature, that destroy bacteria or phage separately. Numerous examples are described by Adams (1954, 1955) and Northrop (1955a) and some have already been referred to in this chapter. We discuss here only a few examples that are at least partly understandable.

The abortive infection of bacteria by phage T2 in the presence of proflavine has already been described. Since proflavine blocks phage growth without preventing bacterial lysis, the loss of capacity to produce phage is to that extent explained and is not in itself very interesting.

A different kind of abortive infection is observed when T5 adsorbs to bacteria in the absence of calcium (Adams, 1949b). In this case the absence of calcium prevents injection (Luria and Steiner, 1954). Bacteria held in the calcium-free medium gradually lose their capacity to produce phage on subsequent addition of calcium (Adams, 1949b). The infected bacteria undergo cytological changes and are unable to multiply (Chapter XII). These results may be summarized by saying that adsorption of phage under conditions in which injection fails causes damage to the bacterium which may prevent subsequent injection when the conditions are changed or, if injection is not irreversibly prevented, the capacity to produce phage is nevertheless irreversibly lost. This effect of noninjecting phage recalls the effects of T2 ghosts on bacteria (Chapter V) and other types of evidence for cellular damage at the time of infection (Chapter XI).

In other instances the progressive loss of capacity to produce phage is subject to nutritional control. Bacteria infected with phage in the presence of cyanide may lose productive potential rapidly in simple media (Doermann, 1952), or very slowly in nutrient broth (Benzer and Jacob, 1953), although injection is probably slowed or prevented by cyanide in both instances (Benzer, personal communication). Similarly, bacteria first starved and then infected with T2 in salt solution lose productive potential by a process that can be partly prevented by feeding amino acids but not by feeding glucose (Gross, 1954b). In this instance, too, there is indirect evidence for delayed injection; the phage-producing potential of the rescuable infected cells remains sensitive to antiphage serum for variable times up to 10 minutes after infection (Gross, 1954a).

For experimental purposes, it is often desirable to be able to infect bacteria under conditions in which abortive infection does not occur, and yet phage growth is arrested at an early stage. The use of cyanide for this purpose, mentioned above, is not always successful, probably because injection is interfered with. Chloramphenicol added before infection may prove more useful. It arrests phage growth at an early stage (Tomizawa and Sunakawa, 1956) but does not interfere with injection of T2 (Melechen and Hershey, personal communication). Low temperatures, on the other hand, are not suitable (Adams 1954, 1955).

5. Noninfective Phage Particles Containing Structural Analogues

In the case of abortive infection, phage development is halted before the completion of a mature phage particle. With other chemical manipulations it is possible to allow phage development to proceed to completion with the formation of structurally mature phage which, however, are noninfective. In effect, still-birth rather than abortion is brought about. This results from the incorporation of an unnatural amino acid or pyrimidine into the protein or nucleic acid of the phage.

In the presence of sulfanilamide, *E. coli* requires thymine and other metabolites for growth. Utilizing this fact, Dunn and Smith (1954) were able to replace thymine in the DNA of T2 and T5 by analogues of thymine in which the 5-methyl group had been replaced with bromine, iodine, or chlorine. For example, T2 DNA, which normally contains 30 per cent thymine among its bases, could be obtained with 6 per cent thymine and 24 per cent 5-bromouracil. The infectivity of such phage progeny was measured in terms of optical density at 2,600 A per plaque-forming particle (Chapter VII). Preparations were obtained in which 50 to 90 per cent of the particles were noninfective. Since the analogues were present before and after infection it is reasonable to assume that all the phage particles, infective or not, contained the unnatural base. Such preparations yield a high proportion of mutants (Litman and Pardee, 1956). It will be of interest to learn more about the properties of these unnatural phage particles.

Attempts to obtain similar incorporation of purine analogues have been disappointing. Incorporation of 8-azaguanine into the RNA of *E. coli* B, but not into bacterial or phage DNA, was obtained by Lasnitzki (1954). A comprehensive discussion of the incorporation of analogues into RNA and DNA may be found in the review by Matthews and Smith (1955).

Proteins may also be modified by replacing a natural amino acid with its structural analogue. The incorporation of 7-azatryptophan into bacterial and phage proteins was demonstrated by Pardee, Shore, and Prestidge (1956). T2 produced after infection in the presence of azatryptophan is noninfective and its protein contains 0.4 per cent azatryptophan. Incorporation was also obtained with tryptozan but not with 5-methyltryptophan.

6. Miscellaneous Inhibitors

a. Antibiotics

In the main, antibiotics prevent phage formation only to the extent of their antibacterial properties. Like other metabolic inhibitors they also may induce premature lysis, thus decreasing the normal phage yield. As mentioned previously, penicillin allows phage production under conditions which inhibit bacterial multiplication.   The yield of phage may be decreased in the manner mentioned, particularly of gram-positive bacteria (Krueger, Cohn, Smith, and McGuire, 1948; Elford, 1948; Himmelweit, 1945; Nicolle and Faguet, 1947).   The accelerated lysis in the presence of penicillin may well be a manifestation of inhibited synthesis of cell wall material.

In most cases, the inhibition of phage production by streptomycin or dihydrostreptomycin parallels bacterial inhibition. However, differential inhibition of phage was demonstrated by Edlinger (1949) and by Bourke, Robbins, and Smith (1952). In both cases the action could not be explained by the previously reported ability of streptomycin to inactivate free phage particles (Cohen, 1947b; Jones, 1945).

Aureomycin affects the production of T3 (Altenbern, 1953) as well as that of other coliphages (Masry, 1953).   In all cases, aureomycin decreases the rate of adsorption, prolongs the latent period, and reduces the burst size by at least one half.

A number of antibiotics with specific antiphage properties, primarily phagicidal, have been described by Asheshov and his associates.   The notable members of this series include phagolessin A58 (Hall and Asheshov, 1953) and chrysomycin (Strelitz, Flon, and Asheshov, 1955).

b. Aromatic Diamidines

The aromatic diamidines, which include propamidine, pentamidine, and stilbamidine, were introduced into the chemotherapeutic arena as trypanosomacidal agents.   Their action in phage-bacterial systems shows two opposite effects.   Pentamidine permits growth of T1, and even increased production, under conditions which are completely bacteriostatic for the uninfected bacteria (Boyd and Bradley, 1951; Amos and Vollmayer, 1957).   On the other hand, propamidine and stilbamidine, but not pentamidine, prevent the production of other phages (Hotchin, 1951; Bourke, Robbins, and Smith, 1952; Bird, 1956).   These findings have particular significance in view of the often recorded similarities between the actions of the diamidines and the acridines.   Indeed, an acridine-like effect is suggested by the fact that propamidine yields sterile lysates of T2-infected bacteria (Bourke, Robbins, and Smith, 1952).

c. Dyestuffs

Antiseptic dyes usually inactivate free phage particles.   The inactivation may be direct or, as in the case of methylene blue, it may require the participation of light and oxidizable substrates.   In a few cases, however, dyes have been shown to differentially inhibit phage production without affecting the activity of the free phage.   Most notable of these include crystal violet (Graham and Nelson, 1954) and malachite green (Wolff and Janzen, 1922; Fitzgerald and Babbitt, 1946; Czekalowski, 1952).

7. Summary

Phage production can be prevented by a wide variety of chemical inhibitors.   These may inhibit phage formation only or, if the reactions which they affect are also required for host metabolism, they may also inhibit the growth of uninfected bacteria.   Infection can be prevented by interfering with the adsorption or penetration processes.   Prevention of adsorption can be obtained by destroying the organ of attachment of the phage with strong oxidizing agents or metal-cyanide complexes, by destroying the complementary receptor sites of the host by a variety of chemical treatments, or by interference at the level of cofactor requirements for adsorption.   Penetration may be prevented by chelating agents, or by inactivating a structure in the phage, presumably an enzyme, necessary for the injection of DNA into the host.   The synthesis of protein and nucleic acid may be inhibited by numerous agents which include respiratory poisons, specific inhibitors of protein synthesis, and analogues of amino acids, purines, pyrimidines, and vitamins.   In the known cases, any interference with protein and nucleic acid synthesis prevents not only phage production, but also multiplication of uninfected bacteria.

Three instances of chemical interference deserve special mention. By the use of chloramphenicol to prevent protein synthesis it is possible on the one hand to show a dependence of DNA synthesis on prior protein synthesis, and on the other hand to demonstrate the sequential synthesis of phage-precursor DNA and protein. The acridines possess the remarkable property of blocking maturation without preventing synthesis of phage DNA and organized protein structures. Finally, by feeding appropriate analogues, intact but noninfective phage particles may be produced whose properties remain to be investigated.

CHAPTER XVI

MUTATION AND PHENOTYPIC VARIATION IN PHAGES

D'Herelle (1926) was so much impressed with the capacity for variation to be observed in phage that he believed all phages to be variants of a single species. Other workers, struck by the constancy of phage types, strongly opposed d'Herelle's view. Some, though certainly aware that not all phages were alike, wrote (and thought) in terms of "the bacteriophage." In part, these different attitudes merely reflected different interests. In effect, however, they produced a confusion of ideas exactly parallel to that afflicting an earlier generation of microbiologists who were trying to sort out the meaning of variability and constancy met with among bacteria.

Today, as a result of systematic study, we know that phages belong to many well-separated types and that limited variation of several kinds is permissible within each type. The present chapter summarizes the observed range of variation.

Many of the early observations on variation in phages have been confirmed by more thorough study and many are probably forever unconfirmable. Many observations of the latter type can doubtless be ascribed to failure to distinguish between variation and simple contamination. Less obvious is the necessity to distinguish between heritable and nonheritable variations. Only in recent times has it become evident that certain types of nonheritable variation in phages are very common.

The material treated in this chapter will be discussed at some length because much of it has not been presented elsewhere as a coherent topic, and because it is the conviction of the author that most of the phenomena mentioned deserve more thorough study than is being devoted to them at present.

1. Definitions

The term *genotype* refers to the genetic constitution of a phage *line*, inherited from ancestors and transmitted to offspring. To determine the genotype of a phage particle one examines a progeny derived from it or, more exactly, to demonstrate a genotypic difference between two phage particles one examines progenies derived from each under conditions as nearly identical as possible. Any constant difference in properties observed in this way is said to be heritable and implies a difference in genotype. Other criteria, such as persistence under a variety of conditions of growth, or genetic recombination when applicable, may be used to further elucidate the difference.

A genotypic difference arising within a single phage line can be ascribed to *mutation*. Here further criteria can always be applied. A mutation originates as a stepwise difference, producing a mutant clone within the parental line. Such clones should recur at random, producing a characteristic distribution of clone sizes (Luria, 1951). A mutation should be identifiable as a local change in genotype when analyzed by genetic recombination (Chapter XVIII). The best studied phage mutations show all these characteristics, but it is fairly certain that other kinds exist (Sections 3h and 5 below).

The term *phenotype*, literally "what shows," refers to directly observable characteristics, as opposed to genotype, which is a somewhat more abstract concept and therefore easier to define. With reference to a phage line, the phenotype corresponds to the genotype (by definition), with the proviso that the phenotype may vary with the conditions of observation whereas the genotype does not, but determines the phenotype under all conditions (again by definition). Particular aspects of the phenotype of a phage particle, therefore, may depend more on the conditions under which the particle was formed than on pertinent aspects of its genotype, though of course the general features of the particle will always reflect its genotype.

To sum up, the word *phenotype* is used to refer to observable characteristics, usually a particular one, of phage particles, whereas the word *genotype* denotes the constant determiner of the recurring phenotype of a phage line observed under standard conditions.   The word *mutation*, in general, refers to any observed change in genotype that occurs in an otherwise pure clone.   A mutation is a heritable change; a change in phenotype may be heritable or not; finally, and unfortunately, the phrase *phenotypic modification* means specifically a nonheritable change in phenotype.

2. Nonhereditary (Phenotypic) Variation

Nonheritable changes in the properties of phage particles occur under a variety of circumstances.   Most of the known examples were reviewed by Luria (1953b) in a definitive manner.   The several kinds may be classified as follows.

a. Host-Induced Modifications

Nonheritable changes in the properties of phage particles in response to growth in different bacterial hosts were called host-induced modifications by Luria (1953b) and host-controlled variations by Bertani and Weigle (1953).   All known examples have many features in common but fall into two classes in one respect.

The larger class is adaptive in the sense explained by the following example.   A phage grown on host A attacks host A with high efficiency of plating but only a small proportion of the particles is able to plate on host B.   However, the progeny of these few particles is able to plate on host A and on host B with approximately equal efficiency.   Host B has brought to light an adaptive modification of the phage.   The result described thus far does not enable one to distinguish between a host range mutation and a phenotypic modification of host range.   When the modified phage are grown again on host A, they revert completely and in one growth cycle to the original host range, with a low plating efficiency on host B as compared with host A.   This manner of reversal of phenotype suggests a phenotypic modification rather than a mutation, which would be expected to revert with much lower frequency. Numerous examples of adaptive host-controlled modifications are described in Chapter XXI, together with additional evidence for their nonmutational origin. The phenomenon has been observed in many phages by Anderson and Felix (1952), Ralston and Krueger (1952, 1954), Frédéricq (1950), N. Collins Bruce (cited by Luria, 1953b), Bertani and Weigle (1953), Frédéricq (1953), Garen and Zinder (1955), Beumer and Beumer-Jochmans (1955), and E. B. Collins (1956).

Only one example of a nonadaptive host-induced modification is known (Luria and Human, 1952), but it was the first host-induced modification to be recognized, and is exceptional also because the modifying host (a particular strain of B/4) is a mutant of the customary host (B). The nonadaptive character of the restricted host range is indicated by the fact that T2 grown on B/4 loses its capacity to grow on B/4, but regains this capacity on being returned to host B.

The common characteristics of all these host-induced modifications may be listed as follows (Luria, 1953b).

1. The modifications of the phage do not affect its ability to adsorb to its various bacterial hosts. The restricted growth on certain hosts is not due solely to failure to inject (Luria and Human, 1952; Garen and Zinder, 1955), though efficiency of injection has not been measured in any instance. The abortive infection may kill the refractory host, as with T2 and with certain Vi phages of *S. typhi,* or not, as with P2 or P22. This difference probably reflects general differences in the properties of the phages, not differences in the nature of the host-induced modification.

2. The few particles of a restricted phage that manage to grow in cells of the refractory host are not exceptional particles; rather the productive bacteria are exceptional. This is indicated by the fact that the proportion of productive bacteria varies with the conditions under which the bacteria were grown before infection and with treatments, such as ultraviolet irradiation, applied to the bacteria before infection. Single bursts of phage issuing from different cells of the modifying host seem to contain identical proportions of particles capable of growing in (exceptional cells of) the refractory host, in contrast to the expectations for mutational changes in the properties of the phage (Luria, 1953b; Ralston and Krueger, 1954). However, it does not follow that the growth potential of all the particles of the modified phage is identical (Luria, 1953b).

3.   In general, all of the phage particles issuing from a given cell of the modifying host exhibit the altered host range. In most instances, too, all the cells of the modifying host produce the same modification of the phage, if they produce phage at all. In one instance this is not true. One strain of B/4 contains cells of which some yield "normal" T2 and some restricted T2, depending on the age of the culture at the time of infection (Luria, 1953b). In other instances, the modifying tendency of the host is determined, in part, by carried prophages unrelated to the phage undergoing modification (Chapter XXI).

The phenomenon of transduction (Chapter XIX) also furnishes examples of nonheritable variations of phage particles controlled by the host. These variations differ from the examples cited above in several respects. In most cases only a minority of the particles is affected. The alteration may or may not affect the growth potential of the phage. The mechanism is presumed to be quite different from that responsible for other examples of host-controlled variation. The only reason for mentioning transduction here is the possibility that it may possess unknown features common to all host-induced modifications.

In summary, nonheritable modifications of host range are produced with very high efficiency when phages multiply in certain hosts. Since these do not in general affect the ability of the phage particles to complete the initial steps of infection, the alteration is probably localized in some of the injected materials (Luria, 1953b). The next question is unanswered: are the modifications localized in DNA or in some of the minor components of the phage particles?

b. Phenocopies

The term *phenocopy* means, literally, a nonheritable variation that mimics in phenotype a heritable variation. We use it here to include all nonheritable variations that seem, like mutations, to arise "spontaneously," that is, under conditions not subject to experimental control. Since only one example has been studied the name is not very important.

Stocks of T5 and related phages contain about one particle per thousand that is unusually resistant to thermal inactivation (Lark and Adams, 1953; Chapter V). In this respect the exceptional particles resemble a much rarer mutant present in the same stocks, but in the majority of the resistant particles the resistance is not heritable. Remarkably enough, the number of phenocopies per single cell yield of T5 is clonally distributed, that is, most yields contain no resistant particles, some contain only one or two, but a few contain 10 or more. Luria (1953b) suggested a kind of pseudo-mutation to account for this result. Probably an equally satisfactory interpretation would ascribe the variation to differences in the conditions of growth in different host cells (Adams, 1953a). In either case some sort of host control seems to be called for, but it is clearly different from that seen in typical host-controlled variations, in which every particle in single bursts is affected. Different phages related to T5 grown in different hosts yields similar proportions of heat resistant particles (Adams, 1953a).

c. Phenotypic Mixing

The typical examples of host-controlled variation reflect an interaction, probably indirect, between the genome of the modifying host and that of the phage to produce phage particles of modified phenotype. In mixed infection with related phages one sometimes sees an interaction between the two phage genomes to produce phage particles of modified phenotype. This phenomenon is called phenotypic mixing and its resemblance to host-controlled variation ends with the somewhat cryptic analogy suggested by the above statements.

The effect is best seen in the experiments of Streisinger (1956c) who studied mixed infections with specially prepared stocks of T2 and T4 that differ only with respect to a single genetic locus controlling the difference in specificity of adsorption in these two phages.   Thus T2 adsorbs to B and to B/4, but not to B/2, and T4 adsorbs to B and to B/2, but not to B/4.   The same locus controls the difference in serological specificity by which it is possible to prepare antisera neutralizing the infectivity of T2 but not T4, and vice versa.   This presumably means that the same component in the phage tail is responsible for specificity of adsorption and neutralization.

The issue of phage from bacteria mixedly infected with these special stocks of T2 and T4 contains particles of only the two expected genotypes: T2, forming clear plaques on the mixed indicator B+B/4, and T4, forming clear plaques on B+B/2, with none forming clear plaques on both indicators.   One can also determine the phenotype of the individual particles, both with respect to specificity of adsorption and specificity of neutralization by antiserum.   Either method reveals three phenotypes: particles resembling T2, particles resembling T4, and a new kind of particle that adsorbs to both B/2 and B/4, and is neutralized by both anti-T2 and anti-T4 sera.   More remarkable still, there is practically no correlation between phenotype and genotype of individual particles.   This result evidently means that the tail of a phage particle contains a certain number of unit structures, different in T2 and T4, and that a phage particle formed in a mixedly infected bacterium receives tail units of either kind, as well as a third structure determining the tail-specificity of its offspring, by more or less independent acts.

The phenomenon was first observed in crosses between T2 and T4 (Delbrück and Bailey, 1946; Novick and Szilard, 1951a) and is also seen in mixed infections with T2 and its *h* mutant (Hershey, Roesel, Chase, and Forman, 1951) and with lambda and its *h* mutant (Appleyard, McGregor, and Baird, 1956).   It has not been observed with respect to any characters not associated with specificity of adsorption.

Phenotypic mixing thus differs from host-induced modifications with respect to the interacting units, the characters affected, and the number of particles affected.   It shows in a remarkable way how two kinds of phage can cooperate in the formation of a single particle.

d. Other Phenotypic Modifications

Agencies such as specific antiserum, radiations, heat, and chemicals applied to extracellular phage particles produce, as far as is known, exclusively phenotypic effects.   They do not, at any rate, produce typical mutations.   Only a few examples are of significance in the present context.

Ralston and Krueger (1954) noted, as is commonly observed with phages, that the rate of loss of infectivity of the staphylococcal phage P14 at 59° C. varies with the host on which titrations are made.   As a result, the effect of heating mimics the effect of the host-induced modification; both produce the same restriction of host range.   This may or may not suggest a common point of action for heat and the host-induced modification, but two items of phage lore are worth citing in this connection.

On the one hand, antiserum and heating can produce similar restrictions of host range (Kalmanson and Bronfenbrenner, 1942).   Both antiserum and heating probably interfere with adsorption or penetration (Chapter VIII; Streisinger and Franklin, 1956).   Thus the effects of heat are probably quite different in principle from typical host-induced modifications. Ralston and Krueger did not make the pertinent test of reacting antiserum with their phage in its unrestricted host range modification.   Neither did they test the ability of the restricted phage produced by heating to adsorb to the refractory host.

It is possible that heat-inactivated phages can sometimes adsorb.   Strongly heated preparations of T2 often show small satellite plaques surrounding the few normal plaques appearing on assay plates (Hershey, Franklin, and Streisinger, personal communications).   This suggests that some of the heated phage particles can adsorb but fail to multiply unless helped out by unknown cofactors. The host-induced modifications, as we have seen, also show a dependence on bacterial physiology that might be interpreted in nutritional terms.

Both heated and host-modified phages might well be investigated to look for cofactor deficiencies (Luria and Human, 1952), and above all to settle the question of penetration. The promising test of penetration is cross-reactivation between phage pairs differing both in genetic markers and phenotypic modifications (Streisinger and Franklin, 1956; Garen and Zinder, 1955).

Another special case of phenotypic modification was described by Sagik (1954). He found that lysates of T2 often contain phage particles that are noninfective because of failure to adsorb. He demonstrated the noninfective particles by reactivating them in various ways, for example by gentle heating. A similar effect was demonstrated in another line of T2, not subject to heat activation, in another way (Hershey and Melechen, 1957). Sagik showed that at least part of the effect could be ascribed to interactions between free phage particles and other products, presumably related to receptor substances, released at the time of lysis. Adams (1955) found that even the active particles in such lysates fail to adsorb at 0°, whereas phage produced in salt-free broth, where it presumably cannot combine with the inhibitor, adsorbs equally well at 0 and 37° C. Y. T. Lanni and F. Lanni, in unpublished experiments, obtained evidence that the defective phage particles can be produced intracellularly, which throws doubt on the adequacy of Sagik's interpretation of the phenomenon.

3. Hereditary Variation (Mutation)

If one examines the properties of related phages such as T2, T4, T6, and C16, one finds both qualitative and quantitative differences in numerous properties. A catalogue of such differences would furnish a good idea of the capacity of the phages in the group to vary by mutation. For practical reasons, it may not be possible to observe all the potential mutations directly. However, by appropriate crossing one can transfer mutant genes from one strain to another for comparison and mapping, just as in higher organisms. This approach to descriptive phage genetics has been exploited particularly by Adams (1951b) and by Streisinger (1956b) with benefits of both expected and unexpected kinds. The information gained in this way will be utilized below when necessary to supplement information obtained by direct isolation of mutants.

a. Mutations Affecting Specificity of Adsorption

A given phage is likely to adsorb only to certain members of a group of closely related bacterial strains. The phage may acquire by mutation the ability to adsorb to a bacterium nonreceptive toward the original type, or lose by mutation an adsorptive capacity it formerly possessed. Such mutations are called, by common consent, host range mutations, and the locus of such mutations is called an h locus (Hershey, 1946b). The term host range in this connection is unsatisfactory because host range can vary in ways not related to adsorption, but the usage is too firmly entrenched to change. The term h mutation, however, should be restricted to its present exact meaning.

The typical procedure for the isolation of h mutants begins with the isolation of a series of bacterial mutants resistant to the wild type phage. The bacterial mutants are then used to select phage mutants capable of infecting them. In general some but not others of the bacterial mutants will prove sensitive to h mutants present in the original stock of phage. The typical result of this procedure is the isolation of a mutant, h, differing by a single mutation from the parental stock, called h^+, as shown by recombination tests. The effect of the mutation is usually an extended host range; the mutant can infect two bacterial strains of which the wild type phage can infect only one.

The extent to which such variation can be carried by successive mutational steps has never been investigated, though the question is of obvious importance to both phage and bacterial taxonomy (Stocker, 1955). As one remarkable instance, mutants of *Pasteurella pestis* phages are known that can infect various *Shigella* species (Girard, 1943; Flu and Flu, 1946; Lazarus and Gunnison, 1947).

In T2, h mutations can occur at a number of widely separated genetic loci (Hershey and Davidson, 1951; Baylor, Hurst, Allen, and Bertani, 1957). Presumably these correspond to physiologically different processes concerned with the organization of tail structure in the phage. Streisinger and Franklin (1956) studied the genetic structure of one of the regions controlling specificity of adsorption in T2. They find that different mutations tend to occur at a number of different sites, which prove to be closely linked but separable by genetic recombination. Reversions to the wild phenotype, however, tend to occur at the site of the original mutation. One can nevertheless recognize several different phenotypes, differing in sensitivity to heat and in other ways, among such reverse mutants.

Remarkably enough, as already mentioned, the two-fold difference in host range between T2 and T4 seems to be due to genetic changes at a single locus. The same locus accounts for the difference in serological specificity (Streisinger, 1956b).

In addition to the examples cited host range mutations have been described by Shwartzman (1927), Sertic (1929b), Sertic and Gough (1930), Luria (1945a, b), Hershey (1946b), Wahl and Blum-Emerique (1950, 1952a), Bresch (1953), Fraser and Dulbecco (1953), and Appleyard, McGregor, and Baird (1956). Probably all of these are mutations affecting specificity of adsorption.

b. Mutations Affecting Growth Potential

We discuss here all those mutations affecting host range that do not influence specificity of adsorption. In principle these could belong to many different classes, but only a few are recognized. For instance, no mutations are known to affect specifically the injection mechanism. The h mutation in T1 is a somewhat borderline case (Chapter X). The mutant can infect B/1. The wild type can adsorb to B/1 but the adsorption is reversible and has no effect on phage or bacterium. For the present this example can be left among the *h* mutations.

The virulent mutants of temperate phages form one category of mutants with altered growth potential (Chapter XIX). The mutations decrease the frequency of lysogenization, and increase the frequency of lytic infection, exhibited by the phage. Virulent mutants produce clear plaques in contrast to the turbid plaques formed by the temperate parent, and are often called *c* mutants for this reason. Examples are described by Burnet and Lush (1936), Gratia (1936b), Rountree (1949a), McCloy (1951), Boyd (1951), Murphy (1952, 1954), Bertani (1953b), Jacob and Wollman (1954), Lwoff, Kaplan, and Ritz (1954), Dickinson (1954), Barksdale and Pappenheimer (1954), Zinder (1955), Levine (1957), Kaiser (1957).

A second category of mutations affecting virulence produces *strong* or *inducing* mutants of temperate phages. Such mutants can overcome the immunity to superinfection exhibited by lysogenic bacteria toward temperate phages closely related to the carried prophage (Chapter XIX). Strong virulent mutants thus form a subclass among virulent mutants, and seem to act by inducing the lytic development of the carried prophage, as well as initiating their own (Jacob and Wollman, 1953). Mutations of this type thus produce an extended host range of a special kind. The inducing mutant of lambda is a multiple mutant (Jacob and Wollman, 1954). Other examples are mentioned by Lwoff (1953) and Bertani (1953b, 1958).

Lysogenic bacteria are also refractory to infection by certain phages unrelated to the carried prophage, including phages that are virulent for the corresponding nonlysogenic bacteria. The well studied example is the resistance of *E. coli* K12 carrying prophage lambda to the *r*II mutants of T4 (Benzer, 1955) (Chapter XVIII). The phage adsorbs to and kills the bacterium, and certainly injects, as shown by mixed infection experiments, but usually fails to multiply. The mutation $r\text{II} \rightarrow r^+$ restores the limited growth potential to normal efficiency. Other examples are cited by Bertani (1953b), and in Chapter XXI

Examples similar to the category last discussed, but unrelated to lysogeny, may exist.   Such examples are unknown and in general might be difficult to establish.

The categories of mutation affecting growth potential summarized above are clearly diverse, and probably many more types exist.   The utility of considering them together is that in each case a block in one or another step in the sequence of reactions essential to phage growth is released by mutation.   Such blocks are potentially identifiable in genetic and metabolic terms (Bertani, 1953b).

c. Mutations Affecting Requirements for Adsorption

Anderson (1948b) found that a line of T4, for which tryptophan is a cofactor of adsorption (Chapter X), can mutate to tryptophan independence.   Delbrück (1948) isolated similar "biochemical mutants" of T4, including some requiring calcium ion in addition to tryptophan.   The requirement for tryptophan (or other cofactors) in T4 ranges all the way from strict dependence to complete independence, with intermediate requirements including "temperature sensitive mutants" that are helped by tryptophan at lower temperatures but not at 37 ° C. (Anderson, 1948c; Wollman and Stent, 1952).

The adsorption of Delbrück's (1948) tryptophan-requiring stocks was inhibited by indole, suggesting competitive interaction of tryptophan and indole at a common site of activation.   However, Anderson's (1948b) stocks are not inhibited by indole, yet show the same kinetics of activation by tryptophan as indole-sensitive stocks (Anderson, 1948a; Stent and Wollman, 1950). The effects of indole and tryptophan on adsorption of different related phages, illustrated in Table XVII, suggests that these two substances act independently, though perhaps on a common activation mechanism.   This mechanism is unknown, but a start has been made toward its identification (Chapter X).

Burnet and Freeman (1937) isolated from phage H (related to T2) a variant that adsorbed more slowly to its host than did the parental phage.   The isolation was accomplished by repeated

TABLE XVII

Role of L-Tryptophan and Indole in Adsorption of Different Phages

Phage stock	Requirement for L-tryptophan	Inhibition by indole
T4,[a] T2L[b]	No	No
T4[c]	Yes	No
T4[a]	Yes	Yes
T2H[b]	No	Yes

[a] Delbrück (1948).
[b] Hershey and Davidson (1951).
[c] Anderson (1948b).

subculture at high bacterial concentrations, recovering the phage after each passage by centrifuging out unlysed bacteria. The procedure is interesting because it suggests a manner in which slowly adsorbing phages might be maintained under ordinary conditions of artificial culture, even though mutations to rapid adsorption were occurring. The variant obtained by Burnet and Freeman differed from the parental stock as follows: slower adsorption, decreased sensitivity to inactivation by bacterial extracts, greatly increased sensitivity to heat, slightly increased rate of inactivation by antiserum, and larger size of plaques. All of these changes, as in h mutants, could reflect a single alteration of the tail protein of the phage particle.

Some results of Schlesinger (1932b) suggested a similar type of variation in coliphage WLL, and a slowly adsorbing mutant of a pyocyanea phage was described by Jacob and Wollman (1953).

d. Mutations Affecting Lysis-Inhibition

Phages related to T2 exist in two forms, subject to *lysis-inhibition* or not (Hershey, 1946a, b). Lysis-inhibition is produced in infected cultures when the concentration of infected bacteria is high enough to cause continuous reinfection during the latent period (not by multiple infection, as is sometimes stated) (Doermann, 1948a). The effect is a greatly extended latent period in most of the cells, and a greatly increased yield of phage.   As a result, wild type phages of this group tend to be of the lysis-inhibiting variety (r^+), but mutate with rather high frequency to the r (rapidly-lysing) form, which does not produce lysis-inhibition.

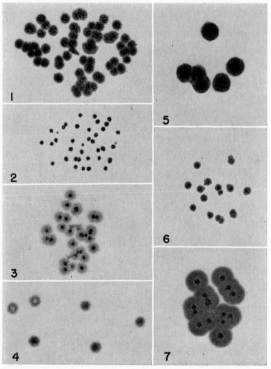

Figure 9.   Plaques of T4 (Doermann strain) and some of its mutants.   1. Wild type, showing one overlapping r mutant plaque.   2. Minute $m41$.   3. Turbid halo $tu44$.   4. Wild type (turbid centers) and $h41$ (clear), from a plating of the mixture on mixed indicator (B + K12/4).   5. The mutant $r48$.   6. The double mutant $r48m41$.   7. The double mutant $t48tu44$. Unpublished photographs by A. H. Doermann.

The r mutations in T2 and T4 occur at many different genetic loci (Hershey and Rotman, 1948; Doermann and Hill, 1953), which accounts for the high over-all frequency of the mutations. The expression of the r character depends on the bacterium;

certain mutants are rapid-lysers on *E. coli* B, but produce lysis inhibition on *E. coli* K12 and other bacteria (Benzer, 1955, 1957).

To produce lysis-inhibition, the primary infection must be with r^+ phage, but some r mutants will serve as the superinfecting phage (Stent and Maaløe, 1953). Different r mutants of the same phage vary greatly in physiological properties (Hershey, 1946b; Benzer, 1957).

The r mutants form characteristic plaques, which explains their importance in early genetic studies. One of these and other mutants of T4 are illustrated in Figure 9.

Cohen (1956) suggested that the r mutants, compared to their parental phages, contain a larger amount of glucose as a constituent of their nucleic acids. Sinsheimer (1956) failed to confirm this, showing that the difference cannot be characteristic of all r mutants. Different phages related to T2 do, however, differ in their content of DNA-glucose (Sinsheimer, 1956).

The loci of all r mutations are widely spread throughout the linkage structure of T4. A certain class of them, restricted to a small region of the linkage structure, affect both the lysis-inhibiting property on *E. coli* B, and the growth potential in lysogenic K12 (Benzer, 1955). The two phenotypic effects are evidently not directly related, but neither one is understood. The remarkable utility of the restricted host-range of the rII mutants is discussed later in this chapter and in Chapter XVIII.

The r mutation was probably first seen by Sertic (1929c) and Demerec and Fano (1945).

e. *Mutations Affecting Plaque Type*

Almost any mutation in a phage is likely to alter the appearance of its plaques. Mention has already been made of virulent mutants of temperate phages, r mutants, and mutants of decreased rate of adsorption. We describe here additional plaque-type mutations the physiological basis for which has not been investigated.

That different phages produce plaques differing in appearance was recognized very early. Examples were illustrated by Gratia

(1922), Asheshov (1924), Burnet (1933d), and Asheshov, Asheshov, Khan, and Lahiri (1933).

Some of the earliest observations of mutation affecting plaque type and host range were made by Sertic (1929b, c). Small plaque mutants in T2 were described by Hershey and Rotman (1949) and in T4 by Doermann and Hill (1953). The use of nutrient agar containing water soluble dyes to recognize "color mutations" in T1 was introduced by Bresch (1953). Several plaque-type mutants of T4 are illustrated in Figure 9.

f. Mutations Affecting Stability

The stability of phages subjected to inactivating agents can be measured with precision (Chapters V and VI). It ought, therefore, to be a simple matter to isolate and recognize resistant mutants. However, this procedure has more often failed than succeeded.

One difficulty was discovered by Adams and Lark (1950). Phage T5 yields heat stable mutants but their presence in a stock is usually obscured by the much more numerous nonmutant heat-stable particles (Adams, 1953a).

Mutants selected for altered adsorption characteristics are often found to differ from the wild stock in sensitivity to heat (Burnet and Freeman, 1937; Hershey and Davidson, 1951; Streisinger and Franklin, 1956).

T2 and T4 differ in resistance to ultraviolet light and this difference can be traced to a single locus by interspecific crosses (Streisinger, 1956a). Attempts to isolate a mutant of T2 having the resistance of T4 have not succeeded, however.

A host range mutant of phage C16 shows an increased susceptibility to inactivation by formaldehyde (Wahl and Blum-Emerique, 1950).

g. Mutations Affecting Antigenic Specificity

The serological difference between T2 and T4 segregates in interspecific crosses with the host range character, both being controlled by the same locus (Streisinger, 1956b). In view of this fact, it is remarkable that the effect of a single host range mutation in T2 does not have a detectable serologic effect (Luria, 1945a; Hershey, 1946a). Lanni and Lanni (1957) have reported serological variation in T5, however. D'Herelle and Rakieten (1935) reported the selection of an antiserum-resistant strain of a staphylococcal phage. Fodor and Adams (1955) obtained segregation and recombination of serological characters in crosses between T5 and the related phage PB.

h. Other Mutations

Mutations affecting the ability to lysogenize, usually from temperate to virulent character, are of unusual genetic interest, but these were mentioned above and are discussed in Chapter XIX. The response of lysogenic bacteria to inducing agents also appears to be subject to genetic control by the prophage and Lwoff (1953) describes a probable mutation with respect to this character.

Ralston and Krueger (1954) obtained variants of a staphylococcal phage differing in capacity to undergo host-induced modification.

Variation in requirements for metal ions have been described. In the case described by Delbrück (1948) calcium is required as a cofactor for adsorption. In other instances calcium serves as a cofactor for injection (Luria and Steiner, 1944). Variation of a staphylococcal phage (Asheshov, 1926) and of a megaterium phage (Wollman and Wollman, 1938) to greater resistance to citrate might be interpreted as a reduced requirement for a cofactor for injection.

Beumer-Jochmans (1951) described a variant of a staphylococcal phage which had acquired the ability to bring about lysis at 44° C.

Mutation to resistance to proflavine in phages has been reported several times (Foster, 1948) (Chapter XV). Resistance can be increased by successive mutational steps. These mutations are of special interest because the action of proflavine has been traced to the maturation step in phage growth.

Sertic (1929a) described a phage whose plaques were surrounded by a spreading halo caused by a rapidly diffusible lysin. Sertic and Gough (1930) reported hereditary variation with respect to this character. Another example is described by Adams and Park (1956), who cite additional pertinent literature. In their case the lysin was identified as an enzyme hydrolyzing the capsular material of Friedlander's bacillus. The enzyme was found both free in phage lysates and attached to phage particles. It was not found in uninfected bacteria. Phage variants were obtained differing in the amount of enzyme produced, with corresponding differences in plaque-type. The possibility of an enzyme under genetic control by the phage is strongly indicated. The role of the enzyme in adsorption of the phage is not yet clear.

Several results of Streisinger's intercrosses between T2 and T4 have been mentioned, but the most remarkable remains to be described. These two phages differ in three characters pertinent in the present context (Streisinger and Weigle, 1956). The DNA of T2 contains 0.77 mole of glucose per mole of hydroxy-methylcytosine, whereas that of T4 contains 1.0 mole (Sinsheimer, 1956). T2 plates with very low efficiency on certain stocks of *E. coli* K12 whereas T4 plates with high efficiency. T4 suppresses the growth of T2 in mixed infections, whereas T2 does not suppress the growth of T4. These three characters will be called bar characters in the remainder of this discussion. They seem to have a common genetic determination or, at any rate, fail to segregate in crosses.

If a bacterium is infected with both T2 and T4 phages, it liberates many particles with the host range genotype of T4 but also some with the host range genotype of T2. Similarly, if the T2 parent carried an *r* marker, some few of the offspring particles will be *r*. When the offspring particles are examined for the bar genotype, however, all of them prove to resemble T4. Moreover, when one of the offspring particles with the host range of T2, now called T2 bar, is backcrossed with T2r (non-bar), the yield (containing some r particles) is again entirely bar in character.

These results are remarkable in several respects. First, the bar character, unlike the familiar genetic markers in these phages, shows "spreading inheritance"; it does not segregate among the offspring of bar by nonbar crosses. Second, it is associated with a gross chemical difference in the DNA, which does not seem to be referable to any antecedent mutational change (tests of this possibility are still rudimentary, however). Third, the ability of T4 to grow in K12 is associated with this gross chemical difference, which offers an opportunity to explore possible causes for the restricted host range of T2. Fourth, the results suggest the possibility of isolating bar mutants of T2, but this possibility has not been adequately tested. Such a mutation would be of an entirely new kind. Fifth, an obvious clue is offered to the nature of one kind of exclusion between dissimilar phages (Chapter XVII).

Additional indications that anomalous types of mutation exist are discussed in section 5 below.

4. Mutation Frequency

Phage mutations are believed to occur exclusively during growth of phage (Luria, 1945a; Hershey, 1946b, 1953d; Weigle, 1953; Jacob, 1954c; Latarjet, 1949, 1954). The rates of natural mutation are not known with great exactness, but probably vary at least over the range from 10^{-4} to 10^{-10} per locus per generation.

Luria (1945a) and Hershey (1946a) measured rates of h mutation in T1 and T2. In T2 the measured rate lies between 10^{-8} and 10^{-9}, which may be too high or ambiguous, depending on how the locus is defined (Hershey, 1953d; Streisinger and Franklin, 1956), and is almost certainly too low since phenotypic mixing is neglected.

Hershey (1946a, b) and Luria (1951) estimated rates of r mutation in T2 at about 10^{-4} per phage particle per generation.

Luria's analysis, furthermore, suggested that the mutants form geometric clones originating at all times during phage growth, which partly justifies the method of calculation. However, the rates measured in this way are complex functions of the large, unknown number of possible sites of mutation (Hershey and Rotman, 1948; Benzer, 1957), and are not therefore very interesting. Hershey (1946a) estimated, by a crude method that is nevertheless free from many types of complication, the rate of reversion from r to r^+ in one of the mutants. The rate fell between 10^{-7} and 10^{-8} per phage per generation. This is probably the rate for a single locus, since the reverse mutations tend to occur at or near the site of the original one (Hershey and Rotman, 1948). However, the rates of reversion at different r loci vary over a wide range (Hershey and Rotman, 1948; Benzer, 1957).

Mutations affecting host range (specificity of adsorption) in T2 show several characteristics in common with the r mutations (Streisinger and Franklin, 1956). Mutations from h to h^+ occur at many closely linked loci with an over-all frequency of the order 10^{-4} per phage per generation. The rates at individual loci must be considerably lower and not too dissimilar from each other. Reversions from h^+ to h, on the other hand, invariably occur at or near the site of the original mutation to h^+. The reversion frequency varies greatly for different h^+ mutants. Thus the h phenotype (like the r^+) seems to call for a rigidly specified genetic configuration that is relatively stable. The h^+ phenotype (like the r) can be produced by many different configurations, many of which are extremely unstable. In both h and r systems, the distinction between "forward" and "reverse" mutations is real, though the distinction between "wild" and "mutant," of course, is somewhat arbitrary. These conclusions were first clearly stated by Streisinger and Franklin.

Adams (1953a) estimated the rate of the mutation to heat stability in T5 at 10^{-7} to 10^{-8} per phage per generation.

These facts seem to permit only a few generalizations. First, mutation rates at individual loci can vary anywhere between an upper limit necessary for the persistence of the phage type, and a lower limit below which the mutation would pass undetected. As a result, the *r* mutations in T4, which can occur in very many loci, actually tend to recur rather frequently in a few (Benzer, 1957). Like the facts mentioned above concerning *h* mutations, this shows that stability at a locus depends on local details of structure. The same conclusion is supported by the suggestion that different mutations at the same locus can be associated with different reversion frequencies at that locus (Benzer, 1957). So far there is no evidence that stability at a given locus is influenced by genetic structure at distant points. Some early indications of this (Hershey, 1946a) have not been borne out by further study (N. Symonds, personal communication).

Luria's (1951) demonstration of a clonal distribution of *r* mutants among single cell yields of T2 provides the chief evidence for a geometric mechanism (as opposed to an observed linear rate) of phage growth.

5. Mutagenic Agents

There is as yet no indication that mutagenic agents produce mutations in extracellular phage particles. In contrast there is considerable evidence that these agents have a pronounced mutagenic effect when applied to infected host cells. There was much scepticism concerning early papers on mutagenesis because of the difficulty of ruling out possible selection by the mutagenic agent. However, the demonstration of the phenomenon with several different mutagens now seems convincing.

Apparently the first experiments were performed by Latarjet (1949), who produced *h* mutations in T2 by ultraviolet irradiation of infected bacteria. The infected bacteria were plated on B/2 to determine the number of infected cells that liberated *h* mutants and on B to determine the number that liberated any phage. The ratio between these two numbers was taken as a measure of the frequency of occurrence of mutations. This frequency for unirradiated controls was 15×10^{-6}. Irradiation during the first third of the latent period before much DNA synthesis had occurred gave doubtful and inconsistent results.

Irradiation during the later two thirds of the latent period gave a marked increase in the frequency of mutations. The frequency was dose-dependent with a threshold of 3,000 ergs per square mm. and a maximum between 5,000 and 6,000 ergs. The maximum frequencies observed were in the range from 100 to 200×10^{-6} to give about a 10-fold increase over the controls. The radiation dose was in the same range as that found to be mutagenic for the host bacterium (Demerec and Latarjet, 1946). Phage T2 and T2h were equally susceptible to ultraviolet inactivation when either extra- or intracellular, but apparently no experiments were done with mixedly infected bacteria to rule out the possibility of selection under these conditions. The actual yield of mutants may well have been higher than observed in these experiments because of the probability that some mutant particles were lost because phenotypic mixing prevented their plating on B/2. In later experiments (Latarjet, 1954) in which phenotypic mixing was eliminated by passage of phage progeny through strain B before plating on B/2, the frequency of mutant particles was raised to 37 times that of unirradiated controls.

The effect of the mutagenic agent, nitrogen mustard, on phage T2 was studied by Silvestri (1949). The agent caused exponential inactivation of phage that was not stopped by dilution into reagents that destroyed nitrogen mustard, but apparently was arrested by adsorption of the phage to susceptible host cells. The rate of inactivation was proportional to the concentration of the mustard. The adsorption of the treated phage particles to strain B, followed by plating of infected bacteria on B/2, revealed a large increase in the frequency of host range mutants among the survivors. The frequency increased from 5×10^{-7} in the controls to 10^{-5} in $M/20$ mustard and 10^{-4} in $M/10$ mustard. The increase in frequency was parallel to the decrease in survival so that a selective effect could be invoked only if the mustard had no effect at all on mutant particles. The most reasonable explanation of the increased frequency of mutants is a direct mutagenic effect of the nitrogen mustard. Although the agent is applied to the phage before infection, the mutagenic effect may well occur within the host cell. Further kinetic study of this system is desirable.

A remarkable example of the induction of mutations in phage was reported by Weigle (1953), who studied effects of ultraviolet light on the temperate phage lambda and its host. He found that the plaque count of ultraviolet-treated phage was much higher when plated on ultraviolet-irradiated bacteria than when plated on normal bacteria. The bacteria could be irradiated before or as long as 30 minutes after adsorption of the phage. Reactivation was also produced by bacteria that had been treated with X-rays and with nitrogen mustard, but not when they had been treated with hydrogen peroxide. Among the offspring of phage particles reactivated in this way were found six distinct kinds of plaque-type mutants but no host-range mutants. The proportion of mutant plaques increased linearly with the dose of ultraviolet light received by the phage and also with the dose received by the bacteria. Treatment of the irradiated bacteria with visible light eliminated the mutagenic effect. Illumination of irradiated bacteria after infection with irradiated phage increased the survival of the phage but no mutants were found. The author concluded that mutations were produced only when both phage and host bacteria had been treated with mutagenic agents. Weigle and Dulbecco (1953) found that the same type of mutagenesis by ultraviolet light is demonstrable with the virulent phage T3, in which case many of the mutants show extended host range.

In the meantime, Fraser and Dulbecco (1953) had obtained unexpected results in crosses between spontaneous h mutants in T3. Their results suggested, among other things, that multiple mutations occur in this phage with a frequency that is unreasonably high relative to the frequency of single mutations. Results of this kind have to be interpreted, in general, as evidence of a mutagenic effect that varies from bacterium to bacterium (Bryson and Davidson, 1951). However, this peculiarity has been seen only in mutants of phage T3, and has not been studied in any detail in this phage.

At this point several facts could be coordinated by making some radical assumptions. The study of lysogenic bacteria had just suggested that prophages occupy a phage-specific site on the bacterial chromosome, with the further implication, perhaps, of genetic homology between phage and bacterium (Lederberg and Lederberg, 1953; Lwoff, 1953; Bertani, 1953b). The experiments of Weigle and of Fraser and Dulbecco suggested an extension of this idea to explain the anomalous aspects of mutagenesis in lambda and T3. The proposal was made that the observed changes are not mutations at all, but effects of genetic recombination between phage and bacterium (Delbrück, 1954). This idea has been elaborated very skillfully by Stent (1958), who shows that it has undeniable merits. These are also illustrated by the following work more or less directly prompted by the idea.

Fraser (in Hershey, Garen, Fraser, and Hudis, 1954) continued work on T3 mutagenesis with the following results. Typically, phage T3 brings about prompt lysis of infected host cells without the production of mutant phage particles. Under certain physiological conditions phage T3 may form a relatively stable complex with the host cell that persists for hours and possibly multiplies. These complexes may be induced to lyse by dilution into broth at 37° C., when they liberate a yield of phage containing about one per cent of host range mutants. Ultraviolet irradiation of the bacteria before infection also produces many mutants among the phage progeny. The mutants produced in this way are of the same phenotype as those liberated from late-lysing unirradiated bacteria. Fraser suggested that these "mutants" might arise as the result of recombination between the phage genetic material and a homologous region in the host cell genetic material. If this were so it might be anticipated that the "mutational patterns" would differ when the same phage strain was used to infect different bacterial strains. This was tested and found to be the case.

Jacob (1954c) studied mutations affecting virulence in phage lambda with results somewhat different from those reported by

Weigle (1953).   The mutation scored by Jacob occurred spontaneously with a frequency of about 10^{-5} per infected bacterium in strain K12S infected with a lambda derivative.   The mutation frequency was increased by increasing doses of ultraviolet light applied to the host bacteria before infection, reaching a maximum of about 5×10^{-4} per infected bacterium.   Similar results were obtained by treating the bacteria with nitrogen mustard before infection with phage.   There was a large increase in the absolute numbers of mutant phage particles as well as in their proportion in the population, that is, treatment of the host bacteria with the mutagen before infection did not cause an appreciable loss of infecting phage particles.   The mutagenic capacity of the treated bacteria varied with the interval between irradiation and infection.   Incubation at 37° C. increased mutagenic capacity to a maximum after 20 to 30 minutes and then decreased it.

Thus Weigle (1953) and Weigle and Dulbecco (1953) observed a mutagenic effect of ultraviolet light in lambda and T3 that required irradiation of both bacteria and phage, whereas Fraser (Hershey, Garen, Fraser, and Hudis, 1954) and Jacob (1954c) obtained mutagenic effects in the same phages by irradiating only the bacteria before infection.   All agree that the bacteria must be irradiated.   All the results can be interpreted in terms of the familiar, if complicated, phenomenon of radio-chemical mutagenesis.   The interesting alternative mentioned above is genetic recombination between bacteria and phage. The discovery that irradiation of the phages increases frequency of genetic recombination in ordinary phage crosses (Jacob and Wollman, 1955), adds to this argument.

Further evidence for a possible genetic homology between phage and host cell was obtained by Garen and Zinder (1955). Their evidence indicates that the sensitivity of phages to inactivation by ultraviolet irradiation places them in two distinct categories; sensitive phages such as T2, T4, and T6 and resistant phages such as T1, T3, and P22.   The authors suggest that the relative resistance of the latter group is due to replacement of damaged phage material by recombination with homologous genetic material present in the host cell. Phages that are highly sensitive to inactivation may have no genetic material homologous to that of their host cell, and this is consistent with the gross chemical differences between the DNA of some of these phages and that of their hosts. The hypothesis of replacement is also supported by the fact that irradiation of bacteria before infection depresses their ability to support growth of irradiated P22 but not that of unirradiated P22 or of irradiated T2.

The general hypothesis of phage-bacterium homology can, however, be placed in a different light, as suggested by the following experiments.

Jacob and Wollman (1953) described the properties of a virulent, "inducing" mutant of the temperate phage lambda. This phage plated with equal efficiency on the lysogenic host K12 (lambda) and on the nonlysogenic strain K12S. However, ultraviolet-inactivated phage gave a much higher plaque count on host strain K12 (lambda) than on K12S. This reactivation occurred only in lysogenic bacteria carrying prophage lambda, not in bacteria carrying unrelated prophages. When the irradiated superinfecting phage carried additional genetic markers, the reactivated phage was predominantly of the superinfecting type, but some bacteria liberated products of recombination with the carried phage. The proportion of recombinants in the phage yield increased with increasing doses of ultraviolet light to the superinfecting phage. Jacob and Wollman interpreted the recombinants as the result of induction of the development of prophage by the infecting particles, following by genetic recombination between the two kinds of vegetative phage.

This example suggests the possibility that apparent mutagenesis could often be the result of genetic recombination between the test phage and an unknown prophage carried by the bacterium. The fact that in this example, the effect is produced by irradiating the phage alone, is unimportant, since the result depends on the special property of this phage to cause the induction of the carried prophage. With other mutants of lambda, the comparable experiment could be performed only if the bacteria were first irradiated to cause induction of prophage development.

The example cited also calls for a distinction between phage-bacterium homology, and phage-prophage homology. At the present time this distinction is not generally possible. It can only acquire meaning, in fact, as the nature of prophage integration into the bacterial genome is elucidated (Chapter XIX) on the one hand, and methods are developed for eliminating unsuspected prophages from bacteria, on the other.

Mutagenic action of proflavine in bacteria infected with T2 was reported by DeMars (1953). The frequency of mutations affecting lysis inhibition was increased at least 10-fold when proflavine was added to the culture at the time of infection. There seemed to be no selective effect of proflavine in mixed infection experiments.

The incorporation of 5-bromouracil into the DNA of T2 (Chapter XV) has mutagenic effects of unusual interest (Litman and Pardee, 1956; Litman, 1956). Both plaque-type and host-range mutants are produced. So far it is doubtful whether the mutational effects are directly related to the incorporation of the analogue. However, the system offers new means of attacking problems of mutagenesis.

In conclusion, numerous examples of induced mutagenesis in phage are known. In several instances, the results can be interpreted in terms of genetic recombination between test phage and phage-like material carried by the host bacterium, though clear recognition of such instances is limited to work with known lysogenic bacteria. In other instances, as with phage T2, chemical and photochemical mutagenesis seems clear. In such instances, the mutagenic agent usually has to act on the infected bacterium; action on the extracellular phage particles is ineffective. In all instances, with trivial exceptions, the bacterium must be exposed to the mutagenic agent. Exposure of the phage may or may not be necessary in addition.

6. Summary

Variation in phages can be divided into two broad classes, hereditary or not, and hereditary variation can be further subdivided into two categories, mutation and genetic recombination. Genetic recombination between phages is a well-defined phenomenon described in Chapter XVIII. Genetic recombination is mentioned here only when it threatens to be confused with mutation, that is, when the initial genetic purity of a phage clone cannot be guaranteed because of possible "contamination" from the host.

Nonheritable variation is most informative in two examples. The first, called phenotypic mixing, calls for interactions between two related phages multiplying in the same host and, specifically, for an interaction between two alleles of an h (host-range) gene in such phages. The effect is to produce phage particles differing in h phenotype and genotype, and phage particles of mixed h phenotype. Particles of mixed genotype (heterozygotes, Chapter XVIII) are also produced, but this probably has little to do with phenotypic mixing.

The second example of nonheritable variation, called host-induced modification, results from unknown causes by which certain characteristics of the phenotype of an entire phage population are determined by the bacteria in which it was produced. The host range character is the principal one affected but, in contrast to phenotypic mixing, not at the level of attachment of phage to bacterium. Both physiological and genetic factors in the bacterium can be recognized to play a role in this phenomenon. The nature of the change in the phage is not known. One instance of spontaneous phenotypic variation in phage has also been described.

Mutations in phages can be classified according to character affected, as is done in this chapter, but this classification is of little theoretical interest. More important is the separation into expected and unexpected categories. The expected categories can be dismissed as follows. They arise spontaneously during phage growth and their frequency can be increased by a few mutagenic agents only when these are applied to the infected bacterium. They arise in a stepwise manner producing mutant subclones, and in most instances prove to carry single mutant loci. These mutations showing expected characteristics have been studied with reasonable care only in T2 and T4.

In crosses between T2 and T4, both unexpected and expected genetic differences are brought to light. The expected ones consist of a pair of allelic genes responsible for the differences in host range and serological specificity, and another pair responsible for the differences in sensitivity to ultraviolet light. The unexpected one is a difference in the DNA-glucose content to which no locus can be assigned, because the gross difference fails to segregate in crosses. This difference is correlated with a difference in host range not affecting adsorption. The origin of a similar difference by mutation has not been observed.

Other anomalous mutations arise under conditions suggesting special interactions between phage and bacterium, possibly genetic recombinations, and possibly involving carried, phagelike materials rather than bacterial chromosomes proper, a distinction that cannot yet be made in most cases. Such mutations have been seen only in T3 and lambda. In T3, the spontaneous mutants arise only under special physiological conditions, and the mutants tend to show multiple-factor differences from wild type. In both T3 and lambda, irradiation of the bacterium before infection increases the frequency of mutation. It is possible, of course, that these are, after all, for the most part photochemically induced mutations of the conventional sort. If so they are no less remarkable, because in this case a clear separation of the inducer, ultraviolet light, from its ultimate target, the phage chromosome, has been achieved.

The physiological effects of mutational changes present a broad field for biochemical exploration, but this has scarcely been started as yet. The topic will be discussed briefly in Chapter XVIII.

CHAPTER XVII

MIXED INFECTION

Mixed infection may be defined as the infection of a single bacterium by at least two distinguishable phage particles. This evidently means something quite different from the mixed infection of a higher plant or animal by two distinct viruses. In the latter case the same cells need not be infected by the two viruses and any interaction between them may be very indirect. For this reason what was long known as "interference" between pairs of plant and animal viruses should not be confused with "mutual exclusion" as described below.

The ratio of infecting phage particles to infected bacteria (the multiplicity of infection) may be varied over a wide range, and independently for the two types of infecting phages. Because one deals with cell populations one cannot determine for any single bacterium exactly how many phage particles of each kind initiated the infection. However, one can calculate by means of the Poisson distribution the proportion of the bacterial population that was infected with any given combination of phage particles. The time between infections with the two viruses can be varied from virtually zero to an interval as long as the minimum latent period, permitting great flexibility in the design of experiments.

Mixed infection with two distinct phages may have one of several results. A given cell may liberate both kinds of phage, only one of the two kinds, or neither kind. In addition it may liberate particles differing from either infecting type. The ease with which the significant variables in mixed infections with phages may be controlled has permitted the rapid development of phage genetics. The rapid progress in this field is due to two major factors, the favorable properties of bacteriophages as materials for genetic research, and perhaps more important, the fact that the research workers were not trained as classical geneticists.

1. Mixed Infection with Unrelated Phages—Mutual Exclusion

The first clear-cut experiments involving the mixed infection of bacterial cells with genetically unrelated phages were performed by Delbrück and Luria (1942). They infected *E. coli* strain B with the two unrelated phages T1 and T2, both of which can grow on this host. The phage yields from such mixedly infected bacteria were identified qualitatively by plating the infected cells before lysis on agar plates seeded with indicator bacteria: B/1 to recognize T2 yielders or B/2 to recognize T1 yielders (Chapter IX). Similarly, the phage yield after lysis could be assayed separately for its content of the two phage types by plating samples on each of the two indicators. (Actually, in this instance, the two phages can also be distinguished by the very different size of plaques.)

Making use of these principles, Delbrück and Luria (1942) performed one-step growth experiments (Chapter II), infecting cells of strain B with the mixed phages T1 and T2, and plating samples of the culture alternately on B/1 and B/2. The early platings showed the proportion of the mixedly infected bacteria that liberated each kind of phage, and the later platings showed the average yield per infected bacterium for each phage type. Following simultaneous mixed infection with an average multiplicity of 4 phage particles of each type, it was found that the mixedly infected bacteria liberated only phage T2. Phage T1 was unable to multiply although it adsorbed normally. If the input ratio of phage T2 was decreased the proportion of infected bacteria liberating T2 decreased and the proportion liberating T1 increased correspondingly. The proportion of bacteria liberating phage T1 corresponded exactly to the expected porportion that escaped infection by T2. This result means that adsorption of a single T2 phage particle to a host bacterium renders that bacterium incapable of serving as a host for phage

T1. Phage T1 is effectively *excluded* from multiplying in bacteria that are infected with phage T2. The T1 phage particles that are adsorbed to T2-infected bacteria are inactivated; they are not recoverable as plaque-forming phage either before or after lysis of the mixedly infected bacteria. In the light of contemporary knowledge, we suppose that both phages inject, but only T2 carries through all the steps necessary to production of new phage particles.

Phage T1 was given a head start of various time intervals before addition of phage T2 to see if it could escape domination by this means. When T1 preceded T2 by 2 or 4 minutes, T2 still dominated growth. When T1 preceded T2 by 6.5 minutes, it accounted for about 60 per cent of the yield. If T1 preceded by 7.5 minutes, it made up nearly 90 per cent of the yield. T1 must precede T2 by about 6 minutes in order to compete on an equal basis with T2 in mixed infection.

In a later study of mixed infection, Delbrück (1945c) introduced a new and valuable technique, the use of mixed indicator bacteria as a test for the simultaneous liberation of different phages from the same bacterium. To detect mixed yields of T1 and T2, for instance, he seeded plates with a mixture of B/1 and B/2, together with about 100 of the mixedly infected bacteria under test. If, on such a plate, an infected bacterium liberates only phage T2, the indicator B/1 is lysed producing a plaque that is turbid due to growth of B/2. Similarly, a bacterium liberating only phage T1 produces a turbid plaque because B/2 is lysed but not B/1. If plaques of T1 and T2 overlap on such a plate, the overlap is completely clear. If a single bacterium liberates both phages, the result is a concentric overlap, the clear center containing both phages, the turbid periphery T1 only. This method permits the detection of mixed yielders in any proportion in excess of about one per cent of the population. An example of mutual exclusion revealed in this way is illustrated in Figure 10.

In applying this technique to the phage pairs T1–T7 and T2–T7, Delbrück could not detect mixed yielders. The results of the mixed indicator method were confirmed by single burst experiments. In mixed multiple infections with T1 and T7 phages, simultaneous infection resulted in about $^1/_3$ of the bacteria liberating only T1 and $^2/_3$ only T7 phages. If either T1

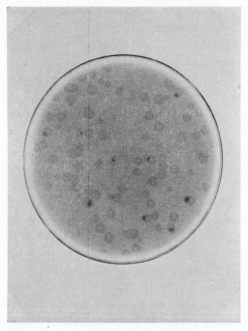

Figure 10. Mutual exclusion between T1 and T7. The mixedly infected bacteria were plated before lysis on the mixed indicator B/1 + B/7. Note that complete lysis occurs only where turbid plaques of the two kinds overlap.

or T7 was given a 4 minute advantage, the other was completely excluded. For the three phages studied, the order of dominance was T2 > T7 > T1.

Mixed multiple infection with two unrelated phages sometimes results in a markedly reduced yield of the phage that wins out (Delbrück, 1945c). This phenomenon is termed "depressor effect." The depressor effect depends on the times of infection with the two phages. The longer the interval between addition of the first and second phages, the less is the depressor effect on the yield of the first phage. Presumably the depressor effect requires the injection of the nucleic acid of the excluded phage into the bacterium because treatment of the culture with either antibacterial serum or antiserum against the second phage markedly decreases the depressor effect. Both types of antiserum interfere with penetration of phage nucleic acid into the host cell (Delbrück, 1945b; Adams and Wassermann, 1956; Chapter VIII).

In a brief report Delbrück (1945d) noted that of 14 pairs of unrelated phages tested in mixed infection all demonstrated the phenomenon of mutual exclusion. In contrast two pairs of related phages, T2–T4 and T4–T6, gave clear evidence that some mixedly infected bacteria would permit multiplication of both infecting types.

Several mechanisms were proposed to explain mutual exclusion, the most generally accepted for some time being the "penetration hypothesis" (Delbrück, 1945c). According to this hypothesis the dominant phage in a given mixedly infected bacterium excludes the other phage by altering the bacterial surface so that the second phage cannot penetrate. There is some evidence that this hypothesis may be applicable to certain examples of exclusion but quite convincing evidence that it does not apply to most cases. In fact, the existence of the depressor effect and the prevention of this effect by both antibacterial and antiphage sera suggest that the second phage penetrates and decreases the rate of multiplication of the dominant phage by an intracellular mechanism. Further evidence that the excluded virus penetrates is derived from isotopic data indicating that chemical components of the DNA of the excluded phage are utilized for synthesis of the dominant phage (see Chapter XIII).

Direct evidence that the penetration hypothesis does not apply to all cases of mutual exclusion was obtained by Weigle and Delbrück (1951) while studying the properties of a lysogenic strain of *E. coli* K12. This bacterium is a satisfactory host for the virulent phage T5, indicating that the carried prophage lambda does not interfere with the multiplication of phage T5. Treatment of K12 with mild doses of ultraviolet light initiates the lytic cycle of growth of phage lambda resulting in lysis some 60 to 80 minutes after irradiation. Mature phage particles first appear in the bacteria 40 to 45 minutes after irradiation.

Suspensions of K12 were irradiated, infected with phage T5 at various intervals after irradiation, and then assayed on appropriate indicators to determine the proportion of cells liberating phage T5 or phage lambda. The proportion of bacteria liberating lambda was less than one per cent at all intervals up to 20 minutes. It reached about 10 per cent after a 37-minute interval and about 80 per cent after a 50-minute interval between irradiation and superinfection. The proportion of bacteria liberating phage T5 was as high as in the nonirradiated control at all intervals up to 20 minutes and then decreased at longer intervals in the same way as the proportion of lambda-yielding bacteria increased. Platings on mixed indicator strains showed that the proportion of bacteria liberating both T5 and lambda was negligible, so that this is a typical example of mutual exclusion. The invading T5 phage is dominant at all times after irradiation until the maturation of lambda begins. After this time lambda is dominant over phage T5. There was no evidence for a depressor effect in these experiments.

It is obvious that in this case the penetration hypothesis cannot be invoked as an explanation of mutual exclusion because the lambda prophage excluded by T5 was already present within the bacteria.

Similar results have been obtained with the unrelated temperate phages P1 and P8 of *Pseudomonas aeruginosa*. In mixed infections of the sensitive host strain 13 with P1 and P8, mutual exclusion occurs and the majority of the mixedly infected bacteria liberate P1. However, lysogenic strain 13(8) is a satisfactory host for P1 and lysogenic host 13(1) supports growth of P8. Therefore mutual exclusion operates in this system only during the lytic cycle of phage growth (Jacob, 1954a). If the lysogenic strain 13(8) is induced with ultraviolet light and then superinfected with P1, the majority of the bacteria liberate P1 and not P8, again demonstrating exclusion of endogenous induced phage by infecting phage. The reverse experiment could not be tried because lysogenic strain 13(1) is not inducible (Jacob, 1952c).

It seems evident that the penetration hypothesis cannot explain many cases of mutual exclusion. The exclusion must depend on some property of intracellular vegetative phage that is not shared by intracellular prophage.

Although mixed infection with unrelated phages usually results in mutual exclusion, there is at least one well documented case in which unrelated phages can mature in the same host cell (Collins, 1957). Phage T1 and phage BG8 have a common host in strain Cullen of *E. coli*. The two phages are not serologically related, are morphologically distinct, differ in their requirement for calcium ion, and differ in the ability of the ultraviolet inactivated particles to kill the host cell and manifest multiplicity reactivation. Despite this strong evidence for lack of any close relationship, mixed infection results in a large proportion of mixed yielders. Evidence of genetic recombination was sought but not found. Any general mechanism for mutual exclusion of unrelated phages must also consider the fact that in certain cases mutual exclusion does not occur. At the present time, no satisfactory mechanism can be suggested.

2. Mixed Infection with Related Phages

a. Absence of Mutual Exclusion

In the early work with the T group of coliphages it had been observed that both burst size and latent period were independent of the multiplicity of infection. Logically it would seem reasonable that infection of a bacterium with two phage particles should give either a shorter latent period or a larger burst size than infection with only one. When neither effect was observed it was concluded that only one phage particle could be involved in infection of a single bacterium regardless of how many particles were adsorbed to the host cell. This notion seemed to be confirmed when it was found that phage T2 inactivated with ultraviolet light interfered under certain conditions with the multiplication of active phage T2 as well as with the multiplication of the unrelated phage T1 (Luria and Delbrück, 1942). These observations were eventually explained in other ways but for several years the hypothesis of the "key enzyme," essential for phage multiplication, was generally accepted. According to this hypothesis competition between virus particles for a limited amount of this key enzyme resulted in exclusion of all but one of them. The key enzyme hypothesis was discarded and replaced by Delbrück (1945c) with the penetration hypothesis already discussed in this chapter. At about the same time clear-cut evidence that more than one phage particle can participate in multiplication within one cell was obtained.

Delbrück and Bailey (1946), working with the closely related phage strains T2, T4, and T6, demonstrated that any pair of these phages could grow together in the same host cell. Delbrück and Bailey also investigated mixed infection with r^+ and r mutant phages by the single burst technique and found that the majority of mixedly infected cells liberated both kinds of phage particles. Similar observations were reported by Hershey (1946a, b) concerning mixed infection with various mutant phages. The experiments of Delbrück and Bailey (1946) and Hershey (1946a, b) showed that related phages are not subject to mutual exclusion. These experiments were also milestones in the history of phage genetics, but this is related in Chapter XVIII.

Many examples of mixed growth of closely related phages have been reported since. When the two phages differ by only a few mutational steps there is no exclusion except for the phenomenon of limited participation which presumably occurs also in multiple infection with a single kind of phage (Dulbecco, 1949b). With less closely related phages there are likely to be varying degrees of partial exclusion discussed below. With unrelated phages mutual exclusion is likely to be complete.

The generalizations just stated refer to the lytic cycle of phage growth. During the lysogenic phase diametrically opposite rules seem to hold (Chapter XIX). Bacteria can often be lysogenized by several unrelated temperate phages, but seldom by two or more related ones.

b. Partial Exclusion

Mixed infection with somewhat distantly related phage pairs such as T2–T4, T2–T6, T4–T6 (Delbrück and Bailey, 1946), or T5-PB (Adams, 1951a) results in one of the pair of infecting phages being partially excluded. Thus less than half of the bacteria to which both T5 and PB particles attach liberate both phages. Using single cell burst experiments, Adams demonstrated that phage PB tends to exclude T5. In mixed infections each bacterium liberates PB-like particles, but only a fraction liberates T5-like particles as well. The number of T5-like particles appearing in mixed bursts is small but variable. The similar example of T2 and T4, in which T2 tends to be excluded, has been studied by Streisinger and Weigle (1956). They find that the ability of T4-like phages to partially exclude T2 is correlated with several characteristics, including high DNA-glucose content, none of which segregates in crosses as do the usual genetic markers. The examples cited above evidently depend on heritable differences between the phages, which may be taken as the diagnostic criterion for partial exclusion of a *first kind*.

A *second kind* of partial exclusion is seen when bacteria are infected first with one and then with another of a pair of very closely related phages. It differs from partial exclusion of the first kind in that it does not depend (except for convenience of demonstration) on genetic differences between the two phages. It has been observed only with T2 and, as the following discussion suggests, may be limited to the T2 and T5 species and very few others. Needless to say, if a bacterium is infected first with T2 and then with T4, both kinds of partial exclusion presumably operate.

Partial exclusion of the second kind was demonstrated by Dulbecco (1952b). He infected bacteria with T2 and reinfected them after various times with an *r* mutant of T2. (This pair does not exhibit partial exclusion of the first kind.) He found that the infected bacteria very quickly develop the ability to exclude the superinfecting phage. The fraction of mixed yielders falls to 0.5 after an interval of one minute and to 0.2 after two minutes. It does not develop in infected bacteria that are starved or whose metabolism is temporarily inhibited by cyanide. It does develop in bacteria "infected" with ultraviolet killed T2. In this instance the superinfecting phage need not be genetically marked.

This excluding mechanism is partial in two senses. First, some bacteria exclude and some do not. Second, some phage particles infecting a given bacterium are excluded and others are not. This was shown by Visconti (1953) who found that at very high multiplicities of superinfection, nearly all the bacteria become mixed yielders again.

Partial exclusion of the second kind can also be demonstrated by chemical methods (Lesley, French, Graham, and van Rooyen 1951; Graham, 1953). Half of the DNA of the excluded phage particles is quickly split into acid-soluble materials and excreted into the culture medium. This effect develops within two minutes, just as the genetic exclusion does. The phenomenon is seen after primary infection with T2, T4, T6, or T5, including irradiated T2, but not after primary infection with T1, T3, or T7. It occurs on secondary infection with T2, but not with T1 or T7. The breakdown is not the cause of the exclusion, because if the bacterial deoxyribonuclease is inhibited, breakdown fails but exclusion persists (French, Graham, Lesley, and Van Rooyen, 1952; Hershey, Garen, Fraser, and Hudis, 1954). The limitation of the breakdown to 50 per cent of the DNA of the superinfecting phage is probably due to the fact that only half of the superinfecting particles inject (Hershey, Garen, Fraser, and Hudis, 1954).

Bacteria infected with T2 also develop resistance to lysis from without by high superinfecting multiplicities of the same phage (Visconti, 1953). This effect seems to develop somewhat more slowly than the exclusion effects described above, but the conditions of study were not quite the same in all cases.

Thus in bacteria infected with T2 and T5 a number of alterations in response to superinfecting phage ensue. The various effects are undoubtedly related but immediate causes have not been identified.

c. Limited Participation

Another kind of partial exclusion, first described by Dulbecco (1949b), is usually called limited participation. Dulbecco demonstrated it as follows. Bacteria were simultaneously infected with 10 to 20 particles of T2 and one or two particles of r mutant per cell. Yields from individual bacteria were scored as mixed or unmixed yields. An appreciable fraction of the yields from the mixedly infected cells always lacked the r marker. Dulbecco interpreted his results in terms of the exclusion of one particle in ten, chosen at random, from participation in growth. Actually, in view of the extreme rapidity of development of partial exclusion of the second kind, it is not clear whether his phenomenon should be distinguished from it.

A more extreme example of limited participation in phage lambda was reported by E.-L. Wollman and Jacob (1954). Only six particles of this phage seemed to be able to infect a single bacterium. Other experiments with phage lambda appear to be incompatible with this conclusion, however. It must be concluded for the present that limited participation is an ill-defined and doubtful phenomenon.

3. Summary

If a bacterial strain is susceptible to two distinguishable phages, it is possible to study the results of mixed infection of single cells with the pair. If the two infecting phages are not related, the usual result is *mutual exclusion;* one phage or the other multiplies but not both.   If one phage is clearly dominant under conditions of simultaneous mixed infection it is possible to transfer the advantage to the second strain by giving it a few minutes head start.   The mechanism of mutual exclusion is not known but it clearly does not involve interference with adsorption, interference with penetration, or competition for a unique key enzyme.   There is one well authenticated case in which two unrelated phages can grow simultaneously in the same host cell.

In contrast to the cases of mutual exclusion, simultaneous mixed infection with related phages permits both to multiply. The mixed growth is usually accompanied by genetic recombination of suitable markers.   If the pair of infecting phages is not very closely related, partial exclusion often results.

Partial exclusion between identical phages occurs under certain conditions.   Primary infection of a bacterium with phage T2 results in very rapid changes in the properties of the infected cell.   Superinfecting T2 phage is excluded from multiplication and half of its DNA is rapidly broken down by deoxyribonuclease. At the same time the bacterium becomes increasingly resistant to lysis from without by high multiplicities of superinfecting phage.

Partial exclusion may occur in all instances of multiple infection.   Thus a bacterium infected with many particles of T2, one of which is genetically marked, is likely not to yield any marked particles.   Results of this kind suggest that only a limited number of particles, about 10 in the case of T2, can participate genetically in multiplication within a single bacterial cell.   The mechanisms of exclusion of all kinds are unknown.

CHAPTER XVIII

BACTERIOPHAGE GENETICS

The mixed growth of two closely related phages in the same host cell with genetic recombination was announced simultaneously by Hershey (1946a, b) and by Delbrück and Bailey (1946). Hershey studied mixed infections with mutant strains of phage T2, such as $T2hr^+$ and $T2h^+r$ and obtained recombinant strains such as $T2h^+r^+$ and $T2hr$. Delbrück and Bailey used related phage strains such as $T2r$ and $T4r^+$, obtaining recombinant types such as $T2r^+$ and $T4r$. Because they were the first phages to be used for genetic studies and because certain properties (highly efficient adsorption to the host cell and useful plaque type and host range mutations) were suitable, phages T2 and T4 have been more thoroughly studied and are better known genetically than any other phages. Most of the important phenomena of phage genetics have been discovered with this pair of phages and so most of this chapter will be devoted to a survey of papers on phage T2 and T4.

1. Mixed Infection and Recombination

Given two related phage strains that differ from each other by at least two distinguishable hereditary characteristics, it is possible to test the pair for genetic recombination, providing only that a common host is available. Genetic recombination has been found in every phage examined with the single exception of coliphage S13 (Zahler, Lennox, and Vatter, 1954). As the list includes temperate and virulent phages, phages for both gram-positive and gram-negative organisms, large phages and small, it seems to be a fairly safe conclusion that genetic recombination between closely related phages under conditions of

mixed growth is a general property of bacteriophages. All
that is necessary to study the genetics of a phage strain is to
isolate an adequate number of variant strains with readily
recognizable genetically controlled characteristics. A description of various kinds of mutants that have been observed in
phages is given in Chapter XVI. Those characteristics that
have been most useful as genetic markers are host range and
plaque morphology, although others such as serological specificity, resistance to heat and ultraviolet light, and virulence have
been used.

In mixed infection experiments it is desirable to infect each
bacterial cell nearly simultaneously with both kinds of phage
particles. This is because an interval between primary infection
and secondary infection may result in genetic exclusion of the
second phage as was discussed in Chapter XVII. In the case of
rapidly adsorbing phages such as T2 one can readily calculate
from the adsorption rate constant the bacterial concentration
and the input ratio of each phage strain to be used in the adsorption mixture so that, for instance, the bacterial cells will be
infected with a mean multiplicity of five phage particles of each
type within one minute. In order to insure mixed infection of
essentially all of the bacterial population it is customary to use
conditions giving an average multiplicity of five phage particles
of each type. Another method of avoiding exclusion of one of
the infecting phage strains is to carry out the adsorption step
using bacteria suspended in buffer (Benzer, 1952) or in cyanide
broth (Benzer and Jacob, 1953). Under these conditions simultaneous mixed infection is achieved starting at the moment of
addition of broth (Chapters XV and XVII). Residual unadsorbed phage is removed by centrifugation or use of antiphage
serum and the infected bacteria are suitably diluted in broth and
permitted to lyse. The proportions of parental and recombinant
types are then determined by suitable assays either on lysates of
a few hundred infected cells or in single cell burst experiments.
The degree of linkage between genetic loci may then be calculated from the relative proportions of parental and recombinant

types found in the yields. These methods were described by Hershey and Rotman (1948, 1949).

2. The Vegetative Phage Pool

Following adsorption of a phage T2 particle to the host cell surface, the phage nucleic acid but not the protein penetrates through the cell wall into the cell interior (Hershey and Chase, 1952). After a lag of a few minutes, copies of the phage DNA begin to be synthesized and this DNA forms a pool of 50 to 100 phage equivalents of DNA per infected cell by 10 minutes after infection. At this time phage DNA begins to be withdrawn from the pool and is coated with protein to form mature phage particles. From this time on new phage DNA is synthesized and added to the pool at the same rate that DNA is withdrawn from the pool by the process of phage maturation so that the pool size remains constant. These processes of DNA synthesis and phage maturation continue until interrupted by host cell lysis. Once phage DNA has been incorporated into a mature phage particle it is isolated biochemically from the DNA pool; maturation is irreversible. Over a considerable period of time the rate of DNA synthesis and of phage maturation is constant presumably because a constant amount of synthetic machinery is functioning at capacity (Hershey, 1953a).

The work of Luria (1951) on the frequency distribution of mutant phage particles in single cell bursts demonstrated clearly a clonal rather than a Poisson distribution with an exponential distribution of clone sizes. This result indicates that each new vegetative phage particle can serve as a pattern for the synthesis of daughter phage particles. This replication of patterns may be interrupted by maturation which withdraws one copy of the pattern for each mature phage. If there is only one copy available at the time it is included in a mature phage particle, the clone size will be one in that bacterium. Maturation results in genetic as well as biochemical isolation.

If a susceptible bacterium is infected simultaneously with two genetically distinguishable phage particles such as $T2h^+r$

and T2hr^{+}, both phage particles are converted to vegetative phage by injection of their nucleic acid, and replication of each begins. Even though the sites of infection may be situated at opposite ends of the bacterial cell the genetic evidence indicates that the two pools of replicating phage DNA soon coalesce and become a single pool. The experiments of Doermann (1953) demonstrated that premature lysates of mixedly infected bacteria contained almost the same proportion of recombinant phage particles at the beginning of phage maturation as at the time of normal lysis. Genetic recombination must have occurred at about the same frequency in the DNA pool before the beginning of maturation as after, and hence the infecting phage particles must have formed a single genetically mixed pool before maturation began. Similar conclusions were drawn from superinfection experiments by Visconti and Garen (1953). The bacteria were singly infected with T2hr phage and after incubation for 6 or 8 minutes were superinfected with an input ratio of 1500 T2$h^{+}r^{+}$ phage particles per bacterium (Chapter XVII). Samples were removed at intervals and diluted into cyanide to stop further phage multiplication and to induce premature lysis. The phage progeny were then assayed for the presence of the genetic markers introduced by the superinfecting phage and present in recombinant phage particles. It was found that the superinfecting parental type and both possible recombinant types were present as mature phage particles as early as 12 minutes after primary infection and 4 minutes after superinfection. The numbers of the complementary recombinant types increased during the latent period in the same way as they would have under conditions of simultaneous mixed infection. Apparently the pool of vegetative phage was established by the primary infection and the superinfecting phage then entered this pool as much as 6 or 8 minutes after the primary infection. The superinfecting phage nucleic acid could enter the pool, replicate, undergo genetic recombination, and reappear in mature phage within 4 minutes after adsorption to the host cell. Such a result would be difficult to visualize if each infecting phage particle in a mixedly infected bacterium formed its own vegetative pool. The efficiency of the recombination process requires thorough mixing of genetic material from the two kinds of parents.

3. The Visconti-Delbrück Theory

By 1953 a considerable body of quantitative data had accumulated as a result of genetic studies with phages T2 and T4, and the time was appropriate for the description of a theoretical mechanism for genetic recombination in these phages. The genetic studies had produced a number of facts with which any proposed mechanism must be consistent. These facts as recognized in 1953 will be briefly reviewed.

a. Many Genetic Loci Are Available

Of 15 independent T2r mutants tested by recombination, all were identical phenotypically by plaque morphology, yet each was distinguishable genetically. Mixed multiple infection with any two mutant r stocks gave a proportion of wild type recombinants that was characteristic of the pair, whereas multiple infection with any single r stock gave only r progeny (Hershey and Rotman, 1948, 1949). Each r mutant of independent origin was given a serial number such as T2r1, T2r2, etc., as a distinctive label. Two distinct host range loci were available for phage T2 (Hershey and Davidson, 1951) and a plaque type mutant m (minute) which is distinct from the r plaque mutations. Another kind of plaque type mutation called tu for turbid was reported in phage T4 by Doermann and Hill (1953) as well as the usual r mutations. A number of distinct tu and m loci are known.

b. Complementary Recombinants Are Formed

In a cross such as $T2rh^+ \times T2r^+h$ one finds both kinds of recombinants among the progeny: $T2rh$ and $T2r^+h^+$. In crosses involving two distinct r mutants such as T2r1 and T2r7, one

obtains as recombinants both T2++ and T2r1r7.   The double
mutant T2r1r7 particles are phenotypically like the T2r parents
but can be identified because on back crossing they give no wild
type recombinants with either parent.   The proportions of the
two recombinant types from a two factor cross are equal when
averaged over the yields of many bacteria.   However, in single
cell bursts the proportions of the complementary recombinants
may be far from equal.   If the recombination frequency is low,
many of the bursts may contain only one of the two possible
recombinant types (Hershey and Rotman, 1949).   This may
mean that the complementary recombinants are produced independently of each other in different recombination events;
or it may mean that each recombination event produces both
kinds of recombinants but that random multiplication and
random maturation may result in unequal numbers of the
complementary recombinants in the yield from a single cell.
The available data do not furnish a crucial test of this important
point but favor the concept of the independent production of
complementary recombinants.

c. Multiple Recombinations

In general, multiple factor crosses give results that might have
been predicted from the two factor crosses.   Crosses of the type
T2r1r5 × T2r1r13 yield no wild recombinants, whereas crosses
of the type T2r1 × T2r4r7 do so.   Multiple factor crosses involving mixed infection with three distinct kinds of phage such
as r7r13 × r4r13 × r4r7 give a small proportion of wild type
recombinants.   This result indicates that at least three different
phage particles can participate in reproduction and recombination within the same host cell.   It also demonstrates that at
least two successive recombination events or matings can contribute genes to a single progeny phage particle;   that is, vegetative phage may undergo several matings with different partners
before maturation.   That triparental matings involve successive
events rather than a single event involving three partners is a
more reasonable assumption because of kinetic and steric con-

siderations. The fact of multiple matings affects the calculation of recombination frequencies because a mating of complementary recombinants would produce parental types again (Hershey and Rotman, 1948). Additional data on triparental matings are given by Hershey and Chase (1951).

d. Linkage and Negative Interference

The proportion of recombinants to total progeny in matings involving a particular pair of gene loci in T2 is essentially constant from experiment to experiment and is not affected by the presence of other mutant loci elsewhere in the parental phage particles. The proportion of recombinants is the same whether the cross involves the parents $h \times r7$ or $hr \times h^+r^+$. The proportion of recombinants to total progeny varies greatly from one pair of gene loci to another, ranging from less than one per cent to as high as 40 per cent. On the basis of the various recombination frequencies observed, Hershey and Rotman (1949) proposed a linkage system involving three linkage groups, and suggested that the gene loci were probably arranged in linear order in each linkage group.

In studies of recombination in phage T4 Doermann and Hill (1953) found evidence for three linkage groups that were homologous to the three linkage groups of Hershey and Rotman (1949) as demonstrated by crosses between T2 and T4. The recombination values between different pairs of loci were strongly indicative of a linear arrangement of the loci in two of the linkage groups. Not enough loci were available for testing linearity in the third linkage group.

Hershey and Rotman (1948, 1949) had found that 8 of the 15 T2r mutants they isolated formed a single closely linked "cluster," giving a low frequency of recombination when tested pairwise. Doermann and Hill (1953) isolated 26 independent *tu* mutants in phage T4 and found these to fall into five distinct clusters. The frequency of recombination between loci within a single cluster was of the order of 1 per cent. They also found an *r* cluster in linkage group II that was homologous with the *r* cluster of Hershey and Rotman. This rII cluster was analyzed in great detail by Benzer (1955, 1957) as will be described later.

A peculiar discrepancy between observed and calculated recombination frequencies was noted by Hershey and Rotman (1949) and by Doermann and Hill (1953). With three linked loci in the linear order 1, 2, 3, if the recombination frequency between locus 2 and 3 is symbolized C_{23}, etc., the recombination frequency between locus 1 and 3, C_{13} should be

$$C_{12} + C_{23} - 2(C_{12} \times C_{23})$$

The negative term is to take account of the fact that if recombination occurs both between 1 and 2 and between 2 and 3 the result will be no recombination between 1 and 3 because the second recombination reverses the effect of the first. When recombination frequencies between terminal loci calculated in this way were compared with observed recombination frequencies, the calculated values were almost invariably higher than those determined experimentally. This suggests that the frequency of double recombinations is greater than that calculated on the basis of the single recombination frequencies, that is, the term 2 $(C_{13} \times C_{23})$ is an underestimate of the frequency of double recombinations. In classical genetics it is usually found that the frequency of double recombinations between closely linked markers is less than that calculated from single frequencies, a phenomenon that has been termed "interference" because the occurrence of a crossover appears to interfere with the occurrence of another crossover in adjacent regions. When the opposite phenomenon was observed in bacteriophages it was referred to as "negative interference" without any necessary implications as to mechanism. The term "negative interference" in phage papers refers then to an excess of double recombinations over those calculated on the basis of single recombination frequencies using the classical genetic formula given above.

e. Multiplication after Recombination

There are a number of possible time relationships among the processes of multiplication, recombination, and maturation.

Some of these can be eliminated on the basis of available evidence. If recombination occurred early as a necessary prelude to multiplication, one would expect to find recombinants primarily in large clones in single cell bursts. In actual experiments with closely linked markers, Hershey and Rotman (1949) found only a small proportion of bursts with more than 10 recombinant particles, so recombination does not necessarily precede multiplication. If recombination were a terminal event followed invariably by maturation, the distribution of recombinants in single cell bursts should be Poissonian, since each act of recombination would be independent of other similar acts. The actual frequency distribution observed by Hershey and Rotman (1949) lies between a purely Poissonian distribution and a purely clonal distribution of the type observed for phage mutations by Luria (1951). These results suggest that each act of recombination is an independent event but that the product or products of the act have a definite probability of replication before being withdrawn from the vegetative pool by the act of maturation. Because the pool size remains constant during maturation, replication and maturation must proceed at the same rate and a newly formed recombinant must have about an even chance of replicating or not before maturation providing that the act of recombination does not alter the probability of subsequent maturation. The latter is not likely to be an important consideration because studies to be discussed later suggest that most of the progeny particles of mixedly infected bacteria have undergone one or more acts of mating. The biochemical evidence indicates clearly that maturation is an irreversible process so that the mature phage particles do not reenter the vegetative pool. One may conclude tentatively from the available evidence that phage particles multiply in the vegetative pool after recombination, but produce on the average only very small clones, before maturation intervenes. Large clones of recombinants could seldom arise unless the recombination occurred early in the development of a particular vegetative pool when the rate of replication was much greater than the rate of maturation.

It is probable that some kind of mating procedure is an un-avoidable if not essential part of phage replication in the vegeta-tive pool. Recombination would then be an incidental result when the mating happens to occur between nonidentical phage particles.

f. Drift toward Genetic Equilibrium

The proportion of recombinants among phage particles found in premature lysates made at various times during the latent period increases as a function of time (Doermann, 1953). With unlinked markers the proportion increases from 0.32 at the start of maturation to 0.42 at the time of lysis. With a given pair of linked markers the proportion of recombinants increases from 0.06 at the start of maturation to 0.12 at the time of normal lysis. Levinthal and Visconti (1953), using the phenomenon of lysis inhi-bition to prolong the latent period in crosses involving the closely-linked markers h and $r13$, found that the recombinant frequency increased from 0.02 at 20 minutes to about 0.09 at 80 minutes. The increase in recombination frequency paralleled the increase in average burst size over this period of time. In a cross involv-ing the less closely linked markers h and $r7$ the recombinant frequency increased from 0.25 at 30 minutes to 0.43 at 90 minutes. This effect had been originally reported by Hershey and Chase (1951) who found that the fraction of recombinants between h and $r7$ was 0.17 at a burst size of 10 (premature lysis), 0.29 at a burst size of 250 (normal lysis), and 0.42 at a burst size of 1,710 (lysis inhibition). The recombinant fre-quency for unlinked or distantly linked markers may approach the equilibrium value of 0.5 but cannot reach this value for several reasons. One obvious reason is that the final phage yield contains phage particles that have matured at various times during the latent period. Particles that have matured early are taken from the vegetative phage pool long before genetic equilibrium has been reached. Because maturation is irreversible, the excess of parental genotypes in the early samples will prevent an equilibrium mixture of recombinants being obtained even if the vegetative pool can reach genetic equilibrium.

The equilibrium value of 0.5 for unlinked markers applies only to bacteria infected with equal numbers of the two parental types. The proportion of the two types in the vegetative pool and in the phage progeny is presumably the same as in the parental phage particles infecting a given bacterium. Any disproportion in the infecting types will result in a decreased opportunity for mating between unlike types, as pointed out by Hershey and Rotman (1949) who developed a correction factor applicable to the yields from single bursts. If a bacterium is infected with m particles of one type and n particles of the other type, the recombinant frequency would be proportional to the factor $4mn/(m + n)^2$. When the average multiplicities of the two infecting types are equal, the random adsorption of the phage particles results in unequal multiplicities in individual bacteria and this decreases the average recombinant frequency. A correction for this effect is given by Lennox, Levinthal, and Smith in an appendix to the paper by Levinthal and Visconti (1953). The observed recombinant frequency should reach about 90 per cent of the theoretical value at an average multiplicity of 5 for each infecting type.

It is evident that some progeny phage particles from mixedly infected bacteria descend from particles that had no opportunity to mate with unlike particles, whereas other progeny phage particles descend from vegetative phage lines in which more than one mating with unlike particles occurred. The observed recombinant frequencies are consistent with the assumption that the act of mating is random with respect to type of partner. As one consequence of repeated matings in the vegetative pool, crosses made with unequal multiplicites of the two parental types may yield a higher frequency of recombinants than of minority parents when the markers are unlinked (Doermann, 1953).

g. A Problem in Population Genetics

On the basis of the observations described above, Visconti and Delbrück (1953) developed a theory to explain quantitatively the frequencies of recombinants observed in various mixed infection experiments involving phages T2 and T4. They made the following specific assumptions that were consistent with the available data. Phage infection involves the introduction of phage DNA into the host cell and as a result mature phage is converted into vegetative phage. Replication and recombination proceed in the pool of vegetative phage until interrupted by lysis of the host cell. Phage is withdrawn from the vegetative pool at the same rate that new phage is produced, and is converted by an irreversible process into mature phage. Mature phage particles do not replicate and do not mix genetically with the vegetative phage pool. Within this pool the vegetative phage particles mate pairwise and at random with respect to partner, and each mating involves a genetically complete phage particle. The authors considered two possibilities with respect to order of mating, synchronous and random, and concluded that random-in-time matings agreed better with data from experiments designed to test this point. Genetic recombination in phage is then a problem in population genetics in which the vegetative phage pool is the population under consideration.

On the basis of these assumptions the authors derived equations to describe the results of mixed infection experiments involving parental phage particles differing by two or three genetic factors. For instance, in the two-factor cross T2hr^+ × T2h^+r the frequency among the progeny of the T2hr recombinant is given by the equation

$$a = (1 - f^2)(1 - e^{-mp})/4$$

In this equation the parameter f is related to the genotype frequencies of the infecting parents by the following expression:

Frequency of majority parent $= (1 + f)/2$

The parameter m is the average number of random matings per progeny phage particle and the parameter p is the probability of recombination between two markers per heterozygous mating. Visconti and Delbrück concluded that for phage T2 under conditions of normal lysis the parameter m had the value of five matings per progeny phage particle. Because the matings are random in respect to both partner and time, some progeny phage particles may have mated only with like particles before maturation. These particles which have had no opportunity for recombination dilute the population in which recombination has occurred, and dilute both single and double recombinants by the same factor. The net effect is an apparent increase in the frequency of double recombinants over that calculated from the frequency of single recombinants by the classical formula. The Visconti-Delbrück theory accounts quantitatively for this apparent excess of double recombinants, the "low negative interference" of phage genetics. When the parameter p, the probability of recombination per heterozygous mating, is used in constructing linkage maps, low negative interference is not observed.

Levinthal and Visconti (1953) tested the assumptions of the Visconti-Delbrück theory by making use of the phenomenon of lysis inhibition to study genetic recombination over a longer period of time than is possible under conditions of normal lysis. Using the closely linked markers h and $r13$ of phage T2 they found that the proportion of recombinants in the total yield increased linearly with time for about the first hour of intracellular multiplication and leveled out when intracellular multiplication ceased. From this observation they deduced that the recombinant frequency in the vegetative pool must also increase as a linear function of time. Because the parameter p, the probability of recombination per heterozygous mating, is independent of time, the average number of matings per progeny particle must increase with time. From their data Levinthal and Visconti calculated that one mating per progeny particle must occur every 2 minutes in the vegetative pool. Phage matured in these experiments at the rate of about 10 particles per minute. If one assumes that the vegetative phage pool remains constant at a size of about 30 particles, then each particle can mate and duplicate every 2 minutes to give the observed rates of genetic recombination and phage maturation. This estimate of the size of the vegetative phage pool is in reasonable agreement with the size of the pool (50 to 100 phage equivalents) estimated by Hershey (1953a) from purely chemical evidence. The experiments of Levinthal and Visconti (1953) are thus consistent with the possibility that mating is a prelude to phage duplication but of course they do not prove the essentiality of such a relationship.

4. Heterozygosis

Although the Visconti-Delbrück theory is an eminently satisfactory description of the kinetics of genetic recombination in bacteriophages it does not attempt to offer a mechanism for genetic recombination, and in particular it does not explain the occurrence of heterozygous phage particles. A detailed description of heterozygous phage particles was given by Hershey and Chase (1951) who discovered them. If bacteria are mixedly infected with r and r^+ phage particles and plated before lysis each mixed yielding bacterium will produce a mottled plaque. The mottled appearance is the result of lysis inhibition in some regions of the plaque where r^+ phage particles are multiplying and complete lysis in other regions where r particles are growing. A mottled plaque is produced whenever both r and r^+ phages grow together, a fact that can be checked by sampling the plaque and demonstrating that both kinds of phage are present.

Hershey and Chase noted that lysates of bacteria mixedly infected with T2r and T2r^+ phage particles contained about 2 per cent of aberrant phage particles that produced mottled plaques. These plaques contained r and r^+ phage particles indicating that the aberrant phage particles segregated to produce both r and r^+ progeny, hence they were heterozygous for the r locus.

The possibility that the mottled plaques might have originated from mixed clumps of r and r^+ phage particles, rather than from single heterozygous particles, was excluded by the fact that the kinetics of inactivation by heat, beta rays, ultraviolet light, and antiserum were the same as those of normal T2 phage particles. There was no evidence that the mottling phage particles gave rise to mottling progeny, but rather the evidence suggested that their progeny were segregants. However, it now seems possible that a heterozygous particle may be used one or more times as a pattern for the synthesis of segregant progeny before its career is interrupted by maturation.

Hershey and Chase (1951) examined five different r loci and one h locus for evidence of heterozygosis and in each case about 2 per cent of the total phage progeny was heterozygous for the marker examined. The proportion of heterozygotes remained constant at about 2 per cent whether the average burst size was 10 (premature lysis), 250 (normal lysis), or 1,700 (lysis inhibition). This was confirmed by Levinthal and Visconti (1953) with a different gene locus. This constant proportion of heterozygotes indicates that heterozygous vegetative phage do not produce heterozygous replicas. It is consistent with the assumption that there is a constant probability per heterozygous mating of producing a phage particle heterozygous for a particular genetic region, and that this phage particle has a constant probability of remaining intact until it matures.

When the parental phage particles differ at two genetic loci, such as h and r, the proportions of different kinds of heterozygotes depend on the linkage between the markers. If the markers are unlinked, the proportion of double heterozygotes is about 3 per cent of all particles heterozygous for either the h or r character. The proportion of double heterozygotes expected on the basis of chance is 1 per cent. The excess is due to the same cause as low negative interference; the frequencies of single and double heterozygotes are calculated on the basis of the total phage population whereas they should be calculated on the basis of heterozygous matings only. For the distantly linked markers h

and $r7$ the proportion of double heterozygotes is also 3 per cent of the total heterozygotes but for the closely linked markers h and $r13$ the proportion of double heterozygotes is much greater, 59 per cent of the total number of heterozygotes for the two loci. This information about the frequencies of single and double heterozygotes was derived from observations of the segregation patterns of heterozygous phage particles by sampling the phage progeny in mottled plaques. For instance in the linked cross $hr7$ by h^+r^+, 44 per cent of the mottled plaques gave only hr^+ and hr particles, 50 per cent gave only h^+r and h^+r^+ particles and 6 per cent gave hr and h^+r^+ particles plus some recombinants. None of 150 mottled plaques that were sampled gave predominantly the two recombinant types hr^+ and h^+r. This means that 6 per cent of the particles that were heterozygous for the r locus were also heterozygous for the h locus, and all of these segregated to give the parental combinations rather than recombinants. The proportion of the different genotypes among the heterozygous particles was controlled by the ratio of the parental particles as expected. For instance, in the unlinked cross with five $hr1$ particles to one h^+r^+ particle, about 80 per cent of the heterozygotes segregated to give the majority parent and recombinant, hr and hr^+, and 20 per cent gave the minority parent and recombinant, h^+r and h^+r^+.

Hershey and Chase (1951) suggested two reasonable genetic structures for the heterozygous particles. One proposed structure is essentially haploid with a small piece of added genetic material derived from the second parent to form a diploid region. The second structure is diploid throughout and contains one parental set and one recombinant set of genes. In each structure the heterozygous region must be limited in extent, being larger than 2 map units, but shorter than 20 units, as judged by the incidence of doubly heterozygous particles in various crosses. The possibility that the formation of heterozygotes is related to the formation of recombinants was pointed out by Hershey and Chase. The singly heterozygous particles as a group give rise in their progeny to half recombinants and half parental types regardless of the linkage relationship of the two markers used, because each singly heterozygous particle gives rise to one parental and one recombinant segregant. Therefore if heterozygous particles were the precursors of all recombinant particles, it would explain the lack of correlation between the frequencies of the sister recombinant types in single cell bursts observed by Hershey and Rotman (1949). Because each of six genetic loci tested contributed 2 per cent of heterozygotes to the total yield and because the heterozygous region is limited in extent relative to the total phage genetic material, it follows that each phage particle in the progeny is potentially heterozygous and is therefore actually diploid for at least a part of its genetic substance. The significance of heterozygosis as a key to the mechanism of genetic recombination in phage was clearly visualized by Hershey and Chase (1951), but the phenomenon was neglected for several years.

The genetic structure and function of heterozygous phage particles was further considered by Levinthal (1954). He proposed two variations of the structures suggested by Hershey and Chase and performed three factor crosses to distinguish between them. The proposed structures are shown in Figure 11. In model I the heterozygous phage consists of one full parental chromosome plus an attached fragment from the second parent to form the heterozygous region. Model II consists of a chromosome fragment from each parent overlapping in the heterozygous region. By using parents differing in three linked markers it is possible to distinguish between the two models by analyzing the segregants obtained from the heterozygous particles. The cross involved the parents $hr2^+r7$ and h^+r2r7^+. The characters $r2$ and $r7$ are mutually epistatic which means that a phage particle carrying either r factor will produce an r plaque. Therefore if a heterozygote from this cross is to produce a mottled plaque it must carry both $r2^+$ and $r7^+$ as well as one of the r genes. For instance a heterozygote of the type $r2^+r7/r2$ will not produce a mottled plaque because it will segregate to produce $r2^+r7$ and $r2r7$ particles which are both pheno-

typically r.   Since only r heterozygotes containing both $r2^+$
and $r7^+$ need be considered, the possible segregation patterns
are (**1**) $r2^+r7^+/r2r7^+$ ($r2$ heterozygotes), (**2**) $r2^+r7^+/r2^+r7$ ($r7$
heterozygotes), (**3**) $r2^+r7/r2r7^+$ (double heterozygotes), (**4**) $r2^+$-
$r7^+/r2r7$ (double heterozygotes).   Patterns (**1**) and (**2**) will lead

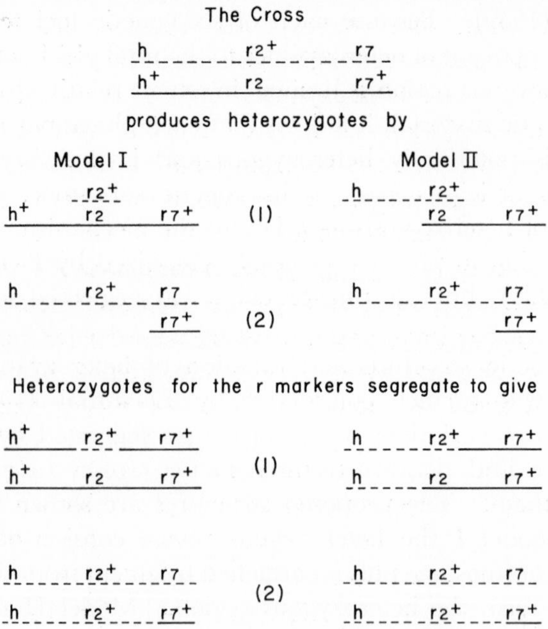

Figure 11. Predictions of two models for the structure of heterozygotes.
Unpublished drawing by M. Delbrück.

to mottled plaques.   Pattern (**3**) will produce primarily r
segregants and will produce mottling only infrequently.   Pattern
(**4**) is a possible type of segregation but was never observed by
Hershey and Chase (1951) who reported that double heterozygotes for linked characters always segregated to give the
parental genotypes.   As may be seen by inspection of Figure 11
the $r7$ heterozygotes will carry only the h allele in either model
I or model II, whereas the $r2$ heterozygotes will carry the h^+
allele in model I and the h allele in model II.   Because the fre-

quencies of $r2$ and $r7$ heterozygotes are equal, one may expect to find the h allele in 50 per cent of the mottled plaques if model I is correct and in all of the mottled plaques if model II is correct. In the case of model II, the frequency of the h allele will be less than 100 per cent because recombination in the vegetative pool will decrease the frequency of the parental phage types in the pool from which the heterozygotes must be drawn. As the vegetative pool approaches genetic equilibrium the frequency of the h allele in the heterozygotes will approach 50 per cent. The frequency of the h allele to be expected can be calculated from the known linkage relationships and the observed frequency of r^+ recombinants which is a measure of the approach to equilibrium. In the case of model I the frequency of the h allele in the heterozygotes will be the same as the frequency in the total population, will be unaffected by the amount of recombination in the vegetative pool, and will be 50 per cent for equal inputs of the two parental types. From the results of Levinthal's experiment given in Table XVIII, it is apparent that the data

TABLE XVIII

The Results of Three-Factor Crosses Made to Determine the Structure of Heterozygotes. The Cross is $hr7 \times r2^a$

Condition	Burst size	Per cent r^+ in progeny	Per cent r heterozygotes in progeny	Per cent h among r heterozygotes		
				Observed	Expected Model I	Expected Model II
Premature lysis	1	2.9	1.3	80	50	80
Normal lysis	100	4.2	1.5	73	50	72
Delayed lysis	350	14	1.2	57	50	54

^{a} Modified from C. Levinthal (1954).

are in good agreement with the predictions for model II, but in complete disagreement with the predictions for model I. The genetic composition of the heterozygous particles changes with time in a manner predictable from the proportion of recombinants in the yield, indicating that both recombinants and heterozygotes are drawn from the same vegetative pool, and that heterozygotes must be formed continuously during phage replication.

Further evidence in support of model II was obtained from an analysis of the genotypes of the segregants from heterozygous particles. The heterozygotes were obtained from the $hr7 \times r2$ cross by premature lysis at an average burst size of one. The r character of 106 mottled plaques was determined by plating a sample from each mottled plaque, picking 5 r plaques from each sample and back-crossing each with both $r2$ and $r7$ stocks. The types obtained were 54 $r7h;$ 7 $r7h^+;$ 34 $r2h;$ 11 $r2h^+$. The proportion of the h alleles among the $r2$ heterozygotes was thus 75 per cent as compared with an expected value of 82 per cent from model II after allowing for recombination that had already taken place in the vegetative pool. As was pointed out above, the $r2$ heterozygotes must have been r^+ at the $r7$ locus in order to have formed mottled plaques, and this is confirmed in the back crossing of the segregants. Therefore 75 per cent of the particles heterozygous for the central $r2$ locus were recombinants for the end markers h and $r7$. As lysis is delayed and the recombinant frequency increases, the fraction of the heterozygotes showing recombination for the end markers decreases, approaching the equilibrium value of 50 per cent as shown in Table XVIII. Because model II has proved correct it is evident that formation of heterozygotes may be a major mechanism of genetic recombination in phage. For instance all segregants of heterozygotes at the $r2$ locus from an $hr7 \times r2$ cross must be recombinants for the h and $r7$ loci, and half of them will be recombinants for the h and $r2$ loci as well. On the basis of the known frequency of formation of heterozygotes and an estimate of the length of the overlap region, Levinthal (1954) calculated the frequency of recombinants between the closely linked h and $r13$ markers that could be formed by the mechanism of the heterozygotes. The calculated frequency of recombinants was the same as the observed frequency leading to the conclusion that formation of heterozygotes is probably the mechanism for all recombinations occurring within linkage groups.

5. Pseudoallelism

The gene is defined by the different operations used in studying its properties. Thus the gene may be defined in terms of its mutability or of crossover distance from some other marker or perhaps eventually in terms of a specific nucleic acid structure. It has become evident that these various definitions are not descriptive of the same physical entity and hence that the gene concept may vary with the operations used to study its properties. This is particularly evident in phage genetics. It was demonstrated by Benzer (1955, 1957) that the rII region in the genetic structure of phage T4 can be divided into subunits in terms of function, mutation, and genetic recombination.

The rII cluster of mutants is located in a definite region of linkage group II of phage T4 and related phages. The mutants are identified by plaque morphology and by a unique host range peculiarity that distinguishes them from other r mutants. The rII mutants are unable to form plaques on the host K12 lysogenic for phage lambda whereas the corresponding r^+ phage particles plate on K12 with the same efficiency as on host strain B. Mixed infection of a susceptible host strain by two phage particles with distinct but closely linked rII markers will result in the liberation in the progeny phage of some wild type particles which can then be detected by plating the progeny on the indicator host K12. The resolving power of this indicator system for closely linked rII markers is limited mainly by the background counts of r^+ particles produced by the spontaneous mutation of the rII parents. Recombinant frequencies between loci separated by a linkage distance as short as 0.01 per cent have been measured and the resolving power is at least 0.0001 per cent for most rII loci. Benzer isolated a large number of independently occurring rII mutants and arranged in a linear map those loci that were resolvable (Figure 12). The map distances are not additive in part because of low negative interference of the kind predicted by the Visconti-Delbrück theory and in part because of "high" negative interference of a second kind that characterizes loci close enough together to fall within the same heterozygous region. Different rII mutations are often distinguishable by other properties such as the rate of spontaneous mutation to wild type, or the "transmission coefficient" defined as the fraction of infected K12 cells that produce T4r progeny. Many of the closely linked mutants that give less than 0.001 per cent recombination are alike in transmission coefficient and rate of reverse mutation and therefore are presumed to be recurrences of identical mutations.

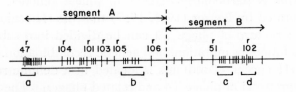

Figure 12. Linkage map of the rII mutants of phage T4. Segments A and B are different cistrons. Reproduced from S. Benzer, 1955, *Proc. Natl. Acad. Sci. U. S.*, **41**, 344, with permission.

a. *The Gene as a Functional Unit*

It is generally assumed that the function of the gene is to determine the specific chemical structure of a protein molecule such as an enzyme. If it is to transmit enough information for this purpose the gene must be a complex structure. As proteins contain some 20 kinds of amino acid, and nucleic acids usually contain only 4 kinds of nucleotide, it seems probable that 3 or 4 nucleotides are necessary to specify one amino acid. Therefore it would take a DNA strand some 1,000 nucleotides in length to determine the structure of a protein of 30,000 molecular weight. The functional unit of the gene may then involve a DNA segment of the order of 1,000 nucleotides in length.

A mutation may involve a chemical change any place in this functional unit, providing only that the chemical change results ultimately in a modified phenotype. The chemical change in the nucleic acid segment might be anything from an exchange of one nucleotide for another to a deletion of the entire functional unit. It is clear that the mutational unit may be much smaller than the functional unit and that many different mutations may occur at different loci within one functional gene unit. If one can determine which mutant loci fall within the functional unit, one can determine the extent of the functional unit in terms of recombination frequency. If one depends on phenotype alone this may be a difficult problem because r mutations, for instance, occur in a number of functional units. A test for "pseudo-allelism" developed in studies with higher organisms is used as a definition of the functional unit. To decide if two mutants with the same phenotype involve the same functional unit, they are tested in diploid heterozygotes containing the two mutations in different configurations. If the heterozygote contains both mutant loci in the same chromosome (*cis* configuration) the phenotype is usually "wild" because the second chromosome provides a complete set of functional units. However, if the heterozygote contains one mutant locus in each chromosome (*trans* configuration) the phenotype depends on whether one or two functional units are involved.

If the two mutations involve different functional units, the *trans* heterozygote will be wild type phenotypically because an intact functional unit corresponding to each mutation will be present. If the two mutations have occurred in the same functional unit, the *trans* heterozygote will have the mutant phenotype because neither chromosome will have a normal functional unit and so neither chromosome can determine the synthesis of a normal protein molecule. Therefore the results of the *cis-trans* test can be used to determine whether two mutations have occurred in the same functional unit or not. If a number of spatially nonidentical mutations in the same functional unit (pseudoalleles) can be mapped, the size of the functional unit can be determined. In phage work mixed infection of single cells with two genetically distinct phage particles simulates a diploid heterozygote because both genetic constitutions are functioning in the same cell.   This is the genetic explanation for the phenomenon of phenotypic mixing (Chapter XVI).   If the two mutations under study are in different phage particles, the mixed infection simulates the *trans* heterozygote, and if the mutant loci are in the same phage and the second phage is wild type, the mixed infection simulates the *cis* heterozygote.

The *r*II mutants of phage T4 have the phenotypic properties of producing *r* plaques on host B and failure to lyse host K12, although infection of this host does occur.   The wild phenotype is characterized by r^+ plaques on host B and efficient lysis of host K12.   All the *r*II mutants are similar in these two properties although they may differ in other characteristics such as map location, transmission coefficient, and frequency of reverse mutation.   If host K12 is mixedly infected with two *r*II mutants and efficient lysis occurs, one concludes that they are in different functional groups.   If the mixedly infected bacteria fail to lyse it is concluded that the mutants are in the same functional group.   On the basis of this test Benzer (1955) concluded that the *r*II region contained two independent functional units as shown in Figure 12.   Benzer (1957) proposed the name *cistron* to describe the functional unit, defined on the basis of the *cis-trans* test as that genetic region in which any two mutants in the *trans* configuration fail to give the wild phenotype, but in the *cis* configuration do give the wild phenotype.

b. The Mutational Unit

Most *r*II mutants can be located unequivocally with reference to other loci in the linkage group by recombination frequency with neighboring mutants.   However, Benzer (1955) found certain anomalous *r*II mutants that failed to give wild type recombinants with a number of closely linked mutants extending over a definite span of the *r*II region, but gave normal recombination with *r*II mutants outside that span.   Such mutants are indicated in Figure 12 by horizontal bars extending over the region of no recombination.   This observation suggests that a mutational event may result in chemical modification of varying lengths of the nucleic acid chain, and raises the question of the minimum extent of the mutation. A minimum-extent mutation might be called a point mutation. A point mutation might involve change in a single nucleotide pair, or any number of pairs. The longer span mutations might be a summation of point mutations or might involve some other type of chromosomal aberration such as a deletion or inversion of genetic material. The observation that these long span mutations do not give rise to reverse mutations is consistent with the recombination data in suggesting that extensive chemical alteration is involved. Benzer (1957) proposed the term *muton* to designate "the smallest element that, when altered, can give rise to a mutant form of the organism." He estimated the size of the muton in phage T4 somewhat as follows. The total amount of nucleic acid in phages of the T4 group is about 2×10^5 nucleotide pairs per infectious particle as determined by chemical analysis. Certain evidence based on isotope tracer studies (Levinthal, 1956) suggests that only 40 per cent of phage T2 DNA may be involved in the transmission of genetic information. Benzer (1955) estimated that the total length of the genetically active nuclear material is about 200 map units (1 map unit gives 1 per cent recombinants in a standard cross) including all known markers. The true map length may differ from this somewhat and a later estimate is 800 map units (Benzer, 1957) after correction for negative interference. If 200 maps units are equivalent to 2×10^5 nucleotide pairs, then 0.01 map unit (the shortest measured distance separating two mutations) is equivalent to 10 nucleotide pairs. As successive resolvable mutations occur at intervals of about 0.01 map unit it is evident that the minimum length of the muton may be less than 10 nucleotide pairs and may be only one. Some of the long span mutons mentioned above may be as long as several hundred nucleotide pairs. The lengths of the two measured functional units or cistrons are of the order of 4,000 nucleotide pairs each. The error in these estimates is probably less than a factor of 10.

c. The Unit of Recombination

On the assumption that the Watson and Crick (1953) model of DNA is a reasonable approximation to the structure of the phage genetic material one can make certain inferences. One might expect that in reference to the phenotypic expression of chemical changes in the genetic material, there would be considerable variation in different regions within one functional unit. If the functional unit controlled the synthesis of an enzyme, a change in a single nucleotide pair in a sensitive region might render the derived enzyme inactive, and extensive change in another region might have no effect on the catalytic properties of the enzyme but might alter its antigenic specificity. Also it would seem probable that genetic recombination might occur at the linkage between any two adjacent nucleotides in the genetic structure. Therefore the minimum unit of mutation and the minimum unit of recombination might involve the same chemical structure, the single nucleotide pair of the Watson-Crick model. Benzer (1957) proposed the term *recon* for the "smallest element in the one-dimensional array that is interchangeable (but not divisible) by genetic recombination." The size of the recon is of the same magnitude as the size of the muton in Benzer's experiments and it is probable that more refined data will show that both units are referable to the nucleotide pair from which the Watson-Crick model is constructed.

By a special technique Benzer (1957) was able to isolate 123 mutants that were not resolvable by recombination and presumably resulted from changes at the same point. These 123 mutant strains could be classified into three categories on the basis of frequency of reverse mutations. One group of 72 strains had reversion frequencies of the order of 0.2×10^{-6} to 4.0×10^{-6}, a second group of 50 strains had reversion frequencies of the order of 0.3×10^{-3} to 4.0×10^{-3}, and 1 strain had a reversion frequency of about 10^{-8}. If a point mutation involves a substitution of a single nucleotide pair by another these differences in reversion frequency may be a result of the substitution of different nucleotides for that present in the wild type genetic material. On this hypothesis there is clearly a modest limit to the number of possible phenotypes that could arise as a result of mutations at a single point. The four phenotypes (wild type plus three mutant types) found by Benzer at a single point might be attributable to the four known nucleotides of T4. Substituents on the nucleotides, such as glucose or hydroxymethylcytosine, might permit a few more types but the total number of variations that can occur at a single point locus is clearly limited if the muton and recon are restricted to a single nucleotide pair.

6. Radiation Genetics

The various effects of ultraviolet light and ionizing radiations on bacteriophages have been discussed in Chapter VI. We will consider here the genetic significance of studies involving radiation and radioactive decay. Certain types of radiation damage are reversible by light (photoreactivation) and by certain chemicals (chemoreactivation) without involving genetic interaction. However, the reactivation of inactivated phages under conditions of multiple infection (multiplicity reactivation), or the rescue of markers of inactivated phages by mixed infection with active phages (cross-reactivation) has features suggestive of genetic interaction between two or more phage particles within an infected cell. As a result radiation has become a tool in the study of the genetics of phages.

a. Multiplicity Reactivation of Phage Inactivated by Ultraviolet Light

Delbrück and Bailey, while assaying ultraviolet-inactivated phage stocks, noted that the plaque counts of surviving phage particles were quite variable and depended on the relative proportions of phage lysate and bacteria in the plating mixtures. In investigating this titration anomaly, Luria (1947) discovered the phenomenon known as *multiplicity reactivation*. A fuller discussion of the experimental methods and results was given by Luria and Dulbecco (1949). An ultraviolet-inactivated phage particle when absorbed to a host cell fails to reproduce itself. However, as we have seen, it is far from inert physiologically. It may kill the host cell, interfere with the multiplication of other phages, or with high intensity visible light undergo photo-reactivation and so regain its ability to reproduce. In multiplicity reactivation, if two or more inactivated phage particles are absorbed to the same host cell, there is a high probability that this multiply-infected bacterium will lyse and liberate viable phage particles. The probability of multiplicity reactivation in multiply-infected bacteria decreases with increasing ultraviolet dosage but is essentially one with low doses. The probability increases with increasing multiplicity so that an increase in multiplicity can to some extent overcome the effect of an increase in ultraviolet dosage. Multiplicity reactivation is a highly efficient and readily demonstrated property of phages T2, T4, T6, and T5, but is barely detectable with T1 and does not occur with T3 and T7. Inactivated T2 may also display multiplicity reactivation in mixed infection with either inactive T4 or inactive T6, but not with inactive T5. The evidence summarized by Bowen (1953) suggests that the major damage involves phage nucleic acid rather than phage protein and hence may be genetic damage. Luria (1947) proposed a hypothesis to explain these results, assuming (1) the inactivation of phage by ultraviolet is due to lethal mutations in a specified number of genetic "units" of the phage particle and (2) that multiplicity reactivation is the result of the recombination of an undamaged unit of each kind to recreate one active phage particle. In order to explain the high efficiency of multiplicity reactivation it was suggested that the undamaged units are capable of independent multiplication before reassembly. Luria and Dulbecco (1949) presented a mathematical formulation of the expected survival based on the following simplifying assumptions: (1) every kind of phage contains a fixed number of genetic units, all equally sensitive to radiation; (2) one undamaged representative of each unit is necessary and sufficient to give viable progeny; (3) there is a Poisson distribution of the number of phages adsorbed on individual cells. According to these assumptions the frequency of productive infection is

$$y = \frac{\sum_{k=2}^{\infty} \frac{x^k e^{-x}}{k!} [1 - (1 - e^{-r/n})^k]^n}{1 - (x + 1)e^{-x}}$$

where y is the fraction of multiply-infected bacteria yielding phage; x is the average multiplicity of infection; r is the average number of lethal damages per phage; n is the number of genetic units in each phage; and k is the exact number of phages absorbed to individual cells.

Since y, x, and r are known for a given experiment, n can be calculated. This equation gave a fairly good fit to the experimental data for ultraviolet doses up to 10 or 20 lethal hits per particle, if n was assumed to be 25 for T2, 15 for T4, and 30 for T6. On carrying these experiments to much higher doses of radiation, Dulbecco (1952a) found two serious discrepancies between the experimental data and the predictions of the theory. The theory predicts the same limiting slope for the dose-survival curve following single and multiple infection. The observed limiting slope for multiple infection is about $1/4$ of that predicted. The theory requires the extrapolated linear portion of the survival curves to intercept the ordinate at the value k^n, whereas the observed intercept is a much smaller value. The discrepancies suggest a kind of ultraviolet damage, lethal in single infection, that can be repaired in multiple infection without substitution of unique phage elements. The value of n can not be equated to any known genetic or chemical structures in the phage.

In a brief note Cairns and Watson (1956) pointed out that the discrepancy between the observed and predicted survival curves could be due to neglect of the deviation from a Poisson distribution of absorbed phage particles expected from the unequal sizes of bacterial cells. If Dulbecco's (1949a) figures for distribution of cell sizes were used, and a Poisson distribution of phage per unit of bacterial surface rather than per bacterial cell was assumed, the calculated survival curves fitted Dulbecco's experimental values well enough to validate the original hypothesis. Thus Cairns and Watson attributed the discrepancies to a faulty assumption rather than to a faulty theory. With very heavy doses of radiation, only a small fraction of the multiply-infected bacteria would show multiplicity reactivation and these would be the cells that had adsorbed the largest number of phage particles. With a skewed distribution of cell size, the largest cells would have adsorbed the most phage particles and the proportion of heavily infected cells in the population would be underestimated by the Poisson distribution.

This explanation of Dulbecco's results was disputed by Harm (1956) on experimental grounds. If the discrepancy between observation and theory is due to the high multiplicity of infection of filamentous cells, it should be possible to decrease the discrepancy by removal of the filaments. Filtration of a washed, concentrated bacterial suspension through fritted glass filters removed essentially all filamentous forms, leaving a much more homogeneous cell suspension. The dose-survival curves were the same whether the filamentous cells had been removed or not. This result is difficult to explain unless the filamentous cells have no greater efficiency of multiplicity reactivation than normal cells regardless of how many additional phage particles they have adsorbed. Harm suggested that his data as well as those of Dulbecco might be explained by assuming that in a part of the DNA damages are reactivated by recombination with a probability of essentially one, whereas the efficiency of multiplicity reactivation is fairly low in another part of the DNA. The theory of two different kinds of lethal damage was first proposed by Barricelli (1956). One kind of damage involves ordinary gene loci. The probability of inactivating any given gene locus is very small in comparison with the probability of inactivating the phage particle. This kind of damage can be corrected by genetic recombination in multiply-infected cells providing the damaged regions are not overlapping. The second kind of damage involves so-called "vulnerable centers" whose probability of inactivation is relatively great. The number of vulnerable centers is small and multiplicity reactivation can occur only if at least one copy of each kind of vulnerable center in a bacterium is undamaged. The quantitative formulation of this theory is rather complex but at higher doses of radiation simplifies to

$$\log W_m = r \log m - 0.43 \ (\lambda V + m\lambda_0 L^{m-1} V^m)$$

where W_m is the probability of multiplicity reactivation; r is the number of vulnerable centers per phage particle; m is the average multiplicity of infection; λ is the average number of inactivations in vulnerable centers per unit V; λ_o is the average number of inactivations in ordinary genes per unit V; L' is the average length of ordinary chromosome damages relative to the total length of ordinary genetic material taken as unity; L is $L' \lambda_o$; V is the dosage of irradiation in lethal hits under conditions of maximum photoreactivation.

This equation gives an excellent fit to the data of Dulbecco (1952a) both in the dark and under conditions of maximum photoreactivation. The values of the constants for phage T2 are:

	r	L'	λ_0	λ	$\lambda_0 + \lambda$
In darkness	3	0.0049	1.83	0.47	2.3
Photoreactivation	1	0.0038	0.895	0.105	1.0

It will be noticed that two of the three vulnerable centers are always photoreactivated. The fact that this formulation fits the experimental data does not prove that the theory is correct and further modifications of the theory are likely to be advanced. However, it does suggest that modifications of the original theory of Luria (1947) can be reconciled with the facts and that genetic recombination may play a role in multiplicity reactivation. A possible clue to the meaning of the vulnerable centers is offered in the work of Krieg (1957), which is not discussed in this book.

b. *Multiplicity Reactivation of Phage Inactivated by Ionizing Radiations or by P³² Decay*

A certain difficulty to explain multiplicity reactivation as a recombination phenomenon arose from the fact that the extent of multiplicity reactivation was found to be strongly dependent on the inactivating agent. Watson (1950) reported very slight multiplicity reactivation after hard X-ray inactivation, and multiplicity reactivation of P^{32}-inactivated phage was not observed at all (Stent and Fuerst, 1955). However, Weigle and Bertani (1956) demonstrated that X-ray inactivated T2 undergoes multiplicity reactivation with high efficiency if the radiation is applied after the phage has been adsorbed to the cell. They concluded that, besides the usual lethal damage, X-rays cause an additional "early step damage" which is expressed only when occurring before adsorption. The fact that under suitable conditions X-ray inactivations may be multiplicity reactivated to a similar extent as ultraviolet inactivations, although the two kinds of radiation are supposed to act in very different ways, argues strongly against a direct chemical reversal of the damage in multiplicity reactivation. The failure to observe multiplicity reactivation following damage by decay of P^{32} remains unexplained.

c. *Cross-Reactivation*

The progeny of mixed infections of bacteria with ultraviolet-inactivated phage and genetically marked viable phage contains genetic markers of the inactivated parent (Luria, 1947). This has been called cross-reactivation, but should perhaps more properly be referred to as "marker rescue," because the inactivated phage is not reactivated as a whole. Both the probability of marker rescue and the partial burst size of phage carrying a given rescued marker decrease with increasing dose of radiation. Extensive analysis of cross reactivation in T4 (Doermann, Chase, and Stahl, 1955; Krieg, 1957) leads to the following conclusions concerning the nature of the radiation damage which causes marker elimination and the nature of the rescue process. The hits are damages of small dimensions located on the linkage structure. Markers hit directly cannot be rescued. Markers which are not directly hit may be rescued during matings with live phage as a result of recombinations occurring between the marker and the nearest hit on either side. The probability of such recombinations decreases with decreasing distance from the marker to the nearest hit, and hence decreases with dose. The matings between the irradiated phage and the viable vegetative population occur with essentially normal mating kinetics. This accounts for the observation that for ultraviolet doses sufficiently high to ensure only one rescue event in a given infected cell, the frequency distribution of the partial burst size of phage carrying the rescued marker is like that for recombinants between very close markers in normal crosses.

Rescue of markers from phage killed by the decay of incorporated P^{32} also occurs (Stent, 1953; Stahl, 1956). In detail the effect of P^{32} differs in a number of ways from that of ultraviolet light. The genetic consequences of a single P^{32} disintegration are greater than that of a single ultraviolet damage; whereas an ultraviolet hit is likely to eliminate only those markers rather closely linked to it, a single P^{32} decay may prevent the contribution even of markers unlinked to the decay. The kinetics of the interaction with the viable vegetative population are also different for the two agents. Whereas rescue from ultraviolet damage occurs with essentially normal mating kinetics, the rescue from P^{32}-inactivated phage occurs immediately following infection about as often as it does at any later generation of the vegetative population.

d. Effects of Ultraviolet Light on Genetic Recombination

Jacob and Wollman (1955) discovered an interesting effect of radiation on genetic recombination. They studied genetic recombination between different mutants of the temperate phage lambda and found that if the parental phages were exposed, before bacterial infection, to doses of ultraviolet light so slight as not to cause appreciable inactivation of the phages, genetic recombination was very much increased. This phenomenon was thoroughly studied in two and three factor crosses, with equal and unequal multiplicities of the parents, either or both irradiated. There are striking differences between the kinetics of recombination with unirradiated and irradiated phages, respectively. With unirradiated phages, recombination in phage lambda occurs relatively rarely and relatively late during the intrabacterial growth cycle. In contrast, with irradiated phage, recombination is much more frequent and it occurs very early, producing large clones of recombinants. It seems that the radiation produces lesions in the genetic material that replication tends to bypass, resulting in an increased number of recombinations. This is very similar to the situation believed to prevail in multiplicity reactivation and cross reactivation, with the difference that in the present case the lesions are not lethal in single infection.

CHAPTER XIX

LYSOGENY*

Although lysogenic bacteria were described many years ago, only recently was the exact nature of the phage-bacterium relationship in such bacteria understood. It is now well established that lysogeny corresponds to an intimate relationship between the genetic materials of a phage and of a bacterium, which are integrated and reproduce as a single unit. Lysogeny occupies therefore a somewhat unique situation at the crossroad of virology and bacterial genetics. Several reviews have covered the main recent advances in the field (Lwoff, 1953; Jacob, 1954a; Bertani, 1958).

1. Definition and Occurrence

Lysogeny is the hereditary property of producing bacteriophage without infection with external particles. A lysogenic bacterium possesses and transmits to its progeny the capacity to produce phage.

Soon after the discovery of phage, it was recognized by many workers (Bordet and Ciuca, 1921; Gildemeister, 1921) that filtrates of bacterial cultures isolated from nature often contain phages that lyse other "indicator" strains of the same bacterial species or of related species. Two types may be distinguished among such phage-producing strains. In the so-called *carrier strains*, phage production can be ultimately ascribed to a population equilibrium between resistant and sensitive cells, the latter being constantly infected by free phage particles. These cultures can easily be freed from phage by successive colony re-isolation or by exposure to antiphage serum.

* Chapter contributed by F. Jacob and E.-L. Wollman.

On the contrary, in *lysogenic* bacteria, each cell can potentially produce phage. Even after many successive reisolations (Bail, 1925; Bordet, 1925) or after prolonged growth in antiphage serum (MacKinley, 1925) every bacterium gives rise to cultures containing bacteriophage. A strain can therefore be considered lysogenic if, on repeated isolations, its cultures or their filtrates regularly form plaques when plated on indicator bacteria. Obviously, the lysogenic character of a strain can be ascertained only if suitable indicator bacteria are available.

Lysogeny appears to be widely spread in nature. When systematic investigations have been carried out, it has been detected in many strains of various species and genera (*Staphylococcus, Vibrio, Pseudomonas, Salmonella, Bacillus, Corynebacterium*, etc.). In certain species of *Salmonella* (Burnet, 1932) and *Staphylococcus* (Williams Smith, 1948), almost every strain is lysogenic. A single bacterial strain may release up to five different types of phage (Williams Smith, 1948; Rountree, 1949a).

2. Prophage

Phages released by lysogenic bacteria are able to establish new lysogenic systems when they infect sensitive cells of the indicator bacterial strain. Such phages are called *temperate* and the process by which they re-establish lysogeny is called *lysogenization*. Lysogenic clones produced in this way in the laboratory differ in no significant respect from the ones isolated from nature. The phage released by lysogenized bacteria remains identical to the phage used for the initial infection. Lysogeny is therefore specific and, after lysogenization, every cell of the progeny carries in some form the genetic information necessary for the biosynthesis of a given type of phage particle.

Phage is not maintained as such within lysogenic bacteria, however. No infective particles can be detected after disruption of the cells (Burnet and McKie, 1929; Wollman and Wollman, 1936b; Gratia, 1936a). One is led therefore to conclude that lysogenic bacteria do not contain phage particles, but carry the information necessary for the production of phage particles in the form of noninfective units. Every individual of a lysogenic population possesses at least one of these units, for which the term of *prophage* has been coined (Lwoff and Gutmann, 1950). The prophage state, in which phage multiplies in lysogenic bacteria without destroying them, must be distinguished from the vegetative state previously considered in this book, which characteristically leads to the production of mature phage particles and lysis of the cell. Thus in lysogenic bacteria, temperate phages may be encountered in three different states: the *prophage state*, in which phage multiplies as a noninfectious unit in perfect coordination with the division of the host; the *vegetative state*, in which phage genetic material is multiplying independently; shortly to be converted to the *infectious state*, characteristic of resting phage particles. Lysogenization represents the process which converts the genetic material of resting phage into prophage. In lysogenic bacteria phage multiplication proper begins with the transition from the prophage state to the vegetative state and ends with the lysis of the cell. This part of the developmental cycle is presumably identical for virulent and temperate phages.

Although no direct information concerning the composition of the prophage has as yet been obtained, most of the available evidence points to its deoxyribonucleic nature. The specificity of lysogenization indicates that the prophage must have the same genetic potentialities as the mature particles of the homologous type, in which the genetic specificity appears to be carried by DNA (Hershey and Chase, 1952). Lysogenic bacteria do not contain any detectable antigen of the homologous phage (Miller and Goebel, 1954). The prophage contains the same amount of phosphorus and probably of DNA as the genetic material of the homologous phage (Stent, Fuerst, and Jacob, 1957).

Once acquired, the lysogenic character is generally stable. Although spontaneous losses of lysogeny have been reported in some bacterial strains (Dooren de Jong, 1931; Gratia, 1936a; E. S. Anderson, 1951; Clarke, 1952), lysogeny seems to be as stable as any other genetic character.

The main problem in the study of lysogeny deals therefore with the nature of the prophage-bacterium relationship. The stability of the lysogenic character implies the transmission of prophage to both daughter cells at each bacterial division. Schematically, such a mechanism can be insured in two ways: either a specific process of replication and segregation of the prophage itself as a nuclear structure; or a random process, provided the number of prophages per bacterium is high enough so that the probability for any daughter cell not to receive at least one is negligible.

All the available evidence supports the former hypothesis. On the one hand, experiments with lysogenic bacteria (Bertani, 1953a; Jacob and Wollman, 1953) point to the existence of a small number of prophages per cell, correlated with the number of nuclei (Section 7 below). On the other hand, analysis by crossing between lysogenic and nonlysogenic bacteria (Lederberg and Lederberg, 1953; Wollman, 1953; Appleyard, 1954a; Frédéricq, 1954c; Jacob and Wollman, 1957) as well as by transduction experiments (Lennox, 1955; Jacob, 1955; Morse, Lederberg, and Lederberg, 1956) indicate that the prophage is indeed located at a given site on the bacterial chromosome and constitutes the sole determinant of lysogeny. Moreover, different types of prophage appear to have different locations each one occupying a specific site of the bacterial chromosome (Jacob and Wollman, 1957). In one case, however, the same prophage has been claimed to occupy, with unequal probabilities, one of three possible sites (Bertani, 1956).

A lysogenic bacterium may thus be visualized as possessing the genetic material of a phage located at a specific site of the bacterial chromosome. The two integrated structures replicate as a whole. Different lines of evidence suggest that the prophage is added to, and not substituted for, an homologous segment of the host chromosome. It does not seem to be inserted into the axis of the bacterial chromosome, but is bound to it in some yet unknown way (Jacob and Wollman, 1957).

3. Properties of Temperate Phages

Temperate phages may be studied by the usual techniques in which sensitive bacteria are infected with phage. Although a certain fraction of the infected bacteria becomes lysogenic, conditions can be obtained in which this fraction is sufficiently low not to impair quantitative analysis. In this way one can determine the characteristics of multiplication, such as adsorption, latent period, burst size, etc.

Temperate phages, like other phages, are composed of DNA and proteins. However, in opposition to what has been observed with the virulent phages T2 and T5, temperate phages previously inactivated by ultraviolet light do not kill sensitive bacteria. Their protein coat appears therefore to be devoid of any lethal action on bacteria.

Many mutations have been described which affect various properties of temperate phages, such as host range, plaque type, plaque size, etc. Among these mutations, are some of a particular interest because they affect the ability to lysogenize. Plaques formed by temperate phages are turbid because their center is occupied by the growth of lysogenic cells. On the contrary, plaques formed by certain mutants are clear because such phages are unable to lysogenize (Dooren de Jong, 1931; Burnet and Lush, 1936; Boyd, 1952a). They have lost the temperate character.

Genetic recombination has been analyzed in several temperate phages (Murphy, 1953; Jacob and Wollman, 1954; Kaiser, 1955; Levine, 1957). The main features are essentially the same as those observed with T2 and T4 (Chapter XVIII) and the Visconti-Delbrück (1953) theory can be applied to them all. In every case studied so far, all the known mutations can be mapped on a single linkage group and the average number of rounds of mating is rather low, 0.5 or less. The frequency of recombination can be increased by exposing the phage particles to ultraviolet light before crossing (Jacob and Wollman, 1955).

4. Lysogenization

Upon infection with a temperate phage, a sensitive bacterium may respond in at least two different ways. In a certain fraction of the population, the infecting phage enters the vegetative state. The bacteria lyse and release phage particles (*productive response*). In another fraction the phage enters the prophage state. The bacterium survives and gives rise to a progeny containing lysogenic bacteria (*lysogenic response*). The relative frequency with which these two responses occur depends on both the conditions of infection and the genetic constitution of the phage.

For a given temperate phage, the frequency of lysogenization can be drastically modified by changing the conditions of infection. The factors which determine such alterations appear to vary widely according to the phage-bacterium system involved. In a phage acting on *Sh. dysenteriae*, 90 per cent of the infected cells produce phage when incubated at 37° after infection, whereas 80 per cent become lysogenic at 20° C. (Bertani and Nice, 1954). With a phage of *S. typhimurium*, the type of response depends upon the multiplicity of infection. When the multiplicity of infection is less than one, most of the infected bacteria lyse and produce phage. If the multiplicity of infection is gradually increased, the frequency of lysogenic response increases and reaches almost 100 per cent with 10 phages per bacterium (Boyd, 1953a). Moreover, in the same system the frequency of lysogenization can be influenced by such treatments as starvation of the cells or addition of various antimetabolites to the cultures (Lwoff, Kaplan, and Ritz, 1954).

It appears, therefore, that the lysogenic response does not result from the selection of preexisting mutants, either of the phage or the bacterium. As first demonstrated by Lieb (1953) in *E. coli*, the decision between lysogenization and lysis must be made after infection. Lieb's work suggests that, in those bacteria that are to become lysogenic, the genetic material of the infecting phage for some time behaves as a cytoplasmic particle. While in this condition it is particularly sensitive to heat, does not multiply, and is randomly distributed to one of the daughter cells at each division.

Although the variability in the bacterial response to infection with a given temperate phage depends on environmental factors, the capacity of a phage to lysogenize is genetically controlled. Mutants can be isolated in which the ability to lysogenize is altered (*c* mutants). Valuable information about the process of lysogenization has been gained through genetic analysis of the *c* mutants (Levine, 1957; Kaiser, 1957). The power of a phage to lysogenize appears to be controlled by a number of closely linked factors in the genetic material of the phage. Moreover, mixed infection with certain pairs of *c* mutants, each of which is unable to lysogenize alone, may result in lysogenization. The mixed infection simulates a heterozygous diploid in the *trans* configuration and each of the mutant phages appears to perform a reaction that the other one cannot. Evidently the temperate parental phage carries out both reactions and by such tests, the existence of two or three different reactions involved in the process of lysogenization has been demonstrated.

5. Production of Phage by Lysogenic Bacteria

a. *Spontaneous Production*

Large cultures of lysogenic bacteria contain free phage particles. During the exponential phase of bacterial growth, the number of phage particles increases proportionally to the number of bacteria. Using single bacteria isolated with a micromanipulator, Lwoff and Gutmann (1950) demonstrated that phages are not secreted by living and multiplying bacteria, but are released by lysis of a small fraction of the bacteria. The constant ratio between free phage particles and bacteria observed in growing cultures expresses the fact that, at each generation, a given fraction of the population lyses and releases a burst of phage. The ratio observed depends on the burst size and the frequency of lysis. Under given conditions of culture the *rate of production*, expressed as the probability per bacterium per generation to produce phage, is constant. For different strains of the same bacterial species, it varies widely (10^{-2} to 10^{-5}) according to the type of prophage carried. The factors yet unknown that determine phage production in lysogenic cultures appear to select at random the small number of cells that lyse in each generation.

b. Induction

In some lysogenic systems the probability of phage production can be increased nearly to one by exposing the cultures to the action of various agents such as ultraviolet light (Lwoff, Siminovitch, and Kjeldgaard, 1950). After irradiation, bacterial growth proceeds for a time corresponding to one or two divisions, then mass lysis occurs and a burst of phage is released by almost every bacterium.

This phenomenon, called induction, allows one to compare phage production by lysogenic bacteria and by sensitive bacteria infected with the identical phage. The characteristics of phage development appear to be similar in both systems, a result taken to mean that after induction and after infection phage multiplication occurs in a common vegetative state (Lwoff, 1953; Jacob and Wollman, 1953).

During the latent period following induction by ultraviolet light, lysogenic bacteria are still able to synthesize respiratory as well as induced enzymes (Siminovich, 1953). It appears to be a general feature of temperate phages and their mutants that their development, both after induction of lysogenic cells and after infection of sensitive cells, does not interfere as strongly with the metabolism of the host as it is the case with the virulent phage T2.

The process of induction is under the control of at least three different factors.

1. Evidence for a *genetic* factor stems from the fact that only certain lysogenic systems are inducible. In general, inducibility behaves as a property of the prophage, not of the bacterial strain.

2. Induction requires exposure of lysogenic bacteria to the action of *inducing* agents. Several inducing agents are known, including ultraviolet light (Lwoff, Siminovitch, and Kjeldgaard, 1950), ionizing radiations (Latarjet, 1951), nitrogen mustard, ethyleneimines, epoxides, and organic peroxides (Lwoff, 1953; Jacob, 1954a). All of these agents are also known to exhibit mutagenic or carcinogenic activity.

Ultraviolet light allows a simple and accurate determination of dose-effect curves for induction of phage development. As a function of dose of ultraviolet light, the fraction of bacteria producing phage first increases, then reaches a maximum which may be greater than 95 per cent, and finally decreases according to a rate which is generally controlled by the bacterial "capacity" to reproduce the homologous phage as measured by irradiation before infection (Jacob, 1954a).

3. Finally, the bacterial response to inducing agents remains under the control of the *physiological condition* of the cultures (Lwoff, 1951). For example, the "aptitude" of inducible lysogenic bacteria to produce phage after irradiation is greatly reduced if they have previously been starved (Jacob, 1952a; Borek, 1952).

Although little is known about the process of induction, several lines of evidence indicate that the primary lesion initiated by inducing agents does not affect the prophage itself, but the bacterial host, the conversion of the prophage to the vegetative state being only a secondary event. On the one hand, careful analysis of induction by X-rays indicates that the target size is much too large to be the prophage itself, but is of the same order of magnitude as the whole bacterial nucleus (Marcovich, 1956). On the other hand, analysis of lysogenic bacteria carrying two different, but related, prophages which can simultaneously develop in the same bacterium points to the existence of a correlation in the production of both types of phage. Such a correlation is incompatible with the hypothesis of a change in the prophage itself as the primary event of induction (Jacob, 1952b). Prophage development must therefore result from some bacterial lesions which, as suggested by the very nature of inducing agents, could be an alteration in the nucleic acid economy of the host.

6. Immunity

Lysogenic bacteria possess the remarkable property of resistance against infection with the homologous phage. As already observed by Bail (1925), Bordet (1925), Burnet and Lush (1936), Wollman and Wollman (1936b), lysogenic bacteria are not sensitive to the phage they release although they may adsorb it. Upon exposure to homologous phage particles, lysogenic bacteria survive and the superinfecting phage does not multiply. This property is called immunity. Lysogenic bacteria are immune against the homologous phage and most of its mutants, with the exception of a special class of virulent mutants (Lederberg and Lederberg, 1953; Bertani, 1953a; Jacob and Wollman, 1953). Immunity of lysogenic bacteria involves a mechanism of resistance to phage infection completely different from inability to adsorb.

That the genetic material of the infecting particles is injected inside an immune bacterium may be demonstrated by infecting lysogenic bacteria with a mutant of the homologous phage (Bertani, 1953a, b; Jacob and Wollman, 1953). The infecting particle is able to multiply in those bacteria in which the prophage develops, either spontaneously or after induction by ultraviolet light. If, for example, lysogenic bacteria are first induced and then infected with a mutant of the homologous phage, they release particles of the superinfecting as well as of the prophage type. Moreover, the ratio between the two types found in the progeny depends upon the multiplicity of infection. A ratio of 1 : 1 is found when the multiplicity of infection is 3 or 4, equal to the average number of nuclei per cell, a result which suggests the presence of one prophage per nucleus in the lysogenic bacterium (Jacob and Wollman, 1953).

The genetic material of the phage which has entered an immune bacterium does not multiply and is diluted out through the course of bacterial multiplication. Immunity reflects a

block in the multiplication of homologous phages as a consequence of the presence of the prophage. Its mechanism is yet
unknown.

The genetic material of a temperate phage which has penetrated inside an immune bacterium has a low probability of
becoming a prophage (Bertani, 1953a). Whereas lysogenic
bacteria carrying several prophages may easily be produced by
successive infections with unrelated temperate phages, there
exists an incompatibility between related prophages. As a
rule, bacteria successively infected with two temperate mutants
of the same phage carry only one type of prophage. Exceptionally, however, the infecting phage may substitute for, or be
added to, the original prophage. In the latter case doubly
lysogenic bacteria carrying two related prophages are formed,
and genetic recombination can be observed between the prophages (Bertani, 1953b; Appleyard, 1954b).

Incompatibility between mutant prophages suggests that, in
a lysogenic bacterium, the number of receptor sites specific for
a given type of prophage is limited.

7. Defective Lysogenic Bacteria

Phage production and immunity constitute the two criteria
by which the presence of a prophage may be detected. In
some lysogenic strains, a mutation of the prophage can prevent
the formation of infectious particles. Strains carrying such mutant prophages are called *defective* lysogenic strains.

Defective lysogenic bacteria have been isolated either after
infection of sensitive bacteria with temperate phages (Jacob,
1950; Lwoff and Siminovitch, 1951) or among the survivors of
normal lysogenic bacteria exposed to ultraviolet light (Lederberg and Lederberg, 1953; Appleyard, 1954b; Jacob and Wollman, 1956). In the cultures of these defective bacteria no,
or very few, phage particles can be detected. If inducible
defective bacteria are exposed to inducing agents, mass lysis
of the culture occurs, but phage particles are produced by only
a small fraction of the bacteria. The presence of a prophage in

defective bacteria is nevertheless demonstrated by the fact that they exhibit the same immunity pattern as normal lysogenic cells.

In defective strains some lesion of the lysogenic system prevents the formation of mature particles. This lesion is generally located on the prophage, since defective bacteria first induced by ultraviolet light and then infected with an homologous phage release a normal burst. By infection with genetically marked phages, it is even possible to localize the defect in the genetic linkage system of the phage. After irradiation, prophage development may be initiated but one of the steps involved in phage formation, such as maturation, is blocked (Jacob and Wollman, 1956). In some strains, defective bacteria induced by ultraviolet light and infected with homologous phages may release, in addition to normal particles, defective particles which, upon infection of sensitive cells, are able to establish new defective systems (Appleyard, 1956).

A defective lysogenic bacterium offers, therefore, the remarkable example of a phage genetic material that can be perpetuated only in the prophage state, restrained by genetic defects from producing infectious particles. Analysis of such strains is likely to yield new information about some of the steps involved in phage production.

8. Lysogeny and Bacterial Genetics

Lysogenization of sensitive bacteria with a temperate phage results in the appearance of new properties of the host, immunity and phage production, which express phenotypically the presence of a prophage. In most cases, these two properties are the only detectable differences between lysogenic and nonlysogenic derivatives of the same strain, which otherwise exhibit the same growth rate and the same biochemical potentialities.

In the last years, however, it has been shown that in some cases temperate phages and lysogeny may modify the genetic potentialities of the host bacterium. On the one hand, in the so-called *transduction* process, certain phages can carry pieces of genetic material of bacterial origin from one bacterium to another. On the other hand, in certain systems, specific alterations of bacterial properties by lysogenization have been reported which appear to be so entangled with the lysogenic character that they can be ascribed to the very presence of a prophage.

a. Transduction

Certain strains of temperate phages are able to carry a piece of genetic material from a donor bacterium, on which the phages have multiplied, to a recipient bacterium which they infect (Zinder and Lederberg, 1952; Zinder, 1953). Among the recipient cells surviving the infection, some have acquired new genetic properties originating in the donor bacterium.

In many cases transduction is not specific and any character of the donor may be transmitted with an equal and low (10^{-5} or 10^{-6}) probability. Everything appears as if the genetic material of the donor was disrupted during the multiplication of the phage permitting segments of this material to be incorporated by chance into occasional phage particles.

Such nonspecific transduction is observed in *Salmonella* (Zinder and Lederberg, 1952) and in *E. coli* (Lennox, 1955). When characters are closely linked, they may be transduced together (Stocker, Zinder, and Lederberg, 1953; Lennox, 1955) and this possibility has been systematically used for genetic analysis of small chromosomal segments of bacteria (Demerec and Demerec 1956).

Among the characters which can thus be transduced from donor to recipient bacteria is the lysogenic character itself. A phage particle acting as a vector may carry, in addition to its own genetic material, a piece of bacterial chromosome carrying one or even more unrelated prophages (Jacob, 1955). In other words, a phage coat may contain the genetic information necessary for the synthesis of two or even three different phages.

Another type of phage-mediated transfer of genetic characters has been recently described in phage lambda (Morse, Lederberg, and Lederberg, 1956). This transduction appears to be specific in the sense that a small fraction of the lambda particles released after induction are able to transfer exclusively the galactose (*gal*) fermentation markers to which prophage lambda is linked in *E. coli* K12. The phage material and the adjacent segment of the bacterial chromosome (*gal*+ for example) are incorporated as a single unit into a phage particle. Upon lysogenization of *gal*− sensitive cells the whole piece is added to the preexisting genome of the cell which becomes a "heterogenote" for the galactose marker, that is, carries both the *gal*+ and *gal*− alleles. Upon induction of such heterogenotes most of the resulting phage particles appear to carry the *gal*+ marker (Weigle, 1957). In this process the specific relationship which, in lysogenic bacteria, ties the prophage to a given region of the bacterial chromosome may therefore persist during the vegetative state and, after maturation, in infectious phage particles.

b. Changes in the Bacterium Resulting from Lysogenization

As a consequence of lysogenization with certain phages, changes may be observed in properties of the host. Such alterations are phage-specific and demonstrate that, besides conferring ability to produce phage and immunity, a prophage may alter host function in a variety of ways.

The best studied case is the production of toxin by *Corynebacterium diphtheriae* (Freeman, 1951). Most of the toxinogenic strains are lysogenic and release phage particles which are active on certain nontoxinogenic strains. Lysogenization of such strains with the phage makes them toxinogenic, and the toxinogenic character can be passed from strain to strain by lysogenization. The correlation between lysogeny and toxin production is complete. Moreover, this property appears to be restricted to certain temperate phages of *C. diphtheriae* (Groman and Eaton, 1955; Barksdale, 1955). Recent experiments even suggest that the ability to confer toxinogenesis segregates in crosses between related phages (Groman and Eaton, 1955).

In other bacterial species the presence of certain prophages can affect properties of the host such as colonial morphology in *B. megaterium* (Ionesco, 1953), synthesis of antigens in *Salmonella* (Iseki and Sakai, 1953), or capacity to reproduce various unrelated phages (Anderson and Felix, 1953b; Bertani, 1953b). Although a prophage does not interfere with the reproduction of unrelated phages in general, it does alter the susceptibility of the bacterium to particular phages. The prophage lambda confers on *E. coli* K12 the ability to distinguish between different mutants of phage T4 (Benzer, 1955). This phenomenon reflects the existence of a phage-specific block in multiplication of infecting particles interposed by the presence of the prophage. In other cases, the prophage plays a role in the phenomenon of host induced modification of superinfecting phage (Chapters XVI and XXI).

Many examples of interference by a prophage with the multiplication of an unrelated phage are now known. Many of them were discovered among the typing phages used to discriminate different strains of a single bacterial species. In most instances this interference is an expression of complex interactions at the intracellular level, of which the outcome is determined by the genetic specificity of all three components, namely, the bacterium, the prophage, and the superinfecting phage, and even sometimes by a fourth factor, the particular modification of the superinfecting phage imposed on it by the bacterium from which it issued. Specific examples of this kind are presented in Chapter XXI.

9. Conclusion

Lysogeny presents a remarkable situation in which the relationships between virology and genetics, dimly seen in previous chapters of this book, are clearly illustrated. Certain phages called temperate can multiply like typical viruses, bringing about the destruction of the cells they infect. Alternatively they can establish a stable association with the surviving host, to be perpetuated in a nonpathogenic form called prophage. Once established as prophage, the genetic material of the phage is integrated in a specific manner with the genetic material of the host and behaves as a normal cell constituent. Although it carries all the information necessary for phage production, it replicates without fatal intervention in the economy of the bacterium. The presence of the prophage at its specific chromosomal site nevertheless endows the bacterium with new properties: the potential ability to produce phage; immunity against superinfection with homologous phages; and new physiological capacities. Thus it is not only the presence, but also the position, of viral material in the cell that characterizes a prophage, and determines the properties of a lysogenic bacterium.

A lysogenic system is very stable. Only when equilibrium is upset by rare or drastic events can lysogenic bacteria produce phage particles. The development of prophage into phage is a lethal process that brings about the destruction of the host. Under ordinary cultural conditions, this is an infrequent, chance occurrence in the bacterial population. In certain strains, however, prophage development can be initiated in nearly all the cells by exposing them to inducing agents such as ultraviolet light. As a consequence of induction, transition occurs from the prophage to the vegetative state. From then on, the series of events leading to cellular lysis and the liberation of infectious particles appears identical both after infection and induction.

The lysogenic character is therefore a genetic property of the bacterium that can be acquired by infection with a virus This is the main feature of lysogeny.

CHAPTER XX

COLICINS AND OTHER BACTERIOCINS*

1. Definition and Criteria

a. Definition

In 1925, Gratia discovered that the filtrates of cultures of a particular strain of *Escherichia coli* strongly inhibited the growth of another strain of the same species. The inhibitory substance, to which the name colicin was later given (Gratia and Frédéricq, 1946), diffused in agar and through cellophane membranes, was resistant to heat and to the action of chloroform, precipitated in acetone, and was apparently not antigenic.

In his early publications, Gratia (1932) drew a parallel between bacteriophages and colicins. Like bacteriophages, colicins are highly specific. In particular, colicinogenic bacteria are resistant to the action of the colicin they produce. From sensitive cultures, resistant derivatives can be isolated. But an essential difference exists between phages and colicins: whereas the former are reproduced by sensitive bacteria the latter are not.

The production of colicin by colicinogenic bacteria is also very similar to the production of phage by lysogenic bacteria. The amount of colicin produced increases during the growth of the culture. Every single bacterium is able to give rise to a colicinogenic culture. When plated on the sensitive indicator, colicinogenic bacteria form minute colonies surrounded by a halo which closely resembles a plaque.

Since Gratia's original observations analogous substances have been found by Frédéricq to be produced by numerous strains of the *Enterobacteriaceae* family, including *Escherichia*, *Aerobacter*,

* Chapter contributed by F. Jacob and E.-L. Wollman.

Salmonella, Shigella, and *Proteus* species. They are all called *colicins,* because a substance produced by any member of the group may be active on strains belonging to any other species of the family, including *E. coli.* These colicins can be distinguished from one another by such properties as specificity of action, the aspect of the zone of inhibition they produce on a given indicator, and other physicochemical properties (Frédéricq, 1948).

Similar antibiotics are produced by certain strains of *Pseudomonas pyocyanea,* but their range of action seems to be restricted to the *Pseudomonadaceae* family. They have therefore been called *pyocins* (Jacob, 1954b). The general term of *bacteriocins* has been proposed to include such antibiotics of protein nature whose production is lethal and whose action, restricted to a narrow range of related species, is conditioned by the presence of specific receptors (Jacob, Lwoff, Siminovitch, and Wollman, 1953). More recently substances possessing most of these properties have been described in gram-positive bacteria and called *megacins* (Ivanovics and Alfoldi, 1954).

In many of their properties, particularly in their specificity of action, bacteriocins resemble bacteriophages (Frédéricq, 1948, 1953), and this explains why a chapter on bacteriocins has been included in this book. The following discussion will be mainly concerned with the properties of colicins, which have been the object of most studies. Other bacteriocins will be described briefly at the end of the chapter.

b. Detection and Titration

The methods used to reveal the presence of a bacteriocin in a culture medium, or its production by a given bacterial strain, are identical with those used for the detection of bacteriophage. Spot tests of the culture medium may be made on the surface of an agar layer seeded with sensitive *indicator* bacteria, or bacteriocinogenic and indicator bacteria may be cross-streaked on the surface of an agar plate. The second method is made more sensitive if separated into two steps: the producing bacteria are inoculated first, incubated, and then sterilized by chloroform vapors (Frédéricq, 1948); the sensitive bacteria are then seeded on the plate. Whatever the method, the presence of a bacteriocin results in an area where growth of the indicator is inhibited. In order to distinguish producing from nonproducing bacteria in a mixed population a triple agar layer is used. A suitable inoculum of the bacteria under test is incorporated into a first layer, which is then covered by a second layer of sterile agar. When, after incubation, isolated colonies have appeared, a third agar layer containing indicator bacteria is added. On further incubation those colonies which produced bacteriocin are made visible by a zone of inhibition in growth of the sensitive bacteria.

As in the case of phage, the existence of a bacteriocin cannot be demonstrated unless a suitable indicator is available. Systematic search for the production of bacteriocins in any group of bacteria therefore involves the same steps as a search for lysogenic strains, namely, collecting a wide variety of strains and testing them against each other in all possible pairs.

Such studies, mainly with enteric bacteria, have revealed that about 20 per cent of the strains investigated produce colicins active against a single selected strain of *Escherichia coli* (Frédéricq, 1948), or *Shigella flexneri* (Halbert, 1948). Seventeen different groups of colicins have been distinguished by Frédéricq using such criteria as host range, morphology of the zone of inhibition, and diffusibility. They are named A, B, C, D, E, etc. A single bacterial strain may produce more than one type of colicin.

The inhibition of growth of the sensitive indicator on agar may be used for titration of bacteriocins. An arbitrary unit of bacteriocin activity may be defined as the highest dilution of the product which still gives a clear zone of inhibition under standard conditions. The range of sensitivity of this method varies greatly according to the type of colicin under study. A more precise method, based on the bactericidal action of colicins, will be described in Section 2b of this chapter

c. Physicochemical Properties

Although they differ in many of their properties, many colicins are rapidly destroyed by proteolytic enzymes (Frédéricq, 1948), and were assumed to be proteins. More recent observations, however, indicate that they may be more complex, perhaps lipo-carbohydrate proteins (Goebel, Barry, Jesaitis, and Miller, 1955). Little work has been done on the properties and nature of colicins. Frédéricq has shown that the different colicins vary widely in properties such as diffusibility, or sensitivity to heat and pH. Different colicins seem to differ in size. For instance colicin V of Gratia forms a very wide zone of inhibition on agar (2 to 3 cm. in diameter) and diffuses through cellophane membranes, whereas a colicin of type A gives a narrow halo of inhibition and is not dialyzable (Frédéricq, 1948). A few colicins have been studied in more detail: one of type V by Heatley and Florey (1946), several of the V and D type by Gardner (1950), and one of type E from *E. coli* ML by Jacob, Siminovitch, and Wollman (1952). These colicins, very soluble in water, are precipitated by ammonium sulfate and organic solvents. Even the large colicins, such as that produced by *E. coli* ML, are not sedimented by centrifugation at 20,000 × *g* for two hours. They are insensitive to ultraviolet light and to ribo- and deoxyribonuclease.

A more detailed analysis of a colicin K was undertaken by Goebel, Barry, and Shedlovsky (1956). They prepared large quantities of this colicin and concentrated and purified it by repeated precipitations with 75 per cent ethanol at 0 ° C. and with 75 per cent ammonium sulfate at pH 4.5, followed by dialysis and treatment with chloroform–octyl alcohol. The material thus obtained is thermostable. A spot test with 0.02 μg completely inhibits the growth on agar of sensitive bacteria. Contrary to what had been reported for other colicins, colicin K is a potent antigen. Antiserum prepared against it agglutinates the bacteria that produce it. In its chemical, physical, immunological, and toxic properties, colicin K appears to be very similar to the somatic or O antigen of the producing bacteria (Goebel, Barry, Jesaitis, and Miller, 1955).

2. Action of Colicins on Sensitive Bacteria

a. Specificity

The action of colicins is very specific. First of all, it is restricted to members of the *Enterobacteriaceae* family. But inside this family, there is a certain degree of group specificity (colicins produced by shigellas, for instance, are mainly active on shigellas), and even of species specificity, among strains of *Shigella sonnei* for example (Frédéricq, 1948). Finally, like the phages, each particular colicin exhibits a definite host-range: some of them act on only a limited number of strains, whereas others have a much wider range of action. This strain specificity depends on the presence of specific receptors on the surface of the susceptible bacteria, as shown by P. Bordet (1948) and by Bordet and Beumer (1948). Specific antibacterial sera protect sensitive bacteria against the action of colicins. Materials contained in bacterial extracts as well as intact sensitive bacteria adsorb colicins and neutralize their activity.

The ability of a bacterial strain to adsorb a colicin and consequent sensitivity to its action may be lost by mutation. In the zones where growth of the sensitive indicator is inhibited rare colonies may be observed (Gratia, 1925). These colonies, like those surviving the action of phage, are formed by resistant mutants which arise spontaneously during bacterial growth (Frédéricq, 1948). The resistant mutants appear to lack the specific receptor for colicin fixation.

In a bacterial population sensitive to various colicins, mutations to resistance against each of the several kinds usually occur independently of each other. For example *E. coli* ϕ, used by Gratia and by Frédéricq for their investigations on colicins, is susceptible to a wide variety of these agents. A mutant resistant to colicin V, called ϕ/V, is still sensitive to other colicins. From ϕ/V one may isolate a double mutant, $\phi/V,E$, resistant to colicins V and E and only to them. This indicates that sensitive cells possess different sites of action for the various types of colicin. A classification of colicins by Frédéricq (1948) is based on such resistance patterns. The factors for resistance to the different types of colicin segregate independently in bacterial crosses (Frédéricq and Betz-Bareau, 1952).

Most remarkable is the observation of Frédéricq (1946) and Bordet (1947) that resistance to certain phages and colicins is correlated. For example, *Sh. sonnei* E90 is sensitive to various colicins (A, B, C, etc.) and to various phages (called I, II, III, etc.). Clones isolated for their resistance to colicin E are also resistant to phage II, but remain sensitive to the other phages and colicins. If mutants are isolated for their resistance against phage II, they are found to be resistant also against colicin E. In the same way, mutants resistant to colicin K are resistant to phage III and *vice versa* (Frédéricq, 1953). Moreover, in bacterial crosses, resistance to colicin E and phage II behaves as a single character (Frédéricq and Betz-Bareau, 1952). It is clear therefore that the action of colicins and phages on sensitive cells is dependent upon specific receptors which may be common to both agents.

b. Mode of Action

Exposure of susceptible bacteria to colicin results in the death of cells which, however, are not lysed. The action of colicin is thus bactericidal but not bacteriolytic. The kinetics of colicin action seems to indicate that the fixation of a small number of molecules is sufficient to bring about the death of a bacterium.

When sensitive bacteria are mixed with a suitable excess of colicin ML, and samples of the mixture are titrated at intervals by dilution and plating to determine the number of colony-forming cells, the number surviving decreases exponentially with time of sampling. The rate of killing is proportional to the initial colicin concentration. These facts suggest that a single particle of colicin is able to kill a bacterium. Moreover, if the colicin is not in excess, the survival curve reaches a plateau that measures the final number of bacteria killed, which proves to be proportional to the amount of colicin added. In this way one measures the number of "lethal particles" in the sample of colicin. Hence the most informative method of colicin titration consists in determining the total number of cells killed by a suitable quantity of colicin. The results may then be expressed in lethal particles per unit volume of the colicin preparation (Jacob, Siminovitch, and Wollman, 1952).

The action of colicin on sensitive bacteria therefore appears to be very similar to the bactericidal action of phage: either may be described as irreversible fixation of lethal particles on specific receptors. Once fixed, colicin interferes strongly with bacterial metabolism (Jacob, Siminovitch, and Wollman, 1952). When colicin ML, for instance, is added in excess to sensitive bacteria, growth is almost immediately arrested, but no lysis occurs. Respiration remains constant during 30 to 60 minutes. Syntheses of ribo- and deoxyribonucleic acids as well as induced enzyme synthesis are promptly inhibited. Furthermore, addition of colicin to bacteria previously infected with phage blocks the development of the phage. Thus in their action on sensitive bacteria, the parallelism between colicin and virulent phages such as T2 appears once more very striking. More especially, since colicins do not induce bacterial lysis nor reproduce in sensitive cells, their behavior is very reminiscent of that of ultraviolet inactivated phages or phage ghosts.

3. Colicinogenic Bacteria

Problems met with in the study of colicinogenic bacteria are in many respects analogous to those of lysogeny. They deal mostly with the mode and genetic determination of colicin production. For technical reasons, answers to these problems are more difficult to obtain with colicinogenic than with lysogenic bacteria. On the one hand, colicins not being reproduced by the bacteria they kill, titration is relatively laborious and insensitive. On the other hand, the colicinogenic character cannot be acquired by infection and therefore many types of experiment which have contributed to our understanding of lysogeny cannot be performed with colicinogenic bacteria.

a. Production of Colicin

The spontaneous production of colicin by bacteria depends very much on the composition of the culture medium, on the conditions of growth, and on the characteristics of the bacterial strain. It is generally found that more colicin is produced in complex than in simple synthetic media (Heatley and Florey, 1946; Jacob, Siminovitch, and Wollman, 1952; Goebel, Barry, and Shedlovsky, 1956). According to the example under study the importance of such factors as aeration (for colicin V) or pH (colicin K) has been stressed. The colicin is sometimes stable in the producing culture, sometimes not. An unfavorable effect of glucose on colicin production has been observed (Gardner, 1950).

The mechanism by which colicin is released by producing bacteria was for a long time unknown. However, the possibility of inducing colicin synthesis in certain colicinogenic strains by exposure to ultraviolet light suggested analogies to induction of lysogenic bacteria that proved fruitful (Jacob, Siminovitch, and Wollman, 1952).

When a culture of *E. coli* ML is submitted to small doses of ultraviolet light, the synthesis of colicin starts almost immediately and colicin accumulates inside the cells. After a latent period of about 80 minutes, the bacteria lyse and release colicin into the medium. The general aspects of induced colicin synthesis are therefore very similar, in this case, to those of induction of phage development in lysogenic bacteria (Chapter XIX).

In particular, the factors that control induction appear to be identical in both lysogenic and colicinogenic bacteria. Thus both depend on genetic factors: certain bacterial strains are inducible, others not. (Inducibility appears to be unrelated to the type, defined by Frédéricq's criteria, of colicin produced, however.) In both cases ultraviolet light, X-rays, and nitrogen mustard are effective inducers. In both cases the physiological conditions of the bacteria, both before and after exposure to inducing agents, are important. Finally, bacterial metabolism during the latent period following induction is similar in both systems. After ultraviolet induction of either colicinogenic or lysogenic bacteria, bacterial growth continues, respiratory enzymes are formed, ribo- and deoxyribonucleic acids are synthesized, and superinfecting virulent phages are able to multiply, until the time of lysis approaches.

Induction of colicin synthesis has been confirmed by Frédéricq (1954b) and by Hamon and Lewe (1955). They found, however, that after exposure to ultraviolet light of a number of inducible colicinogenic strains, release of the colicin was not accompanied by visible lysis of the culture. Whether always accompanied by lysis or not, colicin synthesis brings about the death of the productive cells. Thus, in the same way that the expression of lysogeny is lethal for lysogenic bacteria, the expression of colicinogeny appears to be a lethal process. Both capacities can only be perpetuated in potential form.

b. Genetic Determination of Colicinogeny

The ability to produce a colicin is a hereditary property of a bacterial strain. Colicinogeny is very stable, and no instance of the loss of this character has been reported. Moreover, colicinogenic bacteria are in general immune to the type of colicin they produce. The problems raised by the mode of inheritance of colicinogeny are therefore very similar to those raised by the hereditary transmission of lysogeny. There must exist, in colicinogenic bacteria, specific structures endowed with genetic continuity that confer upon the bacteria the capacity to produce a colicin. Colicins being noninfectious, the only possible approach to the problem of genetic determination seems to lie in genetic analysis by bacterial intercrosses.

It was found by Frédéricq that ability to produce a colicin may be transferred from a colicinogenic to a noncolicinogenic strain in mixed cultures. Different types of colicins are thus transferred with different frequencies, sometimes very high (Frédéricq, 1954a).

Transfer of colicinogeny appears to be a consequence of bacterial conjugation. In crosses between noncolicinogenic and colicinogenic bacteria, the colicinogenic character but not the noncolicinogenic character can be transferred from the donor parent to recombinants. The resulting asymmetry in reciprocal crosses led Frédéricq (Frédéricq, 1954a, 1955; Frédéricq and Betz-Bareau, 1953) to postulate that colicinogeny is under the control of cytoplasmic determinants whose transfer requires direct contact between bacteria of opposite mating types.

Immunity to colicins associated with colicinogeny is distinct from the resistance observed in mutants obtained by selection. For instance, whereas mutants resistant to a given colicin of group E are resistant to all the colicins of that group, bacteria that produce a given colicin of group E may be sensitive to other colicins of the same group. The immunity of colicinogenic bacteria, however, is neither as invariable nor as complete as the immunity of lysogenic bacteria. A striking exception was described by Ryan, Fried, and Mukai (1955). A strain of *E. coli* that does not produce colicin under ordinary conditions of growth releases, after exposure to ultraviolet light, a colicin active on the producing strain.

The transfer of colicinogeny in bacterial crosses enabled Frédéricq (1956) to analyze the immunity pattern of the resulting colicin-producing derivatives. Most of these, although immune to the concentration of colicin they produce, proved to be sensitive to higher concentrations. The genetic relation between the ability to produce a given colicin and immunity to its action seems to be complex.

4. Other Bacteriocins

Strains of *Pseudomonas pyocyanea* are known to produce antibiotic substances active on a wide variety of microorganisms. In filtrates of a certain strain P10 one finds a substance acting only on some other strains of the same species. The synthesis of this substance, called pyocin, can be induced in the whole population by exposure of the cultures to small doses of ultraviolet light or other inducing agents. Pyocin is released into the medium by bacterial lysis. It is adsorbed on specific receptors of susceptible cells. Apparently a single particle of pyocin is sufficient to kill a cell (Jacob, 1954b). The pyocin released by *P. pyocyanea* P10 behaves therefore in every respect as colicins do. The production of such substances is not restricted to strain P10. In the course of a systematic investigation of various strains of *P. pyocyanea*, Hamon (1956) found that about half of them produce one or another pyocin active only on other strains of the same species. Pyocins are protein-like substances that kill but are not reproduced by sensitive cells. They are specifically adsorbed by sensitive strains found only among *Pseudomonas* species. They differ among themselves by such properties as host range, diffusion rate in agar, susceptibility to proteolytic enzymes, inducibility etc. They are typical bacteriocins.

In *B. megaterium* it was observed by Ivánovics and Alföldi (1954) that mutual antagonism between strains is a rather frequent phenomenon attributable to the production of water-soluble antibacterial substances, of a protein-like nature, called *megacins*. As with other bacteriocins, the study of a particular strain showed that exposure of the bacteria to ultraviolet light induces biosynthesis of megacin which, after a latent period of 70 minutes, is released into the medium by lysis of the cells. Efforts to detect phagelike particles in the lysate failed (Ivánovics and Alföldi, 1955).

A striking difference between a megacin and other bacteriocins was found by Ivánovics, Alföldi, and Abraham (1955). The range of action is much broader. Not only does this megacin exert a lethal activity against every strain of *B. megatherium* tested, but it is also active against other bacteria such as *B. subtilis*, *B. anthracis*, and various pigment-forming cocci, such as *Micrococcus aurentiacus* and *M. cinnabareus*. With some exceptions, sensitivity to this megacin appears to parallel susceptibility to lysozyme (Ivánovics and Alföldi, 1957).

5. Bacteriocins and Bacteriophages

Analogy between phages and bacteriocins, first pointed out by Gratia (1925, 1932), was later emphasized by almost every worker in the field. Properties of phages and bacteriocins may be compared at two different levels.

1. The action of phages and of bacteriocins on susceptible cells is similar in many respects. Both agents are adsorbed on specific receptors which, in some instances, may even be common for phages and bacteriocins. The loss of receptors by bacterial mutation results in resistance to the agent. Adsorption of a single particle of either one appears to be sufficient to kill a cell. Finally, bacteriocins interfere with the metabolism of susceptible cells as strongly as virulent phages like T2 (Frédéricq, 1953; Jacob, Siminovitch, and Wollman, 1953).

2. The capacity to produce temperate phages or bacteriocins is a genetic character perpetuated as a potential property the expression of which is lethal. In certain examples of both systems, the lethal biosynthesis can be induced by similar experimental procedures in the whole population (Jacob, Siminovitch, and Wollman, 1953).

In their adsorption specificity and mode of action bacteriocins can best be compared to the proteinaceous "ghosts" obtained by subjecting phage T2 to osmotic shock. Colicin K and phage T6 adsorb on the same bacterial receptors. The killing abilities of these two agents are destroyed at similar rates by X-rays (Latarjet and Frédéricq, 1955), a result which would suggest that the colicin and the protein of the tip of the tail of the phage might be similar in nature and size. These two proteins are antigenically unrelated (Goebel, Barry, Jesaitis, and Miller, 1955), but so are, in general, different phages like T1 and T5 which may nevertheless adsorb to the same receptors.

Although bacteriocins and bacteriophages lend themselves to obvious comparisons, there is no indication for the existence of any direct relationship between these two groups of antibacterial agents, such as a colicin being the product of an incomplete phage development. In particular no case has been as yet found of antigenic similarities between bacteriocins and bacterio-phages. Even when the same bacterial strain is lysogenic and colicinogenic, for instance, no connection between its colicins and phages can be demonstrated. Neither has any instance of conversion from the lysogenic to the colicinogenic state or vice versa been observed.

Material antigenically related to phage has never been found in sensitive or even in lysogenic bacteria, whereas some relationship exists between certain colicins and the bacteria that produce them. Goebel, Barry, Jesaitis, and Miller (1955) found that colicin K is antigenically related to the O antigen of the pro-ducing bacteria. If similar relationships could be established in other systems, particularly where the colicinogenic and non-colicinogenic derivatives of the same strain can be compared (Frédéricq, 1954a), they would have important consequences concerning the relationships between bacteriocins and phages.

One must therefore conclude that, in spite of many remarkable similarities between lysogeny and bacteriocinogeny, there is at present no compelling reason to believe that they are in any way connected.

CHAPTER XXI

USE OF PHAGES IN EPIDEMIOLOGICAL STUDIES*

Species of pathogenic organisms are usually constant in their ecology and produce characteristic reactions in their hosts, and it is often possible to recognize a bacterial species by these reactions. It must be borne in mind, however, that the definition of species in bacteria is not based on such firm foundations as is that of higher organisms. As far as the pathogenic bacteria are concerned, much of the existing classification has resulted from expediency—the search for methods of distinguishing with confidence the pathogenic from the nonpathogenic flora with which they may be fortuitously associated, and of obtaining them in pure culture for diagnostic study. As the efficacy of these methods depends on the more or less constant characters of the bacteria concerned, they are understandably useful to the bacterial taxonomist. But the final validity of bacterial species, in the sense in which the term is employed in the classification of the higher organisms, still remains in doubt.

Communicable bacterial diseases present epidemiologists with the task of determining the avenues by which particular epidemic strains of bacteria have gained access to patients. Moreover, in a given outbreak of an infectious disease such as typhoid fever, it is important to know whether the organisms isolated from patients all have a common origin, that is, whether the epidemic springs from one or multiple sources. Clearly, in an infection caused by a single bacterial species, what is needed is a method of classification at the intraspecific level. In other words, the species should be divisible into "types." In an effi-

* Chapter contributed by E. S. Anderson.

cient typing scheme, the organisms isolated from patients, from vehicles of infection such as food or water and from the carrier responsible for the outbreak of the disease under study, all react identically. If an organism is widely disseminated, and especially if it is commonly carried by otherwise healthy persons, epidemiological study is impossible without such a method.

In order to be practically useful a typing method must satisfy the following requirements: the types and the typing reagents used for their recognition should be stable; the organism should be subdivisible into an adequate number of types; the technique should be simple and the results reproducible and easy to read. The method should be capable of standardization in order that, wherever it is employed, the results are comparable; the results of the test should be available quickly; and, before being accepted for general use, the reliability of the method should be established by exhaustive epidemiological trials.

An early attempt to distinguish between different epidemic strains of an organism was that of Kristensen and Henriksen (1926) in relation to the typhoid bacillus. This method was enlarged upon by Kristensen (1938). It depends on the differential fermentation of l-arabinose and xylose and divides *Salmonella typhi* into three biochemical types. Type I ferments xylose but not arabinose; type II ferments neither xylose nor arabinose; and type III ferments both sugars. As this scheme distinguishes only three types, and as most strains belong to type I, the method is not of great epidemiological value.

Many attempts have been made to classify single bacterial species by serological methods and have met with some success, particularly in the group A haemolytic streptococci. In other instances the number of types distinguishable is too small for epidemiological purposes, or the distinction of types by antisera too difficult.

In 1938 Craigie and Yen introduced their Vi-phage typing scheme for *Salmonella typhi*. This rapidly established itself as the method of choice for the epidemiological recognition of typhoid strains and served as a model for the development of all later schemes for the typing of bacteria by phage.

1. Historical

The practicability of phage typing depends on one of the most important properties of phages, their host specificity. This property was recognized at an early date in phage history. Sonnenschein (1925, 1928) isolated specific phages for *Salmonella paratyphi* B and *S. typhi*, and suggested their use for the rapid identification of these organisms. This method was employed by, among others, Schmidt (1931a, b), who found that Sonnenschein's original paratyphoid B phage could be "adapted" to *S. typhimurium*, *S. cholerae suis*, and *S. enteritidis*. The resulting phages were on the whole specific for the serotypes on which they had been grown, but the phage adapted to *S. enteritidis* was able to lyse *S. cholerae suis*. Marcuse (1931) used specific phages to identify strains of *Shigella flexneri*, and the same author (1934a, b) used Sonnenschein's phages for the identification of *S. paratyphi* B and *S. typhi*. Marcuse confirmed the specificity of these phages. He found that 30 per cent of 469 typhoid strains examined were resistant to the original typhoid phage, but by adaptation of the phage to resistant strains he was able to obtain preparations lysing the remainder. Successive phage adaptation to resistant cultures resulted in the production of five phages, dividing the strains of *S. typhi* into as many groups. This, then, was an early phage typing scheme for the typhoid bacillus.

It will be noted that the word "adaptation" is used above in relation to the propagation of phages on resistant strains. It should be remembered, however, that many if not all salmonellas are lysogenic, and that, in attempts at phage adaptation, there is always the risk of contamination of the original phage with phages carried by strains on which propagation is being carried out. Such contaminating temperate phages may be able to lyse strains resistant to the original phage, and high-titer preparations having new host ranges may then result which would erroneously be regarded as adaptations of the starting phage. This phenomenon certainly proved to be a source of confusion in later phage-typing schemes, and there are strong reasons for suspecting that it played a part in the apparent phage adapta-

tions in earlier days.   Adaptation in phages, which will be discussed later, is of two types, host-induced or phenotypic modification, and host-range mutation.   It can be accepted that
adaptation has occurred if the newly propagated phage is indistinguishable from its unadapted parent in all respects other
than host range, and if a phage that has undergone host-induced
as opposed to mutational modification of host range can be shown
to revert in one growth cycle to the host range of the unadapted
phage when propagated on a suitable bacterial strain.   There is
no evidence that such tests were applied in the earlier work to
establish that true phage adaptation had taken place, and claims
that phages had been adapted must therefore be treated with
caution.

Marcuse (1925) and Hadley (1926) were perhaps the first to
point out the relationship between phage specificity and the
heat-stable surface antigens of Enterobacteriaceae.   The most
important early work in this respect, however, was that of Burnet
and his colleagues (see Burnet, 1927, 1929b, 1930, 1934b;
Burnet and McKie, 1930; Gough and Burnet, 1934).   These
workers showed that, in the phage-host cell systems they studied,
there was a close correspondence between the somatic antigens
and phage sensitivity.   Mutation of the organisms from the
smooth to the rough state, which involved loss of the characteristic somatic antigen, brought about resistance to phage.   Thus,
it was possible to select rough variants of salmonellas with phages
specific for smooth strains.   On the other hand, phages were
found that lysed only rough variants.   Organisms surviving the
attack of "rough-specific" phages were often found to be in the
original smooth state of the host strain.   Burnet (1930) recognized, however, that mutation of bacteria to phage resistance
was possible without demonstrable antigenic change, and he suggested that distinct bacterial agglutinogenic and phage-adsorbing
receptors were carried by a single unit.   Levine and Frisch (1933a,
b, 1934) observed that aqueous extracts of *Shigella shigae* and
Salmonella paratyphi B specifically neutralized the phages to which
these organisms were susceptible, but were virtually without ef-

fect on other phages.   Burnet (1934b) confirmed these observations and Gough and Burnet (1934) demonstrated that the specificity of this phage-inactivating agent was determined by a polysaccharide.   Levine and Frisch (1935, 1936) established, by means of phage sensitivity, differences between certain strains of *S. cholerae suis* which were confirmed by antigenic analysis of the bacteria.   These findings led to the differentiation of the 6_1 and 6_2 somatic antigens in the C group of salmonellas.   Sievers (1943) first identified the somatic antigens of *S. köln* because of the organism's sensitivity to Sonnenschein's phage for *S. paratyphi* B.

2. The Vi-Phage Typing Scheme of Craigie and Yen

In 1934 Felix and Pitt announced their discovery of the Vi antigen of *Salmonella typhi*.   This antigen is present in the great majority of freshly isolated strains of the typhoid bacillus.   Its presence renders the organism inagglutinable by sera containing antibodies against only the somatic (or O) antigen of *S. typhi*. The Vi form of the organism is more virulent for mice than is the non-Vi form, and sera containing Vi and O antibodies offer a more powerful protection to mice against Vi-positive typhoid strains than do sera containing the O antibody alone.   Phages specific for the Vi form of *S. typhi* were isolated independently by three groups of workers (Craigie and Brandon, 1936; Sertic and Boulgakov, 1936a; Scholtens, 1936).   These phages were inactive on and were not adsorbed by the non-Vi (or O) form of the organism.   Two years later, Craigie and Yen (1938) published the Vi-phage typing scheme for *S. typhi*.   These workers had isolated four Vi phages which they designated by the Roman numerals I to IV.   They had originally intended to devise a typing scheme for the typhoid bacillus based on the differential patterns of lysis produced by these phages on different strains of the organism.   The peculiar behavior of one of the phages, Vi-phage II, however, attracted their special attention.   They found that this phage possessed the unusual property of acquiring a high specificity for the last strain on which it had been grown

TABLE XIX

Reactions of Vi-type Strains of *Salmonella typhi* with Routine Test Dilutions of Typing Adaptations of Vi-Phage II

	A	B1	B2	B3	C	D1	D2	D4	D5	D6	E1	E2	F1	F2	G	H	J	K	T	25	26	27	28
A	CL[a]	CL	CL	CL	CL	CL	CL	CL	CL	CL	CL	CL	CL	CL	CL	CL	CL	CL	CL	CL	CL	CL	CL
B1	—	CL	CL	CL	—	—	—	—	—	—	—	—	—	—	—	—	—	—	—	—	—	—	—
B2	—	—	CL	CL	—	—	—	—	—	—	—	—	—	—	—	—	—	—	—	—	—	—	—
B3	—	—	—	CL	—	—	—	—	—	—	—	—	—	—	—	—	—	—	—	—	—	—	—
C	—	—	—	—	CL	—	—	—	—	—	—	—	—	—	—	—	—	—	—	—	—	—	—
D1	—	—	—	—	—	CL	CL	CL	CL	CL	—	—	—	—	—	—	—	—	—	—	—	—	—
D2	—	—	—	—	—	—	CL	—	—	—	—	—	—	—	—	—	—	—	—	—	—	—	—
D4	—	—	—	—	—	—	—	CL	—	—	—	—	—	—	—	—	—	—	—	—	—	—	—
D5	—	—	—	—	—	—	—	—	CL	CL	—	—	—	—	—	—	—	—	—	—	—	—	—
D6	—	—	—	—	—	—	—	—	—	CL	—	—	—	—	—	—	—	—	—	—	—	—	—
E1	—	—	—	—	—	—	—	—	—	—	CL	CL	—	—	—	—	—	—	—	—	—	—	—
E2	—	—	—	—	—	—	—	—	—	—	—	CL	—	—	—	—	—	—	—	—	—	—	—
F1	—	—	—	—	—	—	—	—	—	—	—	—	CL	CL	—	—	—	—	—	—	—	—	—
F2	—	—	—	—	—	—	—	—	—	—	—	—	—	CL	—	—	—	—	—	—	—	—	—
G	—	—	—	—	—	—	—	—	—	—	—	—	—	—	CL	—	—	—	—	—	—	—	—
H	—	—	—	—	—	—	—	—	—	—	—	—	—	—	—	CL	—	—	—	—	—	—	—
J	—	—	—	—	—	—	—	—	—	—	—	—	—	—	—	—	CL	—	—	—	—	—	—
K	—	—	—	—	—	—	—	—	—	—	—	—	—	—	—	—	—	CL	—	—	—	—	—
T	—	—	—	—	—	—	—	—	—	—	—	—	—	—	—	—	—	—	CL	—	—	—	—
25	—	—	—	—	—	—	—	—	—	—	—	—	—	—	—	—	—	—	—	CL	—	—	—
26	—	—	—	—	—	—	—	—	—	—	—	—	—	—	—	—	—	—	—	—	CL	—	—
27	—	—	—	—	—	—	—	—	—	—	—	—	—	—	—	—	—	—	—	—	—	CL	—
28	—	—	—	—	—	—	—	—	—	—	—	—	—	—	—	—	—	—	—	—	—	—	CL

[a] CL = confluent lysis.

400

This capacity for modification of host range was wide enough to enable Cragie and Yen, by progressive adaptation of the phage to a collection of typhoid strains, to recognize 11 types of the typhoid bacillus, and trials of the method soon showed that this subdivision was epidemiologically reliable.   The value of the scheme was recognized by Felix (1943), and it was largely due to his work that it was accepted for international use.   Craigie and Felix (1947) published suggestions for the standardization of the method.   As it was employed by an increasing number of workers it was improved and extended; at present, 58 types and subtypes of the typhoid bacillus are recognizable by the Vi-phage typing scheme, and the flexibility of host range of Vi-phage II is such that it is clear, on theoretical grounds alone, that many more types could be defined.   In this work the terms "type," "Vi-type," and "Vi-phage type" all refer to the bacterium. The typing phages, on the other hand, are simply prefixed by the word "phage."   The original suggestion of Craigie and Yen is retained of designating the Vi-types and the corresponding typing adaptations of Vi-phage II by identical symbols.   Thus, type A is lysed by phage A, type C by phage C, and so on.   Unfortunately, this system of designation has led to considerable confusion among workers not directly concerned with phage typing. However, the routine terminology has found such wide acceptance in the practical field that it is now too late to change it.

Table XIX shows the Vi-phage typing scheme in an abbreviated and simplified form.   Minor cross reactions are omitted from this table.

A number of features are apparent in Table XIX.   Primarily, type A is sensitive to all the typing preparations.   For reasons which will be apparent later, it is believed that A is the most primitive type in this scheme and that phage A represents the wild form of Vi-phage II.   A number of types form associated groups of which one member occupies a similar position relative to the remainder to that occupied by type A in relation to the entire scheme.   In some cases it has been possible to determine the reason for the relationship between some of the members of these groups.   Many types are lysed only by their specific adaptations of Vi-phage II.

Vi-phage typing is now recognized as the method of choice for the epidemiological "fingerprinting" of the typhoid bacillus. It has also established itself as the model for the development of all subsequent schemes for the typing of bacteria by phage.

3. Technical Considerations

a. Isolation of Phages for Typing Purposes

Phages may be isolated from sewage or fecal filtrates, from sensitive bacterial strains contaminated with phage before or during isolation (these are known as carrier strains and show phage-nibbled colonies on plating), and from lysogenic strains of bacteria.   Sewage usually yields virulent phages, but those obtained from feces or carrier strains may be either virulent or temperate. Lysogenic cultures normally produce the most specific phages, but phages of high specificity are occasionally isolated from fecal filtrates or carrier strains, and it is interesting to note that Vi-phage II, the most useful of all typing phages, was originally found in a carrier strain of *Salmonella typhi* (Craigie and Yen, 1938).   It is often an advantage to include in a typing set a phage which is specific only for the bacterial species under test but which will lyse the great majority of strains of that species. By ordinary typing standards, of course, such a phage would be regarded as nonspecific, but, once it has been established that its host range is effectively limited to the one bacterial species, it provides a useful control for the identification of the latter if the more specific typing phages do not produce lysis.   Conn, Botcher, and Randall (1945) used phages for the species identification of soil bacteria.   A phage able to attack an entire bacterial group, such as the salmonellas, may also be usefully employed when it is necessary to confirm that a culture belongs to that group (Cherry, Davis, Edwards, and Hogan, 1954; Wasserman and Saphra, 1955).   It must be remembered, however, that species or group specificity of host range is probably never absolute and, in the absence of other confirmatory tests, lysis of a strain by a single phage is not accepted as offering final proof of species or group identification.

Virulent phages are the most convenient for phage typing, because they produce clear lysis which makes the results easy to read. Naturally, typing phages which are isolated from lysogenic cultures are temperate and, if the rate at which they lysogenize sensitive strains is high, it may be difficult to detect the lysis they produce because of heavy secondary over-growth by lysogenized cells. It is thus advisable to isolate virulent variants of such phages when possible.

b. The Routine Test Dilution

An important principle now observed in phage typing is the use of the "routine test dilution" of the typing phages. In the typing scheme for *Salmonella typhi*, modification of the host range of Vi-phage II does not affect its capacity for adsorption to the host cell, and all the adapted typing preparations are adsorbed by all the Vi-types of the typhoid bacillus irrespective of their specificity (Craigie, 1940). Phage multiplication occurs only when the type of organism and the specificity of the phage coincide. However, adsorption of a Vi-phage II preparation to a heterologous type of the typhoid bacillus is lethal to the cells (Anderson and Fraser, 1956). Thus, when the phage is applied in sufficiently high concentration to a lawn of cells, mass destruction of the bacteria results, and after incubation the culture concerned appears to have undergone phage lysis. It can easily be demonstrated that this is not so by titrating the phage in decimal dilutions on the particular strain concerned. The apparent lysis will then be found to disappear abruptly between two successive dilutions, and no individual plaques can be found. In addition to this direct lethal effect of phage, concentrated lysates may contain bacteriocins which may produce a similar effect to that described above; this also disappears on dilution without yielding discrete plaques. Finally, typing phages often contain particles that can undergo host-induced modification by heterologous bacterial types, or host-range mutants able to multiply in these types. The incidence of either of these two sorts of particle may be sufficiently high (10^{-4} to 10^{-5}) to cause confluent lysis of a number of types when phages are applied undiluted, and type distinction then becomes difficult if not impossible. For these reasons, Craigie and Yen (1938) used each Vi-typing phage in the highest dilution that would produce confluent lysis on its homologous bacterial type. This dilution was originally designated the critical test dilution by Craigie and Yen but is now more generally known as the routine test dilution (RTD). As the result of its use reactions on heterologous types are minimized and type distinction becomes an easy matter. Although no other phage-typing schemes exist that depend on multiple adaptations of a single phage, it has nevertheless been found that the application of a similar principle to schemes employing a number of unrelated phages aids materially in establishing characteristic reaction patterns for epidemiologically distinct bacterial types.

c. Technique

The technique of phage typing is simple and is substantially the same as that described by Craigie and Yen in 1938. The culture to be examined is inoculated into nutrient broth and incubated until a turbidity equivalent to about 5×10^8 organisms per ml. is attained. The initial inoculum is so adjusted that this opacity will be reached in about 2 or $2^1/_2$ hours. The culture is then spread on the surface of a nutrient agar plate, either as a series of discrete areas or as a complete lawn, allowed to dry, and the phages are spotted serially on to these areas in standard amounts of the RTD delivered either by a standardized loop or pipette. When the spots of phage are dry the plates are incubated at a temperature suitable for the system concerned. With the Enterobacteriaceae, first readings are usually possible at 5 to 7 hours and second readings after further overnight incubation. The plates are, of course, suitably marked so that the phages that have caused lysis are easily identified. Two typical typhoid phage typing plates are shown in Figure 13. For routine purposes the phages corresponding to rare Vi-types are pooled so that the test may be completed on one plate. Full details of the media, techniques, and methods of reading

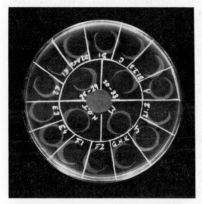 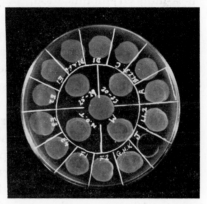

Figure 13. Reactions of *S. typhi* to its typing phages. Left, Vi-type A; right, Vi-type J.

and interpretation are given by Anderson and Williams (1956).

4. Theoretical Aspects of Vi-Phage Typing

a. The Adaptation of Vi-Phage II

All the adapted typing preparations of Vi-phage II are neutralized by an antiserum against phage A, which was the form in which the phage was first isolated, and there is no doubt that all are modifications of the one phage.   The demonstration of the variability of host range of Vi-phage II stimulated considerable interest in the possible mechanism of adaptation, and also aroused curiosity concerning the nature of the differences between the various Vi-types of the typhoid bacillus.   Craigie and Yen (1938) believed that a specific host-range mutant of Vi-phage II existed for each Vi-type of *Salmonella typhi*, and suggested that the process of phage "adaptation" consisted in the selection of its complementary mutant by the type on which phage propagation was carried out. It was shown by Anderson and Felix (1952, 1953a, c) that this suggestion was partly true. However, the latter workers demonstrated that another phenomenon, host-induced modification, played an important role in the elaboration of the typing phages. Host-induced modification in phage was first described by Luria and Human (1952) in phage T2. The subject was examined in some detail by Bertani and Weigle (1953) and Weigle and Bertani (1953) in phages P2 and lambda. A general description of the phenomenon was given by Luria (1953b). As it appears to affect only the phage phenotype, the present author has usually referred to host-induced modification as "phenotypic" modification. A given phage X_A, in which the subscript letter indicates the host range, which will yield a plaque for every particle plated on a particular indicator strain A, may have a low efficiency of plating (EOP), of, say, 10^{-4}, on another strain B. The selection and propagation of plaques appearing on strain B may yield a phage X_{AB} having an EOP of 1 on B. We will assume for the present that, whatever changes it may undergo, the phage always retains an EOP of 1 on strain A. Clearly, the phage newly grown on B could be descended from a host-range mutant able to multiply in B, or from a particle which has been able to adapt itself to B without genetic change. It is possible to distinguish between the two types of change by propagating the phage X_{AB} for a single cycle in strain A, when every particle of a phage changed in phenotype only will revert to phage X_A, whereas a host-range mutant will multiply unchanged as phage X_{AB}. Moreover, if the change to X_{AB} is phenotypic only, the particles destined to undergo it, having no genetic continuity (in terms of the ability to multiply in organism B) in the original phage stock, will exhibit a Poisson distribution in a series of small samples grown for a single cycle in strain A, while host-range mutants will show a clonal distribution (Luria and Delbrück, 1943; Luria, 1951). Bertani and Weigle (1953) observed that phenotypically modifiable particles of phage P2 conformed to a Poisson distribution, and Anderson and Fraser (1956) showed that it was possible, by the use of suitable indicator strains in fluctuation tests, to measure the incidence in the same stock of Vi-phage II of different particles, some undergoing phenotypic modification and others host-range mutation.   It was suggested by Bertani and Weigle (1953) and Weigle and Bertani (1953) that the phenomenon of host-induced modification was probably due not to the presence in the parent phage of a minority of particles able to multiply in any cell of the new host, but to a heterogeneity amongst the host cells which enabled a few organisms to support the multiplication of any particle of the phage.

The host-range flexibility of Vi-phage II was examined by Anderson and Felix (1952, 1953a, c), Anderson (1955a), and Anderson and Fraser (1955, 1956).   It was found that some of the typing adaptations were host-induced modifications, some were host-range mutants, and a third group were host-range mutants with superimposed host-induced modification.

Phage A appears to be the wild form of Vi-phage II and every particle of phages which are pure host-induced modifications of it reverts to phage A when grown in type A which, as Table XIX shows, is fully sensitive to all the typing adaptations of Vi-phage II. Host-range mutants without superadded host-induced modification are unchanged by growth on type A.   However, in a phage showing both varieties of modification, host-induced change is abolished by growth in type A, and the host range of the pure mutant is then expressed.   It can thus be seen that the following combinations affecting host range can occur in Vi-phage II: wild phenotype, wild genotype (phage A); modified phenotype, wild genotype; wild phenotype, modified genotype; modified phenotype, modified genotype.   As would be expected, the widest host ranges are found in the last of these four groups, because the respective phages have the extra range of the host-induced modification added to that of the mutation. A fuller discussion of this subject is given by Anderson and Fraser (1955).

b. *Vi-Type Specificity in* Salmonella typhi

The factors governing the specificity of the Vi-types of *Salmonella typhi* have been clarified to some extent. Craigie (1942, 1946) isolated a temperate phage from type D1 of the organism and found that he could convert type A into type D1 with this phage, which he designated "the latent or gamma agent" of type D1. The significance of this observation does not seem to have been realized, however, and the subject was not pursued. Felix and Anderson (1951), Anderson (1951), and Anderson and Felix (1953b) showed that the Vi-type specificity of many types of *S. typhi* was partly controlled by temperate phages. Such phages were isolated from a number of types, and lysogenization of type A with them produced specific types that seemed similar in all respects to types found in nature. For example, the phage already shown by Craigie to be carried by type D1, converted type A into type D1; that isolated from type D6 transformed A into D6, that from 25 converted A into 25; and so on. Thus, it became clear that Vi-type specificity in *S. typhi*, that is, the spectrum of sensitivity to the many adaptations of Vi-phage II, was to some extent a resistance pattern with which the cells were endowed when they carried particular prophages. The phages concerned were designated "type-determining" phages. They were given small letter symbols when those of the corresponding Vi-types were capitals, and a number with a superscript prime sign when the type carrying them was designated numerically. For example, the determining phage carried by type D1 is designated phage d1, and that carried by type 25 is phage 25′. The observations of Anderson and Felix were confirmed by Ferguson, Juenker, and Ferguson (1955).

Unless otherwise stated, the terms lysogenic and nonlysogenic are used in the present discussion only in relation to the presence or absence of type-determining phages. The determining phages differ from Vi-phage II in not being specific for the Vi form of *Salmonella typhi;* in fact, some of them will even attack other *Salmonella* serotypes. They are also different from the Vi phage in serological, physiological, and physical properties.

Moreover, they affect the sensitivity of their host cells to Vi phages other than Vi-phage II and, more significantly, to non-Vi phages. Bearing in mind the fact that all Vi-types will absorb all Vi-phage II adaptations, irrespective of their specificity, it has become clear as the result of this work that the Vi antigen of the typhoid bacillus provides the Vi-typing phages only with a common receptor of access to the organism. Once this function is carried out it appears to play no further role in the control of Vi-type specificity, which is determined by the presence of prophages, or of other factors hitherto unidentified, elsewhere in the bacterial soma. Anderson and Felix (1953b) found that the specificity of a lysogenic Vi-type was determined by two factors: the identity of the nonlysogenic "ancestral" type; and that of the determining phage with which it was lysogenized. It was observed, moreover, that by the choice of suitable host strains of *S. typhi* to be lysogenized, many new types could be produced with the few determining phages isolated. It was also found, as would be expected, that several naturally occurring lysogenically determined types that differed from each other carried the same phage, and it was apparent that the nonlysogenic host cell and the determining phage each played a precise part in the control of Vi-type specificity. Like most *Salmonella* species, *S. typhi* carries many temperate phages, but relatively few have type-determining properties.

Of the Vi-types shown in Table XIX, types D1, D4, D6, F2, T, 25, and 26 have yielded determining phages. These phages fall into three serological groups and those most closely related to each other serologically show strong similarities in type-determining function and other properties. The phages carried by types D1 and D4 are indistinguishable from each other. Table XX, which is modified from Anderson and Felix (1953b), shows the symbols and serological groups recognized at present. Phages b3, 28', and k, the first two of which constitute a separate serological group, have only limited type-determining properties, but are included for the sake of completeness, since they were isolated at the same time as the remainder of the phages shown.

TABLE XX

Serological Groups of the Type-Determining Temperate Phages of *Salmonella typhi*

Group 1	Group 2	Group 3	Group 4
b3	(a) d1	(a) $\begin{cases} d6 \\ f2 \\ 30' \end{cases}$	t
28'	(b) k	(b) $\begin{cases} 25' \\ 26' \end{cases}$	

Phages d6, f2, and 30' are serologically indistinguishable from each other. Phages 25' and 26' however, which form a separate subgroup, do not show appreciable relationship to the remainder of group 3, nor is their relationship to each other as close as that of the other members of the group.

In view of the constant connection between the specificities of lysogenic Vi-types of *S. typhi* and the prophages they carry, it was suggested by Luria (1953b) that lysogenically determined types be designated by the symbol of the nonlysogenic precursor type followed by that of the determining phage in parentheses. This provides a sort of structural formula for the types concerned and the suggestion was adopted and developed by Anderson (1955a, 1956) and Anderson and Fraser (1955). A few examples of this method of symbolization are shown in Table XXI.

TABLE XXI

Structural Formulae of Vi-Types of *Salmonella typhi*

Original designation	Structural formula
D1	A(d1)
D6	A(d6)
29	A(f2)
33	C(d6)
30	C(f2)
E9	E1(d6)
E7	E1(f2)
F2	F1(f2)

The structural formulae provide more information about the lysogenically determined types than do the symbols in routine use. The relations between many types become obvious and an explanation is found for the ability of some adapted typing preparations to lyse heterologous Vi-types.

It so happens that the nonlysogenic precursors of all the naturally occurring lysogenically determined types impress only a host-induced modification on Vi-phage II. In contrast, all lysogenic types hitherto examined are lysed only by host-range mutants which may or may not have undergone additional host-induced modification. Moreover, the identity of the mutants able to carry out this lysis is decided, as might be expected, by the determining phages. Closely related determining phages such as d6 and f2 erect barriers to the multiplication of Vi-phage II that are overcome by related groups of mutants. Thus, in this system, the interesting phenomenon is found of the selection of easily definable host-range mutants of one phage by lysogenization of cells with other phages, some of which are related to each other, but none of which is demonstrably related to the Vi phage. The mutant selection is so specific that it can be used for the identification of the determining phages that govern it.

Type A seems to be the most primitive form of *Salmonella typhi* in this scheme, because it is sensitive to all the adaptations of Vi-phage II, because it is the ancestral type of many lysogenic Vi-types, and because nonlysogenic types often tend to lose their specificity and to change into type A. A number of Vi-types are known that can be lysed only by host-range mutants of Vi-phage II, yet are not demonstrably lysogenic, and it is not known what controls the specificity of such types. Nor is it known why some nonlysogenic types produce host-induced modification in Vi-phage II, while others select host-range mutants.

All phages studied hitherto show host-range mutations, and phenotypic flexibility of host range is sufficiently frequent to suggest that this also is a widespread phenomenon. The striking feature of Vi-phage II is the latitude over which these changes, separately or in combination, can occur. It has already been pointed out that 58 distinct Vi-types of the typhoid bacillus can now be defined with this phage, and that many more types may exist. What is perhaps still more remarkable is that this phenomenon of wide host-range plasticity seems to be relatively common in Vi phages. The writer (unpublished) has isolated a Vi phage, serologically distinct from Vi-phage II, yet showing a spectrum of host-range modification virtually indistinguishable from that of Vi-phage II. Moreover, the phenotypic and mutational changes exhibit an exactly similar pattern in the two Vi phages. No non-Vi phages have been shown to possess a similar degree of host-range adaptability. There are clearly many intriguing problems still to be solved in this field.

Baron, Formal, and Spilman (1953, 1955) have reported that transduction can be carried out in *Salmonella typhi* with Vi-phage II.

5. The Practical Application of Vi-Phage Typing

This is not the place to embark on a detailed account of the epidemiological value of Vi-phage typing, and only one example will be given. In June, 1948, three children contracted typhoid fever as the result of drinking water from the Wallington river near Winchester in England. The infecting type was E1. Investigation resulted in the isolation of the same Vi-type from the places on the river visited by the children. The organism was traced up the river to a tributary stream, thence to a sewage outlet, through the sewage system, and finally to a single house where a chronic typhoid carrier excreting phage type E1 was found to live. The inquiry ended one year after the children had been infected, and over two miles upstream from the point at which this had occurred. It was controlled throughout by phage typing (see Lendon and MacKenzie, 1951). Typhoid bacilli belonging to various Vi-types are common in river water, and without the precision of phage typing this investigation would have been difficult to conclude satisfactorily. Many more examples could be given of the reliability and value of the method (for references see Anderson and Williams, 1956). There are now about 60 laboratories in over 30 different countries where this work is pursued and among which information is freely exchanged. The type distribution of *S. typhi* has been determined over most of the civilized world, and the routine use of Vi-phage typing has contributed materially to the control of typhoid fever.

6. Phage Typing of *Salmonella paratyphi* **B and** *S. typhimurium*

Phage-typing schemes exist for two further *Salmonella* species of major importance: *S. paratyphi* B and *S. typhimurium* (see Felix and Callow, 1943, 1951; Felix, 1956). In contrast to typhoid phage typing, these methods depend to only a very limited extent on phage adaptation, most of the typing phages being distinct from each other serologically and in other properties. The principle of using the routine test dilution, as described earlier, is also employed in these methods.

As the typing phages of these schemes are not all adaptations of a single phage, few types exist for which there is a single complementary typing preparation. Instead, the differentiation of types is by "pattern reactions." The paratyphoid B typing scheme in current international use is given in Table XXII to illustrate this. A comparison of this table with the typhoid Vi-typing scheme shown in Table XIX will emphasize the difference between the two methods.

In addition to the 10 main types and subtypes shown in Table XXII, a number of constant variant patterns of *S. paratyphi* B with the typing phages have been established. These have shown to be epidemiologically stable and the total number of distinguishable types, subtypes, and variations now recognized is over 30.

The paratyphoid B and typhimurium schemes were originally developed in the belief that the final battery of typing phages for each organism were adaptations of the single starting phage

TABLE XXII

Reactions of Type Strains of *Salmonella paratyphi* B with Routine Test Dilutions of the Typing Phages

Type strains	Typing phages[a]									
	1	2	3a	3b	Jersey	Beccles	Taunton	BAOR	Dundee	1010
1	CL	CL	++	—	CL	—	—	—	SCL	—
2	—	CL	—	—	—	—	—	—	SCL	—
3a	—	—	CL	CL	—	CL	CL	CL	CL	CL
3aI	—	—	CL	—	—	—	CL	—	CL	CL
3b	—	—	—	CL	CL	CL	CL	CL	CL	CL
Jersey	—	—	—	—	CL	CL	CL	CL	CL	CL
Beccles	—	—	—	—	—	CL	CL	—	CL	CL
Taunton	—	—	—	—	—	CL	CL	—	CL	CL
BAOR	—	—	—	—	—	—	—	CL	—	SCL
Dundee	—	—	—	—	—	—	—	—	CL	CL

[a] CL = confluent lysis; SCL = semi-confluent lysis; + + = many individual plaques.

used. As already pointed out, however, it was later observed that adaptation played only a limited part in the evolution of these typing phages, and that many of the phages used were temperate phages which had contaminated the original phage when attempts were made to adapt the latter to lysogenic strains. In spite of this heterogeneity and obligatory use of pattern reactions for type distinction, the paratyphoid B and typhimurium phage-typing schemes have shown themselves to have an order of reliability approaching that of the more elegant scheme for the typhoid bacillus. Furthermore, the various pattern reactions of each serotype are so distinctive that they may be used for the identification of the organisms concerned when flagellar antigenic deficiencies prevent full characterization according to the Kauffmann-White scheme (Anderson, 1955b).

An alternative phage typing method, which was devised by Lilleengen (1948), exists for *S. typhimurium*. This is based on similar principles to the scheme of Felix and Callow. It uses a heterogeneous collection of 12 typing phages and divides the organism into 24 types. It is of interest that transduction was first carried out with a phage isolated from Lilleengen's type 22 (Zinder and Lederberg, 1952).

It has been shown that all the phage types of *S. paratyphi* B are lysogenic (Scholtens, 1950; Felix and Callow, 1951; Hamon and Nicolle, 1951; Nicolle, Hamon, and Edlinger, 1951; Scholtens, 1952, 1955, 1956). The phage or phages carried are characteristic of each type, and it has already been indicated that some of the typing phages are identical with these temperate phages. As with the Vi-types of *S. typhi*, the specific patterns of sensitivity of the paratyphoid B types to the typing phages are controlled to a considerable extent by the characteristic lysogenicity of each type. Hamon and Nicolle (1951) were able to convert type 1 into type 2 (see Table XXII) with the temperate phage carried by type 2, and type 3a into type BAOR with a phage isolated from type BAOR. Similarly, the temperate phages of types Beccles, Taunton, and Dundee converted type 3a into the respective types from which the phages had been isolated. It is thus clear that in the paratyphoid B typing scheme some phages carry out the dual function of typing and of type determination.

There is evidence to show that similar phenomena obtain in the typhimurium phage-typing scheme of Felix and Callow.

7. Phage Typing of Other Salmonellas

In addition to those described above, phage-typing schemes have been devised for *S. paratyphi* A (Banker, 1955); *S. dublin* (Lilleengen, 1950; Williams Smith, 1951c); *S. enteritidis* (Lilleengen, 1950); *S. gallinarum* and *S. pullorum* (Lilleengen, 1952); and *S. thompson* (Williams Smith, 1951a, b). The aim of phage typing is strictly practical in that the various methods are devised for epidemiological purposes only, and there is thus little to be gained from typing organisms that are uncommon. There are, however, a few further salmonella serotypes to which it might be worthwhile applying the method. In Europe, it would probably be an advantage to have a typing scheme for *S. newport*, and, on the American continent, for *S. montevideo* and *S. oranienburg*, which are important contaminants of spray-dried egg (Medical Research Council, 1947; Edwards, Bruner, and Moran, 1948).

Typing schemes for other Enterobacteriaceae, based on the principle of pattern reactions, have been devised for *Shigella sonnei* (Hammerström, 1947, 1949), for *Escherichia coli* of infantile gastro-enteritis (Nicolle, Le Minor, Buttiaux, and Ducrest, 1952), and for *E. coli* of cattle (Williams Smith and Crabb, 1956).

8. Phage Typing of *Staphylococcus aureus*

In the following discussion the term "staphylococcus" signifies coagulase-positive *Staphyloccus aureus*.

The present practice of staphylococcal phage typing started effectively with the work of Fisk (1942) who demonstrated widespread lysogenicity among staphylococci. Fisk's phages were isolated from a number of different strains of staphylococci and proved to be of some value for typing (Fisk and Mordvin, 1944; McClure and Miller, 1946). Wilson and Atkinson (1945), using Fisk's method of isolating phages, introduced a typing scheme in which 21 types were defined with 18 phages. Williams and Rippon (1952) have published a detailed account of the method now in use, which is developed from that of Wilson and Atkinson (1945). As in all the phage-typing schemes other than that of *S. typhi*, phage-type diagnosis in the staphylococci is based on pattern reactions. Twenty-one phages are employed at present for routine work. Because of pattern variability, even in epidemiologically related staphylococci, the custom has been adopted of designating strains by recording the actual spectrum of typing phages to which they are susceptible, and no attempt is now made at type designation as it is employed in salmonellas.

Staphylococcal phage typing presents different problems from the typing of salmonellas. To begin with, the staphylococcus is much more widespread than the pathogenic Enterobacteriaceae. In contrast to the few hundred typhoid carriers known to exist in England, there are probably at least 15,000,000 carriers of staphylococci (Anderson and Williams, 1956). A much greater variety of types might thus be expected to exist among staphylococci than in the typhoid bacillus. Practical experience seems to confirm this expectation, for a random sample of 221 epidemiologically distinct strains, examined with the phages of Williams and Rippon over a six months' period, yielded 169 different patterns (and therefore "types") which fell into 26 pattern groups (Williams, personal communication). With such a variety, the routine use of type designations is clearly impracticable.

The variability in reactions that has been reported between different cultures of apparently epidemiologically uniform groups of staphylococci is greater than would be accepted as satisfactory in a phage-typing scheme for salmonellas. In fact, of course, the widely different ecology of the two groups of bacteria makes the two typing methods valuable in different ways.

Salmonella phage typing provides a system for the stable in-traspecific and epidemiological classification of the organisms, on a local, national, and world-wide basis. Staphylococcal phage typing, on the other hand, is particularly valuable in the local sense, for example, in tracing cross infection or following antibiotic resistant staphylococci in hospital wards, or for in-vestigating outbreaks of staphylococcal food poisoning. Thus, as long as the scheme is locally reliable over relatively short periods (which it is) it fulfils its object. But the reliability goes beyond this point, and staphylococcal phage typing as described by Williams and Rippon (1952) has found wide acceptance. Reference to the many instances in which it has proved useful are given by Anderson and Williams (1956).

The routine staphylococcal typing phages were isolated from lysogenic strains and have been fully described by Rippon (1956). It has been possible to classify them into four serological groups, of which three are currently used in the phage typing of staphylo-coccal strains of human and bovine origin. From the point of view of lytic spectrum, the phages largely fall into five groups. Phages belonging to different lytic groups may nevertheless be serologically indistinguishable. Many attempts at adaptation of the typing phages to different strains of staphylococci have been made and Rippon (1954) and Rountree (1956) claim to have observed host-induced modification in some phages. In view of the widespread lysogenicity found in staphylococci it seems probable that the phage sensitivity patterns of different strains are controlled, in part at least, by lysogenicity, but this subject has not yet been adequately explored.

9. Phage Typing of *Corynebacterium diphtheriae*

Keogh, Simmons, and Anderson (1938) seem to have been the first workers to attempt the phage typing of the diphtheria bacillus. They used only 2 phages, but their results indicated that the method had a possible future. Fahey (1952) defined 9 types of *Corynebacterium diphtheriae* by pattern reactions with 5 phages. The individual phage types recognized did not seem to be characteristic of particular types established on a biological basis (that is, the *mitis*, *intermedius*, and *gravis* varieties of *C. diphtheriae*). Thibaut and Fridéricq (1956) independently produced a typing scheme for this organism in which 8 temperate phages define 9 types. These workers claim that 5 of the typing phages in their scheme are different adaptations of a single phage.

10. Bacterial Typing by Identification of Carried Phages

The typing methods described above depend on the different sensitivities of bacterial strains to a battery of selected phages. It has been shown that these sensitivities are frequently an expression of resistance patterns produced in the bacteria by the presence of prophages, the identity of which varies from type to type. It is thus evident that the identification of these carried phages presents another avenue of approach for bacterial typing. Such an approach has been used by Boyd (1950, 1952), Boyd, Parker, and Mair (1951) and Boyd and Bidwell (1957) for typing *S. typhimurium*, and by Scholtens (1950, 1955, 1956) for *S. paratyphi* B, and there is good evidence to show that the method is reliable. Its value as a routine procedure depends on the ease with which phages can be identified. If this is a simple matter entailing the determination of plaque morphology and host range of the phages concerned, or of the specific changes in phage resistance brought about in selected indicator strains by lysogenization (Anderson, 1956; Anderson and Williams, 1956; Boyd and Bidwell, 1957), the method presents no great technical difficulties, although it is much slower than the more conventional operation of applying a battery of typing phages to the strains to be investigated. If, however, serological identification of the phages and determination of their physical properties are required, the method is too slow for routine use, because the epidemiological value of phage typing, especially in Enterobacteriaceae, is often determined by the speed with which results can be obtained.

One drawback of this method is that the phage resistance

pattern of a lysogenic bacterial strain depends on two factors mentioned above: the character of the nonlysogenic ancestor, and that of the carried phage. If the nonlysogenic precursor of all lysogenic cultures of a given bacterial species always showed the same pattern of phage resistance, identification of the temperate phages would give as much information as would the examination of the sensitivity of the strains to typing phages. Work on the typhoid Vi-types has shown, however, that different nonlysogenic precursors may carry the same determining phage, and the resulting types react quite differently with the Vi-typing phages. Identification of the temperate phage only would erroneously indicate that these types were identical with each other. Moreover, it is not always possible to isolate temperate phages from cultures (this is commonly found in *S. typhi*) and in such instances the method of typing by characterization of temperate phages fails altogether, whereas the examination of sensitivity patterns of a strain to a range of typing phages is still effective. It is evident that a combination of the two methods offers the most precise means of strain characterization, but for routine use the determination of the spectrum of phage sensitivity of bacterial strains is the more practical and reliable approach.

CHAPTER XXII

PHAGE TAXONOMY

Essential for any serious study involving many different objects is the classification of the objects into well defined categories and the development of a nomenclature to designate these categories. Because it is generally accepted that bacteriophages are to be included among the living organisms it seems that the ultimate aim should be to apply to the bacteriophages the Linnean scheme of classification. With this in mind we will inquire briefly into the principles of taxonomy.

1. Purpose and Principles of Taxonomy

The purpose of taxonomy is to give an appropriate and generally acceptable name to each distinct variety of organism, and to place these varieties in a hierarchy of ever larger groups, to indicate their natural relationships to one another. In the original Linnean classification the natural relationships were based on morphological resemblances. With the development of the concept of evolution and the sciences of paleontology and genetics, the Linnaean categories acquired a phylogenetic significance so that natural relationships implied a common ancestry, more or less remote in time.

The basic category of the taxonomist is the *species*, which may be defined as a group of interbreeding natural populations that is reproductively isolated from other such groups. The interbreeding test makes the species a readily delimited category in sexually reproducing organisms. The lack of such a test has resulted in the taxonomic abominations so prevalent in the field of microbiology. For instance, Bergey's Manual (Breed, Murray, and Hitchens, 1948) lists 150 species in the genus *Salmonella*.

The discovery of the phenomenon of transduction (Zinder and Lederberg, 1952) furnished a means for testing the genetic compatibility of strains within the salmonella group. It now seems probable that the 150 "species" really should be considered as 150 serological or biochemical varieties within a single salmonella species.

The next higher category, the *genus*, should include a group of species of presumably common phylogenetic origin, separated by a decided gap from other similar groups (Mayr, Lindsley, and Usinger, 1953). The genus is a category more difficult to define than the species and is a more artificial concept.

In the Linnaean classification each organism has a two-word name, the first specifying the genus and the second the species to which the organism has been assigned. Such a binomial nomenclature has been applied to bacteriophages by Holmes (Bergey's Manual, cited above), who lists 46 species of phage within the genus *Phagus*. The use of such a nomenclature suggests that adequate criteria are available to characterize the species category and the genus category. Such criteria are not available and furthermore it would be virtually impossible to allocate a newly isolated bacteriophage to one of these species on the basis of the published characteristics. Identification of a bacteriophage would require direct comparison with type cultures, yet for many of the species listed by Holmes such type cultures do not exist. At the present stage of development neither the classification nor the nomenclature of Holmes is of any value.

2. Various Proposals for Phage Classification

D'Herelle (1926) proposed that there was only one species of bacteriophage, *Protobios bacteriophagus*, with extreme powers of adaptive variation. He felt that antigenic specificity and resistance to destructive agents could vary as the phage became adapted to growth in different hosts. Yet Bruynoghe and Appelmans (1922) had previously shown that two strains of typhoid phage were antigenically distinct from each other. The antigenic specificity of phages was repeatedly confirmed by various workers, perhaps most thoroughly by Muckenfuss (1928) who suggested the use of neutralizing antisera for the identification and classification of bacteriophages.

Careful investigation by numerous individuals of the properties of pure strains of bacteriophages indicated that there were great differences from one strain to another even of phages attacking a single bacterial strain. However, the properties of any one phage strain were remarkably constant through repeated subculture and were not subject to capricious alteration. The existence of "adaptive" modifications in the properties of a phage strain were early recognized but these usually involved change in only one property at a time. The possibility of a systematic classification of the phages became evident as soon as large numbers of phage strains attacking a single group of bacteria were investigated. Several such schemes for phage classification were proposed nearly simultaneously for different groups of phages.

A classification for the cholera phages was proposed by Asheshov, Asheshov, Khan, and Lahiri (1933) based primarily on serological specificity but including also plaque morphology and the resistance patterns of phage-resistant host cells. The coli-dysentery phages were classified into eleven distinct serological groups by Burnet (1933d) who also demonstrated that this grouping was correlated with plaque morphology, with sensitivity to inactivation by urea and by photodynamic action, and with inhibition of phage growth by citrate. These same criteria were later applied by Burnet and Lush (1935) to the classification of phages attacking strains of *Staphylococcus*. Sertic and Boulgakov (1935) classified 75 strains of typhoid phage into 14 antigenic types and correlated these types with plaque morphology, particle size by ultrafiltration, heat resistance, and virulence. The property of virulence was measured by the length of time it took for a phage infected culture of bacteria to lyse under standard conditions and is roughly proportional to the latent period. Delbrück (1946b) classified seven strains of coliphage into four serological groups and demonstrated that this classification was

correlated with plaque size, morphology in the electron microscope, minimum latent period, and rate of adsorption to the host
cell. Other classifications for limited groups of phages have
been published by McKie (1934) for temperate coli-dysentery
phages, by Rountree (1949b) for staphylococcal phages, by
Friedman and Cowles (1953) for megaterium phages, by Wilkowske, Nelson, and Parmelee (1954) for lactic acid streptococcal
phages, and by Evans (1934) and Evans and Sockrider (1942)
for hemolytic streptococcal phages. The classification of some
enteric phages has been described by Adams (1952) and by
Adams and Wade (1954, 1955).

3. Taxonomic Criteria at the Species Level

As a result of numerous studies with various groups of phages in
different laboratories a number of useful taxonomic criteria for
bacteriophages have been proposed and tested. These were
summarized and discussed by Adams (1953b). Since then certain of these criteria have been further tested with groups of
coliphages and we are in a better position to discuss critically
their taxonomic utility.

a. Serological Relationship

The serological criterion is placed first because it is experimentally simple and because very extensive application has
shown it to be the most useful single test of phylogenetic relationship. The neutralization of the infectivity of one phage strain
by the antiserum to a second phage strain indicates a close biological relationship between the two strains providing certain
sources of error are eliminated. The most obvious of these is that
the antiserum under test may contain unsuspected antibodies
against some unrelated phage, through natural immunization of
the animal with phage in its own intestine or through contamination of the immunizing phage with heterologous phage antigen
through unclean apparatus, or from a lysogenic host bacterium.
To be definitive the serological relationship should be inde-

pendent of the host bacterium on which the immunizing phage is grown. Also the cross-reacting antibody should be removed from the serum by absorption with homologous phage at the same rate as is removal of homologous antibody.

In contrast to the results of a positive reaction, the failure of an antiphage serum to neutralize a heterologous phage does not preclude a close relationship. In the case of two phages for *Serratia marcescens* it was not possible to detect directly a serological relationship, yet each of the two phages was clearly related serologically to other phages of the same group (Adams and Wade, 1954). This serological group which includes phages T3, T7, and D44 is markedly diverse antigenically, suggesting that antigenic specificity in bacteriophages is subject to modification by mutation. Genetic control of serological specificity is also suggested by hybridization experiments in the T5 species (Fodor and Adams, 1955) and in the T2 species (Streisinger, 1956b). There is no evidence so far suggesting large scale changes in serological specificity as a result of single gene mutations. One may conclude that serological relatedness has invariably been correlated with close relationship in other characteristics as well. Absence of serological relationship, however, does not preclude close relationship in other characteristics.

The structural differentiation of phage particles into head and tail portions is correlated with antigenic differentiation into serologically unrelated head antigens and tail antigens. The anti-tail antibodies are involved in neutralization, whereas the anti-head antibodies are detected by agglutination and complement fixation reactions. Serological cross reactions involving the head antigens have been demonstrated with the related phages T2, T4, and T6 by Lanni and Lanni (1953), and with the related phage pair T5 and PB by Fodor and Adams (1955). Rountree (1952) has reported cross reactions by the complement fixation test among staphylococcal phages which failed to cross react in the neutralization test. These experiments suggest the possible taxonomic value of the phage head antigens but not enough work has been done as yet to warrant conclusions. The techniques involved are much more difficult than those of the neutralization test but may well produce worth-while information.

b. Size and Morphology

Phage particle size as determined by ultrafiltration, centrifugation, and X-ray inactivation has been used for purposes of classification. Such methods for size estimation have been superseded by the development of the electron microscope. Size and morphology of phages have been discussed in Chapter IV. It is already evident that there is great variety of size and morphology among the bacteriophages and that these characteristics are likely to be more valuable taxonomic criteria for phages than they have been for bacteria. So far as studies have been carried at present there has been complete agreement between the serological and morphological criteria. It is not unlikely that the morphological criterion may be of value at taxonomic levels above the species but no evidence is yet available on this point.

c. Chemical Composition

The unique occurrence of hydroxymethylcytosine in place of cytosine in the deoxyribonucleic acid of the related phages T2, T4, and T6 suggests that chemical composition may well be of taxonomic value in phage work. However, it is improbable that chemical analyses will be popular for purposes of classification as long as technically simpler and more direct methods are available. A general survey for the presence of hydroxymethylcytosine among a variety of phages may well be enlightening. Only a few phages have so far been analyzed (Chapter VII).

d. Latent Period

The latent period is the elapsed time between adsorption of a phage particle to its host cell and lysis of that cell with release of phage progeny. The minimum latent period is a remarkably constant characteristic of a phage-host cell system when determined under standard environmental conditions. However, the latent period may vary with different host strains, with the nutritional environment, the temperature, and the presence of metabolic poisons. When a number of related phage strains are compared it is found that the minimum latent periods fall within a limited range of times which is characteristic for the group. Because the range of minimum latent periods for different phage groups may overlap, this is not by itself a good taxonomic criterion but in conjunction with other properties may be of value in characterizing a phage species. It suffers from the common fault of all quantitative criteria in not being by itself definitive.

e. Susceptibility to Inactivation

The susceptibility of phages to inactivation by various agents such as heat, urea, photodynamic action, ultraviolet and ionizing radiations, sonic vibration, surface inactivation, changes in salt concentration, and pH all have possible applications to taxonomic problems (Chapters V and VI). The difficulty with inactivation as a taxonomic criterion is that one phage strain differs from another quantitatively rather than qualitatively. Where these criteria have been applied to a group of related phages there is usually found to be considerable variation among the members of the group, and if several different groups are compared there is quite likely to be overlapping in the ranges of variation in the groups. This means that no single type of inactivation, such as temperature sensitivity, can be used as a primary taxonomic criterion, although it may be expected to correlate with classification by the serological and morphological criteria. However, it is quite possible that a given taxonomic group of phages may have a unique pattern of sensitivities when a number of types of inactivation are studied. It may be anticipated on the basis of available evidence that susceptibility of phages to inactivation will not be a very useful taxonomic criterion although it has been used in a number of the classification studies listed in Section 2 above.

It is possible that osmotic shock may be in a different category with respect to taxonomic usefulness. The work of T. F. Anderson (1950) indicated that certain groups of phages were not susceptible to osmotic shock whereas other groups, notably T2, T4, and T6, were highly susceptible. Further study is needed to determine the possible usefulness of this technique in the taxonomy of phages. The same may be said for sensitivity to ultraviolet light (Stent, 1958).

f. Distinctive Physiological Properties

A few tests are known which tend to separate phages into two classes exhibiting qualitatively different responses. The all-or-none properties detected by three tests furnish very useful taxonomic criteria, but unfortunately too few such properties are known, and even the well-known properties have not been looked for in many groups of phages.

The *calcium requirement* of the T5-PB species is an example of such a property. These phages require calcium ion for penetration, and phage reproduction cannot occur without this ion. Many phages have no calcium requirement, and for many other phages in which a calcium requirement has been demonstrated, the precise role of the calcium ion has not been investigated. The literature on this point is surveyed in Chapter XIV. Burnet (1933e) first suggested that the calcium requirement (citrate inhibition) was a useful taxonomic criterion. There is no evidence that the calcium requirement for penetration can be altered by mutation, although the requirement of calcium as an adsorption cofactor can (Delbrück, 1948).

The phenomenon of *multiplicity reactivation* (Luria, 1947) of ultraviolet-inactivated phage is another example of a useful taxonomic criterion. This property is demonstrated by all the strains in the T2 and T5 species but not, or at a much lower level, by strains in the T3 or T1 species. The occurrence of this property outside of the enteric group of phages has not yet been investigated. As far as present knowledge goes, the phenomenon of photoreactivation of ultraviolet-inactivated phages is not likely to be useful in phage taxonomy because it seems to be a general property of all phages so far examined.

The phenomenon of *lysis inhibition* (Doermann, 1948a) and the r^+ to r mutation (Hershey, 1946a) is an example of a physiological property which has been demonstrated only in the T2 species of phages although it has not been looked for outside of the enteric group. This property may be of value only in identifying members of the one species, which seems to be unique in a number of respects.

It seems probable that further research into the physiological properties of phages will turn up other characteristic properties of taxonomic value. One may anticipate that a pattern of behavior with regard to several physiological properties will be more useful than any single property for taxonomic purposes.

g. Results of Mixed Infection Experiments

All of the properties listed above may be used to demonstrate resemblances and differences between any two phage strains. Suppose that we find that the two phage strains are indistinguishable in morphology, serologically related, and similar with respect to several physiological properties. How do we decide on the degree of relationship between them; how do we allocate them to their proper positions in the taxonomic hierarchy? Are they derivatives of the same strain differing in a few mutated genes; are they two varieties within the same species; are they representatives of two different species in the same genus; or should they perhaps be placed in different genera? This is often a difficult problem with higher organisms and in the field of microbiology there are as yet no satisfactory criteria for making such decisions. However, this need not deter us from proposing criteria which then can be put to the test. Such a criterion is the result of the mixed infection experiment. If the two phage strains under comparison have a common host strain of bacteria, it is a simple matter to arrange conditions so that a majority of the bacterial cells are nearly simultaneously infected with at least one phage particle of each kind.

Such a *mixed infection* experiment may have several possible results:

1. *Mutual Exclusion* in which a mixedly infected cell liberates one or the other of the infecting phage types but never both (Delbrück and Luria, 1942). This result has been obtained with 15 pairs of unrelated phage strains in the T-system of coliphages and may be accepted as the usual result of mixed infection with unrelated virulent phages.

2. *Mixed Growth without Genetic Recombination.* In this case mixedly infected bacteria liberate both kinds of phage but no recombinants are found. This result has been found in one case of mixed infection with unrelated phages studied by Collins (1957). How rare or common this result may be we cannot anticipate at present. Many more systems must be studied before the significance of such a result is understocd.

3. *Mixed Growth with Genetic Recombination.* In this type of result the phage progeny from mixedly infected bacteria contain not only the two parental phage types but also phage particles with new combinations of characteristics resulting from recombination of the parental genetic determinants. This type of result is usual in mixed infection experiments with closely related phages; typical examples have been discussed in Chapter XVIII. The occurrence of genetic recombination implies that the two phage strains are similar enough in genetic constitution that genetic determinants may be interchanged between them. This may be considered to be analogous to the criterion of interbreeding populations used to define the species category in higher organisms.

On the basis of the available evidence, one may tentatively propose the use of the results of the mixed infection experiment as a criterion for deciding the relative taxonomic positions of two phage strains with a common host (Adams, 1953b). If the result is mixed growth with genetic recombination, the two strains should be placed in the same species. If the result is mutual ex-

clusion the two strains do not belong in the same species.   If the
result is mixed growth without genetic recombination the criterion is not applicable and other criteria must be used.   If no
common host is available the test cannot be used unless by this
means each strain can be related to a third strain.

In cases in which the criterion of mixed infection is not applicable one must make an arbitrary decision as to whether two
strains are to be placed in the same species or not.   It is suggested that if two phage strains are either morphologically indistinguishable or serologically related and also share a number of
physiological properties in common they should be tentatively
allocated to the same species.   If they are serologically related
and morphologically indistinguishable they are almost certain to
belong in the same species.

4. Possible Taxonomic Criteria at Levels Above the Species

At the present stage of development of phage taxonomy it is
impossible to define the limits of the genus or of higher categories.
However, one can make tentative suggestions for further exploration in this field.   One possible basis for defining the genus
would be morphological resemblance.   For instance, phage
strains which were morphologically similar but serologically and
physiologically dissimilar might be placed in different species in
the same genus.   Another possibility is the use of host range.
The host range pattern is a valuable identifying characteristic
for individual phage strains, but the fact that this can change by
single step mutations limits its value at the species level.   The
total range of hosts available to various phage strains within a
single species is still unknown but it is already evident that among
the enteric phages the host range of a phage species may cover at
least four genera, *Escherichia*, *Serratia*, *Salmonella*, and *Shigella*, in
the family Enterobacteriaceae (Adams and Wade, 1954).   How
much broader than this the host range of a species may be no one
knows but it is quite possible that the hosts for a phage species
may be limited to the various bacterial strains within one family.
In fact it is possible that extensive study of the host ranges of bac-

teriophages may contribute useful evidence about the taxonomy of bacteria (Stocker, 1955). Such studies have lead Girard (1943) to question the present taxonomic position of the plague bacillus.

5. Special Taxonomic Criteria Applicable to Temperate Bacteriophages

Some phages are able to establish lysogeny in the bacteria they infect and are said to be *temperate* on this account (Chapter XIX). This property can of course be used as a taxonomic character. Its use is limited, however, by the fact that for almost every temperate bacteriophage which has been studied to some extent, mutants are known that have lost the ability to establish lysogeny. A virulent phage could thus be a virulent mutant of a yet unknown temperate phage. One may even entertain the view that all phages are or were originally temperate, and that virulence represents a secondary development due to mutation. Against such a generalization stands the fact, however, that some phages are able to kill the host cell by merely adsorbing onto the bacterium, even when active multiplication of the phage is impossible. Such phages of course could not lysogenize in any case unless they first lost such an ability to kill.

Other properties which are observed only with temperate phages could presumably be used as taxonomic criteria.

One of these is the *inducibility* of some temperate phages. Bacteria lysogenic for such phages, upon receiving certain stimuli (ultraviolet light, X-rays, carcinogenic substances, etc.), lyse after a definite latent period, liberating phage. Bacteria lysogenic for other phages do not react in this manner. To date the property of inducibility is not known to be altered by mutation, and may very well be a good taxonomic character.

Another property which can be studied in temperate phages is the ability of a phage to modify genetic properties of the host cells it infects. This phenomenon may occur with various frequencies, mechanisms, and specificities (Chapters XIX and XXI). The difficulty with such properties from a taxonomic point of view seems to be that they require knowledge of the genetics of the host bacterium, which is not generally available.

6. Relationship of Bacteriophages to Other Viruses

In the classification of Holmes (Bergey's Manual) the bacteriophages, plant viruses, and animal viruses are classified as suborders in the order *Virales*. In the modern concept of systematics this implies a common ancestry for these three groups of microorganisms. There are strong resemblances among these three groups, but these can all be attributed to the fact that the viruses are obligate, intracellular parasites with no detectable metabolic activity of their own. These resemblances may be superficial rather than basic and the result of adaptation to a specific environment, much like the superficial resemblance between penguins and seals. It seems probable that each of the three main groups of viruses originated and evolved independently of the other two groups, and it seems possible that different groups of phages have evolved independently of each other. The morphology of the phages as demonstrated in the electron microscope is different from that of all other viruses, which do not possess morphologically distinct head and tail structures. This structural differentiation is correlated with antigenic and functional differentiation. From the chemical point of view, no phage is yet known to contain ribonucleic acid, whereas the latter is present, alone or with deoxyribonucleic acid, in quite a few animal and plant viruses. Also the mode of attack by phage on its host cell differs from the attack of other viruses so far investigated. The injection of phage nucleic acid into the host cell, leaving the phage membrane on the cell surface, seems to be unique.

Perhaps the most compelling evidence for an independent phylogeny for the bacterial viruses may come from studies with temperate phages (Chapter XIX). It has been proposed that there is a homology between the genetic material of the phage and a portion of the chromosome of the host bacterium. The lysogenic state may be the result of crossing over between the infecting phage and the chromosome of the infected bacterium or may consist in a synapsis of phage chromosome with bacterial chromosome to form a heterozygous diploid region which is replicated as such. Some of the evidence for this point of view was presented in Chapters XVI and XIX and will be recapitulated here.

1. In lysogenic bacteria the phage genetic material occupies a definite locus on the bacterial chromosome being linked to recognized bacterial gene loci. For instance, the lambda prophage in strain K12 of *E. coli* is linked to a locus involved in galactose fermentation.

2. Studies by Bertani (1954) with the temperate coliphage P2 suggest that there are several loci available for attachment of the prophage, one site being preferred. Superinfection of a P2 lysogenic bacterium with a genetically marked variant of P2 may result frequently in replacement of the original P2 by the superinfecting P2 at the preferred locus, or less frequently may result in a doubly lysogenic cell with a prophage at each locus. However, superinfection with a different phage, P1, readily gives rise to bacteria doubly lysogenic for P1 and P2, suggesting that these two prophages have different preferred loci in the host cell.

3. Similarly it is possible to make a culture of *Pseudomonas aeruginosa* lysogenic simultaneously for two unrelated phages 1 and 8, or for two related phages 4 and 8 (Jacob, 1952c). However, superinfection of a culture lysogenic for phage 8 with a plaque type mutant of phage 8 does not result in either substitution or in doubly lysogenic cells suggesting that there is a unique site for prophage 8 in this bacterial strain and other sites for prophages 1 and 4 (Jacob and Wollman, 1953).

4. In addition there is another type of evidence suggesting direct recombination between the genetic material of the phage and the host cell and occurring with some virulent as well as temperate phages. Ultraviolet-inactivated temperate phage lambda is reactivated when adsorbed to ultraviolet-treated host cells. Among the reactivated phage particles are found a high proportion (as much as 5 to 10 per cent under certain conditions) of plaque type mutants. These are found only when both bacteria

and phage are treated with ultraviolet light (Weigle, 1953). Similar results were described for the virulent phage T3 by Weigle and Dulbecco (1953). Although various explanations might be suggested for the origin of these mutants, the most interesting is that they result from genetic recombination between the phage genetic material and that of the host cell.

5. Some rather different effects of combined ultraviolet irradiation of salmonella phage P22 and its host cells were interpreted in a similar manner by Garen and Zinder (1955). This phage, like many others, is remarkably resistant to ultraviolet light as compared with phage T2. Its resistance approaches that of T2, however, if one measures the ability of both phages to grow on bacteria that have been heavily irradiated themselves. This could mean that radiation damage to phage P22, but not to T2, can be eliminated by substitution of similar material from the host, provided the latter is not irradiated.

These and other observations, lately reviewed by Stent (1958), are consistent with the hypothesis that part of the genetic material of a phage is often homologous with part of the genetic material of its host. If this hypothesis should prove correct, it might suggest that a given phage is more closely related to its host than to other phages attacking unrelated hosts. The influence that such hypotheses may have on the taxonomy of bacterial viruses and on the relation of bacteriophages to other viruses is obvious and need not be elaborated further.

It seems clear that a Linnaean taxonomy for all viruses, or even for the restricted group of bacterial viruses, is premature at the present state of our information about these organisms. It would seem wise under the circumstances to postpone the use of a binomial nomenclature for these organisms at least until the taxonomic relationships are somewhat clarified (see also Andrewes, 1957).

7. Importance of Type Specimens

In the earlier definition of a species it was customary to place a type specimen in a museum or collection for use as a standard of comparison by later taxonomists. In the new systematics the

type specimen as an individual has been shown to be inadequate and has been replaced by the total gene reservoir of an interbreeding population, which places a limit on the variability
of the individuals within that population. When we turn to
phage taxonomy we find species named and described in terms
that make identification impossible in the absence of any known
type specimens for comparison (Holmes, Bergey's Manual). In
such a taxonomy no attempt is made to describe the limits of
variability of different strains within a species.

One of the principal taxonomic characteristics used in all
schemes of phage classification is serological specificity as demonstrated by the neutralization test. Yet this characteristic is
worthless unless one has either a type specimen for direct comparison, or at least a sample of serum containing the appropriate
antibodies. As noted above in discussing the serological criterion, variability within a species may be sufficiently great so
that one type strain or antiserum is not adequate to describe the
species.

The significance of preserving type strains will be evident when
it is noted that only a few of the type strains for Burnet's eleven
serological groups of coli-dysentery phages are still available, in
spite of the great amount of work done with these phages and in
spite of the fact that they are included in Holmes' taxonomic
scheme. These serological groups may well remain forever
unidentifiable unless the original strains are recovered.

Until recently there was no type culture collection of bacteriophages in existence and only a few private collections of any
size. In 1954 the American Type Culture Collection, Washington, D.C., started a section for phage strains and their host cells
and a fairly representative collection is available from this
source. Other major collections are those of Asheshov, Lister
Institute, London; Boulgakov, Institut Pasteur, Paris; and the
collection of typing phages of the Public Health Laboratories in
Colindale, London.

It is proposed that whenever a new phage strain is described in
the literature attempts be made to identify it by comparison with

known phage strains. If it cannot be related to a known phage strain, type specimens of the phage and a suitable host bacterium should be placed in the ATCC or other culture collection and this fact be recorded in the published paper. The type specimens should be prepared for storage either as lyophilized specimens or in a suitable fluid medium in sealed tubes and 10 to 20 specimens should be included to minimize maintenance problems in the collection. In the case of unstable phage strains the possibility of preserving typing antisera should be considered as an alternative to indefinite maintenance of the phage strains in culture collections. It should be recognized that publications in the field of biology may be of relatively little value unless the biological material used is readily available for study by other investigators.

8. Summary

The taxonomy and nomenclature of bacteriophages is in an unsatisfactory state at the present time for a number of reasons. There are no generally applicable taxonomic criteria available for defining the limits of the species and the genus in the bacteriophages. Tentative suggestions for such criteria have been proposed for further investigation. Because of the lack of information about the phylogeny of phages it is not possible to consider taxonomic categories above the genus level. The relationships among different groups of phages, of phages to other viruses and of phages to their host cells are quite obscure at present. Because of this it would seem that the use of a formal Linnaean binomial nomenclature would be premature. The importance of maintaining type specimens for the use of other investigators is emphasized. Much of the phage literature is worthless for taxonomic purposes because of the impossibility of identifying the phage strains that were used.

GLOSSARY

Abortive infection: Infection accompanied by loss of the infecting phage particle and often death of the bacterium but not yielding a phage progeny under normally sufficient conditions. Infection is abortive because of unusual conditions prevailing before, at the time of, or shortly after infection.

Adsorption: Attachment of phage particle to bacterium, irreversible unless otherwise stated.

Arrhenius constant: The energy of activation of a reaction measured from the dependence of its rate on temperature, explained in elementary texts of physical chemistry.

Burst: Yield of phage liberated by spontaneous lysis of an infected bacterium. This may be measured directly for isolated bacteria in single burst experiments, or as an average burst size in one-step growth experiments. Also the act of liberation.

Capacity: The ability of a bacterium to support growth of phage when infected. Thus one speaks of the capacity of a bacterial culture varying with the dose of ultraviolet light administered to it before infection. To preserve the usefulness of the term, it should not be used to describe the effects of treatment applied after infection.

Clone: The descendants of a single phage particle, issuing either from a single bacterium or from repeated cycles of infection as in the formation of a plaque. Clones also originate within intrabacterial clones, as demonstrated by the appearance of mutant subclones, or recombinant subclones, in single infected cells.

Cross-reactivation: Rescue of genetic markers from inviable phage particles in mixed infection with viable particles.

Doughnuts: Empty heads of phage particles found in lysates of infected bacteria, so called from their characteristic appearance in micrographs of certain types of preparation.

Eclipse period: Elapsed time between infection or induction and the first appearance of infective phage particles in cells, as determined by artificial lysis. The eclipse period of individual cells is variable; that of the culture may be defined as the time required to produce an average of one phage per bacterium. The eclipse period is usually $1/2$ to $3/4$ of the minimum latent period.

Efficiency of plating (EOP): Plaque titer of a phage preparation, determined by plating under stated conditions, relative to some other estimate, usually higher, of the concentration of phage particles.

Exponential killing (or survival): Inactivation kinetics giving a straight line when logarithms of survivors are plotted against time of exposure to, or dosage of, an inactivating agent. The slope of this line is the (fractional) *rate of inactivation* and measures sensitivity of the phage or bacterium in terms relative to dosage. Accumulated dosage is often expressed in multiples of the average lethal dose or *hits*, since e^{-n} survival signifies an average of n hits per phage or bacterium.

Ghost: A phage particle that appears empty in the electron microscope. In several instances ghosts are known to lack nucleic acid.

Host-induced modification: A variant property of phage particles strictly determined by the kind of bacterium in which they last grew. Such modifications are considered nonheritable since they disappear when the phage is transferred to a different host. They form one class of phenotypic variations.

Host range: The range of action of a phage measured in terms of the varieties of bacteria in which it can grow. Host range is often, but not always, determined by success or failure of adsorption.

Immunity: Resistance to infection that does not result from failure of the phage to adsorb and inject, characteristically associated with the lysogenic state.

Indicator bacteria: Bacteria sensitive to a specified kind of phage, usually also resistant to other specified kinds.

Induction: The transition from the prophage to the vegetative state in lysogenic bacteria, occurring spontaneously or after experimental application of inducing agents.

Infection: Used loosely to indicate attachment of phage to bacterium with at least some effects on the cell. One speaks, perhaps improperly, of infection by ghosts of T2 because the cell may be killed, though injection and phage growth are impossible.

Infective center: A plaque-forming particle that may be either a productively infected bacterium or a free phage particle. When one or the other is meant, the term infective center should not be used.

Injection: Entrance of phage DNA into bacterium.

Latent period: Elapsed time between infection or induction and lysis of cells in one-step growth. Latent periods of individual cells vary over a range called the rise period. When reported without qualification, latent period means minimum latent period.

Lysis: Dissolution of an infected bacterium, recognized by release of phage particles, by loss of turbidity of a bacterial suspension, or by microscopic changes of diverse kinds.

Lysis from without: Abortive infection accompanied by prompt lysis of a cell, typically following excessive multiple infection.

Lysogenic bacterium: A bacterium capable of multiplying indefinitely in the infected condition. In lysogenic cultures phage is produced only by exceptional cells that lyse.

Lysogenization: Infection of a bacterium by phage to produce a lysogenic clone or subclone of descendants. Lysogenization occurs some time after, or some bacterial generations after, the initial infection.

Maturation: The conversion of vegetative phage into mature, infective phage particles.

Mixed indicator: A mixture of two bacterial strains capable of distinguishing between phages lysing one strain only, and phages lysing both, on agar plates.

Mixed infection: Multiple infection with each of two or more kinds of phage.

Multiple infection: Multiplicity of infection appreciably greater than one, so that most of the bacteria in a culture are infected with more than one phage particle.

Multiplicity of infection: Ratio of adsorbed phage particles to bacteria in a culture.

Multiplicity reactivation: Production of viable phage progeny in multiple infection with individually inviable phage particles.

Mutant: A phage (or bacterium) showing one or more discrete heritable differences from a standard type called *wild*. Mutations may be accumulated by a succession of steps, defined by the methods of isolation, and may be ascribed to one or more loci, as determined by recombination tests. The useful mutations of phages alter host range or plaque type, though other classes are known. Plaque-type mutants of temperate phages are often virulent.

One-step growth of phage: A single cycle of infection and lysis, nearly synchronous in all the infected bacteria of the culture, usually achieved by the one-step growth experiment (Chapter II).

Phage: Bacteriophage. Used as a noun with a singular verb in this book the word usually means phage species (singular). Used with a plural verb it usually means phage particles. Used in the plural it usually means phage species (plural).

Phenotype: The properties of a phage particle considered independently of the properties of its offspring, which are determined by the *genotype*. In general, a population of phage particles may contain phenotypic and genotypic variants of similar properties, only the latter yielding mutant stocks in which the variation is preserved.

Photoreactivation: Production of viable phage progeny in illuminated bacteria infected with otherwise inviable phage.

Plate: A flat culture dish for nutrient agar; to prepare a culture in such a dish for counting bacterial colonies or plaques. "To plate" usually means "to titrate."

Productive infection: Infection followed by phage production.

Prophage: The form in which phages are perpetuated in lysogenic bacteria.

Resistant bacteria: Bacteria not killed by a given phage, usually owing to failure to adsorb, also called nonreceptive bacteria. See immunity.

Sensitive bacteria: Bacteria killed by a given phage (or other agent). Sensitivity to phage is usually tested by plaque formation, when ability to support growth of phage may also be inferred.

Single infection: Multiplicity of infection considerably less than one, so that most of the infected bacteria in a culture are infected with only one phage particle.

Superinfection: Reinfection of bacteria already infected some minutes before, or reinfection of lysogenic bacteria.

Temperate phage: A phage capable of lysogenizing some fraction, often small, of the bacteria it infects.

Vegetative phage: The form in which phage (or phage genes) multiply during the lytic cycle of phage growth.

Viable: Viable bacteria are able to form colonies. Viable phage particles are able to form plaques following single infection. Viability depends on the conditions of test.

Virulent phage: A phage that lacks the ability to lysogenize. When known to have originated by mutation from a temperate phage, it is called a virulent mutant.

APPENDIX

METHODS OF STUDY OF BACTERIAL VIRUSES

Mark H. Adams

This article originally appeared in Volume 2 of *Methods in Medical Research*,* which has been out of print for a number of years. We are greatly indebted to the publisher and to the Governing Board of *Methods in Medical Research* for the generous permission to reprint a slightly re-edited version of the article.

We believe that the precision of bacterial virus experimentation, only scantily described in most of the literature, and so well portrayed here, will be a valuable stimulus and pattern for the beginner, and for the worker in allied fields of virology, interested in refining his experiments. The original article was, we felt, so well designed by Mark Adams that we seriously contemplated reprinting it without any revision.

The decision to make some small revision was based upon the following principles: The more or less theoretical material for an article intended to stand by itself is not needed and is in some cases outdated by the text of the present book. Such material, as well as an occasional bit of experimental detail judged obsolete, is omitted in this reprinting, each place being indicated by an appropriate ellipsis (. . .). When, after discussion with colleagues, it was judged that omission of certain newer technical methods or details would seem almost to misrepresent current practice, additions were made. These were kept as few and small as seemed reasonable, and all but those of one or two words are enclosed in brackets.

The responsibility for omissions or changes must rest with the undersigned, but we wish to thank the many colleagues who offered advice, and in particular Dr. George Streisinger, Dr. Norton Zinder, Dr. Margeris Jesaitis, and Professor Max Delbrück.

Rollin D. Hotchkiss
Nancy Collins Bruce

January, 1958

* *Methods in Medical Research*, Vol. 2, J. H. Comroe, ed., The Year Book Publishers, Inc., Chicago, 1950, pp. 1–73. Reprinted by permission.

Introduction

It is now generally agreed that the bacteriophage principle of d'Herelle is a group of filtrable viruses, parasitic on bacteria and more closely related chemically and physically to the animal viruses than to the plant viruses. Because of the ease with which they and their host may be grown and studied, because of the high precision with which they may be assayed and because a single infected host cell may be readily isolated and observed in the absence of interaction with other cells, the bacterial viruses have become the subjects of widespread research as models of the host-virus relationship. The bacterial viruses have been used as tools in the study of the synthesis of proteins and nucleic acids in infected cells, as a test system in the search for possible chemotherapeutic and antibiotic agents for virus diseases, in the study of the phenomenon of virus interference, in the study of the action of ultraviolet light and X-radiation on viruses and in the study of the mutational patterns of viruses and bacteria. The possibilities inherent in the bacteriophage as a tool in the study of relationship between virus and host cell have been largely underrated. It is because of the greatly increased interest in recent years in this group of viruses that it was thought worth while to collect in one place the various techniques found most suitable for research in this field.

The author is greatly indebted to Prof. Max Delbrück for a critical reading of the manuscript; many comments and suggestions of his have been incorporated in the text. The author is also grateful to S. E. Luria, R. Dulbecco, T. F. Anderson, and A. H. Doermann for helpful discussions concerning certain portions of the material. However, no one but the author is responsible for any errors or omissions. Some of the photographs showing plaque morphology are included through the kindness of Dr. Delbrück. The author's unpublished experiments which have been included were aided by a grant from the National Foundation for Infantile Paralysis, Inc.

Host Organisms and Viruses

Bacteriophages have been recorded for the various groups of enteric bacteria such as shigella, salmonella, proteus aerobacter, vibrio, and escherichia.   They are also known for bacilli, staphylococci, streptococci, corynebacteria, mycobacteria, and actinomycetes.   Phagelike agents are not known for protozoa, algae, yeasts, or molds.   Extensive investigations have been carried out on certain groups of phages, in particular on the staphylococcus phages by Northrop (1939a) and Krueger (1932), salmonella and coli-dysentery phages by Burnet (1934a), cholera phages by Asheshov, Asheshov, Khan, and Lahiri (1933), typhoid phages by Craigie (1946), and coliphages by Schlesinger (1933a).

In the United States the most intensively investigated phages are the group of 7 coli-dysentery phages described by Demerec and Fano (1945) and studied by Delbrück, Luria, Hershey, Cohen, Beard, Anderson, and many others.   All methods described here have been tested on this group of phages but are more generally applicable.   The work has been reviewed by Delbrück (1946a, b).

Media

In work with strain B of *Escherichia coli* and its phages, the most generally useful medium is nutrient broth which contains 8 g. of Difco nutrient broth and 5 g. of NaCl/liter of water. To this is added 15 g. of Difco agar/liter to make nutrient agar for plates.   For most phage work the agar in the plates should be fairly deep, the requirement being about 30 ml. of nutrient agar/Petri dish.   The plates should be stored in an incubator at 37° C. overnight to dry them before use.   Otherwise water of condensation will cause coalescence of plaques and ruin the plates for quantitative use.   For preparation of agar slants for routine cultivation of the host organism and its mutants, 2 per cent nutrient agar is most suitable since bacteria from such a slant seem to be more readily dispersed in a uniform suspension.

·   ·   ·   ·   ·

Soft agar for the *agar layer technique* contains only 7 g. of Difco agar/liter and is most conveniently put up in 50 ml. amounts in bottles, to be melted and used as needed.

These media are probably suitable for use with any of the enteric bacteria. For more fastidious host organisms special media may have to be devised.

For certain types of work with bacterial viruses it is desirable to grow the host organisms on chemically defined media. [The composition of two simple media used in culturing *E. coli* are given below:

	F medium[a]	M-9 medium
NH_4Cl	1.0 g.	1.0 g.
$MgSO_4$[b]	0.1 g.	0.13 g.
KH_2PO_4	1.5 g.	3.0 g.
NA_2HPO_4	3.5 g.	6.0 g.
Lactic acid[b]	9.0 g.	—
Glucose[b]	—	4.0 g.
Water	1000.0 ml.	1000.0 ml.

[a] Bring to pH 6.8 with NaOH.
[b] Autoclave separately.

Numerous minor modifications of these media will be found in the phage literature.] The media may be enriched if desired with various amino acids, growth factors and salts to support growth of more fastidious organisms. E.g., strain B of *E. coli* will grow abundantly in this medium, but two of its phage-resistant mutants will not grow unless certain amino acids are added. Also, most phages of the T group are produced in high titer on strain B of *E. coli* when grown on F medium, but T5 is not produced unless $CaCl_2$ to a concentration of 0.001 N is added. With such a chemically defined medium it is possible to study the effect of the nutritional environment of the host cell on the yield of phage.

With both broth and chemically defined media, maximal growth of *E. coli* is achieved only with active aeration of the cultures. With an energy source such as lactic acid, aeration is essential for growth. A convenient device for aeration is the Marco air pump.*

A factor of great importance in the design of experiments is the medium in which the host cells have been grown. *E. coli* grown in nutrient broth is from the metabolic point of view very different from *E. coli* grown on the ammonium lactate medium. *E. coli* grown in broth, centrifuged and resuspended in ammonium lactate medium has a long lag period before growth starts, presumably because the organism has to synthesize enzymes necessary for synthesis of amino acids and growth factors furnished in the broth medium. This property of broth-grown *E. coli* was used by Fowler and Cohen (1948) in an investigation of the various constituents of the medium which may play a role in phage synthesis in the organism. The organisms were grown in broth, centrifuged and resuspended in an ammonium lactate medium. The latent period of phage growth and the burst size (p. 473) were then determined on such a culture infected with phage T2. The effect of addition of various amino acids and growth factors on latent period and burst size could then be readily determined.

Isolation of Bacterial Viruses

To isolate a virus lysing *E. coli*, 30 ml. of broth is inoculated with 1 ml. of a visibly turbid culture of the host organism. To this is added with thorough mixing 1 ml. of supernatant obtained by centrifuging pooled sewage for a few minutes. After incubation overnight at 37° C., an aliquot of the culture is centrifuged to remove bacteria and the supernatant is filtered through a Corning ultrafine sintered glass filter. This filtrate is tested for presence of phage.

a. By plating. Dilute the filtrate serially in a broth culture of *E. coli* and spread 0.1 ml. samples of each dilution on agar

* Made by the J. B. Maris Company, Bloomfield, N. J. This company also makes valves and other fittings suitable for low pressure air lines.

plates. Incubate overnight at 37° C. and examine plates for "plaques," small or large circular areas of lysis in the film of bacterial growth. It is well to plate at least 4 serial 1:10 dilutions of the filtrate, since direct plating of a high concentration of virus may result in lysis of all bacteria and absence of plaques, a result often confusing to the uninitiated.

b. By lysis of broth culture. Inoculate 10 ml. of broth with 0.05 ml. of visibly turbid culture of host organism and with 0.1 ml. of the filtrate to be tested for phage. Incubate at 37° C. and examine hourly for turbidity, comparing with a control culture inoculated with bacteria but not with filtrate. If turbidity does not develop or if lysis occurs after turbidity has developed, phage is present and may then be tested for by plating broth dilutions of the culture as described in (*a*).

Once plaques have been obtained on an agar plate, these may be picked and replated twice to insure a pure culture of a single phage type. The plaque is stabbed with a sterile platinum wire and the wire rinsed in 1 ml. of sterile broth. Several dilutions of the broth are then plated as in (*a*).

It should be mentioned that a phage which brings about complete lysis of broth cultures of bacteria may produce very tiny plaques, may have a low efficiency of plating or a slow adsorption rate or may be otherwise unsuitable for quantitative work by plaque-counting techniques. Also, a phage which produces beautiful plaques may not bring about lysis in broth cultures, may yield only low titer stock or be difficult to work with in other ways. The method of isolation may in part determine the properties of the phage isolated, through selection of variants. In fact, repeated subculture of a phage in fluid media using large inocula is a classic method of increasing phage "virulence," probably through selection of mutants with the desired properties.

After isolation, the phage may be characterized by host range characteristics, immunologic properties, plaque morphology, and electron microscopic appearance.

In general, a bacterial virus should be looked for in the natural habitat of its host. For instance, viruses lysing the various enteric bacteria are found in pooled sewage and animal feces. Viruses lysing staphylococci have been found in the nasal passages and on the skin. The soil is often a good place to look for bacterial viruses. Other sources are the so-called lysogenic strains of bacteria. Such strains are contaminated with latent viruses capable of lysing other strains of the same bacterial species. For instance, Rountree (1947a) isolated 5 different lysogenic strains and the appropriate susceptible propagating strains from a series of 40 cultures of pathogenic *Staph. aureus*.

Assay of Host Organisms

For much of the quantitative work with bacterial viruses an accurate estimate of the bacterial concentration is essential. The standard method for determining bacterial concentrations is by viable count. Aliquots (0.1 ml.) of serial dilutions of the bacterial culture are spread over the surface of agar plates with a glass rod, and after incubation the number of colonies are counted. From this count the number of viable organisms/ml. of the original culture may be calculated. It is usually necessary to work with cultures of the host organism which are actively growing at an exponential rate, since in such cultures the percentage of nonviable organisms is small. Presence in the culture of any considerable percentage of dead bacteria will lead to difficulties, since virus particles which become adsorbed to such bacteria do not reproduce themselves or form plaques on agar plates. In the case of bacteria that grow in clumps or chains, such as streptococci, the viable count does not enumerate single cells, but rather the chain is the unit counted. In such cases the clumps or chains must be broken up so that most of the cells are seen singly under the microscope. If this is not possible, some of the statistical methods discussed later cannot be applied to such systems; e.g., estimates of the yield of virus/bacterial cell are likely to be misleading if the calculations are based on chains of cells.

The viable cell count can be used to calibrate a photoelectric colorimeter or a nephelometer so that turbidity of a suspension of bacteria can be used as a measure of bacterial concentration. It must be remembered that the calibration curve so prepared can be used only with bacteria grown under the same conditions and in the same medium as those used in the calibration, since a change in environmental conditions often conspicuously alters size and morphology of the bacteria, reflected in changes in turbidity. Also, changes in turbidity of a culture undergoing lysis by phage cannot be interpreted in terms of numbers of surviving bacteria, since the bacterial debris resulting from lysis of a culture may be quite turbid and yet contain few or no viable bacteria. Also, the phage particles themselves scatter light appreciably.

Assay of Phage by Agar Layer Method

The agar layer method for plating bacterial viruses seems to have been first described by Gratia (1936c), and is in general use by practically all workers.

Procedure. The host bacteria and virus particles are mixed in a small volume of warm 0.7 per cent agar and the mixture is poured over the surface of an ordinary agar plate and allowed to harden to form a thin layer. The bacteria grow as tiny sub-surface colonies in this layer and are nourished by the deep layer of 1.5 per cent agar which is used as foundation. The plaques appear as clear holes in the opaque layer of bacterial growth. The soft 0.7 per cent agar is melted in a boiling water bath and cooled in a 46° C. water bath. It is then transferred with a warmed pipet in 2.5 ml. amounts to warmed test tubes in the 46° C. water bath. The bacterial inoculum is prepared by washing the bacteria from the surface of an agar slant with 5 ml. of broth. One drop of the resultant suspension is added to each tube of soft agar. Then the diluted virus in any volume up to 1 ml. is pipetted into the tubes of soft agar and the mixture poured immediately over the surface of an agar plate. The plate is rocked gently to mix the bacteria and virus particles and set aside to harden. Both the 1.5 per cent agar and the soft

agar layer should be allowed to harden with the Petri dish resting on a leveled sheet of plate glass, to insure uniform distribution of the virus plaques over the plate surface. If the melted
soft agar is held at 46° C. for much over an hour the agar will
start to gel and poor plates will result. Neither bacteria nor
viruses seem to be harmed by a short stay at 46° C.

Advantages of the agar layer method are that the host bacteria
and virus particles may be more uniformly distributed over the
surface of the plate than by the spreading technique and a
larger volume of virus may be plated. The greater porosity of
the soft agar layer permits more rapid diffusion of the phage
particles and development of larger plaques than are obtained
by the spreading technique, and hence variations in plaque
morphology may be more readily studied. The chief disadvan-
tage is that melted agar must be maintained at 46° C. until
used. Use of this method has tremendously facilitated the
plating of bacterial viruses since it is more rapid than the spreading technique.

The dark field colony counter (Spencer Optical Co.) is a good
device for observation and counting of plaques, since the plaques
appear as dark holes in the brightly illuminated layer of bacterial growth. An automatically recording counting apparatus
described by Varney (1935) marks each plaque as it is counted
and at the same time operates an electric recorder.

Efficiency of Plating

The efficiency of plating may be defined as that proportion
of viable phage particles which actually form plaques when
plated. It depends on the ability of the phage particles to become adsorbed to a suitable host cell and on the ability of these
infected cells to liberate more phage again, thus initiating a chain
reaction which results in a plaque. The plaque continues to
increase in size until the stationary phase of bacterial growth is
reached, at which point infected cells no longer liberate virus.
A phage particle which does not become absorbed to a host

cell or an infected host cell which does not liberate phage until near the end of the growth period of the bacteria will not produce a plaque and will not be counted.

Some factors known to affect markedly the efficiency of plating may be mentioned by way of example. Anderson (1945a) found that the coli phage T4, when plated on a chemically defined medium free of amino acids, produced only 10^{-4} the number of plaques produced when it was plated on nutrient agar. Addition of 100 μg. of tryptophan/ml. of the chemically defined medium increased efficiency of plating to that obtained in nutrient broth. Tryptophan is essential for adsorption of phage T4 to the host cell. Hershey, Kalmanson, and Bronfenbrenner (1944) found that the efficiency of plating of a variant of coli phage T2 on tryptose agar was markedly a function of salt concentration. Addition of NaCl to a concentration of 0.2 M increased efficiency of plating by a factor of 10^4 over that of tryptose agar to which no salt was added. Addition of salt in this instance enormously increased the rate of adsorption of phage to bacterium.

The absolute efficiency of plating cannot be determined unless there is an independent method for determining the total number of infective phage particles in a preparation. Perhaps the best available estimate of the efficiency of plating depends on correlation between the size of an infectious unit as estimated by chemical methods and the particle size as determined by means of the electron microscope.

- Hook and co-workers (1946), working with phage T2, found the average dry weight of a plaque-forming particle to be 7×10^{-16} g. and the specific volume of the dried preparation 0.66 ml./g., from which the volume of the lytic particle becomes 5×10^{-16} ml. Assuming the particle to be a sphere, its diameter would be about 100 mμ. From electron micrographs these workers concluded that the head of the phage particle measures about 80 $\times$ 100 mμ and the tail about 120 $\times$ 20 mμ. This close correspondence indicates that the efficiency of plating is certainly not grossly low.

A method for determining the relative efficiency of plating when this is of the order of 0.1–1 and not due to lack of adsorption cofactors or nutritional deficiencies was described by Ellis and Delbrück (1939). In this method, the phage is so diluted in broth that there is somewhat less than 1 infectious particle/ml. and then distributed in tubes to give 50 samples of 1 ml. each. Each sample is inoculated with a few hundred bacteria and incubated overnight. At the end of this time a 0.1 ml. sample from each tube is plated in the usual way to see whether phage is present or not. The proportion of samples containing no phage is determined and the average number of phage particles per sample is calculated from the Poisson formula

$$P(0) = e^{-n}$$

in which $P(0)$ = the fraction of samples containing no phage, n = the average number of phage particles per sample, and e = the base of natural logarithms.

The principle of this method depends on the fact that the chances of a phage particle adsorbing to a bacterium are somewhat greater in a broth culture of bacteria than on a plate, owing to more rapid diffusion and longer time available for contact, as well as a high bacterial concentration—10^9/ml. when growth ceases. Once an infected bacterium has lysed, several hundred phage particles are liberated and the chances of detecting the presence of phage by plating are increased. This method obviously cannot overcome a lowered efficiency of plating due to lack of cofactors for adsorption.

One rather obvious factor which can reduce the efficiency of plating is presence of a considerable proportion of killed bacteria in the culture used for plating. A phage particle adsorbed to a dead bacterium does not multiply or produce a plaque. For this reason only fresh cultures of bacteria should be used for plating.

Stability of Viruses and Selection of Diluents

Most bacterial viruses are remarkably stable when diluted in broth, serum, ascitic fluid and similar diluents, not being inactivated at an appreciable rate even at 60 °C. However, when diluted in salt solutions or chemically defined media, all the phages are less stable and some are strikingly unstable. All the coli-dysentery phages in the T system are rapidly inactivated at gas-liquid interfaces when diluted in media free of protein (Adams, 1948). If dilute suspensions of phages in protein-free media are to be subjected to bubbling or shaking, they should be protected from "surface inactivation" by addition to the medium of a few μg./ml. of gelatin or other protein.

The chemical nature and concentration of salts present in a diluent also affect the stability of some bacterial viruses. The coli-dysentery phages T1 and T5, when diluted in 0.9 per cent saline, are rapidly inactivated even at room temperature. However, addition to the saline of divalent cations such as Mg^{++} or Ca^{++} at a concentration of 10^{-3} M results in a striking increase in stability of these phages (Adams, 1949a).

Viruses in general, when suspended in salt solutions, are subject to very rapid inactivation by small amounts of toxic substances such as cationic and anionic detergents (Stock and Francis, 1943), oxidizing agents and heavy metals (Knight and Stanley, 1944). These materials are much less effective in destroying virus infectivity when the viruses are diluted in broth. When viruses are to be diluted in salt solutions, the most scrupulous care must be exercised to make certain that glassware and solutions are free from traces of acid-dichromate, detergents, heavy metals, and chlorine (which may appear in distilled water).

Preparation of High Titer Phage Stocks

The ability to produce a high titer phage stock at will is largely the result of considerable experience with the particular phage and host cell under consideration. However, certain general principles can be stated which may be of help. Strain

B of *E. coli*, when grown in nutrient broth with aeration, will reach a final concentration of about 5×10^9 cells/ml. but the logarithmic phase of growth will cease at about 10^9 cells/ml. If such a culture is grown to a concentration of 5×10^8–10^9 cells/ml. and is then inoculated with enough phage to reach a final concentration of 2–4×10^9 phage particles/ml. the bacteria will all be infected nearly simultaneously, will all lyse within a few hours, and a final titer of phage of between 10^{10} and 10^{11} infectious particles/ml. should be achieved. Since average yield per infected bacterium is 100–300 phage particles, it might be expected that 10^9 infected bacteria/ml. should liberate at least 10^{11} phage particles/ml. This maximal yield is seldom achieved in practice since large numbers of liberated phage particles are permanently lost by readsorption to infected but not yet lysed bacteria. [Phage will also adsorb to bacterial debris. Bacterial lysates should therefore be centrifuged at low speed to remove the debris and thereby prevent loss of titer on standing.]

Similar results may be achieved with coliphages in the chemically defined media described on p. 446. It should be noted that the medium may have to be reinforced with other substances such as salts, amino acids or other growth factors in special instances. For example, coliphage T5 will not be produced in this medium unless 0.001 N calcium ion is added. . . . In all instances better bacterial growth and higher phage yields are obtained when air is actively bubbled through the medium during the growth period.

[A method of preparing genetically homogeneous phage stocks has been described by Doermann and Hill (1953). Young plaques (4–6 hr of incubation for the T even phages) are used to inoculate young bacterial cultures (about 10^8 cells/ml.).]

Another method of obtaining very high titer phage stocks has been described by Hershey, Kalmanson, and Bronfenbrenner (1943a). It appears simple, but actually requires considerable experience to obtain consistently good yields of phage.

Procedure. Ordinary agar plates are spread with a mixture of heavy broth culture of *E. coli* and enough phage to give barely confluent lysis when the plaques are completely developed, i.e., 10^5–10^6 phage particles/plate. After incubation for 12–18 hr., about 3 ml. of broth is added to each plate and allowed to stand for 15–20 min. The broth is then decanted and centrifuged to remove any bacteria, agar or other debris. Phage stocks prepared thus should have 10^{11}–10^{12} infectious particles/ml. This high concentration is not surprising since a single plaque 2 mm. in diameter may contain between 10^7 and 10^9 recoverable phage particles (T. F. Anderson, 1948b) and confluent lysis requires 10^5–10^6 plaques/plate.

Plates prepared by the agar layer technique can be used in this way also. Four plates were made using 10^5 T5 phage particles/plate and incubated overnight. Five ml. of broth was added to each plate, the soft agar layer was scraped off with a glass rod, and the agar layers shaken in a flask with the 20 ml. of broth. After 30 min. extraction with occasional shaking, the agar and bacterial debris were sedimented at low speed in a centrifuge. Yield was 15 ml. of a T5 stock with 8×10^{11} particles/ml.

[Some of the variables involved in the production of high titer stocks of the T phages by the plate method are discussed in a paper by Swanstrom and Adams (1951).]

Filtration of Phage Stocks

For most purposes it is desirable to use phage stocks which are free from bacteria, molds, and insoluble debris. The first step in such purification should be centrifugation at moderate speed to remove most of the bacteria and larger particulate matter. Another method of removing insoluble materials, which is particularly applicable to large batches of bacterial lysate, is to filter the lysate through a pad of filter paper pulp on a Buchner funnel. Better filtration is often obtained if a layer of infusorial earth, filter cell, or fine sand is placed above the paper pulp. After clarification by either centrifugation or filtration, the lysate is passed through a fine pore bacteriologic filter to remove the few remaining bacterial cells and spores. Filters such as Seitz, Berkefeld, Mandler, porcelain, or sintered glass may be used.   In general, Seitz filters are not satisfactory because a large fraction of the phage is lost in filtration.   Mandler, porcelain, and Corning ultrafine sintered glass filters are usually satisfactory.   The pH of the medium and the salt concentration are important controllable variables which affect the filter-passing ability of viruses.   Gradacol membranes of a porosity which will retain bacteria but permit passage of the virus can also be used for sterilization of phage stocks (Elford, 1938).

[A simple method for the sterilization of phage stocks is to add approximately 0.5 ml. of chloroform per 10–20 ml. of the bacterial lysate, shaking vigorously a few times to saturate with chloroform. After the chloroform has settled (or alternatively is centrifuged) to the bottom, the stock is decanted and aerated until it no longer contains chloroform.   Although this method has been used successfully with the T phages, it is advisable to test the viability of any new phage strain under these conditions.]

Concentration and Purification of Phage

A particularly valuable tool for the concentration and partial purification of large quantities of viruses is the Sharples supercentrifuge.   Stanley applied it to the large scale concentration of tobacco mosaic (1942) and influenza (1944) viruses, and Hook and co-workers used it for concentration of a number of viruses including T2 bacteriophage (1946).   The principles involved in use of the Sharples centrifuge for concentration of viruses were discussed by Markham (1944).   The following description of use of the Sharples centrifuge for concentration of T2 phage is abstracted from the paper by Hook and co-workers (1946).

Procedures.   1. Freshly lysed nutrient broth cultures of T2 phage were stored in the refrigerator 7–14 days, during which time much mucoid material was eliminated by spontaneous precipitation. The lysate was clarified by filtration through a 10 in., 6 or 7 lb. Mandler candle. The filtered lysate was passed through the 50 ml. concentration bowl of the Sharples centrifuge at a rate of 2 liters/hr. Bowl speed was 45,000 r.p.m. (49,000 g). The lysate was followed by 1 liter of sterile 0.9 per cent saline, pH 6.5, at the same rate of flow. The bowl, plugged and capped, was shaken vigorously and set in the refrigerator overnight. The chilled bowl was again shaken vigorously for 10 min., the 50 ml. of concentrate poured into a sterile beaker, and the bowl washed with three 20 ml. portions of sterile saline. The pooled concentrate and washings were spun in 50 ml. Lusteroid tubes in the angle centrifuge at 2,000 g to remove particulate impurities. The supernatant fluid showed a bright blue, opalescent Tyndall effect and contained about 5×10^{11} infectious particles/ml. with an over-all yield of about 90 per cent. The phage in this concentrate was readily sedimented in an ultracentrifuge at 20,000 g in 40 min., forming a gel-like pellet. The pellets were easily resuspended in a few milliliters of saline. This twice-concentrated material was then spun in the angle centrifuge at 2,000 g to remove any insoluble material.

The final product represented a concentration of about 360-fold with an over-all yield of infectivity of better than 80 per cent. Actual yield of purified material was between 5 and 10 mg./liter of broth lysate. The concentrate appeared to be homogeneous and essentially free from extraneous material when examined in the analytical ultracentrifuge and in the electron microscope. If one were to apply this procedure to other phages it might be well to add 10^{-3} M magnesium sulfate to the saline to increase stability of the phage (see p. 454). [The use of this method for phage T6 has been described by Putnam, Kozloff, and Neil (1949) and with some improvements for T4 by Jesaitis and Goebel (1955).]

2. Another simple method for concentration of phage stocks is by removal of water *in vacuo*. A phage stock clarified by

filtration through paper pulp or a coarse Mandler filter is placed in a large Florence flask and connected through an efficient water-cooled condenser and receiving flask with an aspirator or other vacuum pump. Such a system should be designed to operate at an internal pressure of 20–30 mm. Hg and should evaporate several liters of water an hour at a temperature in the distilling flask of about 30 °C. . . .

Example: In a typical preparation 1 liter of T1 phage lysate with a titer of 2×10^{10} particles/ml. was concentrated *in vacuo* to 118 ml. at a concentration of 2.2×10^{11} particles/ml. with no loss of activity. Eighty ml. of this concentrate was spun for 2 hr. at 18,000 r.p.m. in the International refrigerated centrifuge. After the supernatant fluid was decanted and the Lusteroid tubes were drained well on filter paper, the pellets were resuspended in 5 ml. of chemically defined medium and spun at low speed in the angle centrifuge to remove insoluble debris. The discarded supernatant from the high speed centrifugation contained 5.6×10^{10} particles/ml., while the 5 ml. of concentrate had an activity of 3×10^{12} particles/ml., a yield of 80 per cent.

. . . . .

3. Another method of concentrating bacteriophage is by ultrafiltration through a collodion membrane of a permeability which will hold back the phage but permit fairly rapid passage of water and solutes. The medium may be filtered through these membranes at the rate of $1/2$–1 liter/hr. and the phage readily concentrated 100-fold. The method as applied to T2 phage was described in detail by Kalmanson and Bronfenbrenner (1939) and is not included here because the methods described above are more convenient and rapid.

Gradacol membranes are convenient for concentration and purification of phage. Use of a membrane of porosity sufficient to retain the phage permits rapid concentration of large volumes of phage stock while permitting removal of proteins and other high molecular weight substances which will pass the membrane. Use of Gradacol membranes has been thoroughly discussed by Elford (1938).

[4. Herriott and Barlow (1952) have described in detail a method for the preparation and purification of T2 in large quantities (8–10 liters). The essential steps of the purification of the lysate involve (*1*) separation of cell debris by filtration through Hyflow Celite, or by settling and decantation at 5 °C.; (*2*) precipitation of the virus at 5 °C. by acidification to pH 4.0; (*3*) enzymatic digestion of extraneous DNA with DNAase, which decreases the viscosity of the virus suspension, making sedimentation easier, and increases the stability of the phage; and (*4*) differential centrifugation, with selection of the fraction remaining in the supernate at 5,000 *g* but sedimenting in 30 min. at 11,000 *g*. The recovery of active virus in the principal fraction varied from 27 to 85 per cent.

5. In many cases a high recovery of smaller amounts of active phage has been achieved essentially through differential centrifugation similar to the one described above, but omitting the acid precipitation. Such a procedure should be worked out to suit the properties of any individual phage and host to which it is applied.

As an example, for T2 or T4, a culture of *E. coli* B, grown in M-9 synthetic medium and freshly lysed with phage, is either centrifuged at low speed or filtered through Hyflow Celite as described (Herriott and Barlow, 1952). The clear lysate is passed through a Selas filter of porosity #02. It is then centrifuged at high speed (12,000 *g*) for 90 min., the supernate is poured off and the pellet resuspended in $^1/_{50}$ to $^1/_5$ the original volume of 0.15 *M* phosphate buffer containing 20 μg. of gelatin per ml. The simplest method of resuspending the pellet is to leave it undisturbed in the suspension medium a few hours with occasional gentle agitation. (Resuspension of the pellet by pipetting can result in loss of active titer.) The phage concentrate is then treated with DNAase (approximately 1 μg of purified enzyme per ml. for 30–60 min at 37 °C.) and sometimes, if desired, a similar treatment with RNAase. The preparation is then subjected to one or more cycles of high and low speed centrifugation, the final step being a removal of debris at low speed.]

Preparation and Use of Antiphage Sera

Antibodies against viruses have the general property of reacting with the viruses to form an antibody-virus complex which is noninfectious for the host cell by virtue of the fact that adsorption of virus to host cell is prevented. The virus is not damaged by combination with antibody, as demonstrated by the fact that treatment of the virus-antibody complex with papain will result in destruction of antibody and recovery of infectivity of the virus.

Example: In a typical experiment (Kalmanson and Bronfenbrenner, 1943), a sample of phage T2 was incubated with antiserum at a final dilution of 1 : 1,000 for 1 hr. at 37° C., at which time 90 per cent of the infective particles had been neutralized. The neutralized phage was then diluted 1 : 100 in activated papain and incubated at 37° C. Within 20 min. the neutralized phage was completely reactivated. In a control experiment using inactive papain there was no reactivation of phage. The papain solution contained 4 g. of commercial papain/liter of saline and was activated just before use by addition of 0.1 ml. of 16 per cent cysteine–HCl/5 ml. of papain solution and adjustment of pH to 7.4.

Antibodies against viruses are extremely useful tools in virus research since they furnish a convenient means for identification of viruses. They permit serologic classification of the viruses into groups in which the antigenic relationships are correlated with morphologic and biologic resemblances (Delbrück, 1946a). Since antibodies against phages do not inhibit the infectious process once the virus has become adsorbed to the host cell (Delbrück, 1945b), but do prevent further adsorption of free phage, they enable the investigator to, in effect, remove unadsorbed virus from the scene of action without interfering with the growth of adsorbed virus.

Immunization of Animals

The production of a high titer antiserum against a bacterial virus differs in no essential respect from procedures for immunization against bacterial antigens. The important considerations are to inject enough antigen to provide an adequate immunologic stimulus and to use enough animals to allow for individual variation in immunologic response.

Procedure. The rabbit is the most convenient laboratory animal to use for production of antisera. At least 3 animals should be immunized with each antigen because rabbits immunized in the same way with the same antigen may vary 10-fold in the final titer of antibody produced. This also is insurance against loss of animals through sickness or accidental death. The phage stock used for immunization should have at least 10^{10} plaque-forming particles/ml. and may have been produced in either broth or chemically defined media with equally good results. The phages should not be treated with formalin or heat since they are not infectious for the rabbit. However, it is usual to filter the phage stocks to remove bacteria because bacterial infections can occur.

The route of injection seems to be of no significance if high titer stocks are used, for we have obtained equally good results from subcutaneous, intravenous, and intraperitoneal injections. If the stock is of low titer, or the phage a poor antigen, the subcutaneous route is probably preferable.

The time schedule of the injections is not particularly important, provided only that enough antigen is given over a long enough period. We have had good results with 2 injections of 5 ml. each per week for 3 weeks with a test bleeding 1 week after the last injection. Test bleeding is most conveniently made by slitting the marginal ear vein and collecting about 5 ml. of blood. The blood is allowed to clot at 37 °C. in petrolatum-lined centrifuge tubes and placed in the refrigerator overnight. After centrifugation the serum is decanted, centrifuged again if necessary to remove residual red cells, and stored in sterile screw-capped vials in the refrigerator.

The serum is now assayed for antiviral activity and if sufficiently potent for use the rabbit is bled by cardiac puncture. As much as 50 ml. of blood may be removed without damage to the rabbit. After a week's rest the rabbit may be given a second course of injections and bled again.

All operations in bleeding the animals and preparing the sera should be performed with precautions to avoid microbial contamination. If the sera become contaminated they may be sterilized by centrifugation followed by filtration through ultrafine sintered glass or Berkefeld filters. It is most unwise to add preservatives because this will interfere with certain uses of the sera. For instance, the presence of 1 part in 10,000 of Merthiolate in a serum which was then diluted 1:100 for use in one-step growth experiments caused a striking lengthening of the latent period of phage multiplication.

Assay of Antiphage Sera

The reaction between the phage and its antibody is not instantaneous, instead proceeding at a readily measurable rate. This rate is a function of the concentration of virus, of the concentration and activity of the antibody and of the temperature. At constant temperature the rate may be expressed as

$$-dp/dt = Kp/D \text{ (differential)}$$

$$K = 2.3 \ D/t \times \log p_0/p \text{ (integral)}$$

$$p/p_0 = e^{-Kt/D} \text{ (exponential)}$$

in which p_0 = phage assay at zero time, p = phage assay at time t min., D = final dilution of serum in the phage-serum mixture; i.e., if the concentration is $1/100$ that of the undiluted serum, then $D = 100$, K = velocity constant.

This equation holds for inactivation of 90–99 per cent of the phage present in the reaction mixture. The value of K is a characteristic of the particular lot of serum used. Once the K value of a sample of serum has been determined, it can be substituted in the integral form of the equation and used to calculate the dilution D of that serum to be used to inactivate any desired fraction of the phage, e.g., 90 per cent, in any given time, 5 min. or 30 min. It must be remembered that the equation describes the course of the reaction only over a limited range of inactivation, usually between 90 and 99 per cent of the phage, and cannot be used outside this range. Also, the value of K is not absolutely independent of the concentration of serum but usually increases somewhat as D increases. However, the K value is an extremely valuable characteristic of the serum within its limitations.

Procedure. For use, the serum is diluted in the same medium in which the phage is to be diluted, usually broth or some diluent (p. 454), with the additional proviso that the diluent should be approximately isotonic so that the serum globulins will not precipitate. The phage stock is diluted to a titer of $10^7/ml.$ and 0.1 ml. of phage is added to 0.9 ml. of diluted serum at 37 °C. At 5 min. intervals 0.1 ml. samples of the phage-serum mixture are added to 9.9 ml. of diluent to stop antibody reaction and 0.1 ml. samples of this dilution are plated by the agar layer technique. If no inactivation of phage has occurred, about 1,000 plaques will be found after incubation of the plates; after 90 per cent inactivation the count will be 100, etc. The serum should be tested at dilutions of 1:100 and 1:1,000.

From such an experiment it should be possible to calculate the K value of the serum, the range of inactivation over which the equation holds and the effect of serum dilution on the K value. For instance if the serum at a dilution of 1:100 inactivates 90 per cent of the phage in 5 min., the K value = 2.3 × 100/5 × log 100/10 = 46. The higher the K value of a serum, the further it can be diluted and still give satisfactory neutralization of phage. Various phages differ greatly with respect to their rates of reaction with homologous antisera. The K values of antisera against coli phages T3 and T7 usually range between 500 and 3000, and against T2, T4, and T6, between 200 and 1,000. The coliphages T1 and T5 appear to react quite slowly with their antisera since the K values usually range between 20 and 100 and it is most unusual to obtain a serum with a K value higher than 200 for these phages.

Use of K Value of Antiserum to Demonstrate Serologic Relatedness among Phages

If 2 viruses are serologically related, an antiserum against 1 of them will neutralize the infectivity of both. In all cases studied so far, the rate of neutralization has been greater with homologous virus and antiserum than with heterologous systems. The K value of an antiserum when tested with various viruses can be taken as an indication of the degree of relatedness of the viruses. For instance, the coliphages T2, T4, and T6 form a closely related group. An antiserum against T2 had a K value of 200 when measured against T2, a K value of 50 when measured with T4 and of 90 when measured with T6. In contrast, coliphages T3 and T7 are much less similar serologically. A T3 antiserum with a K value of 300 with T3 had a K value of only 1.5 with T7, whereas a T7 antiserum with a K value of 1000 with T7 had a K value of 1 with T3.

Luria (1945a) used this method to test the relatedness of host range mutants of T1 and T2 to the parent strains and found no detectable difference in K values for neutralization of parent and mutant whether tested with antiserum against the parent or the mutant.

With this method Hershey (1946a) attempted to find an antigenic difference between an r type phage mutant and its r^+ ancestor, but failed to detect any difference even when the sensitivity of the method was increased by cross-absorption of the sera with the heterologous phage. Nor could he detect any antigenic difference between host range mutants and their ancestors, confirming Luria. Hershey was, however, able to detect significant immunologic differences in various races of T2 which had been subcultured in different laboratories for some time, indicating that antigenic differences in phage do develop, probably by mutation, during repeated subculture.

This method of antigenic analysis is likely to be useful in a study of the phages released from bacteria simultaneously infected with 2 different types of virus, where there is evidence for exchanges of genetic material (see "Mutations of Bacterio-phages," pp. 501–8).

Other uses of antiphage sera are described in the section on the single-step growth curve (pp. 473–85).

Rate of Adsorption of Virus to Bacterium

The first step in the growth cycle of a virus is adsorption of virus to host cell. Since this step is most accessible to observation it has been more thoroughly studied than the subsequent steps. Knowledge of the adsorption rate is necessary for the design and interpretation of certain kinds of experiments to be described later. Study of the effect of environmental factors and of the physiologic state of the host cell on the rate of the virus adsorption has contributed greatly to understanding of the virus–host cell relationship.

The adsorption of virus to bacteria occurs at a rate that is proportional to the concentrations of virus and of bacteria. It is also a function of temperature, of the viscosity of the medium and of the past history of the bacteria. Under constant environmental conditions and uniform cultural conditions of the host cell, the rate of adsorption follows the equation:

$$-dp/dt = K(B)p$$

$$K = 2.3/(B)t \times \log p_0/p$$

in which p_0 = phage assay at zero time, p = phage not adsorbed at time t min., (B) = concentration of bacteria as number of cells/ml., K = velocity constant with dimensions ml./min.

Example: Coliphage T2 is adsorbed on a broth-grown culture of *E. coli* of a concentration of 5×10^7/ml. at a rate of 80 per cent in 5 min. at 37° C. Substituting in the equation

$$K = \frac{2.3 \times \log 100/20}{5 \times 10^7/\text{ml.} \times 5 \text{ min.}} = 6.4 \times 10^{-9} \text{ ml./min.}$$

The adsorption follows the equation until 90–99 per cent of the virus at least has been adsorbed, provided the ratio of phage to bacteria is not too high. This provision is necessary because the ability of bacteria to adsorb phage is limited, the bacterium becoming saturated when it has adsorbed between 50 and 200 phage particles. The equation is also limited apparently by the fact that the phage is nonhomogenous with respect to rate of adsorption, a small and somewhat variable portion being relatively slowly adsorbed. Delbrück (1940a) investigated the effect of the physiologic state of the host cell on rate of adsorption. The most rapid adsorption of phage to host cell seems to occur when the host cell is in the logarithmic growth phase and growing in a favorable medium. Adsorption is more rapid in stirred adsorption mixtures than in mixtures at rest. However, T. F. Anderson (1949) has observed that violent agitation, as in a Waring Blendor, will prevent adsorption of phage T4 to the host cell.

There are several independent methods for determining the rate of adsorption of phage to bacterium which are applicable under different conditions; these methods will now be described in detail.

1. Assay of Unadsorbed Phage

This method of determining adsorption rate is rather direct and is applicable under conditions in which 20–90 per cent of the total phage present is adsorbed during the experimental period.

Procedure. The bacterial culture is temperature-equilibrated and a sample taken for bacterial assay just before addition of phage. An accurately known quantity of phage is added to the bacteria so that the initial concentration of phage in the adsorption mixture will be known. After thorough mixing, samples of the adsorption mixture are removed at known time intervals and diluted 1:100 to stop the adsorption process. One ml. amounts of the diluted samples are then centrifuged at 3,000 r.p.m. for 5 min. to sediment the bacteria and adsorbed phage. An aliquot of the supernatant fluid is then accurately assayed for residual free phage. The entire procedure from the start of the adsorption process to the assay of free phage in the centrifuge supernatant fluid must be completed before the end of the latent period of phage growth to insure that lysis of infected bacteria does not liberate additional free phage. The dilution may be made into chilled medium and centrifugation carried out in the cold to gain a little more time. This complication can be avoided, of course, by using killed bacteria, but it may be anticipated that the rate of adsorption will be less than with growing bacteria.

A plot of log per cent free phage remaining as a function of time should give a straight line, the slope of which can be used to calculate K. If the rate of adsorption is so slow that less than 20 per cent of the added phage is adsorbed during the available time, this method cannot be used because the accuracy of phage assay is not sufficient to give a reliable set of determinations of free phage. If the proportion of phage adsorbed is much more than 99 per cent, the method becomes unreliable because of incomplete sedimentation of infected bacteria during the centrifugation period, which leads to falsely high values of free phage. This source of error can be reduced by centrifuging for short periods in a high speed angle centrifuge instead of in the relatively slow centrifuge usually used to sediment bacteria.

[A recent method for measuring free (unadsorbed) phage is to treat the infected culture with chloroform which inactivates the infected bacteria. In this procedure the adsorption mixture is diluted into broth containing chloroform (4.5 ml. of broth with 0.5 ml. chloroform), shaken vigorously and then assayed for free phage. This method has been used successfully with T2 and T4 but should be applicable to other phages which are not inactivated by chloroform. Since infected bacteria containing mature phage are lysed by chloroform to yield viable phage (Séchaud and Kellenberger, 1956), it is essential to treat the adsorption mixture with chloroform early in the latent period of phage development.]

2. *Determination of Number of Infected Bacteria*

This method depends on the assumption that each adsorbed phage particle results in an infected bacterium which will produce a plaque when plated. The free phage is eliminated by diluting the adsorption mixture at appropriate intervals into enough antiphage serum to inactivate at least 99 per cent of the free phage during the period of antiserum action. In the case of the coliphages of the T system, antiphage serum has no effect on the ability of infected bacteria to produce plaques provided the antiserum is so diluted that its concentration on the plate does not affect plaque formation (Delbrück, 1945b). In the case of other phages it is well to check this before using the method. The ratio of phage to bacteria in the adsorption mixture must be so low that the probability of a single bacterium adsorbing more than 1 phage particle is negligible. For practical purposes the ratio of adsorbed phage to total bacterial count, the *multiplicity of infection*, should be 0.1 or less. Also, the proportion of bacteria which are dead or otherwise incapable of forming a plaque after adsorption of a phage particle should be less than 5 per cent. If these qualifications are met the number of infected bacteria present at any time should give directly the number of phage particles which have been adsorbed.

Procedure. Bring the bacterial suspension to temperature equilibrium and remove a sample for bacterial assay. Add the required amount of phage stock, mix well, remove a sample, dilute, and assay for phage. If the various qualifications listed in the preceding paragraph are met, this assay will give directly the total number of phage particles put into the adsorption tube since free phage and infected bacteria will both produce plaques. At intervals during adsorption, samples are removed and diluted 1:10 in antiphage serum at an appropriate dilution, as calculated from the K value, to inactivate 99 per cent of the free phage in a convenient time, e.g., 5 min. After this time the sample is further diluted to dilute out the antiserum and plated to determine the number of infected bacteria. The entire procedure must be completed within the latent period of phage growth before lysing bacteria can contribute to the plaque count. A sample of phage stock should be diluted into the antiserum, held at the same temperature for the same length of time, then diluted and plated to insure that the antiserum is really inactivating the required proportion of free phage. The number of infected bacteria at each time interval is then subtracted from the total phage input in the adsorption tube to give the amount of unadsorbed phage remaining. The log per cent unadsorbed phage is then plotted against time and the slope used to calculate K as above.

This method is good for following the reaction from about 1 to 90 per cent adsorption of the phage, the principal limitation being the ability of the antiserum to neutralize a high enough proportion of the free phage in the time allowed.

This method can be combined with method 1 to give directly at the same moment the number of free phage particles and the number of infected bacteria in the adsorption tube. Obviously the sum of the free phage and the infected bacteria should equal the total phage input if the procedure is valid. In fact, this method may be used to demonstrate that antivirus serum has no neutralizing effect on virus once it has become adsorbed to the host cell.

3. Determination of Proportion of Surviving Bacteria

The distribution of phage particles among the various bacteria in the adsorption mixture follows closely the Poisson distribution provided the multiplicity of infection is less than 2. *Multiplicity of infection* is defined as the average number n of phage particles adsorbed/bacterium in the adsorption mixture. The general Poisson formula is

$$P(r) = \frac{n^r}{r!} e^{-n}$$

in which $P(r)$ = the proportion of bacteria adsorbing r phage particles, and n = multiplicity of infection as defined above. The only $P(r)$ which can be determined experimentally is $P(0)$, which is the proportion of bacteria which adsorb no phage particles, since these bacteria are capable of forming colonies when plated on agar. For $P(0)$ the Poisson formula simplifies to

$$P(0) = e^{-n}$$

so that n, the average multiplicity of infection, can be calculated directly from the proportion of noninfected bacteria in the adsorption mixture. The number of phage particles adsorbed is equal to $n \times B$, where B is the total number of bacteria in the adsorption tube. The number of phage particles adsorbed divided by the total phage input gives the proportion of phage particles adsorbed from which the rate of adsorption can be calculated.

Example: A bacterial culture of about 5×10^7 cells/ml. is brought to $37°$ C. and a sample taken for accurate assay.   Coliphage T2 is added to a final concentration of 5×10^7 particles/ml. and well mixed.   After 5 min. adsorption a sample is taken and diluted 1:100 in the same medium to stop further adsorption.   It is then further diluted so that a 0.1 ml. sample would be expected to contain between 50 and 200 surviving bacteria, in this instance a total dilution of 10^{-4}.   Several 0.1 ml. samples of the 10^{-4} dilution are then spread on the surface of agar plates with a glass spreader.   The agar plates should be just previously spread with sufficient anti-T2 serum so that infected bacteria plated with an excess of uninfected bacteria do not form plaques.   This is to prevent free phage and phage liberated from lysing bacteria from attacking the noninfected bacteria.   The amount of antiserum to use per plate must be found by trial.   The plates spread with the diluted adsorption mixture and antiserum are then incubated and the colonies counted.   By this technique the adsorption can be followed right up to the end of the latent period of phage growth.   In this experiment, average colony count on the plates was 225, corresponding to a survival of 2.25×10^7 bacteria/ml. in the adsorption tube after 5 min. of adsorption.   Input of bacteria was 5.0×10^7 and the proportion not infected, $P(0) = 2.25/5.0 = 0.45 = e^{-n}$.   The corresponding value for n, the multiplicity of infection, is 0.8.   The number of phage particles adsorbed is then $5 \times 10^7 \times 0.8 = 4 \times 10^7$/ml.   Phage input in the adsorption tube was 5×10^7/ml.; hence the per cent adsorption in 5 min. at $37°$ C. was 80.

Tables of values of e^{-x} for various values of x are available in handbooks of physics and chemistry, or the values can be calculated by use of log tables and the value of e which is 2.718. . . .

In the spreading technique the agar plates should be dried by pre-incubation overnight so that the sample will be rapidly adsorbed and not remain as fluid pools on the agar surface.

If the adsorption period is long and the rate of adsorption slow the initial bacterial concentration cannot be used in the calculations since the bacterial count is increasing exponentially, doubling in 1 generation time, which is about 20 min for $E.$ $coli$ in broth at 37 °C., so that the count of surviving bacteria will be too high with respect to the initial bacterial assay. The simplest way to avoid this problem with slowly adsorbing phages is to increase phage input so that a reasonable proportion of the bacterial population, about 50 per cent, will be infected in 5–10 min. If less than 20 per cent of the bacteria are infected during $1/2$ generation time, the method is not usable. The method cannot be used with a multiplicity of infection higher than 2 because the Poisson distribution is no longer applicable without correction. The reason for this is that the derivation of the Poisson distribution assumes complete uniformity in the bacterial population with respect to the probability of adsorption. Actually the probability of adsorption of a phage particle to a bacterium is a function of the bacterial surface area, and this is certainly not uniform in bacterial populations. This introduces little error at low multiplicities of infection, but at multiplicities higher than 2 the error begins to exceed the experimental error of plating and leads to low values for n. A method has been worked out by Dulbecco (1949a) for correcting this discrepancy by measuring the size distribution of bacteria in the population and appropriately altering the formula for the distribution. The method is not included here since it is unlikely that one would have to use multiplicities above 2 to determine adsorption rates.

Use of the proportion of surviving bacteria to calculate adsorption rates of phage to bacteria is possible in certain instances in which the first 2 methods given are inapplicable. Phage treated with ultraviolet irradiation is "killed," i.e., unable to reproduce itself, and hence no longer produces plaques when plated with a susceptible host. However, Luria and Delbrück (1942) found that T2 killed in this manner retains its ability to become adsorbed to the host cell and that this adsorption results in death of the host cell. It is possible then to determine the rate of adsorption of such ultraviolet-inactivated phages by this technique when it could not be determined otherwise. The method has been extensively used by Luria (1947) in investigating the conditions necessary for "reactivation" of ultraviolet-inactivated phage (see p. 514).

. . . . .

The Single-Step Growth Curve

One of the most important contributions to phage research in recent years was the development of the one-step growth experiment by Ellis and Delbrück (1939). This technique was designed to determine quantitatively 2 important characteristics of the virus—the latent period of intracellular virus growth and the burst size. The *latent period* is the minimum length of time from adsorption of virus to host cell to lysis of the host cell and release of the progeny of the infecting virus particle. *Burst size* is the average yield of virus particles per infected host cell. Each of these characteristics of the virus can be determined independently by other methods to be described later, but the single-step growth method enables one to determine both in 1 experiment with a minimum of effort. The technique is extremely adaptable, permitting the experimenter to alter the physical and biochemical environment of the host cell at will to see what effect these changes will have on the course of the infection. In particular, the method should prove useful in studying the mode of action of chemotherapeutic agents against virus infections.

The method has been used to compare the effects of *single* infection with 1 virus particle per host cell with those of *multiple* infection with 2 or more virus particles per cell (Delbrück and Luria, 1942). It has also been used in determining the result of *mixed* infection in which bacterial cells are simultaneously infected with 2 different kinds of virus (Delbrück and Luria, 1942).

Procedure. Details of a typical one-step growth experiment will be given, followed by a discussion of the results. The virus used will be coliphage T2 and the host cell, strain B of *E. coli* grown in broth. The medium used throughout will be broth. The number of infected bacteria will be determined by neutralization of unadsorbed phage with anti-T2 serum, followed by plating of a suitable dilution for plaque count. The infection will be *single*, i.e., multiplicity about 0.1. All platings for phage assay will be by the agar layer technique. It is already known from other experiments that with strain B of *E. coli* grown in broth at 37 °C., about 80 per cent of a given sample of phage T2 will be adsorbed in 5 min.; also that with the sample of anti-T2 serum available a dilution of 1:50 will neutralize about 95 per cent of a sample of free phage in 5 min. It has been found from a preliminary trial experiment that the *latent period* for T2 with B grown in broth at 37 °C. is between 20 and 25 min. and that *burst size* is about 100. This experiment is designed to determine these characteristics more precisely.

a. Reagents. 1. Culture of strain B grown in broth with active aeration to a concentration of 5×10^7 cells/ml.

2. Stock of T2 phage diluted in broth to a concentration of 5×10^7 particles/ml.

3. Anti-T2 serum diluted 1:50 in broth.

4. Nutrient broth for dilution of the infected culture. These reagents are accurately dispensed in test tubes according to the protocol and brought to 37 °C. before the start of the experiment so that there will be no effect of temperature variations on bacterial metabolism.

b. Other materials. Tubes containing 2.5 ml. each of 0.7 per cent melted agar inoculated with strain B for the agar layer technique; agar plates, and 0.1 ml. pipets.

c.   Protocol

Time, min.	Tube	Procedure	Expected no. of infected bacteria/ml.
0	1. Adsorption	Add 0.1 ml. of T2 to 0.9 ml. B culture	4×10^6
5	2. Serum	Add 0.1 ml. of #1 to 0.9 ml. serum	4×10^5
10	3. Dilution	Add 0.1 ml. of #2 to 0.9 ml. broth	4×10^4
11	4. F.G.T.[a]	Add 0.1 ml. of #3 to 3.9 ml. broth	10^3
12	5. S.G.T.[b]	Add 0.1 ml. of #4 to 9.9 ml. broth	10

[a] First Growth Tube.
[b] Second Growth Tube.

At 2 min. intervals 0.1 ml. samples from tubes 4 and 5 are plated by the agar layer technique.   After incubation at 37 °C. overnight the plaques are counted.

d. Results.   It is apparent from Table **XXIII** that the plaque counts from the First Growth Tube (F.G.T.) are constant through 21 min. but increase suddenly by 23 min. so the end of the latent period comes between 21 and 23 min.   The counts from the Second Growth Tube (S.G.T.) increase steadily through about 32 min. and remain constant from then on.   Average count during the latent period is 102 which, multiplied by the dilution factor of 4×10^4, indicates 4.1×10^6 infected bacteria/ ml. of the adsorption tube.   The multiplicity of infection is 0.08 and the per cent adsorption in 5 min. is 82.

Average count after bacterial lysis is completed is 111 which multiplied by the dilution factor of 10^2 in going from F.G.T. to S.G.T., gives a count of 11,100 in terms of the F.G.T.   Average burst size is then $11,100/102 = 109$.   Total time interval from the end of the latent period to the completion of bacterial lysis is called the *rise* period, in this case about 10 min.

[Results of a similar experiment are expressed graphically in the control curve of Fig. 4 (p. 172). Phage assays] are plotted

TABLE XXIII
Plaque Counts on Plates from First and Second Growth Tubes

Time, min.	F.G.T.	S.G.T.
15	98	
17	105	
19	93	
20		0
21	110	
22		72
23	520	
24		38
25	About 4000	
26		52
28		78
30		92
32		110
34		123
36		114
40		98
50		107
60		115

against the time after initiation of adsorption. The latent period, rise period and final stationary period are clearly evident, as is burst size.

Discussion

This experiment was designed for a one-step growth curve under conditons of *single* infection; i.e., the proportion of bacteria infected with 2 or more phage particles is small. The input ratio of phage to bacteria was 0.1, and with 80 per cent adsorption the multiplicity of infection was 0.08. Since the distribution of phage particles among the bacterial population follows the Poisson formula (p. 470), the proportion of bacteria not infected at all is 0.923, the proportion infected with 1 phage particle is 0.074, and the proportion infected with 2 or more phage particles is the remainder, or 0.003. Hence the proportion of infected bacteria that are multiply infected is $0.003/0.074 = 4$ per cent. To increase the proportion of multiply infected bacteria, one simply increases the multiplicity of infection by increasing the input ratio. At a multiplicity of 2.3, about 10 per cent of the bacteria are not infected, about 23 per cent are singly infected and the remainder are multiply infected. At a multiplicity of 5, essentially all the bacteria are infected and the proportion of singly infected bacteria is only 3 per cent.

The adsorption period of 5 min. was selected only for convenience. The input ratio was selected to give the desired multiplicity of infection on the basis of the known adsorption rate of phage T2. With a slowly adsorbing phage such as T5 one would have to increase either input ratio or adsorption time to reach the same multiplicity of infection. The adsorption time is limited by the necessity of completing the dilutions before the end of the latent period. Also, a prolonged adsorption time means that initiation of infection in the population is spread over a considerable period and hence that the rise period is also prolonged. If it is desired, for instance, to infect at nearly the same time all the bacteria which are to be infected, the adsorption period should be shortened to 1 min. and the input ratio correspondingly greatly increased.

Dilution of the adsorption mixture 1:10 into the serum tube has 2 purposes. (1) The relative adsorption rate of the phage is decreased to 1:10 because the bacterial concentration is decreased by this factor, while the absolute adsorption rate is reduced to 1:100. (2) The antiserum present rapidly decreases the amount of free phage remaining, thus effectively halting adsorption. In the case of high input ratios and short adsorption periods where it is desired to halt adsorption sharply, dilution should be 1:100.

Since the period of contact with the antiphage serum is designed to inactivate essentially all of the free phage, the plating of an appropriate dilution of this tube gives directly the number of infected bacteria in the adsorption tube. If the total bacterial concentration in the adsorption tube is known from accurate assay just prior to infection, the proportion of the bacterial population which is infected is known and from this the multiplicity of infection can be calculated by use of the Poisson formula. With high multiplicities of infection essentially all the bacteria are infected, and the number of infected bacteria as determined by plaque count are the same as the bacterial assay before infection.

If it is desirable to avoid use of serum in the one-step growth experiment, e.g., in a nutrition study, the adsorption tube can be diluted 1:100 in the growth medium to stop adsorption and F.G.T. and S.G.T. prepared from this dilution. In this instance the number of infected bacteria can be determined by a separate dilution into antiserum followed by plaque assay. This experiment differs from the foregoing in that all plates from F.G.T. and S.G.T. will have some plaques owing to input phage which never became adsorbed, in addition to the plaques caused by infected bacteria. That is, the plates made during the latent period will record total *infective centers*, or free phage plus infected bacteria. In most instances it is not possible to distinguish on the plate the plaques caused by infected bacteria from the plaques caused by free phage. However, the plates made from dilutions of the serum tube will give the number of infected bacteria, and the difference between the total infective centers and the infected bacteria will give the free phage.

The free phage can also be determined directly by centrifugation of a sample of the dilution tube, followed by assay of the supernatant fluid for free phage (described on p. 467). In the case of multiplicities of infection of 0.1 or less, the sum of the free phage and the infected bacteria, i.e., total infective centers, will equal the phage input, since the proportion of multiply infected bacteria is small. However, with higher multiplicities of infection, the proportion of multiply infected bacteria increases and the total of infective centers becomes considerably less than the phage input.

This point is illustrated in the following example in which the results of plaque counts are recalculated in terms of concentrations in the adsorption tube.

Example: Concentration of strain B in the adsorption tube was 5×10^7/ml. Phage input resulted in an initial concentration of T2 in the adsorption tube of 20×10^7/ml., or an input ratio of 4 T2:B. Adsorption was for 5 min. at 37° C. The total infective centers as determined by assay of the adsorption tube at the end of adsorption period was 9×10^7/ml. The number of infected bacteria as determined by assay of the serum tube was 5×10^7, which agrees with the input of bacteria, as it should with such a high multiplicity of infection. Free phage is then the difference: total infective centers, 9×10^7, less infected bacteria, 5×10^7, equals free phage, 4×10^7. Direct determination of free phage in the supernatant of a centrifuge tube from a dilution of the adsorption tube gave 4×10^7, agreeing with the calculated value of free phage. Total phage input, 20×10^7, minus the unadsorbed phage, 4×10^7, equals adsorbed phage, 16×10^7. Since the 16×10^7 phage particles were actually adsorbed on 5×10^7 bacteria, average multiplicity of infection was $16/5 = 3.2$ phage particles per bacterium.

Since 16×10^7 phage particles of a total of 20×10^7 were actually adsorbed, per cent adsorption was $16/20 \times 100 = 80$ per cent during the 5 min. adsorption period. By means of the Poisson formula, the proportion of bacteria not infected for a multiplicity of 3.2 is $P(0) = e^{-n} = e^{-3.2} = 0.041$, which means that 4 per cent of the bacteria should not have been infected. Hence the count of infected bacteria as determined by assay of the serum tube should have been 4 per cent less than the assay of the bacterial input. This difference is within the experimental errors of the assays and was not detected.

The actual number of uninfected bacteria could be determined by plating an appropriate dilution of the serum tube by the spreading technique on an agar plate coated with anti-T2 serum (described in method 3, p. 470) and counting the bacterial colonies. The actual number as determined by this method will be slightly higher than that calculated on the basis of the Poisson formula for the reason discussed on p. 472.

The *dilution factor* in going from the adsorption tube to F.G.T. is chosen so that a reasonable number of plaques, usually 100–200, will be present on the plates during the latent period. The dilution factor in going from F.G.T. to S.G.T. is chosen on the basis of the expected increase in plaque count at the end of the rise period so that the plates from S.G.T. will also contain 100–200 plaques. Considerable latitude in this respect can be obtained by varying the volume of the sample taken from F.G.T. and S.G.T. for plating. When the agar layer technique is used, the sample volume can be varied from 0.05–0.5 ml. without difficulty.

Another consideration in choosing the dilution factor in going from F.G.T. to S.G.T. is the *sampling error*. In the protocol (p. 475) the 0.1 ml. sample from F.G.T. used in preparing S.G.T. contained only 100 infected bacteria. A sample of this size has an expected sampling error of 10 per cent and a possible error of much more so that the burst size determination is subject to at least this error from this cause alone. A larger sample from F.G.T. would decrease this source of error, and the only change involved would be a larger total volume in S.G.T. to keep the dilution factor constant.

Over-all dilution in going from the adsorption tube to S.G.T. is usually of the order of 10^{-5}–10^{-7}. This is very important in the one-step growth experiment in that it essentially prevents readsorption of liberated phage onto surviving bacteria and so enables one to reach a true stationary period in the curve. However, the surviving bacteria continue to grow, increasing by about a factor of 10 every hour, so that the probability of a phage particle adsorbing to a bacterium is also increasing. If the one-step growth experiment is continued for several hours there will be a steady increase in the phage assays which will finally cease only when all susceptible bacteria are lysed. If this type of experiment is carried out at higher concentrations of bacteria but low concentrations of virus, so that the virus released from the first step is readsorbed, it is possible to get a series of steps which become less pronounced and finally become just a smoothly rising curve of phage activity (Ellis and Delbrück, 1939).

An interesting point is demonstrated by the 22 min. sample from S.G.T. This particular plate had 72 plaques, when, judging from F.G.T. samples, it should have had between 1 and 5 plaques. The reason for this high plaque count is that the 0.1 ml. sample withdrawn from S.G.T. contained an infected bacterium which burst and released some 70 phage particles during the procedure of sampling. These 70 phage particles should have been distributed uniformly through the 10 ml. volume of S.G.T., thus actually contributing in the neighborhood of 1 plaque to the 22 min. sample. Owing to the timing of the burst, all 70 particles were contributed to this 1 sample. For this reason any point along the *rise* portion of the single step curve may lie well above the curve. Since there is no compensating error which may lead to correspondingly low counts, these high points must be disregarded in drawing the curve. This is particularly important near the end of the rise period or the early stationary period where a belated burst in the sampling pipet may give an abnormally high plaque count. If this is included in the average value used to calculate the burst size, it may lead to significant error. In the instance cited all 70 plaques were released from the bacterium and dispersed within 30 sec., the time required to withdraw a sample and pour a plate by the agar layer method. This certainly would appear to indicate that the phage is released suddenly by disintegration of the host cell rather than gradually by a process of secretion.

Up to this point it has been assumed in the discussion that release of phage from a bacterium is the result of lysis of the host cell. The fact that in the one-step growth curve the release of phage is not instantaneous but occurs over a period of time, the *rise* period, has been ascribed to the infected bacteria lysing over a period of time rather than simultaneously. There is direct evidence on this point obtained by other methods.

Lysis

1. Direct observation under the miscroscope. An adsorption tube is set up in the usual way with an actively growing culture of bacteria and an input of phage such that multiplicity is about 3, so that nearly all the bacteria will beco ιe infected. The depression of a hollow ground microscope slide is filled with melted 1.5 per cent agar so that a slightly convex agar surface projects above the level of the slide. The rim of the depression is heavily coated with petrolatum. Well before the end of the latent period a loopful of the adsorption mixture is placed on the surface of the hardened agar. After a wait of a few minutes for the broth to be soaked up by the agar, a cover glass is placed in contact with the agar and sealed with petrolatum. This preparation is placed on a warm stage microscope so that incubation of the culture can continue at 37 °C. The bacteria are now observed under the high power or oil immersion lens and a suitable field containing 50–100 bacteria is selected. A map is drawn of this field. This should be completed before the end of the latent period. Then the bacteria are examined at regular intervals. When a bacterium lyses, its image fades out during a minute or so. The time of lysis is then recorded on the map. After lysis of the bacteria has ceased a curve can be drawn of the number of surviving bacteria as a function of time since the initiation of infection. This curve will be the reciprocal of the one-step growth curve for the same phage at the same temperature, indicating that the lysis of bacteria coincides with the liberation of phage. If a warm stage microscope is not available, the entire experiment can be carried out at the temperature of the room and a one-step growth experiment run at the same temperature. Temperature control is important since the temperature coefficient of the latent period is of the same order of magnitude as the temperature coefficient of the bacterial generation time. In the case of a coli phage, both the generation time of the host cell and latent period of the phage doubled when the temperature was decreased from 37 to 25 °C. (Ellis and Delbrück, 1939).

2. Observation by turbidimetric measurements. The measurement of bacterial concentrations by the decrease in light transmission is quite precise but not very sensitive since the minimal concentration which can be measured with any accuracy with a photoelectric colorimeter is about 10^8 bacteria/ml. Photoelectric measurement of the intensity of scattered light in a nephelometer is far more sensitive, enabling accurate estimation of bacterial concentration over the range from 5 ×

10^6 to 10^9/ml. A nephelometer described by Underwood and Doermann (1947) has been used by Doermann (1948a) to follow the course of lysis of bacteria infected with phages. The instrument can be placed in an incubator and a bacterial culture can be grown with aeration in the nephelometer tube so that the culture is under continuous observation. The light scattering of such a culture increases exponentially at the same rate as the bacterial population as determined by plate counts. When such a culture is infected with a sufficient multiplicity of phage that all bacteria are infected within 1–2 min., the turbidity remains essentially constant from the moment of infection to the end of the latent period, indicating that bacterial growth ceases immediately on infection. At the end of the latent period, turbidity rapidly decreases, and simultaneously there is rapid increase in phage titer. These experiments demonstrate that the initiation of lysis as observed by nephelometric measurements in concentrated bacterial cultures occurs after the same latent period as the liberation of virus in F.G.T. and S.G.T. of the one-step growth curve. The evidence indicates that bacterial lysis is coincident with phage liberation. This is also indicated by electron microscope photographs of bursting bacteria caught in the act of spilling out phage particles through a gap in the bacterial membrane (Luria, Delbrück, and Anderson, 1943).

[Adsorption of Phage Without Phage Development

In many types of experiments it is essential that phage growth start almost simultaneously in all of the infected bacteria. This can be accomplished because phage will adsorb to bacteria in media in which phage growth is not possible. Two such methods are given below. (1) Broth-grown bacteria are washed by centrifugation and resuspended in buffered-saline (0.067 M phosphate pH 7.0, 0.1 M NaCl, 0.001 M MgSO$_4$, and gelatin at 20 μg./ml.). Adsorption is allowed to proceed in this environment. The infected bacteria are then centrifuged and resuspended in prewarmed broth. Phage development will proceed from the time of the resuspension. Benzer (1952) has modified this procedure by starving the washed bacteria by incubating them with aeration for one hour before adding the phage. This procedure while ensuring greater precision in the initiation of phage development may also give rise to many abortive infections. (2) The second procedure which was developed by Benzer and Jacob (1953) is even simpler and more useful. Broth-grown bacteria are reversibly poisoned by the addition of KCN (final concentration 0.01 M). After 2 min. have elapsed, the phage is added and adsorption proceeds. The infected bacteria can be safely kept in this manner for periods up to an hour. To initiate phage development the infected bacteria are either diluted a factor of 100 into growth medium or centrifuged and resuspended in growth medium. This technique combined with the chloroform technique for measuring free phage (unadsorbed) makes for a simple method for measuring the rate of phage adsorption.]

Investigations of Chemical Action on Virus Growth

In the one-step growth experiment the adsorption of virus to bacterium is usually carried out under conditions such that the concentration of infected bacteria is between 10^7 and 10^8 cells/ml. This suspension is then diluted during the latent period so that the concentration of infected bacteria in S.G.T. is about 10 cells/ml. This dilution factor of 10^{-6}–10^{-7} permits the addition and removal by dilution of several reagents in succession at definite time intervals during the latent period, permitting great flexibility in the design of experiments.

An obvious example of this is the use of antiphage serum in the one-step growth curve. The adsorption mixture is diluted in antiserum to stop adsorption and neutralize free phage. After sufficient contact with antiserum the suspension of infected bacteria is further diluted to such an extent that the antiserum will have no effect on the phage liberated from lysing bacteria in F.G.T. and S.G.T.

This technique was used by Cohen and Fowler (1947) to

study effects of the antimetabolite, 5-methyltryptophan (5-MT), on phage-infected *E. coli*. The suspension of infected bacteria can be diluted into 5-MT at any time during the latent period, and the action of the inhibitor can be stopped at any subsequent time by further dilution into tryptophan which overcomes the inhibition. As long as 5-MT is present in the growth medium, phage is not liberated from infected bacteria. In fact there is progressive loss of plaque-forming ability of infected bacteria on incubation with the inhibitor. It is a rather general observation that interference with phage synthesis in infected bacteria during the early portion of the latent period results in gradual irreversible inactivation of infected bacteria. This has been found when the interfering agent is 5-MT, KCN (Doermann, 1948a), proflavine (Foster, 1948), and citrate in the case of T5 (Adams, 1949b).

Cohen also found that the *latent* period measured from the time of dilution of 5-MT-inhibited, infected bacteria into tryptophan was the same as it would have been had no inhibitor been used. The time of contact with 5-MT is a hiatus in the latent period.

Similar results were noted by Fowler and Cohen (1948) when methionine sulfoxide was the antimetabolite and inhibition was reversed by dilution into glutamic acid. This method has been extensively used by Foster (1948) in investigation of the inhibitory effect of proflavine on phage multiplication.

The potentialities of the one-step growth method in studying the effects of inhibitors, nutrients, salts and other chemical agents on the multiplication of bacterial viruses have scarcely been realized.

Single-Cell Method of Studying Virus Multiplication

This method consists essentially in diluting a suspension of infected bacteria to the point that small samples of the dilution contain no more than 1 infected bacterium. These samples are incubated until all bacteria have burst, then the samples are plated to determine the phage yield of the single infected bacteria.   The method was originally used by Burnet (1929a) to determine the phage yield from single cells.   Delbrück (1945c) used it in analysis of the phage yields of bacteria simultaneously infected with 2 different types of phage.   This technique is very useful in study of the genetics of bacterial viruses (see pp. 501 ff.).

The distribution of particles among a number of samples follows the Poisson formula if the average number of particles per sample is of the order of 10 or less.   The Poisson formula is

$$P(r) \; = \; \frac{n^r e^{-n}}{r\,!}$$

in which $P(r)$ is the proportion of samples containing r particles when the average number of particles per sample is n.   For the single-cell method the value of n should be made so low that the proportion of samples containing 2 or more infected bacteria will be small in relation to the proportion containing 1.   Usually the value of n is made about 0.3–0.4.   A sample experiment is described to illustrate the principle.

Procedure.   Coliphage T2 will be used to infect a broth-grown culture of *E. coli* at an input ratio such that essentially all bacteria will be infected during a 5 min. adsorption period.   The free phage will be neutralized by antiserum.   The infected bacteria will be about 0.6 bacterium/ml.   This dilution will be distributed into 50 samples of 0.5 ml. each.   After incubation until all bursts have occurred the samples will be plated by the agar layer method.

The adsorption rate for T2 is known to be about 80 per cent in 5 min. at 37 °C. for strain B grown in broth to a concentration of 5×10^7 /ml.   An input ratio of 4 T2/B would then result in an adsorption of $4 \times 0.8 = 3.2$ T2/B in 5 min.   The proportion of uninfected bacteria would be equal to $e^{-3.2} = 4$ per cent, or 96 per cent of the bacteria would be infected.   The concentration of unadsorbed phage in the adsorption tube would be $0.8 \times 5 \times 10^7 = 4 \times 10^7$ ml., which means less than 1 free phage particle/bacterium.   This would be negligible in comparison with the average burst size of the infected bacteria; however, it would mean that a few plates would have 1 or 2 plaques due to free phage particles This can be prevented by diluting the adsorption tube into diluted anti-T2 serum at a concentration which would neutralize 90 per cent of the free phage in 5 min. Then essentially all plaques on the plates would represent phage liberated from infected bacteria.

a. Reagents. 1. Culture of strain B grown with aeration in broth to 5×10^7 cells/ml.

2. Stock of T2 phage diluted in broth to 2×10^9 /ml.

3. Anti-T2 serum diluted 1:50 in broth.

All reagents are to be prewarmed to 37 °C.

b. Protocol.

Time, min.	Tube	Procedure	Expected no. of infected bacteria/ml.
0	1. Adsorption	Add 0.1 ml. of T2 to 0.9 ml. B culture	5×10^7
5	2. Serum	Add 0.1 ml. of #1 to 0.9 ml. serum	5×10^6
10	3. Dilution	Add 0.1 ml. of #2 to 9.9 ml. broth	5×10^4
10.5	4. Dilution	Add 0.1 ml. of #3 to 9.9 ml. broth	5×10^2
11	5. Sample flask	Add 0.1 ml. of #4 to 70 ml. broth	0.71

The broth suspension containing about 0.7 bacterium/ml. is distributed in 0.5 ml. samples into 50 tubes; distribution must be completed before the end of the latent period. The samples and remainder of the suspension in the sample flask are incubated at 37 °C. until well after the end of the *rise* period to insure that all bursts have taken place; in the case of T2 for 40–50 min. from the beginning of the adsorption. A flask of 0.7 per cent agar is melted in a boiling water bath and cooled to 45 °C., then inoculated with plating bacteria washed from the surface of a slant with a few milliliters of broth. With a warmed pipet, 2.5 ml. of inoculated 0.7 per cent agar is added to a sample tube and the contents immediately poured over the surface of an agar plate. The plate is rocked gently for a few seconds to mix the sample with the agar and to insure uniform layering of the agar. Several 0.5 ml. samples from the sample flask containing the remainder of the diluted suspension are also plated to determine average burst size in the suspension.

c. Results. Of the 50 plates, 35 had no plaques, and 15 plates had a total of 1750 plaques, individual plate counts being

8	26	79	123	210
13	43	104	149	261
20	71	121	203	319

Average plaque count on the plates made from the sample flask after the rise period was 39.

d. Calculations. Thirty-five of 50 plates had no plaques, hence no infected bacteria. $P(0) = 35/50 = 0.7 = e^{-n} = e^{-0.35}$, so the average number of infected bacteria/sample was 0.35 and the average number/ml. of the sample flask was 0.7. The dilution factor in going from the adsorption tube to the sample flask was 7×10^7, so the number of infected bacteria in the adsorption tube was 4.9×10^7, thus agreeing closely with the bacterial assay before infection. This could also be checked by plating 0.1 ml. of dilution tube #4 by the agar layer technique before the end of the latent period to determine the actual number of infected bacteria present.

If 50 samples contain an average of 0.35 infected bacteria/ sample, the total number of infected bacteria in the 50 samples should have been $50 \times 0.35 = 17.5$ bacteria. However, only 15 plates had plaques. This must mean that 2 or 3 of the plates had phage yields coming from 2 infected bacteria. The expected distribution calculated from the Poisson formula is

$P(0) = e^{-0.35} = 0.7$, or *35* plates out of 50 with no infected bacteria

$P(1) = \dfrac{0.35^1 \times e^{-0.35}}{1} = 0.245$, or *12* plates out of 50 with *1* infected bacterium

$$P(2) = \frac{0.35^2 \times e^{-0.35}}{2 \times 1} = 0.04,\ \text{or}\ 2\ \text{plates out of 50 with 2 infected}$$
bacteria

$$P(3) = \frac{0.35^3 \times e^{-0.35}}{3 \times 2 \times 1} = 0.005,\ \text{or no plates in 50 with 3 infected}$$
bacteria

Presumably the actual distribution was 13 plates with 1 infected bacterium and 2 plates with 2 each, or 17 infected bacteria in all. These produced a total of 1750 plaques, or an average burst size of $1750/17 = 103$ phage particles/bacterium.

Average plaque count/0.5 ml. sample taken from the sample flask after the end of the rise period was 39, which amounts to an average burst size of the bacteria in the sample flask of $39/0.35 = 111$.

e. Discussion. It must be remembered that in this case the average burst size from the single cell bursts is calculated on but 17 bacteria and from the average in the sample flask from about 32 bacteria, so that neither figure is a reliable estimate of average burst size. This is particularly true since there is such a wide distribution in individual burst sizes, which range from 8 to 319 in the foregoing example. Of course, 2 of the plates contain phage yields from 2 infected bacteria each, but it is impossible to tell *which* plates are involved and there is certainly no a priori reason for suggesting that these are the plates with the highest yields. This broad range in individual burst sizes is the interesting fact brought out by this experiment and one which could hardly be demonstrated in any other way. There is no adequate explanation for this extreme range in burst sizes, but it can hardly be correlated in any simple way with the size of the host cell, since Delbrück found that the spread of burst sizes is much greater than the spread of cell sizes (Delbrück, 1945a). Also, he found that the distribution of burst sizes was not dependent on whether the samples were plated early or late during the *rise* period (Ellis and Delbrück, 1939); i.e., the burst size of a bacterium was not a function of the *latent* period for that particular bacterium.

The only technical difficulty in carrying out such an experiment is the distribution of the large number of accurately measured samples into tubes within the *latent* period. This sampling is greatly facilitated by an automatic pipetting machine, a number of which are on the market. One very convenient device is the Cornwall Pipetting Unit* with which one person can easily distribute 200 samples in 5 min.

Host Cell Mutation to Resistance to Virus Attack

If 10 ml. of a broth culture of strain B of *E. coli* is grown to a concentration of 10^8 cells/ml. and is then inoculated with coli phage T6 to a concentration of 10^8 particles/ml., the culture will clear in a few hours owing to lysis of the susceptible bacteria. However, if the culture is further incubated overnight it will again become turbid owing to growth of phage-resistant variants of strain B.

Isolation of Phage-Resistant Mutants

A phage-resistant mutant can usually be isolated by simply spreading a mixture of host cells and virus on an agar plate, incubating and picking surviving colonies.

Example: One ml. of a bacterial culture containing 2×10^8 cells/ml. is mixed with 1 ml. of T6 phage containing 10^{10} particles/ml., or an input ratio of 50:1. After 5 min. incubation all bacteria which can adsorb phage are infected. One-tenth ml. of the adsorption mixture is placed on the surface of an agar plate and spread uniformly with a glass rod until all of the liquid has been adsorbed by the agar. After incubation the colonies are counted and 12 are found. A single isolated colony is picked from this plate, suspended in 1 ml. of broth and a loopful restreaked on another plate. Two repetitions of this procedure should result in a pure strain of the variant which is free from contaminating virus. If this strain is now plated with phage T6 by the agar layer method, no plaques will be produced. Furthermore, phage T6 is not adsorbed to this variant.

* Made by Becton, Dickinson & Co., Rutherford, N. J.

Presumably in this instance resistance is the result of failure to adsorb the phage particles. However, if this variant is used to assay the other phages of the T group and the results are compared with parallel assays on strain B of *E. coli*, the *efficiency of plating* of the other phages is as high on the variant as on B. This variant is then resistant to T6 but susceptible to all the other phages of the group. This property is transmitted unchanged to the descendants of the cell even though the bacteria are cultivated in the absence of virus T6. The variant is a mutant of strain B and is called B/6. Had the mutant been found to be simultaneously resistant to T6 and T1 it would have been called B/6,1. Had the latter mutant been isolated by use of T1 instead of T6 it would have been called B/1,6.

If we have a mixture of equal numbers of phage T2 and phage T6 and plate an appropriate dilution of the mixture on strain B, the plaque count will be the sum of the T2 and T6 plaques; moreover the T2 plaques cannot be distinguished morphologically from the T6 plaques. However, if the mixture is plated on B/6, only the T2 phage will form plaques and be counted. Similarly, plating of the mixture on B/2 will enable one to assay the T6 phages in the mixture. Such phage-resistant mutants are called *indicator strains* since they enable one to assay any phage to which the strain is susceptible in the presence of any phage to which the strain is resistant. Some of the uses to which indicator strains may be put are discussed later.

In the example cited, all 12 colonies on test are found to be B/6 and all identical. In this particular culture of B, the frequency of B/6 mutants in the population was found to be $12/10^7$ cells. A series of samples taken from the same adsorption tube and plated in the same way would have differed from this only by the expected sampling error.

If a sample of less than 10^6 bacteria had been taken from this culture, probably no mutants would have been found, so it is obvious that the sample size is important. If a mutant occurs infrequently, a much larger sample must be taken. The bacterial culture can be concentrated in the centrifuge and the sample can be spread on Petri dishes 1 ft. in diameter, permitting the sample size to be increased to the order of 10^{10} bacteria. If the mutation is so infrequent that one is not likely to find a mutant in 10^{10} cells, the sample size can be further increased by using 10 liters of broth culture in which the total bacterial population is of the order of 10^{13} cells.

If a series of independent cultures of strain B is made, starting with an inoculum of a few hundred cells in each culture so that the probability of a mutant cell being present in the inoculum is negligible and after incubation each of these cultures is assayed for mutants, it is found that the proportion of mutants varies widely from culture to culture. In one experiment (Luria and Delbrück, 1943) the proportion of B/1 mutants varied from $0/10^8$ to $303/10^8$, with average value $30/10^8$. The reason for this high variability in the proportion of mutants present in independent cultures is that the probability of a mutation occurring in a bacterium is the same for each cell division. For mutations which occur early in the growth of a culture, the descendants of the original mutant cell will form a considerable proportion of the population. For mutations which occur late in the growth of the culture, the number of descendant mutants will be small. This variability in the proportion of mutants found in a series of independent cultures has been used by Luria and Delbrück (1934) to calculate the mutation rate of bacteria.

Mutational Pattern of Strain B of E. coli

The mutational pattern of strain B with respect to resistance to the 7 T phages was first worked out by Demerec and Fano (1945) and further amplified by E. H. Anderson (1946) and Luria (1946). Some of the significant properties of the more useful mutants are listed in Table XXIV.

Additional mutations of strain B are discussed in connection with host range mutations of the viruses (p. 501). Most of the mutants listed in Table XXIV are resistant by virtue of the fact that they have lost the ability to adsorb the phages to which they

TABLE XXIV
One-Step Mutants of Strain B of *E. coli*

Mutant	Susceptible to phages	Mutation rate[a]	Generation time (Min.): broth at 37° C.
B/1, tryptophanless	T2,3,4,5,6,7	10^{-8}–10^{-9}	19–20
B/1,5	T2,3,4,6,7	10^{-8}–10^{-9}	19–20
B/2	T1,3,4,5,6,7	10^{-10}	19–20
B/3,4	T1,2,5,6,7	10^{-7}–10^{-8}	25–26
B/3,4,7	T1,2,5,6	10^{-7}–10^{-8}	25–26
B/3,4,7 prolineless	T1,2,5,6	?	?
B/6	T1,2,3,4,5,7	10^{-7}–10^{-8}	19–20

[a] Mutation rate/bacterium/generation.

are resistant.   However, this is not the only mechanism by which bacteria can become resistant. . . .

Strain B of *E. coli* and most of its phage-resistant mutants grow abundantly on a chemically defined medium free from organic compounds other than an energy source such as glucose or lactic acid (p. 446).   However, E. H. Anderson (1946) discovered that B/1 strains were consistently unable to grow in the basal medium but would grow if tryptophan were added; also that certain B/3,4,7 strains were unable to grow unless proline was present.   The significance of this coupling of a nutritional requirement with phage resistance is not clear.

The mutations of strain B are additive; i.e., strain B can mutate to B/1,5, which can mutate to B/1,5/6, etc.   Moreover, the rate of mutation to a given resistance pattern is usually independent of previous mutations.   B/1,5 mutates to B/1,5/6 at the same rate that B mutates to B/6.   Also, the nutritional deficiencies are additive; i.e., B/1,tryptophanless, can mutate to B/1,tryptophanless/3,4,7, prolineless which requires both tryptophan and proline for growth.

The phages of the T group are properly called coli-dysentery phages since they attack various strains of shigella as well as *E. coli*.   Strains of *Shigella flexneri* I-VI, Boyd I-II, *alkalescens*, *ambigua*, *shiga*, and *sonnei* were all susceptible to 1 or more members of the T group and some were susceptible to all 7. The resistance patterns of the shigella strains and their mutants were the same as those of strain B of *E. coli* as far as tested. However, this group of host cells certainly merits more intensive investigation than it has received.

Indicator Strains and Their Properties

An indicator strain is a strain of bacteria which is resistant to 1 type of phage but susceptible to another type, thus enabling the investigator to assay 1 type of virus in mixtures with the other type. The ideal indicator strain must be completely resistant to the 1 virus strain, not merely unable to support plaque formation. For instance, the B/3,4,7,2,6 strain described by Luria (1946) would not be a suitable indicator strain for T1 and T5 in the presence of T2 or T6 because, although the latter viruses do not form plaques, they do kill the bacteria and hence would interfere with the recording of T1 and T5. This point can be checked by assaying low concentrations of the virus to which the indicator is sensitive in the presence of very large amounts of the virus to which it is resistant, and comparing the efficiency of plating relative to the assay on the usual host strain.

The efficiency of plating of the phage on any prospective indicator strain must always be determined, since it is frequently observed that the efficiency of plating is reduced in mutants relative to that in the parent strain. For instance, the efficiency of plating of phage T2 on certain B/3,4,7 strains is only 20 per cent of that on strain B. Relative efficiency of plating can be readily determined by assaying suitable dilutions of the virus in parallel on the indicator strain and the usual host strain. If efficiency of plating is constant and not too low, the indicator strain can still be used with a suitable correction factor. The relative efficiency of plating of infected bacteria is usually higher than that of free phage, so both should be determined. Also, as already mentioned, the efficiency of plating of the phage to be recorded should be determined in the presence of a large excess of the nonrecorded phage to be certain that there is no interference.

Another important characteristic of an indicator strain that must be determined is the generation time. As noted in Table XXIV, the mutants B/3,4 and B/3,4,7 have a much longer generation time than do the other mutants and the parent strain. This means that with these mutants, whether grown in broth or in plates, the turbidity will develop more slowly. To compensate for this slower growth, a larger initial inoculum must be used.

Strain B/3,4,7 is a relatively "rough" strain in comparison with the other mutants, which means that suspensions of this strain in broth tend to agglutinate spontaneously and settle out of solution. Also, when this mutant is grown on a slant, it is difficult to make a uniform suspension because the organisms tend to stick together in clumps. Unless special pains are taken to disperse such a suspension, by repeated blowing of the suspension through a fine orifice such as a pipet tip, plates inoculated with B/3,4,7 by the agar layer method will present a granular and uneven appearance of the bacterial growth. Another method of dispersing this mutant is to wash the growth from the 2 per cent agar slant with broth and aerate the broth suspension for 20 min. at 37° C.

Also, as noted previously, certain phage-resistant mutants lack the ability to synthesize certain amino acids, so that these mutants cannot be used as indicator strains in chemically defined media unless the amino acids concerned are included in the medium. However, this nutritional deficiency in itself lends a certain versatility to the mutant and permits the investigator to interrupt phage synthesis during the *latent* period by simply diluting the infected bacteria in a medium free from the required growth factor.

Plating of Mixed Viruses with Mixed Indicator Strains

This technique has led directly to important discoveries in the field of bacterial viruses. A specific example of the technique will first be described, then 2 applications of the technique will be discussed which have resulted in new principles.

Procedure. A mixture of equal concentrations of phages T1 and

T7 is made and the mixture diluted so that a 0.1 ml. sample will contain about 100 particles of each kind of virus. This mixture of viruses is to be plated by the agar layer technique on strain B, on each indicator strain separately and on a mixture of the 2 indicator strains. Both phage T1 and phage T7 produce large plaques, but the plaque morphologies are distinctive enough so that an experienced observer can usually distinguish them. In the case of other pairs, such as T2 and T6, this is usually not possible. The appropriate indicator strains to use are B/1,5 and B/3,4,7. The efficiency of plating of each phage on the sensitive indicator strain is better than 90 per cent as compared with strain B, even when an excess of the other phage is present. Slants of 2 per cent agar heavily inoculated with B, with B/1,5 or with B/3,4,7 have been incubated overnight. Two ml. of sterile broth is added to each slant, the bacterial growth is rubbed off with the pipet and dispersed by filling the pipet and forcibly blowing out the contents several times. Strains B and B/1,5 are readily suspended, but B/3,4,7 is difficult to disperse and the broth suspension may have to be aerated for 20 min. at 37 °C. The suspension is allowed to stand for 10 min. so that undispersed clumps will settle out. The bacterial suspensions are then removed with pipets and placed in test tubes. Usually the suspensions of strains B and B/1,5 will be much more turbid than the suspension of B/3,4,7. Broth is added to dilute the more concentrated suspensions until the turbidities of the 3 suspensions appear to be about the same. Then 1 part of the suspension of B/1,5 is added to 4 parts of the suspension of B/3,4,7 to give the *mixed indicator*, and the suspensions of B and B/1,5 are diluted 1/5 with broth. The suspension of B/3,4,7 is not diluted. These relative concentrations have been chosen by experience so that the larger inoculum of B/3,4,7 will compensate for its slower growth rate and result in an equal development of turbidity on the plate in 5–6 hr. when the plaques are well developed. With other combinations of indicator strains the proportions to use in mixtures must be found by trial. A flask of 0.7 per cent agar is melted, cooled to 45 °C. and dispensed in 2.5 ml.

amounts in test tubes in the usual way. Two drops of the appropriate bacterial suspension are used to inoculate each tube of agar. Then 0.1 ml. samples of the diluted virus mixture are plated with the following results:

on B	210 clear plaques-T1 + T7
on B/1,5	113 clear plaques-T7 only
on B/3,4,7	107 clear plaques-T1 only
on B/1,5 + B/3,4,7	201 turbid plaques-T1 + T7

The sample plated on B gives the total number of virus particles, and an experienced eye can in most cases allocate each plaque to either T1 or T7. About 10 per cent of the plaques cannot be positively identified. The sample plated on B/1,5 gives only the T7 plaques, and the sample plated on B/3,4,7 gives only the T1 plaques. The sum of the plaques on these 2 plates should equal the total plaque count on B within the sampling error if the efficiency of plating on the indicator strains is 100 per cent. The sample plated on mixed indicator strains should give the same number of plaques as the sample plated on B, but all the plaques will be turbid. A T1 phage particle will lyse strain B/3,4,7 and so produce a plaque, but strain B/1,5 will not be lysed and will grow within the plaque area forming a turbid background which will, however, be less turbid than the area outside the plaque where both indicator strains are growing. Similarly, the T7 plaques will be turbid because of overgrowth by B/3,4,7. However, where a T1 plaque happens to overlap a T7 plaque there will occur a completely clear area because within the area of overlap *both* indicator strains will be lysed.   If when the agar layer hardened a T1 phage particle happened to come to rest very close to a T7 particle, the 2 plaques will be nearly concentric and a completely clear plaque will result. However, the incidence of such clear plaques should be quite small. Also it is usually possible to distinguish the T1 from the T7 plaques on the mixed indicator plates because despite the disproportionate inoculum the B/1,5 strain grows more rapidly and the T1 plaques are more turbid than the T7 plaques. On long incubation the

T1 plaques may not be distinguishable from the background except for the overlaps, so the plates should be examined after 5 or 6 hr. of incubation.   A plate of mixed viruses on mixed indicator strains is illustrated in Fig. 14.

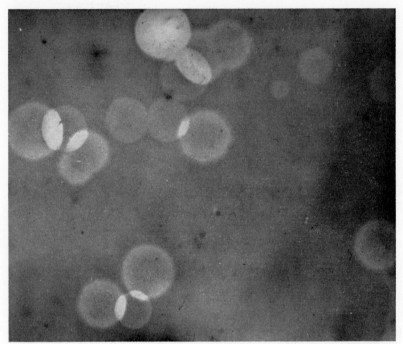

Figure 14. Mixture of phages T1 and T7 plated on mixed indicators B/1,5 and B/3,4,7.   Note the 2 kinds of turbid plaques and clear overlapping areas of complete lysis.   Bright field illumination.

Application.   A most important use of mixed indicator strains is in analysis of the phage yields from mixedly infected bacteria. If a bacterium is mixedly infected with 2 different viruses and then plated on the appropriate mixed indicator strains before the end of the latent period, 2 possible plaque types might be found.   If the infected bacterium liberates *both* kinds of phages, a *clear* plaque will be formed.   This is illustrated in the following examples.

1. Mixed infection of strain B with T1 and T7: Mutual exclusion effect.   The mixed infection experiment was performed to see what would happen when a bacterial cell was simultaneously infected with 2 different viruses (Delbrück, 1945c).   The procedure involved adding a mixture of the 2 viruses to a suspension of bacteria at an input ratio such that after adsorption the average multiplicity of infection would be about 3 for each phage type.   At least 90 per cent of the bacteria would then have adsorbed at least 1 phage particle of each kind and hence would be mixedly infected (p. 479).   At the end of the adsorption period the adsorption mixture was diluted into a mixture of the 2 antisera to stop adsorption and to neutralize unadsorbed phage. After further dilution into F.G.T. the infected bacteria were plated by the agar layer method on strain B, on the separate indicator strains and on mixed indicator strains before the end of the *latent* period.   Also, plates were made from S.G.T. after the end of the *rise* period on the separate indicator strains for determination of burst size.

The number of infected bacteria yielding the 2 types of phage are determined from the plaque counts before the end of the latent period.   Infected bacteria were plated with the following results:

on B   101 plaques (total of T1 and T7 yielders)
on B/1,5   35 plaques (T7 yielders)
on B/3,4,7   70 plaques (T1 yielders)
on mixed indicators   92 turbid plaques (bacteria yielding either T1 *or* T7)
                               3 clear plaques (bacteria yielding both T1 *and* T7)

The sum of the bacteria which liberate T1 and those which liberate T7 equals the total number of infected bacteria when assayed on B, and also is equal to the assay of the bacteria put into the adsorption tube since at a multiplicity of 3 nearly all bacteria are infected.   This result indicates that an infected bacterium liberates either T1 or T7 but not both, within the sampling error, which in this case is about 10 per cent. The plaque count on the mixed indicator plate confirms this, since at the most only 3 of a total of 95 infected bacteria could have liberated both kinds of phage, since only 3 *clear* plaques were found on this plate. These 3 clear plaques might also have been due to accidental overlaps or to a bacterium caught in the act of dividing, 1 member of the pair liberating T1 and the other T7.

In general, when bacteria are mixedly infected with 2 immunologically unrelated phages, they liberate either 1 or the other phage type but not both. This phenomenon has been termed by Delbrück the *mutual exclusion effect.*

The burst size of the mixedly infected bacteria is calculated from plaque counts on the separate indicator plates made from S.G.T. after all bursts have occurred. Burst size is of course calculated on the basis of the number of bacteria which have actually been found to liberate each kind of phage rather than from the total number of infected bacteria; i.e., the total yield of T7 phage divided by the number of infected bacteria which liberate T7 phage gives average burst size of those bacteria which liberate T7. The burst size of mixedly infected bacteria is markedly less than that of bacteria infected with only 1 phage type. This has been termed the *depressor effect* (Delbrück, 1945c).

The average multiplicity of infection for T1 and T7 can be calculated by any of the methods described for the one-step growth experiment (pp. 473 ff.). If the average multiplicity of infection is known for each phage, the proportion of mixedly infected bacteria can be calculated by application of the Poisson distribution. This assumes, of course, that the adsorption of 1 phage particle by a bacterium does not affect the rate of adsorption of another phage particle by that bacterium. This can be readily tested by permitting the bacteria to adsorb T1 phage alone for 5 min. and then adding T7 phage and determining if the rate of adsorption of T7 phage is normal. This is most simply done by centrifuging samples at intervals and plating on B/1,5 so that only the unadsorbed T7 phage in the supernatant is counted.

2. Mixed infection of strain B with even-numbered phages T2, T4, and T6. . . .   When pairs of viruses in the immunologically related group T2, T4, and T6 are investigated, it is found that many mixedly infected bacteria liberate both kinds of phage. When mixedly infected bacteria are plated on mixed indicator strains, from 10 to 90 per cent of the plaques are *clear*.   Also, the sum of the plaques on the separate indicator plates is more than the total number of infected bacteria, indicating that a considerable proportion of infected bacteria liberate both kinds of phage. . . .

Mutations of Bacteriophages

The mutant forms of bacterial viruses are likely to play an important role in the development of our ideas about hereditary mechanisms.   At present, however, only 3 well-defined types of mutations are known among the bacteriophages: (*1*) host range mutations;   (*2*) adsorption cofactor mutations;   (*3*) plaque morphology mutations.   Considerable effort is being expended in an attempt to extend this list of mutant types and to clarify the biochemical basis for the difference between mutant and wild type phage.

1. Host Range Mutations

A host range mutant of a bacterial virus is a variant with an extended host range.   Such variants are usually found as a result of plating a large number of bacteriophage particles with a phage-resistant bacterial mutant and picking an isolated plaque if plaques are produced.   As an example we can take phage T1 and the phage-resistant bacterial mutant B/1,tryptophanless (see p. 493).   If several hundred T1 phage particles are plated with B/1,tr by the agar layer technique no plaques are produced. However, if 10^7 or 10^8 T1 phage particles are plated with B/1,tr a small number of plaques will usually be found.   One of these plaques is stabbed with a sterile platinum wire which is then rinsed in a few milliliters of sterile broth.   This broth will now contain a mixture of the parent T1 phage particles which were originally put on the plate and the new mutant form of T1. Several dilutions of this broth suspension are now plated on B/1,-tr and plaques of the mutant will be produced. Two replatings of this mutant phage in this manner suffice to free it completely from the parent T1 phage since the latter does not multiply on B/1,tr. When the mutant of T1 has been purified a stock may be prepared by growing it on B/1,tr. This stock produces plaques identical in morphology with the parent T1, and there is no detectable difference in immunologic properties between the parent and the mutant. However, the mutant forms plaques on B/1,tr whereas the parent does not. The mutant is called T1h and the parent strain is then called T1h^+ to indicate that it is the wild type with respect to this particular character.

Table XXV shows the host ranges of T1h^+ and T1h and, for comparison, of T5. The host ranges of T1h and T5 are identical, although these phages may be readily distinguished by plaque morphology and by immunologic properties. It is obvious that the host range of a virus is of no value in the primary classification of the virus. However, if the immunologic and morphologic properties are known, the host range is of further value in sub-classification of the virus.

TABLE XXV
Host Ranges of T1h^+, T1h, and T5

When plated on	T1h^+	T1h	T5
B	Plaques	Plaques	Plaques
B/1,tr	No plaques	Plaques	Plaques
B/1,5	No plaques	No plaques	No plaques

If T1h is plated on B/1,tr and the corresponding phage-resistant bacterial mutant isolated as previously described (p. 490), this mutant will be found to be B/1,tr/1,5; i.e., the mutant is resistant to T1h^+, T1h, and T5 and deficient in ability to synthesize tryptophan. No host range mutant of T1 capable of attacking B/1,5 has been found. Similar host range mutants have been found for T2, T3, T4, and T7.   None have been reported for T5 and T6.   Host range mutants in the T group of coliphages have been discussed by Luria (1945a, 1946) and by Hershey (1946b).

Phage stocks, when used for certain purposes, should be relatively free from host range mutants.   For instance, a high proportion of T1h in a stock of T1 phage will interfere with the isolation of the B/1,tr mutant, since this mutant is lysed by T1h.   Also, a high incidence of host range mutants of T2, e.g., in a stock of T2, may interfere with use of the indicator strain B/2 in mixed infection experiments, because a T2h particle will form a plaque on B/2 and may be interpreted as T4 or T6.   The proportion of host range mutants in a stock may be found by assaying appropriate dilutions of the stock on B and on the resistant mutant of B.   It is commonly found that the efficiency of plating of the host range mutant on the phage resistant bacterial mutant is low when compared with assays on strain B.   This must be considered when the host range mutants of the phages themselves are to be studied, in mixed infection experiments, for instance.

2. Adsorption Cofactor Mutations

T. F. Anderson (1945a) discovered that certain stocks of coliphages T4 and T6 required presence in the medium of tryptophan in order that adsorption to the host cell might take place.   Further investigation of this phenomenon disclosed that the tryptophan reacted in a reversible manner with the phage particles to form an "activated complex" which then became capable of adsorption to the host cell.   At concentrations of tryptophan of 0.1 μg./ml. or less there was no detectable activation, whereas at 2 μg./ml., activation of the phage was maximal, all phage particles present being capable of adsorption.   Anderson also was able to demonstrate that his stocks of T4 phage were inhomogeneous with respect to adsorption cofactor requirement (T. F. Anderson, 1948b).   If high concentrations of T4 phage were plated on agar made with a chemically defined medium free of tryptophan a few plaques would be produced.   These plaques gave rise to stocks of T4 which were not cofactor requiring. Stocks of T4 phage prepared from cofactor-requiring plaques retained the cofactor requirement, so that these characteristics were hereditary.

Broth stocks of T4 phage generally contain a mixture of different variants with respect to cofactor requirements. Delbrück (1948) separated these variants from each other by adsorption techniques.

Example: The broth stock was diluted in a tryptophan-free chemically defined medium until the tryptophan concentration was below the threshold for adsorption. Then adsorption of the diluted phage stock with a suspension of B grown in the tryptophan-free medium would remove all non-cofactor-requiring variants. The infected bacteria could be removed by centrifugation and be used to produce a stock lacking a cofactor requirement. L-Tryptophan was then added to the supernatant to a concentration of 4 μg./ml. and a suspension of B grown in tryptophan-free medium added. After sufficient time for adsorption the infected bacteria were removed by centrifugation and a sample of the supernatant plated on nutrient broth agar. Presumably all of the tryptophan-requiring variants should have been removed in this adsorption, yet some phage particles capable of forming plaques on nutrient broth agar remained. One such plaque was picked and used to inoculate a broth culture of B to prepare a stock. This stock gave very low adsorption with tryptophan but high adsorption with broth. Apparently this stock required a cofactor other than tryptophan. Eventually it was found that the adsorption requirement was tryptophan *plus* calcium ion.

This adsorption technique using chemically defined media plus various additions is a good method for separating different cofactor-requiring variants present in a broth stock. A further complication was introduced by Delbrück's (1948) observation that the adsorption of some of the tryptophan-requiring variants was strongly inhibited by *indole*. This inhibition was competitive and the dissociation constant was less for the phage-indole complex. Since *E. coli* rapidly converts tryptophan into indole, this inhibition by indole presents a real difficulty in studying the role of tryptophan in adsorption.

An observation of T. F. Anderson's (1948c) which has greatly simplified study of the cofactor requirement is that a bacterium infected with a cofactor-requiring variant will produce a plaque on a tryptophan-free medium while an unadsorbed phage particle will not. The efficiency of plating of the infected bacterium is enormously higher than that of the free phage particle. The reason for this is not clear, but knowledge of the fact has permitted study of the rate of formation and of decomposition of the tryptophan-phage complex under various conditions (T. F. Anderson, 1948a). This study has been facilitated by Anderson's *"dumping" technique*, a description of which follows.

Procedure. A sample of phage T4 is suspended in a chemically defined medium containing 10 μg./ml. of tryptophan and the mixture incubated until all of the phage has been "activated," i.e., has formed a complex with tryptophan. A 0.1 ml. sample of the activated T4 phage is placed in a large test tube and 10 ml. of a suspension of B in a tryptophan-free medium is dumped in from a second test tube so that the tryptophan is diluted 1 : 100 at the same moment that the bacteria are added. The proportion of T4 phage which is adsorbed onto the bacteria is a function both of the rate of adsorption of activated phage onto bacteria and of the rate of deactivation of phage by dissociation of the phage-tryptophan complex. An estimate of the rate of deactivation is made by dumping in a large volume of tryptophan-free medium at zero time and, after allowing deactivation to proceed for a measured time, dumping in the bacterial suspension and permitting the residual activated phage to adsorb onto bacteria. In all instances the number of infected bacteria is then determined by plating on tryptophan-free medium, on which the infected bacteria produce plaques but the free phage particles do not. Under most conditions the rate of deactivation is more rapid than the rate of adsorption, so that only a fraction of the activated phage-tryptophan complex is registered by this method.

3. Plaque Morphology Mutations

A thoroughly studied plaque morphology mutation occurs in the serologically related family of coliphages T2, T4, and T6.

The mutant is given the symbol r (rapid lysis) and the corresponding wild type is designated r^+, e. g., T2r^+, and T2r. The wild type r^+ particles form small plaques with very turbid halos when plated by the agar layer technique, whereas the mutant r variants form larger plaques with clear halos. Another characteristic distinguishing r^+ from r is the time required for lysis of

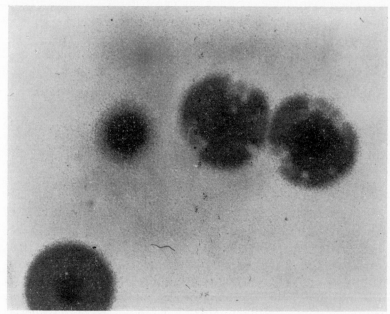

Figure 15. Phage T2, showing 1r^+ plaque, 1r plaque, and 2 *mottled* plaques. Dark field illumination.

visibly turbid cultures.   The *latent* period of phage growth is about 21 min. for members of the T2, T4, T6 family regardless of whether the virus is the r^+ or the r variant. Visibly turbid cultures of bacteria will be lysed by the r mutants between 21 and 30 min. after all the bacteria have been infected.   However, in the case of the r^+ phages, the visibly turbid cultures remain turbid for several hours after all the bacteria have been infected. This phenomenon of *lysis inhibition* was investigated by Doermann (1948), who concluded that when a bacterial cell infected with an r^+ phage was reinfected with a second r^+ phage at least 3 min. after the 1st adsorption, lysis inhibition occurred.   The second infecting particle might be T2r^+, T4r^+, or T6r^+ regardless of the type of the 1st r^+ particle.   The phenomenon of lysis inhibition undoubtedly accounts for the small size and turbid halo characteristic of the r^+ plaques.   The physiologic mechanism responsible for lysis inhibition is not known.

.   .   .   .   .

The characteristic plaque morphologies are best seen when the phages are plated by the agar layer technique using very soft

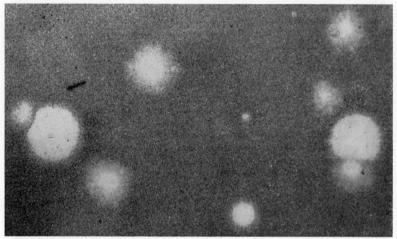

Figure 16. Mixture of phage T2r^+ and T2r plated on strain B, showing inhibition of development of an r plaque by an adjacent r^+ plaque.   Bright field illumination.

agar.   Luria (personal communication) recommended for this purpose that the base agar be made of 1.1 per cent agar instead of the 1.5 per cent agar usually used, and that the soft agar for the agar layer be 0.6 per cent instead of 0.7 per cent.   With an incubation period of 6–8 hr. it is usually possible to distinguish quite sharply between r^+ and r plaques, although there may be a few plaques that cannot be definitely classified.

If a typical stock of T2r^+ phage is diluted and plated so as to have about 10^3 plaques/plate and is examined after 8 hr. incubation, 3 distinct types of plaques (Fig. 15) should be found: (*a*) Most of the plaques will be typical r^+ plaques, quite small and with a turbid halo. (*b*) A few plaques will be typical r plaques, larger with a sharply defined clear halo. (*c*) About 1 per cent of the plaques will be mottled, i.e., will be primarily r^+ type, with a sector of complete lysis owing to the appearance of an r mutant during development of the plaque. If an r^+ plaque overlaps an r plaque, there is a sharp boundary where lysis inhibition by the r^+ phage has prevented development of the r plaque (Fig. 16).

The r mutant can be readily isolated by stabbing either an r plaque or r sector in a mottled plaque with a sterile platinum wire and rinsing the wire in broth. If appropriate dilutions of this broth are then plated by the agar layer technique, many typical r plaques should be found. A well isolated r plaque can then be stabbed and used to inoculate a broth culture of B to produce an r stock.

Mixed Infection and Genetic Recombination

Mixed Infections with r^+ and r Variants of Same Phage Type

Hershey (1946a) made mixed infections of B with T2r^+ and T2r. The input ratio of phage to bacteria was such that the multiplicity of infection was about 2.5 for each variant. Under these conditions about 85 per cent of the bacteria should have adsorbed at least 1 phage particle of each kind; i.e., 85 per cent should be mixedly infected. The free phage was neutralized with antiserum and platings were made on B from F.G.T. before the end of the *latent* period and from S.G.T. after all bursts had taken place. In the plate before the end of the *latent* period the plaque morphologies were carefully examined and showed that 14 per cent of the plaques were r^+, 21 per cent r, and 65 per cent *mottled*. The mottled plaques were due to mixedly infected bacteria which liberated both T2r^+ and T2r phages. In this experiment 65/85 or 76 per cent of the possible mixedly infected bacteria actually liberated both kinds of phage. This must be a minimum estimate since not all mottled plaques can be recognized. Mutual exclusion, if it occurs in this case, must be very weak. Furthermore the *burst size* of the mixedly infected bacteria in this instance was the same as that of bacteria multiply infected with T2r^+ or T2r alone so that there is no depressor effect.

These observations have been confirmed by means of the single-cell burst technique (Delbrück and Bailey, 1946) (pp. 485 ff.).

Recombination of Genetic Characters in Mixedly Infected Bacteria

The discovery of these genetic markers has made it possible to analyze the yields from bacteria infected with phage particles differing in 2 genetic characters (Hershey, 1946b; Hershey and Rotman, 1949), for instance, T2h^+r and T2hr^+. T2h^+ and T2h are readily distinguished from each other by use of a mixture of B and B/2 for plating. When plated on this mixture, T2h^+ will give turbid plaques since it will lyse B but not B/2, while T2h will give clear plaques since it lyses both strains. A culture of B is mixedly infected with equal numbers of T2h^+r and T2$hr.^+$ After adsorption the mixture is diluted into anti-T2 serum to neutralize free phage and further diluted into F.G.T. and S.G.T. An aliquot of F.G.T. is plated on B before the end of the latent period and a sample of S.G.T. on B + B/2 after all bursts have occurred. About 65 per cent of the plaques from F.G.T. are then found to be *mottled*, indicating that at least this proportion of the infected bacteria are liberating both r^+ and r forms. On the mixed indicator plate from S.G.T., r^+ is readily distinguished from r by plaque size and h from h^+ by turbidity. Actually this plate reveals 4 kinds of plaques; T2h^+r and T2hr^+, the parent types, and T2h^+r^+ and T2hr, 2 new types resulting from recombination of the genetic characters of the parents. This method is ideally suited for study of exchanges of genetic characteristics between phages during intracellular growth in mixedly infected bacteria.

[More recent investigations have shown that for a maximum re-combination frequency the multiplicity of infection should be equal and high for each phage type (around eight of each par-ental type is recommended for T2). Dulbecco (1949b) has shown that at least 10 phage particles can participate in growth in a single cell. Adsorption should be performed under condi-tions which permit initiation of phage development to be de-layed (see p. 483) long enough to allow most of the late-reacting phage to be adsorbed before exclusion occurs. If the total num-ber of adsorbed phage is low or unequal, the frequency of ob-served recombinants should be corrected as described by Lennox *et al.* (1953).]

Hershey and Rotman (1948), pursuing this line of research, discovered that not all r mutations are genetically identical al-though the plaques may be indistinguishable morphologically. They isolated a number of independent r mutants of $T2r^+$ and numbered them in the order of isolation as $T2r1$, $T2r2$, etc. A culture of B multiply infected with $T2r1$ gave only r plaques, as did one multiply infected with $T2r2$. However, if B were mixedly infected with $T2r1$ and $T2r2$, about 15 per cent of the progeny were $T2r^+$. Further investigation of the r progeny demonstrated that they were of 3 types, $T2r1$, $T2r2$, and $T2r1r2$. These 3 forms are identical morphologically but can be distin-guished by making mixed infections with the parental types. The $T2r1$ type would give 15 per cent r^+ when tested by mixed infection with a known $T2r2$ stock and no r^+ when tested with a known $T2r1$ stock. However, the $T2r1r2$ type would give no r^+ plaques on mixed infection with either $T2r1$ or $T2r2$. On the basis of his analysis of the r mutants of T2, Hershey con-cluded that there are at least 2 independent linkage groups of dis-tinct r loci.

[Benzer (1955) has developed a method for measuring very small recombination frequencies between members of one of these groups of r mutants (rII, the one containing $r2$). The method is based on the fact that although the wild type phage can grow on the lysogenic bacteria, *Escherichia coli* K-12 (λ), the r

mutants cannot. Thus any wild type progeny that arise in crosses between different r mutants can be found by platings on K-12, as only they will form plaques. The total yield from the cross can be obtained by platings on coli B. In this way recombination frequencies as low as 10^{-8} could be measured, the only limitation being the reverse mutation rate of the parental r strains.]

The exchange of genetic characters occurs not only between mutants of the same phage type but between those of different phage types. In fact, the exchanges were first observed by Delbrück and Bailey (1946), who carried out mixed infections with r^+ and r forms of T2, T4, and T6 in various combinations. For instance, mixed infection of B with T2r^+ and T6r yielded T2r and T6r^+ in addition to the 2 parental types. . . .

Effects of Ultraviolet Irradiation of Bacteriophage

A most convenient and generally accessible source of ultraviolet light is the General Electric germicidal lamp, a low pressure, mercury vapor lamp with about 80 per cent of its ultraviolet output at a wavelength of 2537 A. This wavelength is very close to that found most efficient for sterilization of bacterial suspensions and inactivation of viruses (Gates, 1934). The lamp can be operated in any standard fixture designed to take fluorescent lamps of the same dimensions. A metallic reflector should be avoided, for it will reflect ultraviolet light and complicate the geometry of the irradiation set-up. The lamp must be shaded so that no direct rays reach the eyes of anyone in the vicinity. The ultraviolet output varies with the line potential, so that for reproducible results a constant voltage transformer such as the Sola,* with output of 0.5 amp. at 115 v., should be used with the lamp. For most work this is not necessary. The ultraviolet output varies slightly during the useful life of the lamp. This can be controlled only by calibration of the lamp by photoelectric or biologic methods. The ultraviolet dose varies directly with the

* Made by Sola Electric Company, 4627 West Sixteenth St., Cicero, Ill.

time of irradiation and approximately inversely with the distance of the sample from the tube, so that the dosage can be varied within wide limits quite conveniently. The energy output of a G.E. germicidal lamp calibrated by Luria and Latarjet (1947) was 16 ergs/mm.^{2} sec. for the 2537 A band at a distance of 56 cm. from the lamp. Output varies from lamp to lamp but is usually within 20 per cent of this figure.

The sample to be irradiated should be diluted in a chemically defined medium free from nucleic acids and other substances which absorb strongly near 2537 A. The medium should be so diluted that no mutual screening of phage particles or bacteria can take place. Depth of the sample under irradiation should not be more than 1 or 2 mm., and the sample container should be mounted on a flexible support so that the sample can be constantly agitated during irradiation. A Petri dish is a convenient vessel, and irradiation can be started by removing the cover and stopped by replacing it, since a glass Petri dish absorbs essentially all ultraviolet light at 2537 A.

For the coliphages T1–T7, inactivation by ultraviolet light at 2537 A is an exponential function of the dose of irradiation (Luria, 1947). This indicates that inactivation is probably a "one hit" mechanism, 1 quantum presumably being effective if absorbed in a vulnerable site.

Under constant experimental conditions the rate of inactivation of phage follows the equation

$$- \frac{dp}{dt} = Kp$$

or

$$\log_e \frac{p_0}{p} = Kt$$

This leads directly to a "physiologic unit" of irradiation in which the dose of ultraviolet light is expressed in terms of the inactivation of phage rather than in terms of ergs or other energy units. This is important in that it permits duplication of experiments in

different laboratories without regard for the geometry of the irradiation setup and obviates the need for calibration of the lamp
in energy units. It automatically corrects for loss of radiation by
absorption in the suspending medium. Luria (1947) has defined the physiologic unit r as that dose which will inactivate all
but $1/e$ of the phage particles; i.e., when $p/p_0 = 1/e$ or $\log_e p_0/p =$
1, the phage has received 1 r of radiation.

The energy content of the r dose for different phages varies
with the sensitivity of the phage to ultraviolet radiation. In the
case of phage T2, one r dose corresponds to about 50 ergs/mm.[2],
and this phage can be used to calibrate the output of an ultraviolet light in energy units provided the lamp is nearly monochromatic at 2537 A, as is the G.E. germicidal lamp. The value
of $r = 1/e$ for the proportion of survivors was chosen because at
this per cent survival, the average number of lethal hits/phage
particle is *one*. This follows because the distribution of lethal
hits among the population of phage particles under irradiation is
a Poisson distribution. That is, the proportion of unhit phage
particles, $P(0) = p/p_0 = e^{-n}$. When n (average number of hits/
phage particle) $= 1$, then $p/p_0 = 1/e = 0.3679$. The course of
inactivation is followed by making phage assays in the usual way.
Samples are withdrawn after various doses of radiation, diluted
in broth and assayed for plaque-forming particles by the agar
layer technique. [To avoid photoreactivation of the UV-inac-
tivated phage (see following section) the assay plates should be
kept in the dark.] The inactivation is an exponential function
of the dose of ultraviolet light down to a survival of 10^{-4}–10^{-5}.
In the case of some of the phages the inactivation becomes
markedly slower from this time on, for reasons to be explained
later.

[*Photoreactivation*

Dulbecco (1950) has shown that phage which has been inactivated by UV irradiation can be reactivated (i.e., made able to
produce plaques) if exposed to sufficiently intense visible light
(3,000–5,000 A). This reactivation can take place only when

visible light is administered during a limited period after the inactivated phage particles have been adsorbed to host bacteria.
Illumination of free virus particles or uninfected bacteria has no
reactivating effect on inactivated phage subsequently adsorbed.
For illumination on the plate, Dulbecco used two parallel fluorescent discharge lamps (40 watts each) at a distance of 12 in.
from the plate.   For illumination of liquid media, a General Electric H-5 light source was used together with one or more filters.
Dulbecco (1950) has given a complete description of the apparatus used for illumination in liquid media.]

.   .   .   .   .

Multiplicity Reactivation of Ultraviolet-Inactivated Phages

Luria (1947) found that bacteria singly infected with inactivated phage produced no plaques when plated.   However, any
bacterium infected with 2 or more inactive phage particles did
produce plaques if not too many r doses of irradiation had been
given.

The average multiplicity of infection, n, with ultraviolet-inactivated phage particles can be obtained as described above by
determining the proportion of surviving bacteria at the end of
the adsorption period.   The proportion of uninfected bacteria is
related to n by the Poisson formula $P(0) = e^{-n}$.   Once n has been
determined in this way, the proportion of singly infected bacteria
can be calculated from the formula $P(1) = n\,e^{-n}$.   The proportion of bacteria which had adsorbed 2 or more phage particles is
then $1 - \{P(0) + P(1)\} = 1 - (n + 1)\,e^{-n}$, and the actual
number of bacteria which have been multiply infected is equal
to $1 - (n + 1)\,e^{-n}$ times the total number of bacteria.   The
number of bacteria which have the ability to produce plaques
can be determined by the plating of appropriate dilutions by the
agar layer method and counting the plaques, correcting the
count if necessary for non-inactivated phage particles.

Example: In an actual experiment a suspension of 10^9 B/ml. was mixed
with various amounts of an irradiated T4 phage stock.   The adsorption mix-

tures were incubated for 10 min. at 37° C., then appropriately diluted and assayed for *infective centers* by the agar layer method. Appropriate dilutions
of the adsorption mixture with the highest input ratio of phage to bacteria
were plated to determine the number of surviving bacteria from which the
multiplicity of infection, n, for that particular adsorption tube could be calculated. Once n is known for 1 adsorption mixture it can be calculated for all
the other mixtures made with the same bacterial suspension and phage stock,
assuming only that the percentage adsorption in 10 min, is the same in all adsorption tubes. The data are shown in Table XXVI.

TABLE XXVI[a]

Multiplicity of infection (n)	No. of multiply infected bacteria/ml. (calc.)	No. of infective centers/ml. (exper.)	Ratio (calc.: exper.)
0.67	1.7×10^8	9×10^7	1.9
0.33	5.0×10^7	3×10^7	1.8
0.135	1.1×10^7	6×10^6	1.9
0.067	2.6×10^6	1.3×10^6	2.0
0.033	6.8×10^5	3×10^5	2.1
0.013	1.7×10^5	1×10^5	1.7
			Av. 1.9

[a] From Luria (1947).

As may be seen from Table XXVI about half the bacteria which
adsorbed 2 or more inactivated phage particles actually produced
plaques. The proportion of multiply infected bacteria which
produce plaques depends on the dose of irradiation to which the
phage particles have been subjected. For the phages T2, T4,
and T6, if the physiologic dosage of ultraviolet light is 3 r or less,
i.e., an average of 3 or less lethal hits/phage particle, *all* the multiply infected bacteria produce plaques. As the dose of irradiation is increased, the probability of the bacteria which have adsorbed 2 phage particles forming a plaque is decreased. However, an increase in average multiplicity of infection can overcome this decrease in probability that multiply infected bacteria
will produce plaques. That is, as the number of lethal hits/
phage particle is increased, the number of inactive phage parti-

cles which must be adsorbed to the same bacterium to produce an infective center must be increased. . . .

.   .   .   .   .

Another interesting observation made by Luria is that cross-reactivation can occur within the group T2, T4, and T6. That is, mixed infection of bacteria with inactivated T2 and inactivated T6 will result in liberation of both T2 and T6 in an active form. In order for reactivation to take place, both phages must be capable of adsorption on the same host cell. For instance, inactivated T2 is not reactivated by T6 when B/6 is the host cell.

.   .   .   .   .

Methods of Studying Intracellular Growth of Bacteriophage

The methods described so far have been devoted to study of the properties of extracellular phage up to the moment of adsorption to the host cell and after lysis of the host cell. Little has been said about what happens inside an infected bacterium during the latent period of intracellular phage growth. A number of widely differing techniques have been applied to this problem, some of the more novel of which will be described in detail, and others briefly mentioned with references to the literature.

Biochemical Methods

Cohen and Anderson (1946) used the Warburg respirometer to study the respiration of normal and phage-infected host cells. The bacteria were grown in the chemically defined ammonium lactate medium called F medium (p. 446). The Warburg vessels contained 1.5×10^9 bacteria in a total volume of 2 ml. of F medium. To 1 was added 8×10^9 active $T2r^+$ particles, to a second was added the same number of ultraviolet-inactivated T2 particles, and the third vessel was a virus-free control. The experiment was conducted at 38° C. Oxygen uptake was measured continuously and the total CO_2 evolution determined at the end of the experiment. The bacteria in the virus-free control took up oxygen at a rate which increased exponentially with time in the same way that the bacterial population increased. The bacteria infected with either active T2 or ultraviolet-inactivated T2 continued to take up oxygen at the rate which prevailed at the moment of infection. There was no increase in oxygen absorption rate or in bacterial turbidity in the vessels containing phage. The respiratory quotient was the same in all 3 vessels, about 1.05. This experiment indicates that both active and ultraviolet-inactivated T2 phage can interrupt the multiplication of infected host cells without altering the rate of oxygen uptake or CO_2 evolution. Infection with phage does not affect host cell respiration. Use of $T2r^+$ phage in these experiments resulted in the phenomenon of lysis inhibition (p. 506) and enabled continuation of experiments for several hours before lysis began to interfere with the observations.

Cohen (1948) continued his study of virus-infected host cells by making chemical analyses for protein and nucleic acid at intervals during the latent period. This was done by adding trichloroacetic acid to aliquots of the culture to a final concentration of 5 per cent. The mixture was chilled 15 min. and centrifuged 10 min. The supernatant fluid was decanted, the tubes were drained and the precipitate washed with cold 5 per cent trichloroacetic acid. The precipitate could then be analyzed for total phosphorus, for nitrogen by Kjeldahl, for pentose by quantitative Bial (Mejbaum, 1939) or for desoxyribosenucleic acid (DNA) by the diphenylamine reaction (Dische, 1930). About 10^9 bacteria are required for these analyses except for Kjeldahl N, for which about 10^{10} bacteria are needed.

.   .   .   .   .

Another method of following intracellular phage synthesis was developed by Racker and Adams (unpublished experiments) as a result of Cohen's work. Nucleic acids have a high absorption of ultraviolet radiation at 2,600 A. Since phage particles contain about 40 per cent nucleic acid in contrast to 20 per cent for the host cell, and since apparently only phage nucleic acid is synthesized following infection, it should be possible to study phage nucleic acid synthesis in infected bacteria by measuring changes in light absorption at 2600 A in the Beckman spectrophotometer. In cultures of *E. coli* growing in a chemically defined medium the absorption at 2600 A increases exponentially with time, doubling in 1 generation time. In cultures of *E. coli* infected with a 5-fold multiplicity of phage T2, nucleic acid synthesis as measured by absorption at 2600 A ceases completely for 5–10 min. following infection, then proceeds at a rate that is a linear function of time. . . . The concentration of bacteria should be about 10^8/ml. and the medium and reagents used must not absorb too much light at 2600 A.

Radiation Methods

As discussed in the preceding section, the inactivation of free phage by ultraviolet light is a simple exponential function of the dose of radiation as might be expected if 1 hit were enough to inactivate a phage particle. It is possible that individual phage particles inside an infected bacterium might be inactivated in the same way and that the destruction of the plaque-forming potentiality of an infected bacterium would require as many hits as the number of phage particles it contained at the time of irradiation. The destruction of infective centers at a given time during the latent period would follow the course of a multiple hit curve if 2 or more phage particles were present, and a series of such curves at appropriate intervals during the latent period would enable one to determine the course of virus synthesis.

This type of analysis was attempted by Luria and Latarjet (1947). The bacteria were singly infected with T2 phage, diluted into anti-T2 serum to inactivate free phage and further diluted in a chemically defined medium of low ultraviolet absorption. Samples of the highly diluted suspension of infective centers were taken at intervals, exposed to ultraviolet irradiation and assayed for surviving infective centers by plating before the end of the latent period. The killing curve for singly infected bacteria immediately after infection is a single hit curve very close to that for free phage. It differs only in that the infective centers are slightly more resistant to ultraviolet light than free phage, as might be expected owing to the screening effect of the bacterium. The killing curve for multiply infected bacteria immediately after infection was a multiple hit curve. This indicates that the killing of infective centers is due to destruction of the reproducibility of the phage itself rather than to damage to the host cell.

.   .   .   .   .

[The UV method for following early stages of phage development has subsequently been used and refined by Benzer (1952) and Symonds (1957).]

This experimental approach to the mechanism of virus growth was modified by Latarjet (1948), using X-rays as the inactivating agent to avoid the screening effect of intracellular nucleic acid. The experimental procedure was the same as that already described except that X-radiation of 0.95 A wavelength was used at doses as high as 250 kiloroentgens.

Methods Involving Interruption of Growth During the Latent Period Followed by Disruption of Host Cells

These methods, developed by Doermann (1948b), constitute an important contribution to phage methodology because they permit assay of intracellular phage particles during the latent period of phage growth. The methods involve an interruption of phage growth at intervals during the latent period by means of cell poisons or low temperature, followed by release of intracellular phage by means of lysis from without (Delbrück, 1940b) or sonic vibration (T. F. Anderson, Boggs, and Winters, 1948).

1. Lysis from without. In a typical experiment the *growth medium* consisted of acid-hydrolyzed casein, tryptophan, salts, and glycerol. Phage T4r was the infecting virus, $0.01M$ KCN

was the metabolic poison, and phage T6 was used to liberate
the T4 phage by lysis from without. The *lysing medium* was
the growth medium plus $0.01M$ KCN and 4×10^9 T6 particles/
ml. All assay platings were by the agar layer technique on B/6,
since this indicator strain permits assay of T4 in the presence
of T6. A culture of B was grown to 10^8/ml. and concentrated
to 10^9/ml. so that phage adsorption would be rapid. A stock
of T4r phage was diluted to 10^9/ml. in the growth medium.
Anti-T4 serum diluted in the growth medium was used to neutralize free phage.

Protocol

Time, min.	Tube	Procedure	Conc. of infected bacteria/ml.
0	1. Adsorption	Add 0.1 ml of T4 to 0.9 ml B culture	10^8
2	2. Serum	Add 0.1 ml of #1 to 0.9 ml serum	10^7
6	3. Dilution	Add 0.1 ml of #2 to 9.9 ml medium	10^5
6.5	4. F.G.T.	Add 0.1 ml of #3 to 1.9 ml medium	5×10^3
7	5. S.G.T.	Add 0.1 ml F.G.T. to 9.9 ml medium	5×10^1

Platings made at intervals from F.G.T. and S.G.T. gave the
usual one-step growth curve which was used as a control on
latent period and burst size.

At intervals during the latent period 0.1 ml. samples from the
dilution tube were diluted into 1.9 ml. samples of the lysing medium
chilled to $0°$ C., kept cold for 10 min., then incubated for 30
min. at $37°$ C. The chilling and the KCN in the lysing medium
interrupted phage growth, and the high concentration of T6
phage brought about lysis from without, liberating any T4
phage which had been produced up to the time of dilution
into the lysing medium. After the 30 min. incubation period
an aliquot of each lysing medium tube was plated on B/6 to

determine the amount of T4 phage produced/infected bacterium up to the time of sampling.

Using this technique, there is no detectable intracellular T4 phage present from the earliest samples taken at about 9 min. after infection until about 14 min. after infection, at which time about 1 phage particle/bacterium is demonstrable. The number of intracellular phage particles that can be liberated per infected cell then increases at an approximately linear rate until the normal burst size is reached at about 28–30 min. after infection. This maximal yield is reached several minutes before the end of the normal rise period.

.   .   .   .   .

It is obvious that the effect of many other cell poisons on the growth of phage could be studied in this manner. For instance, 5-methyltryptophan, shown by Cohen and Anderson (1946) to prevent phage growth, was used by Doermann with results very similar to those with KCN. This inhibitor, however, does not stop synthesis promptly in host cells able to synthesize their own tryptophan so that the mutant B/1,tr was used as the host cell in experiments involving 5-methyltryptophan.

[2. Premature lysis of infected cells by chloroform. A simple technique for obtaining premature lysis of phage infected cells has been described by Séchaud and Kellenberger (1956). They found that chloroform effects a rapid lysis of infected cells when they contain at least one infectious unit per cell. Lysis of such cells is complete two minutes after exposure to chloroform. To follow the intracellular development of infectious phage the infected culture was diluted to contain around 3×10^4 infected bacteria per ml. At intervals during the latent period, samples were taken and diluted further in a diluent containing chloroform (3–6 drops of chloroform per 5 ml. of diluent). These suspensions were shaken vigorously for several seconds and 15–30 min. later assayed for phage. The action of chloroform was found to be independent of the media used (i.e., tryptone, M-9, phosphate buffer). It was noted, however, that in the case of T2 the pH should be between 7.5 and 8 for maximum recovery of plaque formers. These studies were carried out using phages T2, T4, and lambda on their respective hosts strains B and K12 of *E. coli*.

3. Estimation of intracellular phage development by use of streptomycin. Symonds (1957) has developed a technique to measure, at any time during the latent period, the number of bacteria that contain infective phage. This technique involves the use of a streptomycin-resistant mutant as indicator organism. The infected bacteria are streptomycin sensitive. During the latent period samples are plated in streptomycin-containing agar with the resistant mutant as the indicator. The infected bacteria are therefore killed by the streptomycin and no further phage development proceeds. However, those of the infected bacteria which contained, at the time of plating, infective phage, now lyse and release this phage, thereby forming a plaque on the streptomycin-resistant indicator.]

4. Lysis by sonic vibration. This method of lysing infected bacteria during the latent period is restricted to small phages such as T1, T3, and T7, which are relatively slowly inactivated by the sonic treatment. The method is the same as the foregoing except that samples withdrawn from the dilution tube at intervals were diluted into tubes of growth medium which had been prechilled to 0° C. This diluted sample was placed in the sonic vibrator and treated for 5 min. at 5° C. Appropriate samples were then plated by the agar layer method for phage assay.

Experiments in which separate samples from the same dilution tube were treated by lysis from without or by sonic vibration demonstrated an extremely close agreement between the methods.

BIBLIOGRAPHY

A

Ada, G. L., 1957. "Ribonucleic Acid in Influenza Virus." In G. E. W. Wolstenholme and E. C. P. Millar, eds., *The Nature of Viruses*, pp. 104–15. Little, Brown, Boston.

Adams, M. H., 1948. Surface inactivation of bacterial viruses and of proteins. *J. Gen. Physiol.*, **31,** 417.

Adams, M. H., 1949a. The stability of bacterial viruses in solutions of salts. *J. Gen. Physiol.*, **32,** 579.

Adams, M. H., 1949b. The calcium requirement of coliphage T5. *J. Immunol.*, **62,** 505.

Adams, M. H., 1951a. Mixed infection of a bacterium with coli-dysentery phage T5 and a serologically related Salmonella phage. *J. Immunol.*, **66,** 477.

Adams, M. H., 1951b. The hybridization of coliphage T5 and salmonella phage PB. *J. Immunol.*, **67,** 313.

Adams, M. H., 1952. Classification of bacterial viruses: characteristics of the T5 species and of the T2, C16 species. *J. Bacteriol.*, **64,** 387.

Adams, M. H., 1953a. The genotypically and phenotypically heat resistant forms in the T5 species of bacteriophage. *Ann. inst. Pasteur*, **84,** 164.

Adams, M. H., 1953b. Criteria for a biological classification of bacterial viruses. *Ann. N.Y. Acad. Sci.*, **56,** 442.

Adams, M. H., 1954. "Abortive Infection with Viruses." In F. W. Hartman, F. L. Horsfall, and J. G. Kidd, eds., *The Dynamics of Virus and Rickettsial Infections*, p. 86. Blakiston, New York.

Adams, M. H., 1955. *Virology*, **1,** 336.

Adams, M. H., and H. Lark, 1950. Mutation to heat resistance in coliphage T5. *J. Immunol.*, **64,** 335.

Adams, M. H., and B. Park, 1956. *Virology*, **2,** 719.

Adams, M. H., and E. Wade, 1954. Classification of bacterial viruses: the relationship of two *Serratia* phages to coli-dysentery phages T3, T7 and D44. *J. Bacteriol.*, **68,** 320.

Adams, M. H., and E. Wade, 1955. Classification of bacterial viruses: characteristics of the T1,D20 species of coli-dysentery phages. *J. Bacteriol.*, **70,** 253.

Adams, M. H., and F. Wassermann, 1956. Frequency distribution of phage release in the one-step growth experiment. *Virology*, **2,** 96.

Ajl, S. J., 1950. Metabolic studies on T2 *E. coli* bacteriophage. *J. Bacteriol.*, **60,** 393.

Alper, T., 1948. Hydrogen peroxide and the indirect effect of ionizing radiations. *Nature*, **162,** 615.

Alper, T., 1954. *J. Gen. Microbiol.*, **11,** 313.

Altenbern, R. A., 1953. The action of aureomycin on the *Escherichia coli* bacteriophage T3 system. *J. Bacteriol.*, **65,** 288.

Amos, H., and E. Vollmayer, 1957. Accelerated bacteriophage synthesis in pentamidine-treated *Escherichia coli*. *J. Bacteriol.*, **73,** 178.

Anderson, E. H., 1946. Growth requirements of virus resistant mutants of *E. coli* strain "B". *Proc. Natl. Acad. Sci. U. S.*, **32,** 120.

Anderson, E. S., 1951. *J. Hyg.*, **49,** 458.

Anderson, E. S., 1955a. *Nature*, **175,** 171.

Anderson, E. S., 1955b. *J. Gen. Microbiol.*, **12,** 379.

Anderson, E. S., 1956. *J. Gen. Microbiol.*, **14,** 676.

Anderson, E. S., and A. Felix, 1952. *Nature*, **170,** 492.

Anderson, E. S., and A. Felix, 1953a. *J. Gen. Microbiol.*, **8,** 408.

Anderson, E. S., and A. Felix, 1953b. *J. Gen. Microbiol.*, **9,** 65.

Anderson, E. S., and A Felix, 1953c. *Intern. Congr. Microbiol., 6th Congr.*, Rome, 1953, *Rept. Proc.*, **3,** 462.

Anderson, E. S., and A. Fraser, 1955. *J. Gen. Microbiol.*, **13,** 519.

Anderson, E. S., and A. Fraser, 1956. *J. Gen. Microbiol.*, **15,** 225.

Anderson, E. S., and R. E. O. Williams, 1956. *J. Clin. Pathol.*, **9,** 94.

Anderson, T. F., 1944. Virus reactions inside of bacterial host cells. *J. Bacteriol.*, **47,** 113.

Anderson, T. F., 1945a. The role of tryptophane in the adsorption of two bacterial viruses on their host, *E. coli*. *J. Cellular Comp. Physiol.*, **25,** 17.

Anderson, T. F., 1945b. *Science*, **101,** 565.

Anderson, T. F., 1946. *Cold Spring Harbor Symposia Quant. Biol.*, **11,** 1.

Anderson, T. F., 1948a. The activation of the bacterial virus T4 by L-tryptophan. *J. Bacteriol.*, **55,** 637.

Anderson, T. F., 1948b. The inheritance of requirements for adsorption cofactors in the bacterial virus T4. *J. Bacteriol.*, **55,** 651.

Anderson, T. F., 1948c. Influence of temperature and nutrients on plaque formation by bacteriophages active on *E. coli* strain B. *J. Bacteriol.*, **55,** 659.

Anderson, T. F., 1948d. The growth of T2 virus on ultraviolet-killed host cells. *J. Bacteriol.*, **56,** 403.

Anderson, T. F., 1949. The reactions of bacterial viruses with their host cells. *Botan. Rev.*, **15,** 464.

Anderson, T. F., 1950. Destruction of bacterial viruses by osmotic shock. *J. Appl. Phys.*, **21,** 70.

Anderson, T. F., 1951. Techniques for the preservation of three dimensional structure in preparing specimens for the electron microscope. *Trans. N.Y. Acad. Sci.*, **13,** 130.

Anderson, T. F., 1952. Stereoscopic studies of cells and viruses in the electron microscope. *Am. Naturalist*, **86,** 91.

Anderson, T. F., 1953. The morphology and osmotic properties of bacteriophage systems. *Cold Spring Harbor Symposia Quant. Biol.*, **18,** 197.

Anderson, T. F., S. Boggs, and B. S. Winters, 1948. The relative sensitivities of bacterial viruses to intense sonic vibration. *Science*, **108,** 18.

Anderson, T. F., and A. H. Doermann, 1952a. The intracellular growth of bacteriophages II. The growth of T3 studied by sonic disintegration and by T6-cyanide lysis of infected cells. *J. Gen. Physiol.*, **35,** 657.

Anderson, T. F., and A. H. Doermann, 1952b. Sonic reactivation of antiserum-neutralized bacteriophage T3. *J. Bacteriol.*, **63,** 291.

Anderson, T. F., C. Rappaport, and N. A. Muscatine, 1953. On the structure and osmotic properties of phage particles. *Ann. inst. Pasteur*, **84,** 5.

Andrewes, C. H., 1957. *Advances in Virus Research*, **4,** 1.

Andrewes, C. H., and W. J. Elford, 1932. The "killing" of bacteria by bacteriophage. *Brit. J. Exptl. Pathol.*, **13,** 13.

Andrewes, C. H., and W. J. Elford, 1933a. Observations on antiphage sera: I. "The percentage law." *Brit. J. Exptl. Pathol.*, **14,** 367.

Andrewes, C. H., and W. J. Elford, 1933b. Observations on antiphage sera: II. Properties of incompletely neutralized phage. *Brit. J. Exptl. Pathol.*, **14,** 377.

Anson, M. L., 1946. *Ann. N.Y. Acad. Sci.*, **46,** 347.

Appleyard, R. K., 1954a. *Genetics*, **39,** 429.

Appleyard, R. K., 1954b. *Genetics*, **39,** 440.

Appleyard, R. K., 1956. *J. Gen. Microbiol.*, **14,** 573.

Appleyard, R. K., J. F. McGregor, and K. M. Baird, 1956. Mutation to extended host range and the occurrence of phenotypic mixing in the temperate coliphage lambda. *Virology*, **2,** 565.

Arkwright, J. A., 1924. The source and characteristics of certain cultures sensitive to bacteriophage. *Brit. J. Exptl. Pathol.*, **5,** 23.

Armitage, P., 1953. Statistical concepts in the theory of bacterial mutation. *J. Hyg.*, **51,** 162.

Asheshov, I. N., 1924. Experimental studies on bacteriophage. *J. Infectious Diseases*, **34,** 536.

Asheshov, I. N., 1925. The antigenic power of ultrasterile lysates. *Compt. rend. soc. biol.*, **93,** 643.

Asheshov, I. N., 1926. Action du citrate de soude sur le bactériophage. *Compt. rend. soc. biol.*, **94,** 687.

Asheshov, I. N., E. A. Hall, and H. Flon, 1955. Action of test compounds on bacterial viruses. *Cancer Research Suppl. 3*, 57.

Asheshov, I. N., I. Asheshov, S. Khan, and M. M. Lahiri, 1933. *Indian J. Med. Research*, **20,** 1101.

Astrachan, L., and E. Volkin, 1957. Chromatographic detection of differences between bacteriophage-related deoxyribonucleic acids. *J. Am. Chem. Soc.*, **79,** 130.

B

Bail, O., 1925. *Med. Klin. Munich*, **21,** 1277.

Baker, E. E., W. F. Goebel, and E. Perlman, 1949. The specific antigens of variants of *Sh. sonnei. J. Exptl. Med.*, **89,** 325.

Baker, S. L., and S. H. Nanavutty, 1929. *Brit. J. Exptl. Pathol.*, **10,** 45.

Banker, D. D., 1955. *Nature*, **175,** 309.

Barksdale, L., 1955. *Compt. rend. soc. biol.*, **240,** 1831,

Barksdale, L. W., and A. M. Pappenheimer, Jr., 1954. Phage host relationships in non-toxigenic and toxigenic diphtheria bacilli. *J. Bacteriol*, **67,** 220.

Barlow, J. L., and R. M. Herriott, 1954. *Bacteriol. Proc. Soc. Am. Bacteriologists*, **54,** 46.

Barner, H. D., and S. S. Cohen, 1954. The induction of thymine synthesis by T2 infection of a thymine requiring mutant of *Escherichia coli. J. Bacteriol.*, **68,** 80.

Baron, L. S., S. B. Formal, and W. Spilman, 1953. *Proc. Soc. Exptl. Biol. Med.*, **83,** 292.

Baron, L. S., S. B. Formal, and W. Spilman, 1955. *J. Bacteriol.*, **69,** 177.

Barricelli, N. A., 1956. *Acta Biotheoretica*, **11,** 8.

Barrington, L. F., and L. M. Kozloff, 1956. *J. Biol. Chem.*, **223,** 615.

Barry, G. T., 1954. A study of the antigenicity of T3 and T4 coli-dysentery bacteriophages during the vegetative stage of development. *J. Exptl. Med.*, **100,** 163.

Barry, G. T., and W. F. Goebel, 1951. The effect of chemical and physical agents on the phage receptor of phase II *Shigella sonnei. J. Exptl. Med.*, **94,** 387.

Baylor, M. B., D. D. Hurst, S. L. Allen, and E. T. Bertani, 1957. *Genetics* **42,** 104.

Baylor, M. R. B., J. M. Severens, and G. L. Clark, 1944. Electron microscope studies of the bacteriophage of *Salmonella pullorum. J. Bacteriol.*, **47,** 277.

Bayne-Jones, S., and L. A. Sandholzer, 1933. Changes in the shape and size of *B. coli* and *B. megaterium* under the influence of bacteriophage. *J. Exptl. Med.*, **57,** 279.

Beard, J. W., 1948. Purified animal viruses. *J. Immunol.*, **58**, 49.

Bentzon, M. W., O. Maaløe, and G. Rasch, 1952. An analysis of the mode of increase in number of intracellular phage particles at different temperatures. *Acta Pathol. et Microbiol. Scand.*, **30**, 243.

Benzer, S., 1952. Resistance to ultraviolet light as an index to the reproduction of bacteriophage. *J. Bacteriol.*, **63**, 59.

Benzer, S., 1953. Induced synthesis of enzymes in bacteria analysed at the cellular level. *Biochim. et Biophys. Acta*, **11**, 383.

Benzer, S., 1955. *Proc. Natl. Acad. Sci. U. S.*, **41**, 344.

Benzer, S., 1957. "The Elementary Units of Heredity." In W. D. McElroy and B. Glass, eds., *The Chemical Basis of Heredity*, p. 70. Johns Hopkins Press, Baltimore.

Benzer, S., M. Delbrück, R. Dulbecco., W. Hudson, G. S. Stent, J. D. Watson, W. Weidel, J. J. Weigle, and E. L. Wollman, 1950. In M. Delbrück, ed., *Viruses*. California Institute of Technology, Pasadena.

Benzer, S., and F. Jacob, 1953. Etude du développement du bactériophage au moyen d'irradiations par la lumière ultra-violette. *Ann. inst. Pasteur*, **84**, 186.

Bertani, G., 1951. Studies on lysogenesis: I. Mode of phage liberation by lysogenic *Escherichia coli*. *J. Bacteriol.*, **62**, 293.

Bertani, G., 1953a. *Ann. inst. Pasteur*, **84**, 273.

Bertani, G., 1953b. *Cold Spring Harbor Symposia Quant. Biol.*, **18**, 65.

Bertani, G., 1954. Studies on lysogenesis: III. Superinfection of lysogenic *Shigella dysenteriae* with temperate mutants of the carried phage. *J. Bacteriol.*, **67**, 696.

Bertani, G., 1956. *Brookhaven Symposia in Biol.*, **8**, 50.

Bertani, G., 1958. Lysogeny. *Advances in Virus Research*, **5**, 151.

Bertani, G., and S. J. Nice, 1954. *J. Bacteriol.*, **67**, 202.

Bertani, G., and J. J. Weigle, 1953. *J. Bacteriol.*, **65**, 113.

Beumer, J., 1947. Les relations entre bactériophages et bactéries. *Rev. Belge Pathol. et Méd.*, **18**, 244, 289.

Beumer, J., 1953. *Ann. inst. Pasteur*, **84**, 15.

Beumer, J., and M. P. Beumer-Jochmans, 1951. Les exigences en calcium du phage de Lisbonne. *Ann. inst. Pasteur*, **81**, 489.

Beumer, J., and M. P. Beumer-Jochmans, 1955. Importance de l'hote bactérien pour les besoins en calcium d'un bactériophage. *Ann. inst. Pasteur*, **89**, 394.

Beumer, J., and L. Quersin, 1947. *Compt. rend. soc. biol.*, **141**, 1280.

Beumer-Jochmans, M. P., 1951. Etude comparative du comportement à 44° de deux phages staphylococciques. *Ann. inst. Pasteur*, **80**, 536.

Beutner, E. H., P. E. Hartman, S. Mudd, and J. Hillier, 1953. *Biochim. et Biophys. Acta.*, **10**, 143.

Birch-Andersen, A., O. Maaløe, and F. S. Sjostrand, 1953. High resolution electron micrographs of sections of *E. coli*. *Biochim. et Biophys. Acta*, **12**, 395.

Bird, T. J., 1956. The effects of drugs on various aspects of bacteriophagy. Ph.D. Dissertation, University of Pennsylvania.

Bonifas, V., and E. Kellenberger, 1955. *Biochim. et Biophys. Acta*, **16**, 330.

Bordet, J., 1925. *Ann. inst. Pasteur*, **39**, 717.

Bordet, J., and M. Ciuca, 1921. *Compt. rend. soc. biol.*, **84**, 276.

Bordet, J., and E. Renaux, 1928. *Ann. inst. Pasteur*, **42**, 1283.

Bordet, P., 1947. *Rev. immunol.*, **11**, 323.

Bordet, P., 1948. *Compt. rend. soc. biol.*, **142**, 257.

Bordet, P., and J. Beumer, 1948. *Compt. rend. soc. biol.*, **142**, 259.

Borek, E., 1952. *Biochim. et Biophys. Acta*, **8**, 211.

Borrel, A., 1928. *Compt. rend. soc. biol.*, **98**, 947.

Borrel, A., 1932. *Compt. rend. soc. biol.*, **111**, 923.

Bourke, A. R., M. L. Robbins, and P. K. Smith, 1952. Studies on the chemical inhibition of T2r+ bacteriophage. *J. Immunol.*, **69**, 75.

Bowen, G. H., 1953. Studies of ultraviolet irradiation phenomena—an approach to the problems of bacteriophage reproduction. *Cold Spring Harbor Symposia Quant. Biol.*, **18**, 245.

Boyd, J. S. K., 1949a. The symbiotic phages of *S. typhi murium*. *J. Pathol. Bacteriol.*, **61**, 127.

Boyd, J. S. K., 1949b. *Nature*, **164**, 874.

Boyd, J. S. K., 1950. *J. Pathol. Bacteriol.*, **62**, 501.

Boyd, J. S. K., 1951. Observations on the relationship of symbiotic and lytic bacteriophage. *J. Pathol. Bacteriol.*, **63**, 445.

Boyd, J. S. K., 1952. *Brit. Med. J.*, **1952 II**, 679.

Boyd, J. S. K., 1953. In P. Fildes and W. E. Van Heyningen, eds., *The Nature of Virus Multiplication* (2nd Symposium Soc. Gen. Microbiol.) pp. 119–48. Cambridge Univ. Press, London.

Boyd, J. S. K., and D. E. Bidwell, 1957. *J. Gen. Microbiol.*, **16**, 217.

Boyd, J. S. K., and P. L. Bradley, 1951. On the assessment of the influence of chemical compounds on bacteriophage multiplication. *Brit. J. Exptl. Pathol.*, **32**, 397.

Boyd, J. S. K., M. T. Parker, and N. S. Mair, 1951. *J. Hyg.*, **49**, 442.

Bozeman, F. M., C. L. Wisseman, Jr., H. E. Hopps, and J. X. Danauskas, 1954. Action of chloramphenicol on T1 bacteriophage. *J. Bacteriol.*, **67**, 530.

Braun, W., 1953. *Bacterial Genetics*. Saunders, Philadelphia.

Breed, R. S., E. G. D. Murray, and A. P. Hitchens, 1948. *Bergey's Manual of Determinative Bacteriology*, 6th ed. Williams and Wilkins, Baltimore.

Bresch, C., 1953. Genetical studies on bacteriophage T1. *Ann. inst. Pasteur*, **84,** 157

Bronfenbrenner, J., 1925. Effect of electrolytes on the rate of inactivation of bacteriophage during precipitation. *Proc. Soc. Exptl. Biol. Med.*, **23,** 187.

Bronfenbrenner, J., 1928. "The Bacteriophage, Present Status of the Question of Its Nature and Mode of Action. In Jordan and Falk, *The New Knowledge of Bacteriology and Immunology*, pp. 525–56. Univ. of Chicago Press, Chicago.

Bronfenbrenner, J., R. S. Muckenfuss, and D. M. Hetler, 1927. *Am. J. Pathol.*, **3,** 562.

Brown, D. D., and L. M. Kozloff, 1957. Morphological localization of the bacteriophage tail enzyme. *J. Biol. Chem.*, **225,** 1.

Bruynoghe, R., and B. Appelmans, 1922. La neutralisation des bactériophages de provenance differente. *Compt. rend. soc. biol.*, **87,** 96.

Bryson, V., and H. Davidson, 1951. *Proc. Nat. Acad. Sci. U. S.*, **37,** 784.

Burnet, F. M., 1925. The nature of acquired resistance to bacteriophage action. *J. Pathol. Bacteriol.*, **28,** 407.

Burnet, F. M., 1927. *Brit. J. Exptl. Pathol.*, **8,** 121.

Burnet, F. M., 1929a. A method for the study of bacteriophage multiplication in broth. *Brit. J. Exptl. Pathol.*, **10,** 109.

Burnet, F. M., 1929b. *J. Pathol. Bacteriol.*, **32,** 15.

Burnet, F. M., 1930. *J. Pathol. Bacteriol.*, **33,** 647.

Burnet, F. M., 1932. *J. Pathol. Bacteriol.*, **35,** 851.

Burnet, F. M., 1933a. Immunological studies with phage-coated bacteria. *Brit. J. Exptl. Pathol.*, **14,** 93.

Burnet, F. M., 1933b. *Brit. J. Exptl. Pathol.*, **14,** 100.

Burnet, F. M., 1933c. Specific agglutination of bacteriophage particles. *Brit. J. Exptl. Pathol.*, **14,** 302.

Burnet, F. M., 1933d. The classification of *dysentery-coli* bacteriophages: II. The serological classification of coli-dysentery phages. *J. Pathol. Bacteriol.*, **36,** 307.

Burnet, F. M., 1933e. *J. Pathol. Bacteriol.*, **37,** 179.

Burnet, F. M., 1934a. The bacteriophages. *Biol. Rev.*, **9,** 332.

Burnet, F. M., 1934b. *J. Pathol. Bacteriol.*, **38,** 285.

Burnet, F. M., and M. Freeman, 1937. A comparative study of the inactivation of a bacteriophage by immune serum and by a bacterial polysaccharide. *Australian J. Exptl. Biol. Med. Sci.*, **15,** 49.

Burnet, F. M., E. V. Keogh, D. Lush, 1937. Immunological reactions of filterable viruses. *Australian J. Exptl. Biol. Med. Sci.*, **15,** 227.

Burnet, F. M., and D. Lush, 1935. *J. Pathol. Bacteriol.*, **40,** 455.

Burnet, F. M., and D. Lush, 1936. *Australian J. Exptl. Biol. Med. Sci.*, **14,** 27.

Burnet, F. M., and D. Lush, 1940. Action of certain surface active agents on viruses. *Australian J. Exptl. Biol. Med.*, **18,** 141.

Burnet, F. M., and M. McKie, 1929. *Australian J. Exptl. Biol. Med. Sci.*, **6,** 277.

Burnet, F. M., and M. McKie, 1930. *J. Pathol. Bacteriol.*, **33,** 637.

Burnet, F. M., and M. McKie, 1933. The classification of dysentery-coli bacteriophages: I. The differentiation by Bail's method of phages lysing a typical *E. coli* strain. *J. Pathol. Bacteriol.*, **36,** 299.

Burton, K., 1955. The relation between the synthesis of deoxyribonucleic acid and the synthesis of protein in the multiplication of bacteriophage T2. *Biochem. J.*, **61,** 473.

Buzzell, A., and M. A. Lauffer, 1952. X-ray studies on T5 bacteriophage. *Arch. Biochem.*, **39,** 195.

C

Cairns, H. J. F., and G. S. Watson, 1956. Multiplicity reactivation of bacteriophage. *Nature,* **177,** 131.

Campbell-Renton, M. L., 1937. Radiation of bacteriophage with ultraviolet light. *J. Pathol. Bacteriol.*, **45,** 237.

Campbell-Renton, M. L., 1942. Experiments on shaking bacteriophage. *J. Pathol. Bacteriol.*, **54,** 235.

Cann, J. R., and E. W. Clark, 1954. On the kinetics of neutralization of bacteriophage T2 by specific antiserum. *J. Immunol.*, **72,** 463.

Cann, J. R., and E. W. Clark, 1955. Effect of salt concentration and pH on the rate of virus neutralization by purified fractions of specific antiserum. *Biochem. et Biophys. Acta*, **18,** 430.

Castagnoli, C., P. Donini, and F. Graziosi, 1955a. Inactivation of phage due to assimilated P-32 and the recovery of host cells. *Nature,* **175,** 992.

Castagnoli, C., P. Donini, and F. Graziosi, 1955b. Indagine biofisica del complesso virus-cellula ospite durante i primi stadi dell'infezione. *Giorn. Microbiol.*, **1,** 52.

Chang, S. L., M. Willner, and L. Tegarden, 1950. Kinetics of thermodestruction of bacterial virus in water. *Am. J. Hyg.*, **52,** 194.

Chapman, G., J. Hillier, and F. H. Johnson, 1951. Observations on bacteriophagy of *Erwinia carotovora*. *J. Bacteriol.*, **61,** 261.

Cherry, W. B., B. R. Davis, P. R. Edwards, and R. B. Hogan, 1954. *J. Lab. Clin. Med.*, **44,** 51.

Cherry, W. B., and D. W. Watson, 1949. The Str. Lactis host-virus system: II. Characteristics of virus growth and the effect of electrolytes on virus adsorption. *J. Bacteriol.*, **58,** 611.

Clarke, N. A., 1952. *J. Bacteriol.*, **63,** 187.

Clifton, C. E., 1931. Photodynamic action of certain dyes on the inactivation of staphylococcus bacteriophage. *Proc. Soc. Exptl. Biol. Med.*, **28,** 745.

Cohen, S. S., 1947a. The synthesis of bacterial viruses in infected cells. *Cold Spring Harbor Symposium Quant. Biol.*, **12,** 35.

Cohen, S. S., 1947b. Streptomycin and desoxyribonuclease in the study of variations in the properties of a bacterial virus. *J. Biol. Chem.*, **168,** 511.

Cohen, S. S., 1948. The synthesis of bacterial viruses: I. The synthesis of nucleic acid and protein in *Escherichia coli* B infected with T2$r+$ bacteriophage. *J. Biol. Chem.*, **174,** 281.

Cohen, S. S., 1949. Growth requirements of bacterial viruses. *Bacteriol. Rev.*, **13,** 1.

Cohen, S. S., 1952. The enzymes of the host cell as a requirement for virus synthesis. *Ann. N.Y. Acad. Sci.*, **54,** 902.

Cohen, S. S., 1953a. Chemotherapeutic aspects of studies on bacterial viruses. *Pediatrics*, **11,** 89.

Cohen, S. S., 1953b. Studies on controlling mechanisms in the metabolism of virus-infected bacteria. *Cold Spring Harbor Symposium Quant. Biol.*, **18,** 221.

Cohen, S. S., 1956. Molecular bases of parasitism of some bacterial viruses. *Science*, **123,** 653.

Cohen, S. S., and T. F. Anderson, 1946. Chemical studies on host-virus interactions: I. The effect of bacteriophage adsorption on the multiplication of its host, *Escherichia coli* B. *J. Exptl. Med.*, **84,** 511.

Cohen, S. S, and R. Arbogast, 1950a. VI. Immunochemical studies on the purity of concentrates of various bacterial viruses prepared by differential centrifugation procedures. *J. Exptl. Med.*, **91,** 607.

Cohen, S. S., and R. Arbogast, 1950b. VII. A comparison of some properties of three mutant pairs of bacterial viruses, T2$r+$ and T2r, T4$r+$ and T4r, T6$r+$ and T6r. *J. Exptl. Med.*, **91,** 619.

Cohen, S. S., and R. Arbogast, 1950c. *J. Exptl. Med.*, **91,** 637.

Cohen, S. S., and H. D. Barner, 1954. Studies on unbalanced growth in *E. coli*. *Proc. Natl. Acad. Sci. U. S.*, **40,** 885.

Cohen, S. S., and C. B. Fowler, 1947. Chemical studies on host-virus interactions: III. Tryptophane requirements in the stages of virus multiplication in the *Escherichia coli*-T2 bacteriophage system. *J. Exptl. Med.*, **85**, 771.

Cohen, S. S., and C. B. Fowler, 1948. V. Some additional methods of determining nutritional requirements for virus multiplication. *J. Exptl. Med.*, **87**, 275.

Collins, E. B., 1956. Host-controlled variation in bacteriophages active against lactic streptococci. *Virology*, **2**, 261.

Collins, E. B., F. E. Nelson, and C. E. Parmelee, 1950. Relation of calcium and other constituents of a defined medium to proliferation of lactic streptococcus phage. *J. Bacteriol*, **60**, 533.

Collins, N. J., 1957. Thesis, New York University, N. Y.

Conn, H. J., E. J. Botcher, and C. Randall, 1945. *J. Bacteriol.*, **49**, 359.

Costa Cruz, J. da, 1923. *Compt. rend. soc. biol.*, **89**, 759.

Craigie, J., 1940. *Intern. Congr. Microbiol., 3rd Congr., New York, Rept. Proc.*, p. 296.

Craigie, J., 1942. *Can. Public Health J.*, **33**, 41.

Craigie, J., 1946. *Bacteriol. Rev.*, **10**, 73.

Craigie, J., and K. F. Brandon, 1936. *J. Pathol. Bacteriol.*, **43**, 233.

Craigie, J., and A. Felix, 1947. *Lancet*, **1**, 823.

Craigie, J., and C. H. Yen, 1937. *Trans. Roy. Soc. Can.*, **V, 31**, 79.

Craigie, J., and C. H. Yen, 1938. *Can. Public Health J.*, **29**, 448, 484.

Csáky, T. Z., D. Beard, E. S. Dillon, and J. W. Beard, 1950. *J. Biol. Chem.*, **185**, 311.

Czekalowski, J. W., 1952. Studies on the reproduction of bacterial viruses: II. Effect of enzyme-inhibitors on the multiplication of the coliphage T2. *Brit. J. Exptl. Pathol.*, **33**, 57.

D

Delaporte, B., 1949. *Carnegie Inst. Wash. Year Book*, **48**, 166.

Delaporte, B., 1952. *Ann. inst. Pasteur*, **83**, 555.

Delaporte, B., and L. Siminovitch, 1952. *Ann. inst. Pasteur*, **82**, 90.

Delbrück, M., 1940a. Adsorption of bacteriophage under various physiological conditions of the host. *J. Gen. Physiol.*, **23**, 631.

Delbrück, M., 1940b. The growth of bacteriophage and lysis of the host. *J. Gen. Physiol.*, **23**, 643.

Delbrück, M., 1945a. The burst size distribution in the growth of bacterial viruses. *J. Bacteriol.*, **50**, 131.

Delbrück, M., 1945b. Effects of specific antisera on the growth of bacterial viruses. *J. Bacteriol.*, **50**, 137.

Delbrück, M., 1945c. Interference between bacterial viruses: III. The mutual exclusion effect and the depressor effect. *J. Bacteriol.*, **50**, 151.

Delbrück, M., 1945d. The breakdown of the mutual exclusion mechanism. *Ann. Rept. L.I. Biol. Assoc.* **56,** 28.

Delbrück, M., 1946a. Experiments with bacterial viruses, *Harvey Lect.*, **41,** 161.

Delbrück, M., 1946b. Bacterial viruses or bacteriophages. *Biol. Revs. Cambridge Phil. Soc.*, **21,** 30.

Delbrück, M., 1948. Biochemical mutants of bacterial viruses. *J. Bacteriol.*, **56,** 1.

Delbrück, M., 1954. Wie vermehrt sich ein Bakteriophage? *Angew. Chem.*, **66,** 391.

Delbrück, M., and W. T. Bailey, Jr., 1946. Induced mutations in bacterial viruses. *Cold Spring Harbor Symposia Quant. Biol.*, **11,** 33.

Delbrück, M., and S. E. Luria, 1942. Interference between bacterial viruses: I. Interference between two bacterial viruses acting upon the same host, and the mechanism of virus growth. *Arch. Biochem.*, **1,** 111.

Delbrück, M., and G. S. Stent, 1957. "On the mechanism of DNA replication." In W. D. McElroy and B. Glass, eds., *The Chemical Basis of Heredity*, p. 699. Johns Hopkins Press, Baltimore.

DeMars, R. I., 1953. Chemical mutagenesis in bacteriophage T2. *Nature*, **172,** 964.

DeMars, R. I., 1955. The production of phage-related materials when bacteriophage development is interrupted by proflavine. *Virology*, **1,** 83.

DeMars, R. I., S. E. Luria, H. Fisher, and C. Levinthal, 1953. The production of incomplete bacteriophage particles by the action of proflavine and the properties of the incomplete particles. *Ann. inst. Pasteur*, **84,** 113.

Demerec, M., and Z. E. Demerec, 1956. *Brookhaven Symposia Biol.*, **8,** 75.

Demerec, M., and U. Fano, 1945. Bacteriophage-resistant mutants in *Escherichia coli*. *Genetics*, **30,** 119.

Demerec, M., and R. Latarjet, 1946. *Cold Spring Harbor Symposia Quant. Biol.*, **11,** 38.

Dickinson, L., 1948. The bacteriophages of *Pseudomonas pyocyanea*. 1. The effect of various substances upon their development. *J. Gen. Microbiol.*, **2,** 154.

Dickinson, L., 1954. The behavior of a temperate phage of *Ps. Aeruginosa* compared with that of a serologically related virulent mutant. *J. Gen. Microbiol.*, **11,** 105.

Dische, Z., 1930. Some new characteristic color tests for thymonucleic acid. *Mikrochemie*, **8,** 4.

Doermann, A. H., 1948a. Lysis and lysis inhibition with *E. coli* bacteriophage. *J. Bacteriol.*, **55,** 257.

Doermann, A. H., 1948b. Intracellular growth of bacteriophage. *Carnegie Inst. of Wash. Year Book*, **47,** 176.

Doermann, A. H., 1952. The intracellular growth of bacteriophages: I. Liberation of intracellular bacteriophage T4 by premature lysis with another phage or with cyanide. *J. Gen. Physiol.*, **35,** 645.

Doermann, A. H., 1953. The vegetative state in the life cycle of bacteriophage: evidence for its occurrence, and its genetic characterization. *Cold Spring Harbor Symposia Quant. Biol.*, **18,** 3.

Doermann, A. H., M. Chase, and F. W. Stahl, 1955. Genetic recombination and replication in bacteriophage. *J. Cellular Comp. Physiol.*, **45,** Suppl. **2,** 51.

Doermann, A. H., and M. B. Hill, 1953. Genetic structure of bacteriophage T4 as described by recombination studies of factors influencing plaque morphology. *Genetics*, **38,** 79.

Dolby, D. E., 1955. The effect of enzyme inhibitors on the multiplication of T2 bacteriophage. *J. Gen. Microbiol.*, **12,** 406.

Dooren de Jong, L. E. den, 1931. *Zentr. Bakteriol. Parasitenk., Abt.* **1 Orig. 120,** 1.

Dooren de Jong, L. E. den, 1936. *Zentralbl. Bakteriol. Parasitenk. Abt. I Orig.*, **136,** 404.

Dulbecco, R., 1949a. On the reliability of the Poisson distribution as a distribution of the number of phage particles infecting individual bacteria in a population. *Genetics*, **34,** 122.

Dulbecco, R., 1949b. The number of particles of bacteriophage T2 that can participate in intracellular growth. *Genetics*, **34,** 126.

Dulbecco, R., 1950. Experiments on photoreactivation of bacteriophages inactivated with ultraviolet radiation. *J. Bacteriol.*, **59,** 329.

Dulbecco, R., 1952a. A critical test of the recombination theory of multiplicity reactivation. *J. Bacteriol.*, **63,** 199.

Dulbecco, R., 1952b. Mutual exclusion between related phages. *J. Bacteriol.*, **63,** 209.

Dulbecco, R., 1952c. Production of plaques in mono-layer tissue cultures by single particles of an animal virus. *Proc. Natl. Acad. Sci. U. S.*, **38,** 747.

Dulbecco, R., 1955. In A. Hollaender, ed., *Radiation Biology: Vol. II. Ultraviolet and Related Radiations*, p. 455. McGraw-Hill, New York.

Dulbecco, R., and J. J. Weigle, 1952. Inhibition of bacteriophage development in bacteria illuminated with visible light. *Experimentia*, **8,** 386.

Dunn, D. B., and J. D. Smith, 1954. Incorporation of halogenated pyrimidines into the deoxyribonucleic acids of *Bacterium coli* and its bacteriophages. *Nature*, **174,** 305.

E

Edlinger, E., 1949. *Ann. inst. Pasteur*, **76,** 396.

Edlinger, E., 1951. Etude de l'action de la chloromycetin sur la multiplication du bactériophag. *Ann. inst. Pasteur*, **81,** 514.

Edwards, P. R., D. W. Bruner, and A. B. Moran, 1948. *J. Infectious Diseases*, **83,** 220.

Eisenstark, A., S. S. Goldberg, and L. B. Bernstein, 1955. Lysogenicity in *Xanthomonas pruni*. *J. Gen. Microbiol.*, **12,** 402.

Elford, W. J., 1938. "The Sizes of Viruses and Bacteriophages and Methods for Their Determination." In Doerr and Hallauer, eds., *Handbuch der Virusforschung*, pp. 126–76. Julius Springer, Vienna.

Elford, W. J., 1948. The influence of antibacterial substances on the interaction of bacteria and bacteriophages: I. The influence of penicillin. *J. Gen. Microbiol.*, **2,** 205.

Elford, W. J., and C. H. Andrewes, 1932. The sizes of different bacteriophages. *Brit. J. Exptl. Pathol.*, **13,** 446.

Ellis, E. L., and M. Delbrück, 1939. The growth of bacteriophage. *J. Gen. Physiol.*, **22,** 365.

Ellis, E. L., and J. Spizizen, 1941. The rate of bacteriophage inactivation by filtrates of *Escherichia coli* cultures. *J. Gen. Physiol.*, **24,** 437.

Epstein, H. T., and S. Englander, 1954. *Arch. Biochem. Biophys.*, **52,** 394.

Evans, A. C., 1934. Streptococcus bacteriophage: A study of four serological types. *Public Health Repts. (U.S.)*, **49,** 1386.

Evans, A. C., and E. M. Sockrider, 1942. Another serologic type of streptococcic bacteriophage. *J. Bacteriol.*, **44,** 211.

Evans, E. A., Jr., 1952. *Biochemical Studies of Bacterial Viruses*. Univ. of Chicago Press, Chicago.

Evans, E. A., Jr., 1954. *Ann. Rev. Microbiol.*, **8,** 237.

Exner, F. M., and S. E. Luria, 1941. Sizes of streptococcus bacteriophages determined by X-ray inactivation. *Science*, **94,** 394.

F

Fahey, J. E., 1952. *Can. Public Health J.*, **43,** 167.

Felix, A., 1943. *Brit. Med. J.*, **I,** 435.

Felix, A., 1953. In P. Fildes and W. E. Van Heyningen, eds., *The Nature of Virus Multiplication* (2nd Symposium Soc. Gen. Microbiol.), p. 203. Cambridge Univ. Press, London.

Felix, A., 1956. *J. Gen. Microbiol.*, **14,** 208.

Felix, A., and E. S. Anderson, 1951. *Nature*, **167,** 603.

Felix, A., and B. R. Callow, 1943. *Brit. Med. J.*, **II,** 127.

Felix, A., and B. R. Callow, 1951. *Lancet*, **2,** 10.

Felix, A., and R. M. Pitt, 1934. *Lancet*, **2,** 186.

Ferguson, W. H., A. Juenker, and R. A. Ferguson, 1955. *Am. J. Hyg.*, **62,** 306.

Fildes, P., D. Kay, and W. K. Joklik, 1953. "Divalent Metals in Phage Production." In P. Fildes and W. E. Van Heyningen, eds., *The Nature of Virus Multiplication* (2nd Symposium Soc. Gen. Microbiol.), p. 194. Cambridge Univ. Press, London.

Fischer, G., 1950. On the occurrence of heat-resistant variants in a pure anti-coli bacteriophage. *Acta Pathol. Microbiol. Scand.*, **27,** 129.

Fisk, R. T., 1942. *J. Infectious Diseases,* **71,** 153, 161.

Fisk, R. T., and O. E. Mordvin, 1944. *Am. J. Hyg.*, **40,** 232.

Fitzgerald, R. J., and D. Babbitt, 1946. Studies on bacterial viruses: I. The effect of certain compounds on the lysis of *Escherichia coli* by bacteriophage. *J. Immunol.*, **52,** 121.

Fitzgerald, R. J., and M. E. Lee, 1946. Studies on bacterial viruses: II. Observations on the mode of action of acridines in inhibiting lysis of virus-infected bacteria. *J. Immunol.*, **52,** 127.

Flu, P., and H. Flu, 1946. *Leeuwenhoek ned. Tijdschr.*, **11,** 195.

Fluke, D. J., and E. C. Pollard, 1949. Ultraviolet action spectrum of T1 bacteriophage. *Science,* **110,** 274.

Fodor, A. R. and M. H. Adams, 1955. Genetic control of serological specificity in bacteriophage. *J. Immunol.*, **74,** 228.

Foster, R. A. C., 1948. An analysis of the action of proflavine on bacteriophage growth. *J. Bacteriol.*, **56,** 795.

Foster, R. A. C., F. H. Johnson, and V. K. Miller, 1949. The influence of hydrostatic pressure and urethane on the thermal inactivation of bacteriophage. *J. Gen. Physiol.*, **33,** 1.

Fowler, C. B., and S. S. Cohen, 1948. Chemical studies in host-virus interactions: IV. A method for determining nutritional requirements for bacterial virus multiplication. *J. Exptl. Med.*, **87,** 259.

Fraenkel-Conrat, H., 1956. *J. Am. Chem. Soc.*, **78,** 882.

Franklin, R. M., M. Friedman, and R. B. Setlow, 1953. The ultraviolet action spectrum of a *Bacillus megatherium* bacteriophage. *Arch. Biochem. Biophys.*, **44,** 259.

Fraser, D., 1951a. An apparatus for the growth of aerobic bacteria and the preparation of bacteriophage. *J. Bacteriol.*, **61,** 115.

Fraser, D., 1951b. Bursting bacteria by release of gas pressure. *Nature,* **167,** 33.

Fraser, D., and R. Dulbecco, 1953. A genetic analysis of the factors controlling the *h* character in bacteriophage T3. *Cold Spring Harbor Symposia Quant. Biol.*, **18,** 15.

Fraser, D., and E. A. Jerrell, 1953. The amino acid composition of T3 bacteriophage. *J. Biol. Chem.*, **205,** 291.

Frédéricq, P., 1946. *Schweiz. Z. allgem. Pathol. u. Bakteriol.*, **9,** 385.

Frédéricq, P., 1948. Actions antibiotiques réciproques chez les *Enterobacteriacae. Rev. Belge Path. et Med. exptl.*, **19, suppl. 4.**

Frédéricq, P., 1950. Anomalies observées lors du titrage d'un bactériophage sur des souches microbiennes heterologues. *Compt. rend. soc. biol.*, **144,** 1284.

Frédéricq, P., 1952a. Emploi du chloroforme pour mesurer le taux de fixation des entérobactériophages par les bactéries vivantes. *Compt. rend. soc. biol.*, **146,** 327.

Frédéricq, P., 1952b. Action bactéricide des bactériophages des types II et III sans multiplication des corpuscules. *Compt. rend. soc. biol.*, **146,** 622.

Frédéricq, P., 1953. *Ann. inst. Pasteur*, **84,** 294.

Frédéricq, P., 1954a. *Compt. rend. soc. biol.*, **148,**399.

Frédéricq, P., 1954b. *Compt. rend. soc. biol.*, **148,** 1276.

Frédéricq, P., 1954c. *Compt. rend. soc. biol.*, **148,** 1501.

Frédéricq, P., 1955. *Ann. soc. roy. sci. méd. et nat. Bruxelles*, **8,** 15.

Frédéricq, P., 1956. *Compt. rend. soc. biol.*, **150,** 1514.

Frédéricq, P., and M. Betz-Bareau, 1952. *Ann. inst. Pasteur*, **83,** 283.

Frédéricq, P., and M. Betz-Bareau, 1953. *Compt. rend. soc. biol.*, **147,** 1100, 1113, 1653, and 2043.

Freeman, M., 1937. *Australian J. Exptl. Biol. Med. Sci.*, **15,** 221.

Freeman, V. J., 1951. *J. Bacteriol.*, **61,** 675.

French, R. C., 1954. The contribution of protein from parent to progeny in T2 coliphage. *J. Bacteriol.*, **67,** 45.

French, R. C., A. F. Graham, S. M. Lesley, and C. E. Van Rooyen, 1952. The contribution of phosphorus from $T2r^+$ bacteriophage to progeny. *J. Bacteriol.*, **64,** 597.

French, R. C., and L. Siminovitch, 1955. *Can. J. Microbiol.*, **1,** 754.

Friedman, M., 1954. The effect of the host on the properties and sensitivity of a bacterial virus. *J. Bacteriol.*, **68,** 274.

Friedman, M., and P. B. Cowles, 1953. The bacteriophages of *Bacillus megaterium:* I. Serological, physical, and biological properties. *J. Bacteriol.*, **66,** 379.

G

Gardner, J. F., 1950. *Brit. J. Exptl. Pathol.*, **31,** 102.

Garen, A., 1954. Thermodynamic and kinetic studies on the attachment of T1 bacteriophage to bacteria. *Biochim. et Biophys. Acta*, **14,** 163.

Garen, A., and T. T. Puck, 1951. The first two steps of the invasion of host cells by bacterial viruses. II. *J. Exptl. Med.*, **94,** 177.

Garen, A., and N. D. Zinder, 1955. Radiological evidence for partial genetic homology between bacteriophage and host bacteria. *Virology*, **1,** 347.

Gates, F. L., 1934. Results of irradiating *Staph. aureus* bacteriophage with monochromatic ultraviolet light. *J. Exptl. Med.*, **60,** 179.

Gest, H., 1943.   The effects of inorganic salts on the multiplication of bacterial viruses.   *J. Infectious Diseases*, **73,** 158

Gildemeister, E., 1921.   *Berlin. klin. Wochschr.*, **58,** 1355.

Girard, P., 1943.   *Ann. inst. Pasteur*, **69,** 52.

Giuntini, J., P. Lépine, P. Nicolle, and O. Croissant, 1947.   *Ann. inst. Pasteur*, **73,** 579.

Goebel, W. F., 1950.   Studies on bacteriophage: II.   Inhibition of lysis of *E. coli* B by somatic antigen of phage II Shigella sonnei.   *J. Exptl. Med.*, **92,** 527.

Goebel, W. F., G. T. Barry, M. A. Jesaitis, and E. M. Miller, 1955.   *Nature*, **176,** 700.

Goebel, W. F., G. T. Barry, and T. Shedlovsky, 1956.   *J. Exptl. Med.*, **103,** 577.

Goebel, W. F., and M. A. Jesaitis, 1952.   The somatic antigen of a phage resistant variant of phase II *Sh. sonnei*.   *J. Exptl. Med.*, **96,** 425.

Goebel, W. F., and M. A. Jesaitis, 1953.   *Ann. inst. Pasteur*, **84,** 66.

Gold, W., and D. W. Watson, 1950.   Studies on the bacteriophage infection cycle: I.   A lytic activity assay for bacteriophages of *Clostridium madisonii*.   *J. Bacteriol.*, **57,** 13.

Goldwasser, E., and F. W. Putnam, 1951.   Physicochemical properties of bacteriophages: III.   Diffusion of bacteriophage T6.   *J. Biol. Chem.* **190,** 75.

Goodgal, S. H., C. S. Rupert, and R. M. Herriott, 1957.   "Photoreactivation of *Hemophilus Influenzae* Transforming Factor for Streptomycin Resistance by an Extract of *Escherichia coli* B."   In W. D. McElroy and B. Glass, eds., *Symposium on the Chemical Basis of Heredity*, pp. 341–43.   Johns Hopkins Press, Baltimore.

Gots, J. S., and G. R. Hunt, Jr., 1953.   Amino acid requirements for the maturation of bacteriophage in a lysogenic *Escherichia coli*.   *J. Bacteriol.*, **66,** 353.

Gough, G. A. C., and F. M. Burnet, 1934.   *J. Pathol. Bacteriol.*, **38,** 301.

Graham, A. F., 1953.   *Ann. inst. Pasteur*, **84,** 90.

Graham, D. M., and F. E. Nelson, 1954.   Inhibition of lactic streptococcus, bacteriophage by crystal violet and other agents.   *J. Gen. Physiol.*, **37,** 121.

Gratia, A., 1922.   The Twort-d'Herelle phenomenon: II.   Lysis and microbic variation.   *J. Exptl. Med.*, **35,** 287.

Gratia, A., 1925.   *Compt. rend. soc. biol.*, **93,** 1040.

Gratia, A., 1932.   *Ann. inst. Pasteur.* **48,** 413.

Gratia, A., 1936a.   *Compt. rend. soc. biol.*, **122,** 812.

Gratia, A., 1936b. Mutation d'un bactériophage du *Bacillus megatherium*. *Compt. rend. soc. biol.*, **123**, 1253.

Gratia, A., 1936. *Ann. inst. Pasteur*, **57**, 652.

Gratia, A., 1940. De l'action antagoniste du calcium contre la toxicité exercée par le potassium sur un bactériophage du *Bacillus megatherium*. *Compt. rend. soc. biol.*, **133**, 702.

Gratia, A., and P. Frédéricq, 1946. *Compt. rend. soc. biol.*, **140**, 1032.

Groman, N. B., and M. Eaton, 1955. *J. Bacteriol.*, **70**, 637.

Gross, S. R., 1954a. Abortive infection of a strain of *Escherichia coli* by coliphage T2. *J. Bacteriol.*, **68**, 36.

Gross, S. R., 1954b. *J. Bacteriol.*, **68**, 43.

H

Hadley, P., 1926. *Proc. Soc. Exptl. Biol. Med.*, **23**, 443.

Hahn, F. E., and J. Ciak, 1957. *Science*, **125**, 119.

Halbert, S. P., 1948. *J. Immunol.*, **58**, 153.

Haldane, J. B. S., 1939. *J. Hyg.*, **39**, 289.

Hall, E. A., and I. N. Asheshov, 1953. A study of the action of phagolessin A58 on the T phages. *J. Gen. Physiol.*, **37**, 217.

Hall, E. A., F. Kavanagh, and I. N. Asheshov, 1951. Action of forty-five antibacterial substances on bacterial viruses. *Antibiotics & Chemotherapy*, **1**, 369.

Hammerström, E. H., 1947. *Lancet*, **1**, 102.

Hammerström, E. H., 1949. *Acta Med. Scand.*, **Suppl. 133.**

Hamon, Y., 1956. *Ann. inst. Pasteur* **91**, 82.

Hamon, Y., and Z. V. Lewe, 1955. *Ann. inst. Pasteur*, **89**, 336.

Hamon, Y., and P. Nicolle, 1951. *Ann. inst. Pasteur*, **80**, 496.

Harm, W., 1956. *Virology*, **2**, 559.

Hartman, P. E., S. Mudd, J. Hillier, and E. H. Beutner, 1953. Light and electron microscopic studies of *E. coli*-coliphage interactions: III. Persistence of mitochondria and reductase activity during infection of *E. coli* B with T2 phage. *J. Bacteriol.* **65**, 706.

Heagy, F. C., 1950. The effect of 2,4-dinitrophenol and phage T2 on *Escherichia coli* B. *J. Bacteriol.*, **59**, 367.

Heatley, N. G., and H. W. Florey, 1946. *Brit. J. Exptl. Pathol.*, **27**, 378.

Hedén, C., 1951. Studies of the infection of *E. coli* B with the bacteriophage T2. *Acta Pathol. Microbiol. Scand.*, **Suppl. No. 88.**

Herčík, F., 1955. *Biochem. et Biophys. Acta*, **18**, 1.

d'Herelle, F., 1917. Sur un microbe invisible antagonists des *bacilles dysenteriques*. *Compt. rend.*, **165**, 373.

d'Herelle, F., 1921. *Le bactériophage: son rôle dans l'immunité*. Masson, Paris.

d'Herelle, F., 1926. *The Bacteriophage and Its Behavior.* Williams & Wilkins, Baltimore.

d'Herelle, F., 1930. Elimination du bactériophage dans les symbioses bactérie-bactériophage. *Compt. rend. soc. biol.*, **104,** 1254.

d'Herelle, F., and T. L. Rakieten, 1934. Mutations as governing bacterial characters and serologic reactions. *J. Infectious Diseases*, **54,** 313.

d'Herelle, F., and T. L. Rakieten, 1935. The adaptation of a staphylococcus bacteriophage to an artificially produced antibacteriophagic serum *J. Immunol.*, **28,** 413.

Herriott, R. M., 1948. Inactivation of viruses and cells by mustard gas. *J. Gen. Physiol.*, **32,** 221.

Herriott, R. M., 1951a. Nucleic acid–free T2 virus "ghosts" with specific biological action. *J. Bacteriol.*, **61,** 752.

Herriott, R. M., 1951b. Nucleic acid synthesis in mustard gas treated *E. coli* B. *J. Gen. Physiol.*, **34,** 761.

Herriott, R. M., and J. L. Barlow, 1952. Preparation, purification and properties of *E. coli* virus T2. *J. Gen. Physiol.*, **36,** 17.

Herriott, R. M., and W. H. Price, 1948. The formation of bacterial viruses in bacteria rendered non-viable by mustard gas. *J. Gen. Physiol.*, **32,** 63.

Hershey, A. D., 1941. The absolute rate of the phage-antiphage reaction. *J. Immunol.*, **41,** 299.

Hershey, A. D., 1943. Experiments with bacteriophage supporting the lattice hypothesis. *J. Immunol.*, **47,** 77.

Hershey, A. D., 1946a. Mutation of bacteriophage with respect to type of plaque. *Genetics*, **31,** 620.

Hershey, A. D., 1946b. Spontaneous mutations in bacterial viruses. *Cold Spring Harbor Symposia Quant. Biol.*, **11,** 67.

Hershey, A. D., 1953a. Nucleic acid economy in bacteria infected with bacteriophage T2: II. Phage precursor nucleic acid. *J. Gen. Physiol.* **37,** 1.

Hershey, A. D., 1953b. Intracellular phases in the reproductive cycle of bacteriophage T2. *Ann. inst. Pasteur*, **84,** 99.

Hershey, A. D., 1953c. Functional differentiation within particles of bacteriophage T2. *Cold Spring Harbor Symposia Quant. Biol.*, **18,** 135.

Hershey, A. D., 1953d. *Advances in Genetics*, **5,** 89.

Hershey, A. D., 1954. "Some Central Problems of Viral Growth." In F. W. Hartman, F. L. Horsfall, and J. G. Kidd, eds., *Dynamics of Virus and Rickettsial Infections*, pp. 13–15. Blakiston, New York.

Hershey, A. D., 1955. An upper limit to the protein content of the germinal substance of bacteriophage T2. *Virology*, **1,** 108.

Hershey, A. D., 1956a. In D. E. Green, ed., *Currents in Biochemical Research*, pp. 1–28. Interscience, New York-London.

Hershey, A. D., 1956b. *Brookhaven Symposia in Biol.*, **8,** 6.

Hershey, A. D., 1957. Bacteriophages as genetic and biochemical systems. *Advances in Virus Research*, **4,** 25.

Hershey, A. D., and J. Bronfenbrenner, 1952. "Bacterial Viruses: Bacteriophages." In T. M. Rivers, ed., *Viral and Rickettsial Infections of Man*, 2nd ed., p. 190. Lippincott, Philadelphia.

Hershey, A. D., and E. Burgi, 1956. *Cold Spring Harbor Symposia Quant. Biol.*, **21,** 91.

Hershey, A. D., and M. Chase, 1951. *Cold Spring Harbor Symposia Quant. Biol.* **16,** 471.

Hershey, A. D., and M. Chase, 1952. Independent functions of viral protein and nucleic acid in growth of bacteriophage. *J. Gen. Physiol.*, **36,** 39.

Hershey, A. D., and H. Davidson, 1951. Allelic and non-allelic genes controlling host specificity in a bacteriophage. *Genetics*, **36,** 667.

Hershey, A. D., J. Dixon, and M. Chase, 1953. Nucleic Acid economy in bacteria infected with bacteriophage T2: I. Purine and pyrimidine composition. *J. Gen. Physiol.*, **36,** 777.

Hershey, A. D., A. Garen, D. K. Fraser, and J. D. Hudis, 1954. *Carnegie Inst. Washington Yearbook*, **53,** 210.

Hershey, A. D., G. Kalmanson and J. Bronfenbrenner, 1943a. Quantitative methods in the study of the phage-antiphage reaction. *J. Immunol.*, **46,** 267.

Hershey, A. D., G. Kalmanson, and J. Bronfenbrenner, 1943b. Quantitative relationships in the phage-antiphage reaction: Unity and homogeneity of the reactants. *J. Immunol.*, **46,** 281.

Hershey, A. D., G. Kalmanson, and J. Bronfenbrenner, 1944. Coordinate effects of electrolyte and antibody on infectivity of bacteriophage. *J. Immunol.*, **48,** 221.

Hershey, A. D., M. D. Kamen, J. W. Kennedy, and H. Gest, 1951. The mortality of bacteriophage containing assimilated radioactive phosphorus. *J. Gen. Physiol.*, **34,** 305.

Hershey, A. D., F. Kimura, and J. Bronfenbrenner, 1947. Uniformity of size of bacteriophage particles. *Proc. Soc. Exptl. Biol. Med.*, **64,** 7.

Hershey, A. D., and N. E. Melechen, 1957. *Virology*, **3,** 207.

Hershey, A. D., C. Roesel, M. Chase, and S. Forman, 1951. *Carnegie Inst. Washington Year Book*, **50,** 195.

Hershey, A. D., and R. Rotman, 1948. Linkage among genes controlling inhibition of lysis in a bacterial virus. *Proc. Natl. Acad. Sci. U. S.*, **34,** 89.

Hershey, A. D., and R. Rotman, 1949. Genetic recombination between host range and plaque-type mutants of bacteriophage in single bacterial cells. *Genetics*, **34,** 44.

Hill, R. F., 1956. Effects of illumination on plaque formation by *Escherichia coli* infected with T1 bacteriophage. *J. Bacteriol.* **71,** 231.

Hill, R. F., and H. H. Rossi, 1954. The ultraviolet sensitivity and photoreactivability of T1 bacteriophage. *Radiation Research*, **1**, 282.

Himmelweit, F., 1945. Combined action of penicillin and bacteriophage on staphylococci. *Lancet*, **249**, 104.

Hirst, G. K., 1948. *J. Exptl. Med.*, **87**, 301.

Hofer, A. W., 1947. Bacteriophage under the ordinary microscope. *J. Bacteriol*, **53**, 781.

Hollaender, A., 1954. Ed., *Radiation Biology: Vol. I. High Energy Radiation.* McGraw-Hill, New York.

Hollaender, A., 1955. Ed., *Radiation Biology: Vol. II. Ultraviolet and Related Radiations.* McGraw-Hill, New York.

Holweck, F. S., Luria, and E. Wollman, 1940. *Compt. rend.*, **210**, 639.

Hook, A. E., D. Beard, A. R. Taylor, D. G. Sharp, and J. W. Beard, 1946. Isolation and characterization of T2 bacteriophage of *Escherichia coli*. *J. Biol. Chem.*, **165**, 241.

Hoshino, T., 1954a. The influence of the host character of *Escherichi coli* upon its lysis by bacteriophage: I. New screening method for the observation on the antiphage action of a compound. *Japan J. Exptl. Med.*, **24**, 59.

Hoshino, T., 1954b. The influence of the host character of *Escherichia coli* upon its lysis by bacteriophage: II. The influence of host character on the acriflavine tolerance of bacteriophage T3. *Japan. J. Exptl. Med.*, **24**, 63.

Hotchin, J. E., 1951. The influence of acridines on the interaction of *Staphylococcus aureus* and staphylococcus K phage. *J. Gen. Microbiol.*, **5**, 609.

Hotchin, J. E., 1954. The purification and electron microscopical examination of the structure of staphylococcal bacteriophage K. *J. Gen. Microbiol.*, **10**, 250.

Humphries, J. C., 1948. Enzymic activity of bacteriophage culture lysates. *J. Bacteriol.*, **56**, 683.

I

Ionesco, H., 1953. *Compt. rend.*, **237**, 1794.

Iseki, S., and T. Sakai, 1953. *Proc. Japan Acad.*, **29**, 127.

Ivànovics, G., and L. Alföldi, 1954. *Nature*, **174**, 465.

Ivànovics, G., and L. Alföldi, 1955. Observations on lysogenesis in *B. megatherium* and on megacine, the antibacterial principle of this bacillus species. *Acta Microbiol. Acad. Sci. Hung. II*, **3**, 275.

Ivànovics, G., and L. Alföldi, 1957. *J. Gen. Microbiol.*, **16**, 522.

Ivànovics, G., L. Alföldi, and E. Abraham, 1955. *Zentr. Bakertiol. Parasitenk.*, **Abt. I Orig.**, **163**, 274.

J

Jacob, F., 1950. *Compt. rend.*, **231,** 1585.

Jacob, F., 1952a. *Ann. inst. Pasteur*, **82,** 578.

Jacob, F., 1952b. *Ann. inst. Pasteur*, **83,** 295.

Jacob, F., 1952c. Développement spontané et induit des bactériophages chez des *Pseudomonas pyocyanea* polylysogènées. *Ann. inst. Pasteur*, **83,** 671.

Jacob, F., 1954a. *Les bactéries lysogènes et la notion de provirus.* Masson, Paris.

Jacob, F., 1954b. *Ann. inst. Pasteur*, **86,** 149.

Jacob, F., 1954c. Mutation d'un bactériophage induite par l'irradiation des seules bactéries hôtes avant l'infection. *Compt. rend. Acad Sci.*, **238,** 732.

Jacob, F., 1955. *Virology*, **1,** 207.

Jacob, F., A. Lwoff, L. Siminovitch, and E. L. Wollman, 1953. *Ann. inst. Pasteur*, **84,** 222.

Jacob, F., L. Siminovitch, and E. L. Wollman, 1952. *Ann. inst. Pasteur*, **83,** 295.

Jacob, F., L. Siminovitch, and E. L., Wollman, 1953. *Ann. inst. Pasteur*, **84,** 313.

Jacob, F., A. M. Torriani, and J. Monod, 1951. L'effet du rayonnement ultraviolet sur la biosynthèse de la β galactosidase et sur la multiplication du bactériophage T2 chez *E. coli*. *Compt. rend. Acad. Sci.*, **233,** 1230.

Jacob, F., and E.-L. Wollman, 1953. *Cold Spring Harbor Symposia Quant. Biol.*, **18,** 101.

Jacob, F., and E.-L. Wollman, 1954. *Ann. inst. Pasteur*, **87,** 653.

Jacob, F., and E.-L. Wollman, 1955. *Ann. inst. Pasteur*, **88,** 724.

Jacob, F., and E.-L. Wollman, 1956. *Ann. inst. Pasteur*, **90,** 282.

Jacob, F., and E.-L. Wollman, 1957. In W. D. McElroy and B. Glass, eds., *Symposium on the Chemical Basis of Heredity*, pp. 468–98. Johns Hopkins Press, Baltimore.

Jerne, N. K., 1952. Bacteriophage inactivation by antiphage serum diluted in distilled water. *Nature*, **169,** 117.

Jerne, N. K., 1956. The presence in normal serum of specific antibody against bacteriophage T4 and its increase during the earliest stages of immunization. *J. Immunol.*, **76,** 209.

Jerne, N. K., and P. Avegno, 1956. The development of the phage-inactivating properties of serum during the course of specific immunization of an animal: reversible and irreversible inactivation. *J. Immunol.*, **76,** 200.

Jerne, N. K., and L. Skovsted, 1953. The rate of inactivation of bacteriophage T4r in specific antiserum: I. Salt effect II. Cofactor. *Ann. inst. Pasteur*, **84,** 73.

Jesaitis, M. A., and W. F. Goebel, 1952. The chemical and antiviral properties of the somatic antigen of phase II *Sh. sonnei*. *J. Exptl. Med.*, **96,** 409.

Jesaitis, M. A., and W. F. Goebel, 1953. The interaction between T4 phage and the specific lipocarbohydrate of phase II *Sh. sonnei*. *Cold Spring Harbor Symp. Quant. Biol.*, **18,** 205.

Jesaitis, M. A., and W. F. Goebel, 1955. Lysis of T4 phage by the specific lipocarbohydrate of phase II *Shigella sonnei*. *J. Exptl. Med.*, **102,** 733.

Joklik, W. K., 1952. Intracellular growth of phages T1 and T2. *Brit. J. Exptl. Pathol.*, **33,** 359.

Jones, D., 1945. The effect of antibiotic substances upon bacteriophage. *J. Bacteriol.*, **50,** 341.

Jones, D., and A. Schatz, 1946. Methods of study of antiphage agents produced by microorganisms. *J. Bacteriol.*, **52,** 327.

K

Kaiser, A. D., 1955. *Virology*, **1,** 424.

Kaiser, A. D., 1957. *Virology*, **3,** 42.

Kalmanson, G., and J. Bronfenbrenner, 1939. Studies on the purification of bacteriophage. *J. Gen. Physiol.*, **23,** 203.

Kalmanson, G., and J. Bronfenbrenner, 1942. Evidence of serological heterogeneity of polyvalent "pure line" bacteriophage. *J. Immunol.*, **45,** 13.

Kalmanson, G. M., and J. Bronfenbrenner, 1943. Restoration of activity of neutralized biologic agents by removal of the antibody with papain. *J. Immunol.*, **47,** 387.

Kalmanson, G. M., A. D. Hershey, and J. Bronfenbrenner, 1942. Factors influencing the rate of neutralization of bacteriophage by the antibody. *J. Immunol.*, **45, 1.**

Kalter, S. S., V. D. Mordaunt, and O. D. Chapman, 1946. Isolation of *E. coli* phage by means of cationic detergents. *J. Bacteriol.*, **52,** 237.

Kay, D., 1952. The intracellular multiplication of coli bacteriophage T5st. *Brit. J. Exptl. Pathol.*, **33,** 236.

Kay, D., and P. Fildes, 1950. Calcium requirement of a typhoid phage. *Brit. J. Exptl. Pathol.*, **31,** 338.

Kellenberger, E., and W. Arber, 1955. Die Struktur des Schwanzes der Phagen T2 und T4 und der Mechanismus der irreversiblen Adsorption. *Z. Naturforsch.*, **10b,** 698.

Kellenberger, E., and W. Arber, 1957. *Virology*, **3,** 245.

Kellenberger, G., and E. Kellenberger, 1952. *Schweiz. Z. allgem. Pathol. u. Bakteriol.*, **15,** 225.

Kellenberger, G., and E. Kellenberger, 1956. Etude de souches colicinogènes au microscope électronique. *Schweiz. Z. allgem. Pathol. Bakteriol.*, **19,** 582.

Kellenberger, E., A. Ryter, and W. Schwab, 1956. *Experientia*, **12,** 421.

Kellenberger, E., and J. Séchaud, 1957. *Virology*, **3,** 256.

Kelner, A., 1949. *Proc. Natl. Acad. Sci. U. S.*, **35,** 73.

Kelner, A., 1953. Growth, respiration and nucleic acid synthesis in ultraviolet-irradiated and in photoreactivated *Escherichia coli.* *J. Bacteriol.*, **65,** 252.

Keogh, E. V., R. T. Simmons, and G. Anderson, 1938. *J. Pathol. Bacteriol.*, **46,** 565.

Kerby, G. P., R. A. Gowdy, E. S. Dillon, M. L. Dillon, T. Z. Csàkay, D. G. Sharp, and J. W. Beard, 1949. Purification, pH stability and sedimentation properties of the T7 bacteriophage of *Escherichia coli.* *J. Immunol.*, **63,** 93.

Kleczkowski, A., 1957. Effects of nonionizing radiations on viruses. *Advances in Virus Research,* **4,** 191.

Kleczkowski, J., and A. Kleczkowski, 1954. A study of the mechanism of inhibition of bacteriophage multiplication by chymotrypsin. *J. Gen. Microbiol.*, **10,** 285.

Klein, M., S. S. Kalter, and S. Mudd, 1945. The action of synthetic detergents upon certain strains of bacteriophage and virus. *J. Immunol.*, **51,** 389.

Kligler, I. J., and E. Olenick, 1943. Inactivation of phage by aldehydes and aldoses and subsequent reactivation. *J. Immunol.*, **47,** 325.

Knight, C. A., and W. M. Stanley, 1944. The effect of some chemicals on purified influenza virus. *J. Exptl. Med.*, **79,** 291.

Koch, A. L., F. W. Putnam, and E. A. Evans., Jr., 1952. *J. Biol. Chem.*, **197,** 113.

Koch, G., and W. Weidel, 1956a. Uber die receptorsubstanz fur den phagen T5: IV Mitteil. Eine einfache Methode zur quantitativen Bestimmung von Aminosauren und ihre Anwendung fur Vergleiche zwischen Receptorsubstanz und mutativen Abwandlungsprodukt. *Z. physiol. Chem.*, **303,** 213.

Koch, G., and W. Weidel, 1956b. *Z. Naturforsch.*, **11b,** 345.

Koerber, W. L., G. Greenspan, and A. F. Langlykke, 1950. Observations on the multiplication of phages affecting *Streptomyces griseus.* *J. Bacteriol.*, **60,** 29.

Kozloff, L. M., 1952a. Biochemical studies of virus reproduction: VI. Breakdown of phage T6r⁺. *J. Biol. Chem.*, **194,** 83.

Kozloff, L. M., 1952b. *J. Biol. Chem.*, **194,** 95.

Kozloff, L. M., 1952c. The fate of the infecting virus particle. *Exptl. Cell Research Suppl.*, **2,** 367.

Kozloff, L. M., 1953. Origin and fate of bacteriophage material. *Cold Spring Harbor Symposia Quant. Biol.*, **18,** 209.

Kozloff, L. M., and K. Henderson, 1955. Action of complexes of the zinc group metals on the tail protein of bacteriophage T2r⁺. *Nature,* **176,** 1169.

Kozloff, L. M., K. Knowlton, F. W. Putnam, and E. A. Evans, Jr., 1951. *J. Biol. Chem.*, **188,** 101.

Kozloff, L. M., and F. W. Putnam, 1949. Biochemical studies of virus reproduction: II. Chemical composition of *E. coli* bacteriophage T6 and its host. *J. Biol. Chem.*, **181**, 207.

Kozloff, L. M., and F. W. Putnam, 1950. Biochemical studies of virus reproduction. III. The origin of virus phosphorus in the Escherichia coli T6 bacteriophage system. *J. Biol. Chem.*, **182**, 229.

Krieg, D. R., 1957. Thesis, University of Rochester, Rochester, N. Y.

Kristensen, M., 1938. *J. Hyg.*, **38**, 688.

Kristensen, M., and H. C. D. Henriksen, 1926. *Acta Pathol. Microbiol. Scand.*, **3**, 551.

Krueger, A. P., 1930. A method for quantitative determination of bacteriophage. *J. Gen Physiol.*, **13**, 557.

Krueger, A. P., 1931. The sorption of bacteriophage by living and dead susceptible q acteria. *J. Gen. Physiol.*, **14**, 493.

Krueger, A. P·, 1932. The heat inactivation of an antistaphylococcus bacteriophage. *J. Gen. Physiol.*, **15**, 363.

Krueger, A. P., and D. M. Baldwin, 1934. The reversible inactivation of bacteriophage by HgCl₂. *J. Gen. Physiol.*, **17**, 499.

Krueger, A. P., T. Cohn, P. N. Smith, and C. D. McGuire, 1948. Observations on the effect of penicillin on the reaction between phage and staphylococci. *J. Gen. Physiol.*, **31**, 477.

Krueger, A. P., and J. Northrop, 1930. *J. Gen. Physiol.*, **14**, 223.

Krueger, A. P., and E. J. Scribner, 1939. Intracellular phage precursor. *J. Gen. Physiol.*, **22**, 699.

Krueger, A. P., E. J. Scribner, and T. Mecracken, 1940. Photodynamic inactivation of phage precursor by methylene blue. *J. Gen. Physiol.*, **23**, 705.

L

Labaw, L. W., 1951. Origin of phosphorus in *E. coli* bacteriophages. *J. Bacteriol.*, **62**, 169.

Labaw, L. W., 1953. The origin of phosphorus in the T1, T5, T6, and T7 bacteriophages of *E. coli*. *J. Bacteriol.*, **66**, 429.

Labaw, L. W., V. M. Mosely, and R. W. G. Wyckoff, 1949. Lysis of formalinized bacteria by phage. *Science*, **110**, 275.

Labaw, L. W., V. M. Mosley, and R. W. G. Wyckoff, 1950a. *Exptl. Cell Research*, **1**, 353.

Labaw, L. W., V. M. Mosley, and R. W. G. Wyckoff, 1950b. Electron microscopy of ultraviolet irradiated bacteria and their interaction with bacteriophage. *Biochim. et Biophys. Acta*, **5**, 327.

Labaw, L. W., V. M. Mosley, and R. W. G. Wyckoff, 1953. Development of bacteriophage in X-ray inactivated bacteria. *J. Bacteriol.*, **65,** 330.

Lanni, F., and Y. T. Lanni, 1953. Antigenic structure of bacteriophage. *Cold Spring Harbor Symposia Quant. Biol.*, **18,** 159.

Lanni, F., and Y. T. Lanni, 1956. Mutational reduction of host range in coliphage T5. *Proc. Soc. Am. Bacteriol.*, p. 51.

Lanni, F., and Y. T. Lanni, 1957. Serological mutants and structure of phage T5. *Federation Proc.*, **16,** 421.

Lanni, Y. T., 1954. Infection by bacteriophage T5 and its intracellular growth —A study by complement fixation. *J. Bacteriol.*, **67,** 640.

Lark, K. G., and M. H. Adams, 1953. The stability of phages as a function of the ionic environment. *Cold Spring Harbor Symposia Quant. Biol.*, **18,** 171.

Lasnitzki, I., 1954. Incorporation of 8-azaguanine into nucleic acids. *Nature*, **173,** 346.

Latarjet, R., 1942. *Ann. inst. Pasteur*, **68,** 561.

Latarjet, R., 1946. *Rev. can. Biol.*, **5,** 9.

Latarjet, R., 1948. Intracellular growth of bacteriophage studied by roentgen irradiation. *J. Gen. Physiol.*, **31,** 529.

Latarjet, R., 1949. Mutation induite chez un virus par irradiation ultraviolette de cellules infectées. *Compt. rend. Acad. Sci.*, **228,** 1354.

Latarjet, R., 1951. *Ann. inst. Pasteur*, **81,** 389.

Latarjet, R., 1953. "Multiplication of Bacterial Viruses Studied by Radiobiological Methods." In P. Fildes and W. E. Van Heyningen, eds., *The Nature of Virus Multiplication* (2nd Symposium Soc. Gen. Microbiol.), p. 175. Cambridge Univ. Press, London.

Latarjet, R., 1954. *Acta Cancrol.*, **10,** 136.

Latarjet, R., and E. Ephrati, 1948. Influence protectrice de certaines substances contre l'inactivation d'un bacteriophage par les rayons-X. *Compt. rend. Soc. Biol.*, **142,** 497.

Latarjet, R., and P. Frédéricq, 1955. *Virology*, **1,** 100.

Latarjet, R., and B. Milétic, 1953. *Ann. inst. Pasteur*, **84,** 205.

Latarjet, R., and P. Morenne, 1951. Inactivation d'un bactériophage par un rayonnement ultraviolet de très faible intensité. *Ann. inst. Pasteur*, **80,** 220.

Latarjet, R., and R. Wahl, 1945. Précisions sur l'inactivation des bactériophages par les rayons ultraviolets. *Ann. inst. Pasteur*, **71,** 336.

Lazarus, A. S., and J. B. Gunnison, 1947. Action of *P. pestis* phage on strains of Pasteurella, Salmonella and Shigella. *J. Bacteriol.*, **53,** 705.

Lea, D. E., 1946. *Actions of Radiations on Living Cells*. Cambridge Univ. Press, London.

Lea, D. E., and C. A. Coulson, 1949. The distribution of the numbers of mutants in bacterial populations. *J. Genetics*, **49,** 264.

Lea, D. E., and M. H. Salaman, 1946. Experiments on the inactivation of bacteriophage by radiations, and their bearing on the nature of bacteriophage. *Proc. Roy. Soc. (London)*, **133B**, 434.

Lederberg, J., 1957. Mechanism of action of penicillin. *J. Bacteriol.*, **73**, 144.

Lederberg, J., and E. M. Lederberg, 1952. Replica plating and indirect selection of bacterial mutants. *J. Bacteriol.*, **63**, 399.

Lederberg, E. M., and J. Lederberg, 1953. *Genetics*, **38**, 51.

Lendon, N. C., and R. D. Mackenzie, 1951. *Monthly Bulletin Ministry Health (London)*, **10**, 23.

Lennox, E. S., 1955. *Virology*, **1**, 190.

Lennox, E. S., C. Levinthal, and F. Smith, 1953. The effect of finite input in reducing recombinant frequency. *Genetics*, **38**, 508.

Lennox, E. S., S. E. Luria, and S. Benzer, 1954. On the mechanism of photoreactivation of ultraviolet inactivated bacteriophage. *Biochim. et Biophys. Acta*, **15**, 471.

Lépine, P., P. Bonét-Maury, N. Boulgakov, and J. Giuntini, 1944. *Compt. rend. soc. biol.*, **138**, 728.

Lesley, S. M., R. C. French, and A. F. Graham, 1950. Breakdown of infecting coliphage by the host cell. *Arch. Biochem.*, **28**, 149.

Lesley, S. M., R. C. French, and A. F. Graham, and C. E. Van Rooyen, 1951. *Can. J. Med. Sci.*, **29**, 128.

Levin, B. S., and I. Lominski, 1936. Sur le méchanisme de l'inhibition du bactériophage par la lécithine. *Comp. rend. soc. biol.*, **122**, 1286.

Levine, M., 1957. *Virology*, **3**, 22.

Levine, P., and A. W. Frisch, 1933a. *Proc. Soc. Exptl. Biol. Med.*, **30**, 993.

Levine, P., and A. W. Frisch, 1933b. *Proc. Soc. Exptl. Biol. Med.*, **31**, 47.

Levine, P., and A. W. Frisch, 1934. *J. Exptl. Med.*, **59**, 213.

Levine, P., and A. W. Frisch, 1935. *Proc. Soc. Exptl. Biol. Med.*, **32**, 883.

Levine, P., and A. W. Frisch, 1936. *J. Immunol.*, **30**, 63.

Levinthal, C., 1954. Recombination in phage T2: its relationship to heterozygosis and growth. *Genetics*, **39**, 169.

Levinthal, C., 1956. The mechanism of DNA replication and genetic recombination in phage. *Proc. Natl. Acad. Sci. U. S.*, **42**, 394.

Levinthal, C., and H. Fisher, 1952. The structural development of a bacterial virus. *Biochim. et Biophys. Acta*, **9**, 419.

Levinthal, C., and H. W. Fisher, 1953. Maturation of phage and the evidence of phage precursors. *Cold Spring Harbor Symposia Quant. Biol.*, **18**, 29.

Levinthal, C., and C. A. Thomas, Jr., 1957. "The Molecular Basis of Genetic Recombination in Phage." In W. D. McElroy and B. Glass, eds.,

Symposium on the Chemical Basis of Heredity, pp. 737–43. Johns Hopkins Press, Baltimore.

Levinthal, C., and N. Visconti, 1953. Growth and recombination in bacterial viruses. *Genetics*. **38,** 500.

Lieb, M., 1953. *J. Bacteriol.*, **65,** 642,

Lilleengen, K., 1948. *Acta Pathol. Microbiol. Scand.*, **Suppl. 78**.

Lilleengen, K., 1950. *Acta Pathol. Microbiol. Scand.*, **27,** 625.

Lilleengen, K., 1952. *Acta Pathol. Microbiol. Scand.*, **130,** 194.

Lisbonne, M., and L. Carrère, 1923. Influence des electrolytes sur la lyse microbienne transmissible. *Compt. rend. soc. biol.*, **89,** 865.

Litman, R. M., 1956. *Cold Spring Harbor Symposia Quant. Biol.*, **21,** 109.

Litman, R. M., and A. B. Pardee, 1956. Production of bacteriophage mutants by a disturbance of deoxyribonucleic acid metabolism. *Nature*, **178,** 529.

Lunan, K. D., and R. L. Sinsheimer, 1956. A study of the nucleic acid of bacteriophage T7. *Virology*, **2,** 455.

Luria, S. E., 1944. *Proc. Natl. Acad. Sci. U. S.*, **30,** 393

Luria, S. E., 1945a. Mutations of bacterial viruses affecting their host range. *Genetics*, **30,** 84.

Luria, S. E., 1945b. Genetics of bacterium-bacterial virus relationship. *Ann. Missouri Botan. Garden*, **32,** 235.

Luria, S. E., 1946. Spontaneous bacterial mutations to resistance to antibacterial agents. *Cold Spring Harbor Symposia*, **11,** 130.

Luria, S. E., 1947. Reactivation of irradiated bacteriophage by transfer of self-reproducing units. *Proc. Natl. Acad. Sci. U. S.*, **33,** 253.

Luria, S. E., 1950. Bacteriophage: an essay on virus reproduction. *Science*, **111,** 507.

Luria, S. E., 1951. *Cold Spring Harbor Symposia Quant. Biol.*, **16,** 463.

Luria, S. E., 1953a. *General Virology*. Wiley, New York.

Luria, S. E., 1953b. *Cold Spring Harbor Symposia Quant. Biol.*, **18,** 237.

Luria, S. E., 1955. In A. Hollaender, ed., *Radiation Biology: Vol. II. Ultraviolet and Related Radiations*, p. 333. McGraw-Hill, New York.

Luria, S. E., and M. Delbrück, 1942. Interference between bacterial viruses: II. Interference between inactivated bacterial virus and active virus of the same strain and of a different strain. *Arch. Biochem.*, **1,** 207.

Luria, S. E., and M. Delbrück, 1943. *Genetics*, **28,** 491.

Luria, S. E., M. Delbrück, and T. F. Anderson, 1943. Electron microscope studies of bacterial viruses. *J. Bacteriol.*, **46,** 57.

Luria, S. E., and R. Dulbecco, 1949. Genetic recombinations leading to production of active bacteriophage from ultraviolet inactivated bacteriophage particles. *Genetics*, **34,** 93.

Luria, S. E., and F. M. Exner, 1941. *Proc. Natl. Acad. Sci. U. S.*, **27**, 370.

Luria, S. E., and M. L. Human, 1950. Chromatin staining of bacteria during bacteriophage infection. *J. Bacteriol.*, **59**, 551.

Luria, S. E., and M. L. Human, 1952. *J. Bacteriol.*, **64**, 557.

Luria, S. E., and R. Latarjet, 1947. Ultraviolet irradiation of bacteriophage during intracellular growth. *J. Bacteriol.*, **53**, 149.

Luria, S. E., and J. L. Palmer, 1946. *Carnegie Inst. Wash. Yearbook*, **45**, 153.

Luria, S. E., and D. L. Steiner, 1954. The role of calcium in the penetration of bacteriophage T5 into its host. *J. Bacteriol.*, **67**, 635.

Luria, S. E., R. C. Williams, and R. C. Backus, 1951. Electron micrographic counts of bacteriophage particles. *J. Bacteriol.*, **61**, 179.

Lwoff, A., 1951. *Ann. inst. Pasteur*, **81**, 370.

Lwoff, A., 1953. *Bacteriol. Rev.*, **17**, 269.

Lwoff, A., and A. Gutmann, 1950. *Ann. inst. Pasteur*, **78**, 711.

Lwoff, A., A. S. Kaplan, and E. Ritz, 1954. *Ann. inst. Pasteur*, **86**, 127.

Lwoff, A., and L. Siminovitch, 1951. *Compt. rend.*, **233**, 1397.

Lwoff, A., L. Siminovitch, and N. Kjeldgaard, 1950. *Ann. inst. Pasteur*, **79**, 815.

M

Maaløe, O., 1950. Some effects of changes of temperature on intracellular growth of the bacterial virus T4r. *Acta. pathol. et microbiol. Scand.*, **27**, 680.

Maaløe, O., A. Birch-Andersen, and F. S. Sjöstrand, 1954. *Biochim. et Biophys. Acta*, **15**, 12.

Maaløe, O., and A. Birch-Andersen, 1956. "On the Organization of the Nuclear Material in *Salmonella typhimurium*." In E. T. C. Spooner and B. A. D. Stocker, eds., *Baterial Anatomy*, pp. 261–78. Cambridge Univ. Press, London.

Maaiøe, O., and G. S. Stent, 1952. *Acta Pathol. Microbiol. Scand.*, **30**, 149.

Maaløe, O., and N. Symonds, 1953. Radioactive sulfur tracer studies on the reproduction of T4 bacteriophage. *J. Bacteriol.*, **65**, 177.

Maaløe, O., and J. D. Watson, 1951. The transfer of radioactive phosphorus from parental to progeny phage. *Proc. Natl. Acad. Sci. U. S.*, **37**, 507.

Mackal, R. P., and L. M. Kozloff, 1954. Biochemical studies of virus reproduction: XII. The fate of bacteriophage T7. *J. Biol. Chem.*, **209**, 83.

McCloy, E., 1951. Unusual behavior of a lysogenic Bacillus strain. *J. Gen. Microbiol.*, **5**, XIV (Proceedings).

McClure, W. B., and A. M. Miller, 1946. *Can. Med. Assoc. J.*, **55**, 36.

McKie, M., 1934. The lysogenicity of coliform bacilli. *Australian J. Exptl. Biol.*, **12,** 169.

MacKinley, E. B., 1925. *Compt. rend. soc. biol.*, **93,** 1050.

McLauchlan, T. A., E. M. Clark, and F. W. Boswell, 1947. *Nature*, **160,** 755.

MacNeal, W. J., F. C. Frisbee, and E. Krumwiede, 1937. *J. Infectious Diseases*, **61,** 222.

Mandell, J. D., 1955. Thesis, California Institute of Technology.

Manson, L. A., 1954. Effect of proflavine on bacteriophage synthesis. *Federation Proc.*, **13,** 503.

Manson, L. A., 1957. The biosynthesis of T5 coliphage. *Bacteriol. Proc. Soc. Am. Bacteriologists*, p. 37.

Marcovich, H., 1956. *Ann. inst. Pasteur*, **90,** 458.

Marcuse, K., 1925. *Z. Hyg. Infektionskrankh.*, **105,** 17.

Marcuse, K., 1931. *Klin. Wochschr.*, **10,** 732.

Marcuse, K., 1934a. *Zentr. Bakteriol. Parasitenk.*, **Abt. I 131,** 49.

Marcuse, K., 1934b. *Zentr. Bakteriol. Parasitenk.*, **Abt. I 131,** 206.

Markham, R., 1944. The isolation of viruses by means of the electrically driven Sharples super-centrifuge. *Parasitology*, **35,** 173.

Marshak, A., 1951. Absence of cytosine in bacteriophage T2. *Proc. Natl. Acad. Sci. U. S.*, **37,** 299.

Masry, F. L. G., 1953. The action of aureomycin on the relation between a virus and a cell as shown on the T system of coliphages. *J. Egypt. Med. Assoc.*, **36,** 299.

Matthews, R. E. F., and J. D. Smith, 1955. The chemotherapy of viruses. *Advances Virus Research*, **3,** 49.

Maurer, F. D., and D. W. Woolley, 1948. Protection of Escherichia coli against bacteriophage with citrus pectin. *Proc. Soc. Exptl. Biol. Med. U. S.*, **67,** 379.

Mayers, V. L., and J. Spizizen, 1954. The isolation of desoxyribonucleic acid from bacteriophages by an improved method. *J. Biol. Chem.*, **210,** 877.

Mayr, E., E. B. Lindsley, and R. L. Usinger, 1953. *Methods and Principles of Systematic Zoology.* McGraw-Hill, New York.

Medical Research Council, 1947. Med. Research Council (Brit.) Spec. Rep. Ser. No. 260.

Mejbaum, W., 1939. Estimation of small amounts of pentose, especially in derivatives of adenylic acid. *Z. physiol. Chem.*, **258,** 117.

Melechen, N. E., 1955. The relationship of phage DNA synthesis to protein synthesis in replication of bacteriophage T2. *Genetics*, **40,** 585.

Merling-Eisenberg, K. B., 1938. *Brit. J. Exptl. Pathol.*, **19,** 338.

Merling-Eisenberg, K. B., 1941. *J. Pathol. Bacteriol.*, **53,** 385.

Merrill, M. H., 1936. The mass factor in immunological studies upon viruses *J. Immunol.*, **30,** 169.

Miller, E. M., and W. F. Goebel, 1949. *J. Exptl. Med.*, **90,** 255.

Miller, E. M., and W. F. Goebel, 1954. *J. Exptl. Med.*, **100,** 525.

Mondolfo, U., and E. Hounie, 1948. *Giorn. batteriol. e immunol.*, **39,** 47.

Monod, J., and E.-L. Wollman, 1947. *Ann. inst. Pasteur*, **73,** 937.

Morse, M. L., E. M. Lederberg, and J. Lederberg, 1956. *Genetics*, **41,** 142.

Muckenfuss, R. S., 1928. *J. Exptl. Med.*, **48,** 709.

Mudd, S., J. Hillier, E. H. Beutner, and P. E. Hartman, 1953. *Biochim. et Biophys. Acta*, **10,** 153.

Murphy, J. S., 1952. Mutants of a bacteriophage of *Bacillus megatherium*. *J. Exptl. Med.*, **96,** 581.

Murphy, J. S., 1953. *J. Exptl. Med.*, **98,** 657.

Murphy, J. S., 1954. Some mutant phages produced directly by *B. megatherium* 899a with their rate of occurrence. *J. Exptl. Med.*, **100,** 657.

Murray, R. G. E., D. H. Gillen, and F. C. Heagy, 1950. Cytological changes in *E. coli* produced by infection with phage T2. *J. Bacteriol.*, **59,** 603.

Murray, R. G. E., and J. F. Whitfield, 1953. Cytological effects of infection with T5 and some related phages. *J. Bacteriol.*, **65,** 715.

Mutsaars, W., 1950. Influence de la cysteine sur la bactériophage. *Combt. rend. soc. biol.*, **144,** 1435.

Mutsaars, W., 1951a. Influence des colorants basiques sur la phagostase par la trypaflavine. *Ann. inst. Pasteur*, **80,** 343.

Mutsaars, W., 1951b. Résistance du bactériophage aux acridines. *Ann. inst. Pasteur*, **80,** 65.

N

Nagano, Y., and M. Mutai, 1954a. Etudes sérologiques sur le bactériophage. Neutralisation du bactériophage adsorbé sur la bactérie sensible. *Compt. rend. soc. biol.*, **148,** 757.

Nagano, Y., and M. Mutai, 1954b. Etudes sérologiques sur le bactériophage. Adsorption du bactériophage neutralisé sur la bactérie hôte. *Compt. rend. soc. biol.*, **148,** 766.

Nagano, Y., and M. Oda, 1954. Etudes sérologiques sur le bactériophage. Propriétés sérologiques du phage T2 inactivé par le "choc osmotique." *Compt. rend. soc. biol.*, **148,** 1318.

Nagano, Y., and M. Oda, 1955. Adhésion du bactériophage neutralisé sur le bacille sensible. *Compt. rend. soc. biol.*, **149,** 863.

Nagano, Y., and S. Takeuti, 1951. Etudes sérologiques sur le bactériophage. *Japan. J. Exptl. Med.*, **21,** 427.

Nanavutty, S. H., 1930. The thermal death rate of bacteriophage. *J. Pathol. Bacteriol.*, **33,** 203.

Nelson, J. B., 1927. Variations in the scours type of *B. coli* from the standpoint of bacteriophagic action. *J. Exptl. Med.*, **46,** 549.

Newcombe, H. B., 1948. Delayed phenotypic expression of spontaneous mutations in *E. coli. Genetics,* **33,** 447.

Newcombe, H. B., 1949. *Nature,* **164,** 150.

Nicolle, P., and M. Faguet, 1947. La synergie lytique de la pénicilline et du bactériophage, etudiée au microbiophotomêtre. *Ann. inst. Pasteur,* **73,** 490.

Nicolle, P., Y. Hamon, and E. Edlinger, 1951. *Ann. inst. Pasteur,* **80,** 479.

Nicolle, P., A. Jude, and G. Diverneau, 1953. Antigènes entravant l'action de certain bactériophages. *Ann. inst. Pasteur,* **84,** 27.

Nicolle, P., L. LeMinor, R. Buttiaux, and P. Ducrest, 1952. *Bull. acad. natl. med., Paris,* **136,** 480, 483.

Nicolle, P., and M. Mimica, 1947. Bactériophages et antiseptiques analyses du phénomène de l'anneau de culture. *Ann. inst. Pasteur,* **73,** 1072.

Northrop, J. H., 1938. Concentration and purification of bacteriophage. *J. Gen. Physiol.,* **21,** 335.

Northrop, J. H., 1939a. *Crystalline Enzymes.* Columbia Univ. Press, New York.

Northrop, J. H., 1939b. *J. Gen. Physiol.,* **23,** 59.

Northrop, J. H., 1955a. Inactivation and reactivation of B. megaterium phage. *J. Gen. Physiol.,* **39,** 225.

Northrop, J. H., 1955b. Concentration and purification of B. megaterium phage. *J. Gen. Physiol.,* **39,** 259.

Novick, A., and L. Szilard, 1951a. Virus strains of identical phenotype but different genotype. *Science,* **113,** 34.

Novick, A., and L. Szilard, 1951b. *Cold Spring Harbor Symposia Quant. Biol.* **16,** 337.

O

Oparin, A. I., 1938. *The Origin of Life,* Macmillan, New York.

Ore, A., and E. Pollard, 1956. Physical mechanism of bacteriophage injection. *Science,* **124,** 430.

Otto, R., and Winkler, W. F., 1922. *Deut. Med. Wochschr.,* **48,** 383.

P

P'an, H. S., Y. Tchan, and J. Pochon, 1949. Etudes cytologiques de *Pasteurella pestis* soumis à l'influence du bactériophage specifique: I. Modifications morphologiques de l'appareil nucleaire. *Ann. inst. Pasteur,* **76** 468.

Pardee, A. B., V. G. Shore, and L. S. Prestidge, 1956. Incorporation of aza-tryptophan into proteins of bacteria and bacteriophage. *Biochim. Biophys. Acta*, **21, 406.**

Pardee, A. B., and I. Williams, 1952. The increase in desoxyribonuclease of virus infected *E. coli*. *Arch. Biochem. Biophys.*, **40,** 222.

Pardee, A. B., and I. Williams, 1953. Enzymatic activity and bacteriophage infection: III. Increase of desoxyribonuclease. *Ann. inst. Pasteur*, **84,** 147.

Park, B. H., 1956. An enzyme produced by a phage-host cell system: I. The properties of a *Klebsiella* phage. *Virology*, **2,** 711.

Park, J. T., and J. L. Strominger, 1957. Mode of action of penicillin. *Science*, **125,** 99.

Parmelee, C. E., P. H. Carr, and F. E. Nelson, 1949. Electron microscope studies of bacteriophage active against *Str. lactis*. *J. Bacteriol.*, **57,** 391.

Perdrau, J. R., and C. Todd, 1953. The photodynamic action of methylene blue on bacteriophage. *Proc. Roy. Soc. (London)*, **B112,** 277.

Perlman, D., A. F. Langlykke, and H. D. Rothberg, 1951. Observations on the chemical inhibition of *S. griseus* bacteriophage multiplication. *J. Bacteriol.*, **61,** 135.

Pfankuch, E., and G. A. Kausche, 1940. *Naturwiss.*, **28,** 46.

Pijper, A., 1945. Bacteriophage action on *B. typhosum* and *B. megatherium* as displayed by darkground cinemicrography. *J. Pathol. and Bacteriol.*, **57,** 1.

Pollard, E., 1953. *The Physics of Viruses*. Academic Press, New York.

Pollard, E., 1954. The action of ionizing radiation on viruses. *Advances in Virus Research*, **2,** 109.

Pollard, E. C., and F. Forro, 1949. Examination of target theory by Deuteron bombardment of T1 phage. *Science*, **109,** 374.

Pollard, E., and M. Reaume, 1951. Thermal inactivation of bacterial viruses. *Arch. Biochem.*, **32,** 278.

Pollard, E., and J. Setlow, 1953. Action of heat on the serological affinity of T-1 bacteriophage. *Arch. Biochem. Biophys.*, **43,** 136.

Polson, A., 1948. Diffusion constants of the *E. coli* bacteriophages. *Proc. Soc. Exptl. Biol. Med.*, **67,** 294.

Polson, A., and C. C. Shepard, 1949. On the diffusion rates of bacterio-phages. *Biochim. et Biophys. Acta*, **3,** 137.

Polson, A., and R. W. G. Wyckoff, 1948. *Science*, **108,** 501.

Potter, N. F., and F. E. Nelson, 1953. *J. Bacteriol.*, **66,** 508.

Pausnitz, C., 1922. *Zentr. Bakteriol. Parasitenk*, **Abt. I 89,** 187.

Price, W. H., 1947a. Bacteriophage formation without bacterial growth: I. Formation of Staphylococcus phage in the presence of bacteria inhibited by penicillin. *J. Gen. Physiol.*, **31,** 119.

Price, W. H., 1947b. Bacteriophage formation without bacterial growth: III. The effect of iodoacetate, fluoride, gramicidin, and azide on the formation of bacteriophage. *J. Gen. Physiol.*, **31,** 135.

Price, W. H., 1952. Bacterial viruses. *Ann. Rev. Microbiol.*, **6,** 333.

Puck, T. T., A. Garen, and J. Cline, 1951. The mechanism of virus attachment to host cells: I. The role of ions in the primary reaction. *J. Exptl. Med.*, **93,** 65.

Puck, T. T., and H. H. Lee, 1954. Mechanism of cell wall penetration by viruses: I. An increase in host cell permeability induced by bacteriophage infection. *J. Exptl. Med.*, **99,** 481.

Puck, T. T., and H. H. Lee, 1955. *J. Exptl. Med.*, **101,** 151.

Puck, T. T. and B. Sagik, 1953. Virus and cell interaction with ion exchangers. *J. Exptl. Med.*, **97,** 807.

Puck, T. T., and L. J. Tolmach, 1954. *Arch. Biochem. Biophys.*, **51,** 229.

Putnam, F. W., 1950. Molecular kinetic and electrophoretic properties of bacteriophages. *Science*, **111,** 481.

Putnam, F. W., 1951. Sedimentation of bacteriophage T6. *J. Biol. Chem.*, **190,** 61.

Putnam, F., 1952. The origin of bacteriophage nitrogen, carbon, and phosphorus. *Exptl. Cell. Research Suppl.*, **2,** 345.

Putnam, F. W., 1953. Bacteriophages: nature and reproduction. *Advances in Protein Chem.*, **8,** 175.

Putnam, F. W., 1954. Ultracentrifugation of bacterial viruses. *J. Polymer Science*, **12,** 391.

Putnam, F. W., and L. M. Kozloff, 1950. *J. Biol. Chem.*, **182,** 243.

Putnam, F. W., L. M., Kozloff, and J. C. Neil, 1949. Biochemical studies of virus reproduction: I. Purification and properties of *E. coli* bacteriophage T6. *J. Biol. Chem.*, **179,** 303.

Putnam, F. W., D. Miller, L. Palm, and E. A. Evans, Jr., 1952. Biochemical studies of bacteriophage reproduction: X. Precursors of bacteriophage T7. *J. Biol. Chem.*, **199,** 177.

Q

Quersin, L., 1948. Images nucleaires au cours de divers phénomènes de lyse microbienne. *Ann. inst. Pasteur*, **75,** 522.

R

Ralston, D. J., and A. P. Krueger, 1952. Phage multiplication on two hosts. Isolation and activity of Staphyloccus phage Pl. *Proc. Soc. Exptl. Biol. U. S.*, **80,** 217.

Ralston, D. J., and A. P. Krueger, 1954. The isolation of a staphylococcal phage variant susceptible to an unusual host control. *J. Gen. Physiol.*, **37,** 685.

Reiter, B., 1949. *Nature*, **164,** 667.

Reiter, B., 1956. Inhibition of coli bacteriophage T2 by apple pectin. *J. Gen. Microbiol.*, **14,** 323.

Rice, M. M., E. McCoy, and S. G. Knight, 1954. *Proc. Soc. Exptl. Biol. Med.*, **86,** 344.

Rifkind, D., and M. J. Pickett, 1954. *J. Bacteriol.*, **67,** 243.

Rippon, J. E., 1954. Ph.D. Thesis, London University.

Rippon, J. E., 1956. *J. Hyg.*, **54,** 213.

Rita, G., and L. G. Silvestri, 1950. Studio morfologico delle modificazioni del cosiddetto nucleo in cellule batterische infettate con virus (batteriofagi): I. *E. coli* B virus della serie T. *Boll. soc. ital. biol. Sper.*, **26,** 1.

Robinow, C. F., 1944. *J. Hyg.*, **43,** 413.

Rountree, P. M., 1947a. *Australian J. Exptl. Biol. Med. Sci.*, **25,** 9.

Rountree, P. M., 1947b. Staphylococcal bacteriophages: II. Bacteriophage absorption by straphylococci. *Australian J. Exptl. Biol. Med. Sci.*, **25,** 203.

Rountree, P. M., 1949a. *J. Gen. Microbiol.*, **3,** 153.

Rountree, P. M., 1949b. *J. Gen. Microbiol.*, **3,** 164.

Rountree, P. M., 1951a. *J. Gen. Microbiol.*, **5,** 673.

Rountree, P. M., 1951b. *Brit. J. Exptl. Pathol.*, **32,** 341.

Rountree, P. M., 1952. Serological studies of the multiplication of a staphylococcal bacteriophage. *Australian J. Exptl. Biol. Med. Sci.*, **30,** 567.

Rountree, P. M., 1955. The role of divalent cations in the multiplication of staphylococcal bacteriophages. *J. Gen. Microbiol.*, **12,** 275.

Rountree, P. M., 1956. *J. Gen. Microbiol.*, **15,** 266.

Rouyer, M., and R. Latarjet, 1946. Augumentation du nombre de bactèriophages en presence de bactéries sterilisées par irradiation. *Ann. inst. Pasteur*, **72,** 89.

Ruska, H., 1940. *Naturwiss.*, **28,** 45.

Ruska, H., 1943. *Ergeb. Hyg., Bakteriol. Immunitätsforsch. u. Exptl. Therap.* **25,** 437.

Rutten, F. J., K. C. Winkler, and P. G. DeHaan, 1950. The action of sulfanilamide on bacteriophages T1-T7. *Brit. J. Exptl. Pathol.*, **31,** 369.

Ryan, F. J., P. Fried, and F. Mukai, 1955. *Biochim. et Biophys. Acta*, **18,** 131.

S

Sagik, B. P., 1954. A specific reversible inhibition of bacteriophage T2. *J. Bacteriol.*, **68,** 430.

Sato, G., 1956. *Science*, **123,** 891.

Schlesinger, M., 1932a. *Z. Hyg. Infektionskrankh.*, **114,** 114.

Schlesinger, M., 1932b. *Z. Hyg. Infektionskrankh.*, **114,** 136.

Schlesinger, M., 1932c. *Z. Hyg. Infektionskrankh.*, **114,** 149.

Schlesinger, M., 1933a. *Biochem. Z.*, **264,** 6.

Schlesinger, M., 1933b. *Z. Hyg. Infektionskrankh.*, **115,** 774.

Schlesinger, M., 1934. Zur Frage der chemischen Zusammensetzung des Bakteriophagen. *Biochem. Z.*, **273,** 306.

Schmidt, A., 1931a. *Zentr. Bakteriol. Parasitenk.*, (**Abt. I**) **Ref. 123,** 202.

Schmidt, A., 1931b. *Zentr. Bakteriol. Parasitenk.*, (**Abt. I**) **123,** 207.

Scholtens, R. T., 1936. *J. Hyg.*, **36,** 452.

Scholtens, R. T., 1950. *Leeuwenhoek ned. Tijdschr.*, **16,** 256.

Scholtens, R. T., 1952. *Leeuwenhoek J. Microbiol. Serol.*, **18,** 257.

Scholtens, R. T., 1955. *J. Hyg.*, **53,** 1.

Scholtens, R. T., 1956. *Leeuwenhoek J. Microbiol. Serol.*, **22,** 65.

Schüler, H., 1935. Stoffwechsel- und Fermentuntersuchungen an Bakteriophagen. *Biochem. Z.*, **276,** 254.

Schultz, E. W., and L. P. Gebhardt, 1935. Nature of formalin inactivation of bacteriophage. *Proc. Soc. Exptl. Biol. Med.*, **32,** 1111.

Schultz, E. W., J. S. Quigley, and L. T. Bullock, 1929. The antigenic properties of the bacteriophage. *J. Immunol.*, **17,** 245.

Schultz, E. W., P. R. Thomassen, and L. Marton, 1948. *Proc. Soc. Exptl. Biol. Med.*, **68,** 451.

Schwerdt, C. E., and F. L. Schaffer, 1955. Some physical and chemical properties of purified poliomyelitis virus preparations. *Ann. N.Y. Acad. Sci.* **61,** 740.

Scribner, E. J., and A. P. Kreuger, 1937. *J. Gen. Physiol.*, **21,** 1.

Séchaud, J., and E. Kellenberger, 1956. *Ann. inst. Pasteur*, **90,** 102.

Sertic, V., 1929a. Origine de la lysine d'une race du bactériophage. *Compt. rend. soc. biol.*, **100,** 477.

Sertic, V., 1929b. *Compt. rend. soc. biol.*, **100,** 612.

Sertic, V., 1929c. *Compt. rend. soc. biol.*, **100,** 614.

Sertic, V., 1937. Sur le différence d'action des électrolytes sur le développement des diverses races de bactériophages. *Compt. rend. soc. biol.*, **124,** 98.

Sertic, V., and N. A. Boulgakov, 1935. Classification et identification des typhiphages. *Compt. rend. soc. biol.*, **119,** 1270.

Sertic, V., and N. A. Boulgakov, 1936a. *Compt. rend. soc. biol.*, **122,** 35.

Sertic, V., and N. A. Boulgakov, 1936b. *Compt. rend. soc. biol.*, **123,** 887.

Sertic, V., and N. A. Boulgakov, 1937. *Compt. rend. soc. biol.*, **126,** 734.

Sertic, V., and W. Gough, 1930. Modification d'une race de bacteriophage par adaptation sur des formes bacteriénnes secondaires. *Compt. rend soc. biol.*, **105,** 199.

Setlow, R., S. Robbins, and E. Pollard, 1955. Action spectrum for latent period extension of T1 bacteriophage. *Radiation Research*, **2,** 262.

Sharp, D. G., A. E. Hook, A. R. Taylor, D. Beard, and J. W. Beard, 1946. Sedimentation characters and pH stability of the T2 bacteriophage of *E. coli. J. Biol. Chem.*, **165,** 259.

Shew, D. I., 1949. Effect of calcium on development of streptococcal bacteriophages. *Nature*, **164,** 492.

Shropshire, R. F., 1947. Bacterial dispersion by sonic energy. *J. Bacteriol.*, **54,** 325.

Shwartzman, G., 1927. A powerful lytic principle against hemolytic streptococci of erysipelas origin. *J. Exptl. Med.*, **46,** 497.

Siddiqui, M. S. H., L. M. Kozloff, F. W. Putnam, and E. A. Evans, 1952. *J. Biol. Chem.*, **199,** 165.

Siegel, A., and S. J. Singer, 1953. The preparation and properties of desoxypentosenucleic acid of bacteriophage T2. *Biochim. Biophys. Acta*, **10,** 311.

Sievers, M., 1943. *Zentr. Bakteriol. Parasitenk.*, **Abt. I 150,** 52.

Silvestri, L., 1949, *Boll. Inst. sieroterap. Milan*, **28,** 193.

Siminovitch, L., 1953. *Ann. inst. Pasteur*, **84,** 265.

Sinsheimer, R. L., 1954. Nucleotides from T2r^+ bacteriophage. *Science*, **120,** 551.

Sinsheimer, R. L., 1956. The glucose content of the deoxyribonucleic acids of certain bacteriophages. *Proc. Natl. Acad. Sci. U. S.*, **42,** 502.

Sinsheimer, R. L., 1957. Some properties of bacteriophage ϕX174 *Federation Proc.*, **16,** 250.

Smiles, J., F. V. Welch, and W. J. Elford, 1948. The influence of antibacterial substances on the interaction of bacteria and bacteriophages. *J. Gen. Microbiol.*, **2,** 220.

Smith, A. G., 1949. The effect of acriflavine and phosphine GRN on lysis of bacteria by bacteriophage. *J. Immunol.*, **61,** 57.

Smith, J. D., and G. R. Wyatt, 1951. The composition of some microbial deoxypentose nucleic acids. *Biochem. J.*, **49,** 144.

Sonneborn, T. M., 1955. Heredity, development and evolution in Paramecium. *Nature*, **175,** 1100.

Sonnenschein, C., 1925. *Münch. med. Wochschr.*, 1443.

Sonnenschein, C., 1928. *Deut. med. Wochschr.*, 1034.

Spizizen, J., 1943a. Biochemical studies on the phenomenon of virus reproduction: I. Amino acids and multiplication of bacteriophage. *J. Infectious Diseases*, **73,** 212.

Spizizen, J., 1943b. Biochemical studies on the phenomenon of virus reproduction: II. Studies on the influence of compounds of metabolic significance on the multiplication of bacteriophage. *J. Infectious Diseases*, **73,** 222.

Spizizen, J., B. Hampil, and J. C. Kenney, 1951. Biochemical studies on the phenomenon of virus reproduction: IV. The inhibition of coliphage T2r^+ multiplication by sulfhydryl compounds and its prevention by ethylenediaminetetraacetic acid and metallic ions. *J. Bacteriol.*, **62**, 331.

Spizizen, J., J. C. Kenney, and B. Hampil, 1951. Biochemical studies on the phenomenon of virus reproduction: III. The inhibition of coliphage T2r^+ multiplication by sodium salicylate and sodium gentisate. *J. Bacteriol.*, **62**, 323.

Stahl, F. W., 1956. The effects of the decay of incorporated radioactive phosphorus on the genome of bacteriophage T4. *Virology*, **2**, 206.

Stanley, W. M., 1942. The concentration and purification of tobacco mosaic, virus by means of the Sharples supercentrifuge. *J. Am. Chem. Soc.*, **64**. 1804.

Stanley, W. M., 1944. An evaluation of methods for the concentration and purification of influenza virus. *J. Exptl. Med.*, **79**, 255.

Stassano, H., and A. C. de Beaufort, 1925. Action du citrate de soude sur le principe lytique transmissible. *Compt. rend. soc. biol.*, **93**, 1380.

Stent, G. S., 1953. Cross reactivation of genetic loci of T2 bacteriophage after decay of incorporated radioactive phosphorus. *Proc. Natl. Acad. Sci. U. S.*, **39**, 1234.

Stent, G. S., 1955. Decay of incorporated radioactive phosphorus during reproduction of bacteriophage T2. *J. Gen. Physiol.*, **38**, 853.

Stent, G. S., 1958. Mating in the reproduction of bacterial viruses. *Advances in Virus Research*, **5**, 95.

Stent, G. S., and C. R. Fuerst, 1955. Inactivation of bacteriophages by decay of incorporated radioactive phosphorus. *J. Gen. Physiol.*, **38**, 441.

Stent, G. S., C. R. Fuerst, and F. Jacob, 1957. *Compt. rend.*, **244**, 1840.

Stent, G. S., and N. K. Jerne, 1955. The distribution of parental phosphorus atoms among bacteriophage progeny. *Proc. Natl. Acad. Sci. U. S.*, **41**, 704.

Stent, G. S., N. K. Jerne, and G. Sato, 1957. See Delbrück and Stent, 1957.

Stent, G. S., and O. Maaløe, 1953. Radioactive phosphorus tracer studies on the reproduction of T4 bacteriophage. *Biochim. et Biophys. Acta*, **10**, 55.

Stent, G. S., and E.-L. Wollman, 1950. Studies on activation of T4 bacteriophage by cofactor: II. Mechanism of activation. *Biochim. et Biophys. Acta*, **6**, 307.

Stent, G. S., and E.-L. Wollman, 1951. Studies on activation of T4 bacteriophage by cofactor: III. Conditions affecting the activation process. *Biochim. et Biophys. Acta*, **6**, 374.

Stent, G. S., and E.-L. Wollman, 1952. On the two step nature of bacterio-phage adsorption. *Biochim. et Biophys. Acta*, **8**, 260.

Stock, C. C., and T. Francis, Jr., 1940. *J. Immunol.*, **47**, 303.

Stock, C. C., and T. Francis, Jr., 1943. The inactivation of the virus of lymphocytic choriomeningitis by soaps. *J. Exptl. Med.*, **77**, 323.

Stock, C. C., W. Jacobson, and M. Williamson, 1951. An influence of 2,6-diaminopurine upon the content of Kappa in *Paramecium aurelia*, variety 4. *Proc. Soc. Biol. Med. U. S.*, **78**, 874.

Stocker, B. A. D., 1955. Bacteriophage and bacterial classification. *J. Gen. Microbiol.*, **12**, 375.

Stocker, B. A. D., N. D. Zinder, and J. Lederberg, 1953. *J. Gen. Microbiol.*, **9**, 410.

Streisinger, G., 1956a. The genetic control of ultraviolet sensitivity levels in bacteriophages T2 and T4. *Virology*, **2**, 1.

Streisinger, G., 1956b. The genetic control of host range and serological specificity in bacteriophages T2 and T4. *Virology*, **2**, 377.

Streisinger, G., 1956c. Phenotypic mixing of host range and serological specificities in bacteriophages T2 and T4. *Virology*, **2**, 388.

Streisinger, G., and N. C. Franklin, 1956. *Cold Spring Harbor Symbosia Quant. Biol.*, **21**, 103.

Streisinger, G., and J. Weigle, 1956. Properties of bacteriophages T2 and T4 with unusual inheritance. *Proc. Natl. Acad. Sci. U. S.*, **42**, 504.

Strelitz, F., H. Flon, and I. N. Asheshov, 1955. Chrysomycin: a new antibiotic substance for bacterial viruses. *J. Bacteriol.*, **69**, 280.

Swanstrom, M., and M. H. Adams, 1951. Agar layer method for production of high titer phage stocks. *Proc. Soc. Exptl. Biol. Med.*, **78**, 372.

Symonds, N., 1957. Effects of ultraviolet light during the second half of the latent period on bacteria infected with phage T2. *Virology*, **3**, 485.

T

Tanami, J., and H. Kawashima, 1953. *Virus (Tokyo)*, **3**, 129.

Tanami, Y., and Y. Miyajima, 1956. Evidence of serological heterogeneity of T2 bacteriophage. *J. Bacteriol.*, **72**, 721.

Taylor, A. R., 1946. Chemical analysis of T2 bacteriophage and its host *E. coli.* strain B. *J. Biol. Chem.*, **165**, 271.

Taylor, A. R., D. G. Sharp, D. Beard, and J. W. Beard, 1943. Isolation and properties of equine encephalitis virus (Eastern strain). *J. Infectious Diseases*, **72**, 31.

Taylor, N. W., H. T. Epstein, and M. A. Lauffer, 1955. *J. Am. Chem. Soc.*, **77**, 1270.

Terada, M., 1956. *Studies on Bacterial Viruses*. Naya Co., Tokyo.

Thibaut, J., and P. Frédéricq, 1956. *Compt. rend. soc. biol.*, **150**, 1039.

Tobin, J., 1953. *Brit. J. Exptl. Pathol.*, **34,** 635.

Tolmach, L. J., 1957. *Advances in Virus Research*, **4,** 63.

Tolmach, L. J., and T. T. Puck, 1952. The mechanism of virus attachment to host cells: III, *J. Am. Chem. Soc.*, **74,** 5551.

Tomizawa, J., and S. Sunakawa, 1956. The effect of chloramphenicol on deoxyribonucleic acid synthesis and the development of resistance to ultraviolet irradiation in E. coli infected with bacteriophage T2. *J. Gen. Physiol.*, **39,** 553.

Toshach, Sheila, 1950. Bacteriophages for *C. diphtheriae, Can. J. Public Health,* **41,** 332.

Twort, F. W., 1915. An investigation on the nature of ultramicroscopic viruses. *Lancet,* **2,** 1241.

U

Uetake, H., T. Nakagawa, and T. Akiba, 1955. The relationship of bacteriophage to antigenic changes in group E salmonellas. *J. Bacteriol.*, **69,** 571.

Underwood, N., and A. H. Doermann, 1947. A photoelectric nephelometer. *Rev. Sci. Instruments,* **18,** 665.

V

Van Vunakis, H., J. L. Barlow, and L. Levine, 1956. Neutralization of bacteriophage by the properdin system. *Proc. Natl. Acad. Sci. U. S.* **42,** 391.

Varney, P. L., 1935. An automatically recording colony counting apparatus. *J. Lab. Clin. Med.*, **21,** 207.

Visconti, N., 1953. Resistance to lysis from without in bacteria infected with T2 bacteriophage. *J. Bacteriol.*, **66,** 247.

Visconti, N., and M. Delbrück, 1953. *Genetics*, **38,** 5.

Visconti, N., and A. Garen, 1953. Unity of the vegetative pool in phage-infected bacteria. *Proc. Natl. Acad. Sci. U. S.*, **39,** 620.

Volkin, E., 1954a. A desoxyribonucleoprotein in bacteriophage $T4_r{}^+$. *Federation Proc.*, **13,** 315.

Volkin, E. 1954b. The linkage of glucose in coliphage nucleic acids. *J. Am. Chem. Soc.*, **76,** 5892.

Volkin, E., and L. Astrachan, 1956a. Phosphorus incorporation in E. coli ribonucleic acid after infection with bacteriophage T2. *Virology*, **2,** 149.

Volkin, E., and L. Astrachan, 1956b. Intracellular distribution of labeled ribonucleic acid after phage infection of Escherichia coli. *Virology* **2,** 433.

Volkin, E., and L. Astrachan, 1956c. The absence of ribonucleic acid in bacteriophage $T2r^+$. *Virology*, **2,** 594.

W

Wahl, R., 1939.   *Compt. rend. soc. biol.*, **131**, 234.

Wahl, R., 1946a.   *Ann. inst. Pasteur*, **72**, 73.

Wahl, R., 1946b.   *Ann. inst. Pasteur*, **72**, 284.

Wahl, R., 1946c.   *Ann. inst. Pasteur*, **72**, 287.

Wahl, R., 1953.   La semi-résistance aux bactériophages.   *Ann. inst. Pasteur*, **84**, 51.

Wahl, R., and L. Blum-Émerique, 1946.   *Ann. inst. Pasteur*, **72**, 959.

Wahl, R., and L. Blum-Émerique, 1947.   *Ann. inst. Pasteur*, **73**, 741.

Wahl, R., and L. Blum-Émerique, 1949a.   *Ann. inst. Pasteur*, **76**, 103.

Wahl, R., and L. Blum-Émerique, 1949b.   *Ann. inst. Pasteur*, **77**, 561.

Wahl, R., and L. Blum-Émerique, 1950.   *Ann. inst. Pasteur*, **78**, 336.

Wahl, R., and L. Blum-Émerique, 1951.   *Ann. inst. Pasteur*, **80**, 155.

Wahl, R., and L. Blum-Émerique, 1952a.   *Ann. inst. Pasteur*, **82**, 29.

Wahl, R., and L. Blum-Émerique, 1952b.   Les bactéries semi-résistantes au bacteriophage: IV.   Influence de la concentration des certains ions sur le comportement des bactéries semi-résistantes vis-à-vis du phage.   Signification de ces bactéries.   *Ann. inst. Pasteur*, **82**, 266.

Wahl, R., and A. Guelin, 1942.   *Ann. inst. Pasteur*, **68**, 245.

Wahl, R., and R. Latarjet, 1947.   Inactivation de bactériophages par des radiations de grande longeur d'onde (3,400–6,000 A).   *Ann. inst. Pasteur*, **73**, 957.

Wahl, R., and S. Lewi, 1939.   *Compt. rend. soc. biol.*, **131**, 749.

Wahl, R., A. Terrade, and G. Monceaux, 1950.   *Ann. inst. Pasteur*, **79**, 429.

Wasserman, M. M., and I. Saphra, 1955.   *J. Bacteriol.*, **69**, 97.

Watanabe, I., 1957.   *J. Gen. Physiol.*, **40**, 521.

Watanabe, I., G. S. Stent, and H. K. Schachman, 1954.   On the state of the parental phosphorus during reproduction of bacteriophage T2.   *Biochim. et Biophys. Acta*, **15**, 38.

Watson, J. D., 1950.   The properties of X-ray inactivated bacteriophage: I.   Inactivation by direct effect.   *J. Bacteriol.*, **60**, 697.

Watson, J. D., 1952.   The properties of X-ray inactivated bacteriophage: II.   Inactivation by indirect effects.   *J. Bacteriol.*, **63**, 473.

Watson, J. D., and F. H. C. Crick, 1953.   The structure of DNA.   *Cold Spring Harbor Symposia Quant. Biol.*, **18**, 123.

Watson, J. D., and O. Maaløe, 1953.   Nucleic acid transfer from parental to progeny bacteriophage.   *Biochim. et Biophys. Acta*, **10**, 432.

Weed, L. L., and S. S. Cohen, 1951.   The utilization of host pyrimidines in the synthesis of bacterial viruses.   *J. Biol. Chem.*, **192**, 693.

Weidel, W., 1951.   Über die Zellmembran von *E. coli* B: I.   Präparierung der Membranen gegenüber den Bakteriophagen. *Z. Naturforsch.*, **6b,** 251.

Weidel, W., 1953a. Further studies on the membrane of "*E. coli*" B. *Ann. inst. Pasteur*, **84,** 60.

Weidel, W., 1953b. Phage receptor systems of *E. coli* B. *Cold Spring Harbor Symposia Quant. Biol.*, **18,** 155.

Weidel, W., and E. Kellenberger, 1955. The *E. Coli* B receptor for the phage T5: II. Electron microscope studies. *Biochim. et Biophys. Acta*, **17,** 1.

Weidel, W., and G. Koch, 1955. Uber die Rezeptorsubstanz fur den Phagen T5: III. Serologische Untersuchungen. *Z. Naturforsch.*, **10b,** 694.

Weidel, W., G. Koch, and K. Bobosch, 1954. Uber die rezeptorsubstanz fur den Phagen T5. *Z. Naturforsch.*, **9b,** 573.

Weigle, J. J., 1953. *Proc. Natl. Acad. Sci. U. S.* **39,** 628.

Weigle, J. J., 1957. *Virology*, **4,** 14.

Weigle, J. J., and G. Bertani, 1953. *Ann. inst. Pasteur*, **84,** 175.

Weigle, J. J., and G. Bertani, 1956. Multiplicity reactivation of bacteriophage inactivated by ionizing radiations. *Virology*, **2,** 344.

Weigle, J. J., and M. Delbrück, 1951. *J. Bacteriol.*, **62,** 301.

Weigle, J. J., and R. Dulbecco, 1953. *Experientia*, **9,** 372.

Welsh, J. N., and M. H. Adams, 1954. Photodynamic inactivation of bacteriophage. *J. Bacteriol.*, **68,** 122.

Whitfield, J. F., and R. G. E. Murray, 1954. A cytological study of the lysogenization of *Shigella dysenteriae* with P1 and P2 bacteriophages. *Can. J. Microbiol.*, **1,** 216.

Whitfield, J. F., and R. G. E. Murray, 1956. The effects of the ionic environment on the chromatin structures of bacteria. *Can. J. Microbiol.*, **2,** 245.

Whitfield, J. F., and R. G. E. Murray, 1957. Observations on the initial cytological effects of bacteriophage infection. *Can. J. Microbiol.*, **3,** 493.

Whittaker, E., 1950. Two bacteriophages for *M. smegmatis*. *Can. J. Public Health*, **41,** 431.

Wilkowske, H. H., F. E. Nelson, and C. E. Parmelee, 1954. Serological classification of bacteriophages active against lactic streptococci. *App. Microbiol.*, **2,** 243.

Williams, R. C., 1953. The shapes and sizes of purified viruses as determined by electron microscopy. *Cold Spring Harbor Symp. Quant. Biol.*, **18,** 185.

Williams, R. C., and D. Fraser, 1953. Morphology of the seven T-bacteriophages. *J. Bacteriol.*, **66,** 458.

Williams, R. C., and D. Fraser, 1956. *Virology*, **2,** 289.

Williams, R. E. O., and J. E. Rippon, 1952. *J. Hyg.*, **50,** 320.

Williamson, K. I., and W. S. Bertaud, 1951. A new bacteriophage active against a lactic streptococcus. *J. Bacteriol.*, **61,** 643.

Williams Smith, H., 1948. *J. Hyg.*, **46,** 74.

Williams Smith, H., 1951a. Some observations on lysogenic strains of Salmonella. *J. Gen. Microbiol.*, **5**, 458.

Williams Smith, H., 1951b. *J. Gen. Microbiol.*, **5**, 472.

Williams Smith, H., 1951c. *J. Gen. Microbiol.*, **5**, 919.

Williams Smith, H., and W. E. Crabb, 1956. *J. Gen. Microbiol.*, **15**, 556.

Wilson, G. S., and J. D. Atkinson, 1945. *Lancet*, **1**, 647.

Wisseman, C., J. Smadel, F. Hahn, and H. Hopps, 1954. *J. Bacteriol.*, **67**, 662.

Wolff, L. K., and J. W. Janzen, 1922. Action de divers antiseptiques sur le bactériophage de d'Herelle. *Compt. rend. soc. biol.*, **87**, 1087.

Wollman, E., and Mme. E. Wollman, 1936a. *Compt. rend. soc. biol.*, **121**, 302.

Wollman, E., and Mme. E. Wollman, 1936b. *Compt. rend. soc. biol.*, **122**, 190.

Wollman, E. and Mme. E. Wollman, 1938. Production experimentale de souches de bactériophages determinant la lyse en absence de Calcium soluble. *Compt. rend. soc. biol.*, **128**, 379.

Wollman, E., and A. Lacassagne, 1940. *Ann. inst. Pasteur*, **64**, 5.

Wollman, E.-L., 1947. *Ann. inst. Pasteur*, **73**, 348.

Wollman, E.-L., 1953. *Ann. inst. Pasteur*, **84**, 281.

Wollman, E.-L., and F. Jacob, 1954. *Ann. inst. Pasteur*, **87**, 674.

Wollman, E.-L., and G. S. Stent, 1950. Studies on activation of T4 bacteriophage by cofactor: I. The degree of activity. *Biochim. et Biophys. Acta*, **6**, 292.

Wollman, E.-L., and G. S. Stent, 1952. Studies on activation of T4 phage by cofactor: IV. Nascent activity. *Biochim. et Biophys. Acta*, **9**, 538.

Woodruff, H. B., T. D. Nunheimer, and S. B. Lee, 1947. A bacterial virus for *Actinomyces griseus*. *J. Bacteriol.*, **54**, 535.

Wooley, J. G., and M. K. Murphy, 1949. Metabolic studies on T2 *Escherichia coli* bacteriophage: I. A study of desoxypyridoxine inhibition and its reversal. *J. Biol. Chem.*, **178**, 869.

Wooley, J. G., M. K. Murphy, H. W. Bond, and T. D. Perrine, 1952. The effect of certain chemical compounds on the multiplication of T2 bacteriophage. *J. Immunol.*, **68**, 523.

Wyatt, G. R., 1952. Deoxyribonucleic acid in insect viruses. *J. Gen. Physiol.*, **36**, 201.

Wyatt, G. R., and S. S. Cohen, 1953. The bases of the nucleic acids of some bacterial and animal viruses: the occurrence of 5-hydroxymethyl cytosine. *Biochem. J.*, **55**, 774.

Wyckoff, R. W. G., 1949a. Multiplication of the T3 bacteriophage against *E. coli*. *Proc. Soc. Exptl. Biol. Med.*, **71**, 144.

Wyckoff, R. W. G., 1949b. *Electron Microscopy Techniques and Applications*. Interscience, New York-London.

Y

Yamamoto, N., 1956.   *Virus (Tokyo)*, **6,** 510.

Z

Zahler, S. A., E. S. Lennox, and A. E. Vatter, 1954.   Growth and mutation of the small bacteriophages S13 and φX174.   *Bact. Proc. Soc. Am. Bacteriologists*, **54,** 47.

Zelle, M. R., and A. Hollaender, 1954.   Monochromatic ultraviolet action spectra and quantum yields for inactivation of T1 and T2 *Escherichia coli* bacteriophages.   *J. Bacteriol.*, **68,** 210.

Zinder, N. D., 1953.   *Cold Spring Harbor Symposia Quant. Biol.*, **18,** 261.

Zinder, N. D., 1955.   *J. Cellular Comp. Physiol.*, **45,** *Suppl.*, **2,** 23.

Zinder, N. D., and J. Lederberg, 1952.   *J. Bacteriol.*, **64,** 679.

INDEX

A

Abortive infection, 178, 283
  definition, 282, 439
Absorption spectra, of ultraviolet-
  inactivated bacteriophages,
  66, 67
Absorption spectrum, of nucleic acid,
  67
Acridines, effect on bacteriophage reproduction, 278–81, 287
Acriflavine, effect on bacteriophage
  reproduction, 278–80
Actinomyces phage, reproduction, inhibition, 279
Action spectra, of ultraviolet-inactivated bacteriophages, 66, 67
Activation, of coliphages by cofactors,
  144–46
Adaptation, in typing phages, 398,
  405–12, 418, 419
Adenine, in coliphages, 90, 91
Adenosine triphosphatase (ATPase),
  in coliphage T2, 239
Adsorption, of bacteriophage to host
  cell, 15, 16, 137–60, 392
  bacterial antigens effect on, 123,
  124, 152–59
  effect on plaque size, 23, 24, 137
  inhibition, 267–70
  irradiation effect on, 77, 148
  mutations affecting, 298, 299,
  301, 302
  as taxonomic criterion, 424
  techniques in study of, 466–73,
  503–5
  of colicins to host cells, 385, 392
  definition, 439

Aeration, 446, 447, 455, 496
  effect on colicin production, 388
Aerobacter species, colicins in, 381
Agar, concentration, effect on plaque
  size, 24
  effect on bacteriophage adsorption,
  268
Agar filtration method, in morphological study of bacteriophages,
  184
Agar layer method, in assay of
  bacteriophage, 29, 30, 450, 451
  media for, 446, 507
Agglutination, of phage-coated
  bacteria, 106, 107
Aggregation, of coliphages by antiphage sera, 105, 106
Alanine, in coliphages, 90
Albumin, egg, effect on adsorption of
  bacteriophages, 268
  effect on irradiation of bacteriophages, 75
  effect on neutralization of bacteriophages, 112
  serum, effect on irradiation of bacteriophages, 75
  effect on neutralization of bacteriophages, 112
Alcohols, effect on bacteriophages, 53
Alpha particles, effect on bacteriophages, 78, 79
Amino acids, analogues, effect on
  bacteriophage reproduction,
  273–75, 283, 284
  in coliphages, 90
  as growth factors for coliphage T2,
  244, 283

Papain, in coliphage WLL, 238
  in reactivation of neutralized phage, 101, 102, 461
Partial exclusion, see *Exclusion, partial*
Pasteurella phage, growth factors, 235
Pasteurella species, 121
Pasteurella pestis, effect of infection on, 197
Pasteurella pestis phage, host range, 122
  mutants, 298, 299
Pectin, effect on bacteriophage adsorption, 269, 270
Penetration, of bacteriophage into host cell, 17, 18, 161–68
  inhibition, 270, 271
Penicillin, effect on bacteria, 246, 266, 284, 285
  effect on latent period of bacteriophages, 170
Pentamidine, effect on bacteria, 266
  effect on reproduction of bacteriophages, 285
Peptone, effect on adsorption of bacteriophage, 41, 55
Periodate, effect on adsorption of bacteriophage, 152
Permanganate, effect on bacteriophages, 54
Peroxides, see also *Hydrogen peroxide*
  effect on bacteriophages, 54, 77, 79,
  effect on lysogenic bacteria, 9
  organic, effect on lysogenic bacteria, 373
pH, effect on bacteriophages, 50, 146, 150, 151
  as taxonomic criterion, 427
  effect on colicin production, 388
  effect on surface inactivation of coliphages, 55, 56
Phage, see *Bacteriophage*
Phage-inhibiting agent (PIA), 103

effect on adsorption of bacteriophages, 152–59
Phagolesin, effect on bacteriophage reproduction, 285
Phenocopies, of bacteriophages, 294
Phenol, effect on adsorption of bacteriophage, 151, 152
Phenotype, definition, 290, 291, 441
Phenotypic mixing, in bacteriophages, 132, 133, 317, 354
Phenotypic modification, in bacteriophages, 132–35, 291–97
  definition, 132, 291
  in *S. typhi* phage Vi II, 399, 403, 406, 407, 411
  of staphylococcal typing phages, 418
Phenylalanine, in coliphages, 90
  effect on adsorption of coliphages, 143
  effect on irradiation of bacteriophages, 75
Phosphatases, in bacteriophages, 238, 239
Phosphate, effect on heat inactivation of coliphage T5, 58
  effect on proflavine inhibition of bacteriophage reproduction, 281
Phosphine GRN, effect on bacteriophage reproduction, 279
Phosphorus, assimilation in bacteriophage reproduction, 257–62
  labeled, effect on bacteriophages, 80–82, 180–82, 362, 363
  in study of bacterial changes following infection, 166, 167
  in study of bacteriophage penetration into host cell, 17, 161–63
  in study of DNA synthesis in bacteriophages, 248, 257–61
  in study of doughnuts, 184